Fracture Behaviour of Polymers

Fracture Behaviour of Polymers

A. J. KINLOCH

Ministry of Defence, Procurement Executive, Propellants, Explosives and Rocket Motor Establishment, Waltham Abbey, Essex, UK

and

R. J. YOUNG

Department of Materials, Queen Mary College, University of London, Mile End Road, London, UK

APPLIED SCIENCE PUBLISHERS

LONDON and NEW YORK

APPLIED SCIENCE PUBLISHERS LTD
Ripple Road, Barking, Essex, England

Sole Distributor in the USA and Canada
ELSEVIER SCIENCE PUBLISHING CO., INC.
52 Vanderbilt Avenue, New York, NY 10017, USA

British Library Cataloguing in Publication Data

Kinloch, A. J.
 Fracture behaviour of polymers.
 1. Polymers and polymerisation
 I. Title   II. Young, R. J.
 547.7'04541

ISBN 0-85334-186-9

WITH 162 ILLUSTRATIONS AND 34 TABLES

© APPLIED SCIENCE PUBLISHERS LTD 1983

Printed in Northern Ireland at The Universities Press (Belfast), Ltd.

Preface

Over recent years there has been a tremendous upsurge in interest in the fracture behaviour of polymers. One reason for this is the increasing use of polymers in structural engineering applications, since in such circumstances it is essential to have as complete an understanding as possible of the polymer's fracture behaviour. This book is designed to meet the requirements of those who need to be informed of the latest developments in the field of polymer fracture. It is written particularly for research workers but it should also prove invaluable for advanced students taking final-year undergraduate or postgraduate courses.

The main emphasis is upon the use of fracture mechanics in the study of polymer fracture but this approach is then developed to cover the micromechanisms of the fracture process. Particular prominence is given to the relationship between structure, mechanical properties and the mechanics and mechanisms of fracture. The first chapter is a brief introduction which has several aims. One is to introduce polymers to the reader who does not have a strong background in the subject and another is to provide background material that will be used at later stages. The book is then split into two main parts: the first deals with the mechanics and mechanisms whilst the second is concerned with materials. In Part I phenomena such as molecular fracture, fracture mechanics, shear yielding and crazing are covered from a general viewpoint. In Part II the properties of the different types of polymer are discussed separately. One problem with this approach is that some topics are dealt with in several different places and some repetition and cross-referencing is inevitable. For example, crazing is often studied as a general phenomenon but it is also important in controlling crack

v

propagation in glassy thermoplastics and as a major toughening mechanism in multiphase polymers. However, the usefulness of covering the topic in several different chapters is that the interrelationship between the different aspects can more readily be appreciated. Also the mathematical aspects of a topic such as crazing can be developed separately from the discussion of crazing during the fracture of particular types of polymer.

The authors would like to thank many of their friends and colleagues in the field of polymer fracture for many useful discussions and help in the preparation of this book. They are particularly grateful to E. H. Andrews, C. B. Bucknall, A. M. Donald, E. J. Kramer, G. J. Lake, P. E. Reed, S. J. Shaw, A. Thomas, D. Tod and J. G. Williams who have read various chapters, provided copies of manuscripts in advance of publication and supplied original micrographs. They are also grateful to Gillian Kinloch and Karen Wiggins for typing the manuscript. Finally they would like to extend their gratitude to their wives and families for their great patience and support throughout the period of preparation of the book.

A. J. KINLOCH
R. J. YOUNG

Acknowledgements

The authors wish to thank the following publishers for permission to reproduce illustrations from previous publications:

Chapman and Hall Ltd—Figs 1.7, 4.6, 4.8, 4.9, 4.14, 5.11, 5.12, 6.8, 7.7(c), 7.12, 7.16, 9.6, 11.2;
John Wiley and Sons Inc.—Figs 4.11, 4.13(a), 11.1.
Springer Verlag—Fig. 6.10 (b–d).
Taylor and Francis Ltd—Figs 5.2, 7.14(a, b).
IPC Science and Technology Press Ltd—Figs 4.12, 4.13(b), 9.13(b, c).
Society of Plastics Engineers Inc.—Fig. 10.12.

A number of other figures in the book are based upon already published material and, in these cases, an appropriate acknowledgement appears in the caption.

Contents

Preface v

Acknowledgements vii

Main Notation xvii

Main Abbreviations xxv

Chapter 1 **Introduction** 1
  1.1   Basic Concepts 2
      1.1.1   Definitions 2
      1.1.2   Classification of polymers 3
      1.1.3   Molar mass 7
  1.2   Synthesis and Characterisation of Polymer Molecules 8
      1.2.1   Synthesis 8
      1.2.2   Identification of polymers 10
      1.2.3   Measurement of molar mass 10
      1.2.4   Macromolecules in solution 11
  1.3   Structure of Solid Polymers 12
      1.3.1   Amorphous polymers 12
      1.3.2   The glass transition 14
      1.3.3   Crystalline polymers 15
      1.3.4   Crystallisation and melting 15
  1.4   Stress and Strain 18
      1.4.1   Stress 18
      1.4.2   Strain 20
      1.4.3   Plane stress and plane strain 20
      1.4.4   Relationship between stress and strain 22
  1.5   Deformation of Polymers 23
      1.5.1   Elastic deformation 23

1.5.2   Viscoelasticity   26
1.5.3   Hysteresis and plastic flow   29
1.5.4   Shear yielding   31
1.5.5   Crazing   31
1.6   Fracture of Polymers   32
1.6.1   General approaches   32
1.6.2   General behaviour   33
1.6.3   Stresses at crack tips   33
1.6.4   Griffith fracture   35
1.6.5   Toughening mechanisms   36
1.7   Concluding Remarks   37
References   37

PART I—MECHANICS AND MECHANISMS

Chapter 2   **Molecular Aspects**   43
2.1   Introduction   43
2.2   Fracture on the Molecular Level   44
2.2.1   Theoretical strength of a solid   44
2.2.2   Molecular fracture in polymers   47
2.3   Kinetic Approach to Fracture   50
2.4   Techniques for Studying Molecular Deformation and Fracture . 54
2.4.1   Techniques for studying bond straining   55
2.4.2   Study of bond breakage   57
2.4.3   Void formation and growth   60
2.5   Micromechanisms of Polymer Fracture   61
2.5.1   Molecular fracture during deformation   62
2.5.2   Microvoid formation and craze growth   69
2.6   Concluding Remarks   70
References   71

Chapter 3   **Fracture Mechanics**   74
3.1   Introduction   74
3.2   Energy Balance Approach   75
3.2.1   Basic principles   75
3.2.2   Linear elastic fracture mechanics   77
3.2.3   Bulk non-linear elastic behaviour   79
3.2.4   Bulk inelastic behaviour   84
3.3   Stress-Intensity Factor Approach   86
3.3.1   Basic principles   86
3.3.2   Small scale yielding   88
3.4   Relationship between G and K   92
3.5   Thickness Effects   93
3.6   Experimental Considerations   97
3.6.1   Flexible polymers   97
3.6.2   Rigid polymers   97

3.6.3 Value of G_{Ic} and K_{Ic} 101
3.7 Concluding Remarks 104
References 104

Chapter 4 **Shear Yielding** 107
4.1 Introduction 107
4.2 General Aspects of Yield Behaviour 108
    4.2.1 Definitions 108
    4.2.2 Mechanical tests 110
    4.2.3 Viscoelastic nature of yield behaviour 111
    4.2.4 Criteria for shear yielding 114
    4.2.5 Molecular theories 117
4.3 Inhomogeneous Deformation 119
    4.3.1 Causes 120
    4.3.2 Types of inhomogeneous deformation 120
    4.3.3 Shear bands in glassy polymers 122
    4.3.4 Crystalline polymers 127
4.4 Shear Yielding and Crack Initiation 128
4.5 Shear Yielding and Crack Propagation 132
    4.5.1 Mechanisms 132
    4.5.2 Criteria 139
4.6 Concluding Remarks 142
References 143

Chapter 5 **Crazing** 147
5.1 Introduction 147
5.2 Microstructure 149
5.3 Micromechanics 152
    5.3.1 Mechanical properties of crazes and craze fibrils 152
    5.3.2 Models of craze shape and stress distribution 155
5.4 Craze Initiation 158
    5.4.1 Mechanisms and criteria 158
    5.4.2 Kinetics 165
5.5 Craze Growth 165
    5.5.1 Mechanisms 165
    5.5.2 Kinetics and criteria 167
5.6 Craze Breakdown 169
    5.6.1 Mechanisms 169
    5.6.2 Kinetics 171
    5.6.3 Criteria 173
5.7 Effect of Polymer Structure 174
    5.7.1 Molar mass 174
    5.7.2 The role of molecular entanglements 175
    5.7.3 Orientation 176
    5.7.4 Chemical structure 177
5.8 Concluding Remarks 177
References 178

Chapter 6 **Impact and Fatigue** 182
6.1   Introduction 182
6.2   Impact Tests 182
      6.2.1   Introduction 182
      6.2.2   Experimental methods 185
      6.2.3   Effect of specimen geometry 188
      6.2.4   A fracture mechanics approach 192
6.3   Dynamic Fatigue 197
      6.3.1   Introduction 197
      6.3.2   Experimental considerations 197
      6.3.3   Thermal fatigue failure 200
      6.3.4   Mechanical fatigue failure 202
6.4   Static Fatigue 211
      6.4.1   Introduction 211
      6.4.2   Mechanisms 212
      6.4.3   Life-prediction 214
6.5   Concluding Remarks 220
      References 220

PART II—MATERIALS

Chapter 7 **Glassy Polymers I—Thermoplastics** 229
7.1   Introduction 229
7.2   Brittle Fracture 230
      7.2.1   Effect of testing variables 231
      7.2.2   Effect of polymer structure 237
7.3   Crack Propagation 241
      7.3.1   Crack velocity 242
      7.3.2   Temperature 245
      7.3.3   Relaxations and crack propagation 247
      7.3.4   Adiabatic/isothermal transitions 247
      7.3.5   Specimen thickness 249
      7.3.6   Molar mass 251
      7.3.7   Orientation 252
      7.3.8   Environment 254
7.4   Micromechanisms 255
      7.4.1   Craze initiation and growth 256
      7.4.2   Environmental crazing 256
      7.4.3   The structure of crazes 260
      7.4.4   Shear yielding 261
      7.4.5   Crazing versus shear yielding: entanglements 263
      7.4.6   Crack propagation 267
      7.4.7   Crack healing 269
7.5   Impact and Fatigue 270
      7.5.1   Impact 270

7.5.2 Dynamic fatigue 273
7.5.3 Static fatigue 277
7.6 Concluding Remarks 279
References 280

Chapter 8 Glassy Polymers II—Thermosets 286
8.1 Introduction 286
8.2 Brittle Fracture 287
  8.2.1 Stress/strain behaviour 287
  8.2.2 Fracture strength, fracture energy and flaws 289
  8.2.3 Cross-link density 290
8.3 Crack Propagation 291
  8.3.1 Fracture mechanics testing 291
  8.3.2 Material variables 293
  8.3.3 Testing variables 296
  8.3.4 Crack velocity 298
  8.3.5 Causes of unstable propagation 300
8.4 Failure Mechanisms 301
  8.4.1 Crack propagation 301
  8.4.2 Plastic deformation 304
  8.4.3 Crazing 306
  8.4.4 Polymer microstructure 307
8.5 Failure Criteria 309
  8.5.1 Constant crack-opening displacement 309
  8.5.2 Critical stress/distance criterion 311
8.6 Impact and Fatigue 315
  8.6.1 Impact 315
  8.6.2 Dynamic fatigue 316
  8.6.3 Static fatigue 317
8.7 Concluding Remarks 320
References 320

Chapter 9 Crystalline Polymers 324
9.1 Introduction 324
  9.1.1 General mechanical behaviour 324
9.2 Deformation 326
  9.2.1 Elastic deformation of polymer crystals 326
  9.2.2 Elastic deformation of semicrystalline polymers . . . 330
  9.2.3 Plastic deformation and drawing 331
9.3 Fracture of Polymer Crystals 332
  9.3.1 Molecular fracture: macroscopic single crystals . . . 333
  9.3.2 Intermolecular cleavage 337
9.4 Fracture of Isotropic Semicrystalline Polymers 338
  9.4.1 Effect of morphology and structure 338
  9.4.2 Crack propagation and fracture mechanics 342
  9.4.3 Effect of testing conditions 346

          9.4.4   Environmental fracture and crazing   354
    9.5   Fracture of Oriented Semicrystalline Polymers   357
          9.5.1   Tensile strength   358
          9.5.2   Fatigue   360
          9.5.3   Failure mechanisms   361
    9.6   Concluding Remarks   363
          References   365

Chapter 10   **Rubbers**   370
    10.1   Introduction   370
    10.2   Energy Dissipating Mechanisms   371
    10.3   Initiation of Fracture   377
           10.3.1   Introduction   377
           10.3.2   Initiation under triaxial stresses   378
           10.3.3   Intrinsic fracture energies   382
    10.4   Crack Propagation   386
           10.4.1   Stresses at crack tips   386
           10.4.2   Amorphous rubbers   388
           10.4.3   Strain-crystallising rubbers   393
           10.4.4   Filled rubbers   394
           10.4.5   Fatigue failure   395
    10.5   Tensile Fracture   398
           10.5.1   Failure under combined stresses   398
           10.5.2   Effect of rate and temperature   400
           10.5.3   Effect of degree of cross-linking   403
           10.5.4   Energy dissipating mechanisms and tensile fracture .   405
           10.5.5   Multiphase rubbers   406
           10.5.6   Theories of tensile failure   411
    10.6   Concluding Remarks   416
           References   416

Chapter 11   **Toughened Multiphase Plastics**   421
    11.1   Introduction   421
    11.2   Mechanisms of Toughening   423
           11.2.1   Particle deformation   423
           11.2.2   Shear yielding   425
           11.2.3   Crazing   428
           11.2.4   Simultaneous shear yielding and crazing   432
           11.2.5   Crack pinning   434
    11.3   Stress/Strain Relationships   438
    11.4   Structure/Property Relationships   442
           11.4.1   Concentration and size of second-phase particles . .   442
           11.4.2   Particle/matrix adhesion   448
           11.4.3   Matrix properties   451
    11.5   Test Variables   452
           11.5.1   Effect of temperature and rate   452
           11.5.2   Dynamic fatigue   462

11.5.3   Static fatigue 465
11.6   Concluding Remarks 467
       References 467

Author Index 473

Subject Index 489

Main Notation

a	crack length or semimajor axis of elliptical hole		change in toughening mechanism
$\dot{a}$	crack velocity	d_v	mean distance between void centres
$\dot{a}_c$	critical crack velocity	e	strain
a_f	crack length at which propagation becomes relatively fast	e_a	strain amplitude
		e_c	critical craze strain
		e_f	fracture strain
a_T	time–temperature shift factor	e_m	mean strain
		e_y	yield strain
a_0	intrinsic, or inherent, crack, or flaw, length	e_0	applied strain
		f	a damage function
b	specimen thickness	$f(\ )$	a function
b_{min}	specimen thickness at ductile/brittle transition	g	distribution function
		g_e	spectroscopic splitting factor
b_n	specimen thickness in plane of crack	h	specimen height
		$\mathbf{h}$	Planck's constant
c	critical distance ahead of crack	h_a	thickness of adhesive layer
c_{ijkl}	tensor containing stiffness constants	h_m	value of h_a at maximum adhesive fracture energy, $G_{Icm}(\text{joint})$
c_p	specific heat capacity		
d_f	fibre diameter		
d_p	interparticle distance	h_p	equilibrium separation of atomic planes
d_{pc}	critical value of d_p for		

h_r	hysteresis ratio		zone radius at crack growth
$\bar{k}$	thermal conductivity		
k	Boltzmann's constant	r_{yc}''	plane-stress plastic-zone radius at crack growth
$k_1 \rightarrow k_i$	constants		
l	specimen length		
l_e	chain contour length between entanglements	s	span
		$\mathbf{s}_e$	spin vector
		s_f	stress ratio
l_m	length of moment arm	t	time
l_r	length of slow crack growth region	t_{cr}	critical time for crack healing
Δl	fitting length constant	t_f	time-to-failure
m	constant in Paris fatigue equation	t_i	time for crack initiation phase
m_p	plastic constraint factor	t_l	loading period
m_w	Weibull modulus	t_0	pre-exponential constant
n	constant in craze/crack growth equations		
$\bar{n}_b$	average number of primary main chain bonds between cross-links	t_p	time for crack propagation phase
		v	volume
		v^*	activation volume
		v_f	volume fraction
p	hydrostatic component of the stress tensor	v_{fp}	volume fraction of particles
$\bar{p}$	pressure driving fluid into a craze	v_{fv}	volume fraction of voids
p_c	critical value of p	w	specimen width
p_f	failure probability	w_{sl}	width of shear lip
q	constant in fatigue equation	x	separation of atomic planes
r	distance (polar coordinate)	$\dot{y}$	rate of extension
r_p	particle radius	A	area
r_y	plastic-zone radius	A_f	constant in Paris fatigue equation
r_y'	plane-strain plastic-zone radius	A_v	constant in craze/crack growth equation
r_y''	plane-stress plastic-zone radius	A_E	pre-exponential constant in Eyring equation
r_{yc}	plastic-zone radius at crack growth		
r_{yc}'	plane-strain plastic-	A_I	constant relating infra-

red vibration fre-
quency to applied
stress

A_L ligament area

A_R constant relating
Raman vibration fre-
quency to applied
strain

B_f constant in fatigue equation

B_s constant

B_G constant

C compliance

C_1, C_2 constants in Williams–
Landel–Ferry equa-
tion

C_c constant in Williams
theory of craze
growth

C_f constant in fatigue equation

D_{cr} creep compliance

D_f constant in fatigue equation

E Young's modulus

E_0 unit time Young's modulus

ΔE difference in energy

ΔE^* activation energy for
yielding

F work done

G_c fracture energy

G_c' plane-strain fracture
energy

G_c'' plane-stress fracture
energy

G_{cm} maximum value of G_c

G_{co} energy needed to cause
crazing

G_{ic} interfacial fracture
energy

G_0 intrinsic fracture energy
(Subscripts I, II or III to the
above indicate mode of
failure—see Fig. 3.6)

ΔG fracture energy range
during fatigue cycling

ΔG^* activation energy for
fracture

ΔG_{AB}^* activation energy for
chain scission

$\mathscr{G}$ shear modulus

H magnetic field strength

ΔH^* activation enthalpy

I_1 first stress invariant

$I(\theta)$ intensity of scattered
X-rays

J contour integral

J_c value of J for fracture

$\mathscr{J}_{loss}$ loss compliance

$\mathscr{J}_{storage}$ storage compliance

K stress-intensity factor

K_c stress-intensity factor at
fracture, or fracture
toughness

K_c' plane-strain value of K_c

K_c'' plane-stress value of K_c

K_c^* stress-intensity factor
for instability

K_{ca} stress-intensity factor at
crack arrest

K_{cf} value of K_c at which
relatively rapid crack
propagation occurs

K_{ci} stress-intensity factor at
crack initiation

K_d dynamic fracture toughness

K_i value of K to initiate
crazing

K_m critical value of K for
craze growth

K_{max} maximum value of K

K_{min} minimum value of K

K_n critical value of K for rapid craze growth

ΔK stress-intensity factor range during fatigue cycling $(= K_{max} - K_{min})$

(Subscripts I, II or III to the above indicate mode of failure—see Fig. 3.6)

$\bar{L}$ average distance between cross-links in the unstrained state

L_m dimension of a cavity

M molar mass

$\bar{M}_c$ average molar mass between cross-links

$\bar{M}_e$ average molar mass between physical entanglements

$\bar{M}_n$ number-average molar mass

$\bar{M}_v$ viscosity-average molar mass

$\bar{M}_w$ weight-average molar mass

M_0 'zero strength' molar mass

N number of cycles

$\mathbf{N}$ Avogadro's number

N_a number of backbone bonds per unit area

N_b number of chains per unit volume

N_f number of cycles to failure

N_m number of cavities per unit volume

P applied load

P_a applied load at crack arrest

P_c applied load at onset of crack propagation

Q geometry constant

R plastic-zone length in Dugdale model

$\mathbf{R}$ molar gas constant

R_c plastic-zone length at crack growth

$\langle \bar{R}^2_{rms} \rangle^{\frac{1}{2}}$ root mean square end-to-end distance of a polymer molecule

$\langle \bar{R}^2_{rms} \rangle_e^{\frac{1}{2}}$ root mean square end-to-end distance of a chain of molar mass M_e

$\langle \bar{R}^2_{rms} \rangle_0^{\frac{1}{2}}$ unperturbed dimensions of a polymer molecule

S shape factor

T temperature

$\bar{T}$ crack tip temperature for instability

T_b ductile-to-brittle transition temperature

T_c crystallisation temperature

T_g glass transition temperature

T_m crystalline melting temperature

T_m° equilibrium melting temperature

T_r reference temperature

T_L line energy per unit length of crack front

U stored elastic energy

U_b bond dissociation energy

U_c	stored elastic energy at crack growth		criteria
$\dot{U}_d$	energy dissipation rate	Z	dimensional geometry factor
U_H	loss in pendulum energy during an impact test	Z_g	factor related to cavity geometry
U_I	energy consumed in tossing the broken impact specimen out of the machine	α_c	factor reducing craze surface stress in active environments
ΔU^*	activation energy for thermal bond dissociation	α_f	reduction in stress in fatigue damage zone
W	strain-energy density (i.e. strain-energy per unit volume)	α_r	primary molecular-relaxation
		β	Bohr magneton
W_a	thermodynamic work of adhesion for an interface	β_g	coefficient relating the pressure dependence of T_g
W_c	applied strain-energy density for crack growth	β_r	secondary molecular-relaxation
		γ	surface free-energy
W_d	hysteresis, or loss, strain-energy density	γ_a	surface free-energy of adhesive
W_{df}	value of W_d at fracture	γ_{as}, γ_{SL}	interfacial free-energies
W_f	applied strain-energy density for tensile fracture	γ_s	surface free-energy of substrate
W_r	retraction, or recoverable, strain-energy density	δ	crack-opening displacement
		δ_c	craze thickness
		δ_r	phase angle
		$\tan \delta_r$	loss factor
W_{tc}	strain-energy density around crack tip at crack growth	δ_s	solubility parameter
		δ_t	crack-opening displacement at crack tip
W_0	applied, or input, strain-energy density	δ_{tc}	crack-opening displacement at crack tip at crack growth
X, X_1	constants in Bowden and Oxborough craze criteria	η	stress concentration
		η_v	viscosity
Y, Y_1	constants in Bowden and Oxborough craze	θ	angle (polar coordinate or X-ray scattering)

θ_{sb}	angle of shear bands	ξ	$\left(1-\dfrac{r}{R}\right)^{\frac{1}{2}}$
θ_{sz}	angle of inclined neck		
λ	extension ratio	ρ	crack tip radius
λ_c	extension ratio at crack growth	ρ_c	crack tip radius at crack growth
λ_{cf}	craze fibril extension ratio	ρ_d	density
		σ	stress
λ_f	extension ratio at fracture	σ_a	stress amplitude
		σ_b	stress bias
λ_{max}	maximum value of applied extension ratio	σ_c	applied stress at crack growth
λ_{sz}	extension ratio in shear deformation zone	σ_{cf}	craze fibril stress
		σ_{cs}	craze surface stress
λ_w	wavelength	σ_f	fracture stress, or strength
λ_{wc}	wavelength in meniscus instability craze growth model	σ_{fc}	critical tensile strength at the ductile/brittle transition
λ_0	applied extension ratio		
μ, μ_M, μ_C, μ_T	coefficients in yield criteria to model the effect of pressure	$\sigma_{f\infty}$	fracture strength of polymer with infinite molar mass
μ_{mag}	magnetic moment of free electron	σ_{ic}	interfacial debonding stress
ν	Poisson's ratio	σ_{ij}	component of the stress tensor
ν_d	applied frequency in dynamic-fatigue tests	σ_m	mean stress level
ν_e	Raman vibration frequency	σ_{max}	maximum value of σ_0
		σ_{min}	minimum value of σ_0
ν_{ef}	effective number of network chains per unit volume	σ_p	plastic-zone surface stress
		σ_t	stress at crack tip
ν_{em}	frequency of electron magnetic radiation	σ_{tc}	critical stress at crack tip
ν_r	rate of bond breakage	σ_{th}	threshold stress
ν_{r0}	temperature-independent constant for bond breakage	σ_{theo}	theoretical fracture stress
ν_σ	Infra-red vibration frequency	σ_y	uniaxial tensile yield stress
		σ_0	applied stress

$\sigma_1, \sigma_2, \sigma_3$ principal stresses

τ time variable

τ_{oct} octahedral shear stress

τ_y pure-shear yield stress

τ_C shear stress needed for yield in Coulomb yield criterion

τ_M shear stress needed for flow in von Mises yield criterion

τ_T shear stress needed for yield in Tresca yield criterion

(Superscript ^{0} indicates value in pure shear, i.e. in absence of any hydrostatic component to the stress tensor)

ϕ energy to fracture per unit volume of shear lip

ψ energy dissipated in viscoelastic and plastic deformations at the crack tip

Δ displacement

Θ theta temperature

Φ loss function

Ω pressure activation volume

Main Abbreviations

ABS   acrylonitrile–butadiene–styrene copolymer
HDPE   high-density polyethylene
HIPS   high-impact polystyrene
LDPE   low-density polyethylene
MDPE   medium-density polyethylene
NR   natural rubber
PBA   poly(p-benzamide)
PBT   poly(p-phenylenebenzobisthiazole)
PC   polycarbonate
PES   poly(ether sulphone)
PET   poly(ethylene terephthalate)
PMMA   poly(methyl methacrylate)
POM   polyoxymethylene ≡ polyacetal
PP   polypropylene
PPD-T   poly(p-phenylene terephthalamide)
PPO   poly(2,6-dimethyl 1,4-phenylene oxide)
PTFE   polytetrafluoroethylene
PVC   poly(vinyl chloride)
SAN   styrene–acrylonitrile copolymer
SBR   styrene–butadiene rubber

Chapter 1

Introduction

Polymers are an important class of materials made up of long-chain covalently bonded molecules and include plastics, rubbers and adhesives. Polymers are now finding increasing use in engineering applications due to factors such as lightness, low cost and ease of fabrication, although many polymers have unique properties not found with other materials. For example, rubbers have the property of being able to be stretched to very high strains and to rapidly spring back to their original dimensions on the removal of the applied stress. Epoxy resins can be used as high-performance adhesives to make joints which may be significantly superior in mechanical properties, e.g. strength and fatigue resistance, compared to bolted or welded structures.

A vital consideration for the use of polymers in engineering applications is the need for knowledge of the way they respond to mechanical deformation and, in particular, of their ultimate properties. In some respects polymers have gained a bad reputation for being rather weak and easily fractured. This is to a certain extent unfair as many of the faults are due to incorrect design or materials selection rather than inferior materials. The ease of deformation can in many respects be an advantage and means that flexible and tough polymers such as polyethylene make excellent materials for packaging. The unique properties of rubbers have been utilised since the last century. However, there are problems with certain polymers, such as poor impact or fatigue resistance and environmental stress cracking. This book will be concerned with the mechanics and mechanisms of these and other failure processes. In addition we will also be pointing out how these problems can be overcome, such as by modifications to the existing polymer or the use of alternative polymers.

1

In this chapter the scene is set for the rest of the book and essential background material which will not be covered elsewhere is presented. Emphasis is placed upon areas which will be referred to in detail later. Basic concepts and ideas are discussed first of all and the synthesis and structure of polymers are reviewed briefly. The deformation of polymers is then discussed for both the elastic case and for inelastic or plastic deformation. Finally the state of stress at cracks and the fracture of polymers are considered from a general viewpoint.

1.1 BASIC CONCEPTS

There are several words and concepts used throughout this book which need to be defined especially for readers who are unfamiliar with the subject of polymer science.

1.1.1 Definitions

A *polymer* is a long molecule containing atoms held together by primary covalent bonds along the molecule. Polymers are made by a process called *polymerisation* whereby *monomer* molecules react together chemically to form linear or branched chains or a three-dimensional polymer network as shown in Fig. 1.1. The details of the polymerisation process control the type of polymer produced and the structure of the polymer governs its properties.

If only one type of monomer is used the resulting polymer is called a *homopolymer* whereas if more than one type of monomer is used the polymer is termed a *copolymer*. There are several types of copolymers and a wide variety of structures and properties can be obtained. If two types of monomer unit are used, A and B, then different geometrical arrangements of these units lead to different types of copolymer such as[1]

Random copolymer   A—A—A—B—B—A—B—B—A—A—A—B—B—

Block copolymer   A—A—A—A—A—A—B—B—B—B—B—B—A—A—A—A—A

Graft copolymer   A—A—A—A—A—A—A—A—A—A—A—A—A—A—A—

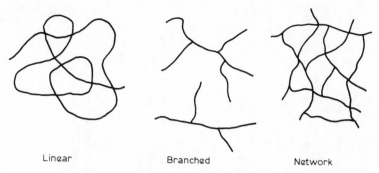

| Linear | Branched | Network |

Fig. 1.1. Schematic representation of different types of polymer molecule.

and the different arrangements of monomer units lead to polymers with different properties.

1.1.2 Classification of Polymers

There are now a large number of polymers available, many with complex chemical structures and long names. In this book we will be concerned mainly with the properties of the most common polymers and the structures of some of these are given in Table 1.1—because of the length of their names abbreviations will sometimes be used especially in Part II and the abbreviations are also given in the table. Although many of the properties of a polymer are controlled solely by its chemical structure there are considerable variations in properties due to differences in physical structure such as chain length or molecular architecture.[1] Hence polymers tend to be classified into types with similar molecular architecture rather than similar chemical structure. Of course, any attempts to classify polymers into particular groups tend to be somewhat arbitrary. One way is to put them into groups displaying similar physical properties which reflect the underlying molecular structure, as shown in Fig. 1.2. Polymers can be separated into three distinct groups: *thermoplastics, rubbers* and *thermosets,* and in addition thermoplastics can be separated into two subgroups, *crystalline* and *non-crystalline* (amorphous). Thermoplastics are linear or branched polymers which melt upon heating. Rubbers are lightly cross-linked polymers which have elastomeric properties, and thermosets are rigid, highly cross-linked polymers which degrade rather than melt upon the application of heat. This general classification is used to differentiate between the types of polymer in Part II.

TABLE 1.1
SOME COMMON THERMOPLASTIC POLYMERS (AFTER REFERENCE 1)

Monomer	Polymer	Comments and uses
Ethylene $CH_2=CH_2$	Polyethylene (PE)	Moulded objects, tubing, film, electrical insulation, e.g. 'Alkathene'.
Propylene $CH_2=CH(CH_3)$	Polypropylene (PP)	Similar uses to PE; lighter, stiffer, e.g. 'Propathene'.
Tetrafluoroethylene $CF_2=CF_2$	Polytetrafluoroethylene (PTFE)	Mouldings or film. High-temperature polymer. Excellent electrical insulator. Low coefficient of sliding friction. Expensive, e.g. 'Teflon', 'Fluon'.
Styrene $CH_2=CH(C_6H_5)$	Polystyrene (PS)	Cheap moulded objects. Polymerised with butadiene to make high impact polystyrene (HIPS). Expanded to make plastic foam.

Methyl methacrylate
$CH_2=C(CH_3)COOCH_3$

Poly(methyl methacrylate) (PMMA)

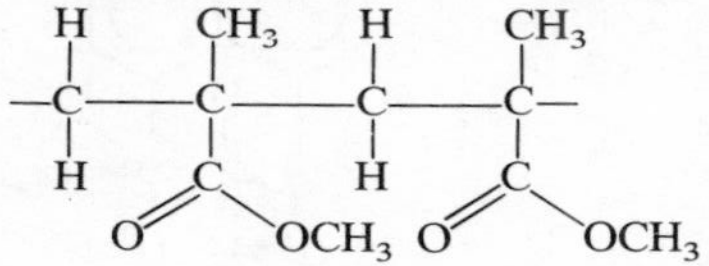

Transparent sheets and tubing. More expensive than PS. Aeroplane windows, e.g. 'Perspex', 'Lucite'.

Vinyl chloride
$CH_2=CHCl$

Poly(vinyl chloride) (PVC)

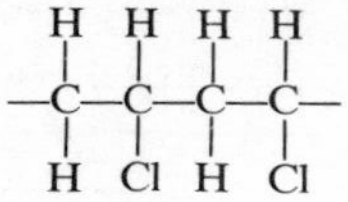

Gramophone records, water pipes, gutters etc. Plasticised to make raincoats, garden hoses and orange squash bottles, e.g. 'Darvic', 'Welvic'.

Vinyl acetate
$CH_3COOCH=CH_2$

Poly(vinyl acetate) (PVA)

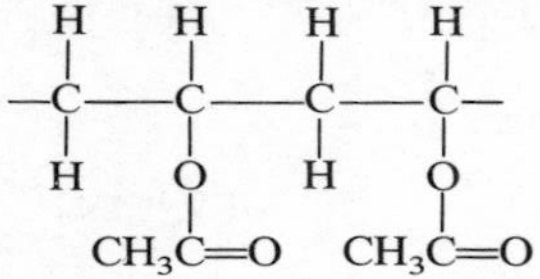

Chewing gum, adhesives, surface coatings.

Acrylonitrile
$CH_2=CHCN$

Polyacrylonitrile (PAN)

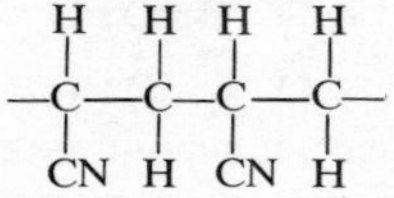

Textile fibres, e.g. 'Orlon', 'Acrilan'.

TABLE 1.1—contd.

Monomer	Polymer	Comments and uses
Ethylene glycol $HOCH_2—CH_2OH$ and terephthalic acid $HOOC—\bigcirc—COOH$	Polyethylene terephthalate (PET)	Textile fibres, e.g. 'Terylene'. Thin drawn film, e.g. 'Mylar', 'Melinex'.
Hexamethylene diamine $H_2N—(CH_2)_6—NH_2$ and sebacic acid $HOOC—(CH_2)_8—COOH$	Nylon 6.10	Textile fibres, also moulded objects. Bearing and gear wheels.

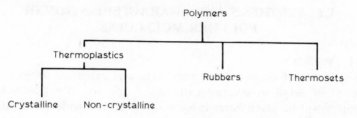

Fig. 1.2. Classification scheme for polymers.

1.1.3 Molar Mass

As many of the physical properties of polymers are intimately dependent upon the size of the polymer molecules it is essential to have a
parameter to describe this size. This is normally done by quoting the
molar mass, M, which is the mass of 1 mole of the polymer and has
units of $g\,mol^{-1}$ or $kg\,mol^{-1}$. In many texts the molar mass is called the
'molecular weight' but this is not preferred because it can be misleading. The weight of a polymer molecule is very small ($\sim 10^{-20}$ g) and the
term 'molecular weight' really means the relative molecular mass (i.e.
the mass of a polymer molecule divided by the mass of a hydrogen
atom).

In a typical polymer sample there is a *distribution* of molar mass and
so an average value needs to be defined. Two particular averages are
often quoted: the number average, $\bar{M}_n$, and the weight average, $\bar{M}_w$,
both of which are capable of being measured experimentally. They can
be defined as[1]

$$\bar{M}_n = 1/\sum (w_i/M_i) \qquad (1.1)$$

and

$$\bar{M}_w = \sum (w_i M_i) \qquad (1.2)$$

where w_i is the weight fraction of molecules of molar mass M_i in the
distribution. In many polymers there is a wide distribution of molar
mass and $\bar{M}_n$ and $\bar{M}_w$ are only two points on the distribution. Some
idea of the nature of the distribution can be obtained from the value of
$\bar{M}_w/\bar{M}_n$. For sharp fractions (i.e. a narrow distribution) $\bar{M}_w/\bar{M}_n \sim 1$.
Many polydisperse polymers have the ideal distribution of molar mass[1]
for which $\bar{M}_w/\bar{M}_n = 2$ but there is often a very broad distribution and
$\bar{M}_w/\bar{M}_n \gg 2$, especially for branched polymers.

1.2   SYNTHESIS AND CHARACTERISATION OF POLYMER MOLECULES

1.2.1   Synthesis

The synthesis of polymers is a very large and extensive subject. It is covered in detail in several textbooks[1-3] and so only a very brief summary will be given here. It is conventional to divide the synthesis of polymers into two main categories, namely *condensation* polymerisation and *addition* polymerisation, although other types of polymerisation reaction are also used.

Condensation polymerisation reactions take place between polyfunctional monomer molecules such as a diacid and a diol. An example of this is given below for the production of a linear polyester, poly(ethylene terephthalate)

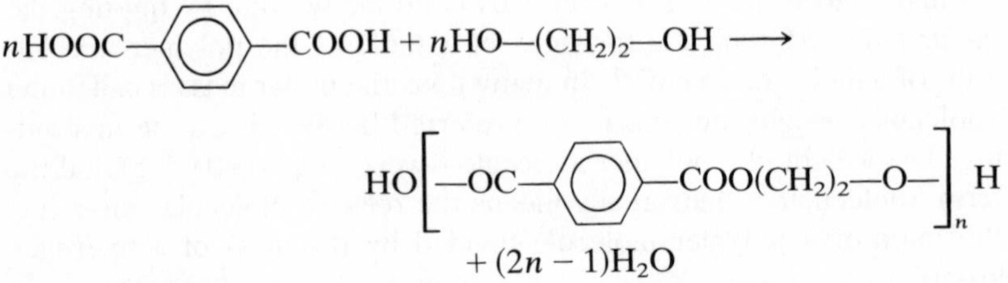

$$n\,HOOC-\!\!\left\langle\bigcirc\right\rangle\!\!-COOH + n\,HO-(CH_2)_2-OH \longrightarrow$$

$$HO\left[-OC-\!\!\left\langle\bigcirc\right\rangle\!\!-COO(CH_2)_2-O-\right]_n H$$
$$+ (2n-1)H_2O$$

The molar mass of the polymer increases with increasing reaction time. If the functionality of the monomer molecules is greater than two then a network polymer may be produced.

Addition polymerisation is the second main category and differs from condensation polymerisation in several ways. The monomers contain double bonds which are susceptible to attack by either free-radical or ionic initiators. The monomer molecules add on, one at a time, to an activated molecule which is eventually neutralised by a termination reaction. The reaction has three distinct steps: initiation, propagation and termination, and can be summarised as shown below for the polymerisation of styrene to give polystyrene

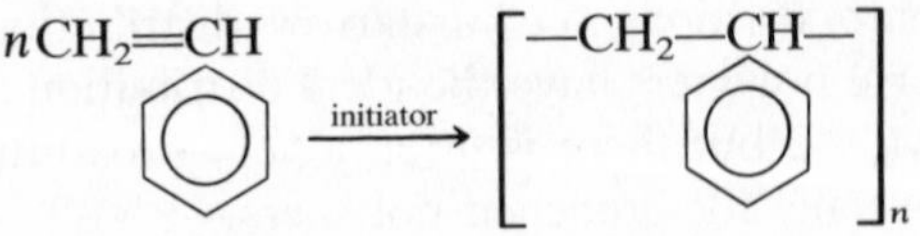

$$n\,CH_2\!\!=\!\!CH \atop \left\langle\bigcirc\right\rangle \quad \xrightarrow{\text{initiator}} \quad \left[-CH_2-CH- \atop \left\langle\bigcirc\right\rangle\right]_n$$

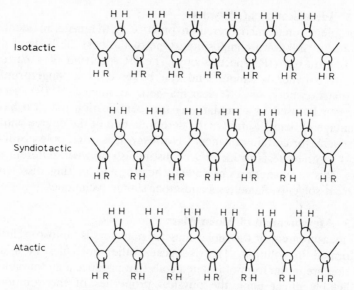

Fig. 1.3. Different stereochemical configurations of polymers formed from the general vinyl monomer $CH_2{=}CHR$.

The molar mass of the polystyrene produced depends upon the concentrations of monomer and initiator and the reaction temperature.[1] If a mixture of monomers is used a copolymer may be produced.

There is now an increasing need for polymer molecules with well-defined molecular structures such as controlled levels of branching, molar mass and tacticity (Fig. 1.3). This can be achieved by using special types of catalyst to control polymerisation. For example, Ziegler–Natta catalysts[2,3] can be used to produce vinyl polymers, such as polystyrene or polypropylene, with no branching and controlled types of tacticity. Also special ionic initiators can be used to produce polymers with very narrow distributions of molar mass ($\bar{M}_w/\bar{M}_n \sim 1$) and controlled tacticities. Recent developments in the field of solid-state polymerisation[1,4] have allowed macroscopic polymer crystals to be produced in which the molecules are completely ordered and fully aligned.

These polymers with controlled structures are particularly useful for the study of the effect of molecular structure upon mechanical properties and their use has allowed many significant advances in our understanding of structure/property relationships in polymers.

1.2.2 Identification of Polymers

A problem often encountered in practice is the need to identify a polymer of unknown composition. One of the best methods of doing this is infra-red (IR) spectroscopy. The IR spectrum of a particular type of polymer is unique and can be used as a 'fingerprint' for identification purposes.[5] Nuclear magnetic resonance (NMR) spectroscopy can be used in a similar way for identification but also has the advantage of being useful for the determination of the degree and type of tacticity for certain polymers.[1] However, it is often only possible to resort to crude tests to identify or distinguish between different polymers. This can sometimes be done by heating and melting, dissolving in different solvents, flame tests and other simple techniques.

1.2.3 Measurement of Molar Mass

The measurement of the molar mass of polymers is almost exclusively performed in solution. This is because the molecules in a dilute solution are in the form of isolated coils that produce a measurable and predictable effect upon the physical properties of the solution. In particular the thermodynamic behaviour of polymer solutions is relatively well understood and the *osmotic pressure* of a polymer solution can be used to determine the number-average molar mass, $\bar{M}_n$, of the polymer molecules in the solution.[1] Polymer coils also scatter light in a well-defined way and measurement of *light scattering* can be used to determine both $\bar{M}_w$ and the dimensions of the polymer coils. A particularly simple method of determining the molar mass of a polymer is by measuring the *viscosity* of a dilute solution of the polymer. However, this produces the viscosity-average molar mass, $\bar{M}_v$, where $\bar{M}_n < \bar{M}_v < \bar{M}_w$, which can only be accurately related to $\bar{M}_n$ and $\bar{M}_w$ when the whole molar-mass distribution is known.[1]

An extremely useful method of determining molar mass is gel permeation chromatography (GPC) which can also be used for polymer fractionation.[1,6] This technique is finding increasingly more use and involves streaming a polymer solution through a column packed with porous glass beads. The larger molecules cannot enter the pores and so pass through the column more rapidly than smaller molecules and the molar-mass distribution becomes spread out. Analysis of the solution leaving the column therefore allows the complete distribution to be determined as shown in Fig. 1.4. In addition GPC can be used as a preparative technique to split the distribution up into different molar-mass fractions.[1,6]

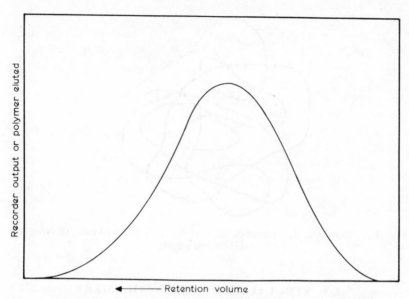

Fig. 1.4. Typical gel permeation chromatograph. It can be related directly to the molar mass distribution for the polymer.

1.2.4 Macromolecules in Solution

Many of the methods of polymer characterisation involve the measurement of properties of polymer solutions—the conformations of polymer molecules in solution are related to their organisation in the solid state. In dilute solution the molecules of many polymers are in the form of a random Gaussian coil[1] as shown in Fig. 1.5. The dimensions of the coil are characterised in terms of the distance between the chain ends, the displacement length, which is normally quoted as its root mean square (RMS) value, $\langle \bar{R}^2_{rms} \rangle^{\frac{1}{2}}$, which can be determined from light-scattering measurements.[1] In good solvents the coils are expanded whereas in poor solvents they are contracted and in certain polymer/solvent systems at a particular temperature (the Theta temperature, Θ) the polymer chain has its unperturbed dimensions $\langle \bar{R}^2_{rms} \rangle_0^{\frac{1}{2}}$.[1,7] In addition the polymer solution behaves in a pseudo-ideal manner when $T = \Theta$.

The conformations of polymer molecules in the solid state are now known to be similar to those in dilute solution and this is important in determining the structure of amorphous and semicrystalline polymers and in the theoretical analysis of rubber elasticity.

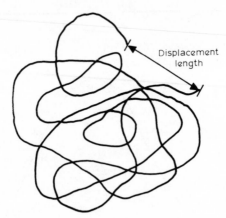

Fig. 1.5. Schematic representation of a coiled polymer molecule showing the displacement length.

1.3   STRUCTURE OF SOLID POLYMERS

Many molecular solids are crystalline but an unusual aspect of the structure of polymers is that they can be obtained in both amorphous and crystalline forms, and, in addition, crystalline polymers are only semicrystalline when containing a significant amorphous component.[1] There is an increasing realisation that there is an intimate relationship between the structure and the mechanical properties for both amorphous and crystalline polymers—because of this the structure of both types of polymer will be discussed in detail.

1.3.1   Amorphous Polymers

Certain polymers cannot be crystallised at all whereas others are obtained in a semicrystalline form when they are cooled slowly from the molten state and are only non-crystalline when they are cooled rapidly or quenched. For example, atactic polystyrene cannot be crystallised whereas poly(ethylene terephthalate) is amorphous when cooled rapidly from the melt but can be crystallised by slow cooling or annealing at an elevated temperature.

Over the years there has been a great deal of dispute as to whether amorphous polymers are truly amorphous or contain domains of order.[8] There is now strong evidence from small-angle X-ray scattering[9] and careful electron microscopy[10] that the domains of order are probably an artefact and that amorphous polymers are non-crystalline. Although the structures must be random it is of considerable interest to know the conformations of the molecules in an amorphous polymer. Many years ago Flory[11] predicted that the molecules in an amorphous polymer would have the same conformations as they have in a Theta solvent and hence an RMS displacement length of $\langle \bar{R}_{rms}^2 \rangle_0^{\frac{1}{2}}$. It is only relatively recently that this has been proved experimentally from small-angle neutron scattering studies upon mixtures of protonated and deuterated polymers.[12]

Another feature in the structure of amorphous polymers which is now being recognised as affecting the mechanical properties is *entanglements*. As polymer solutions become more concentrated it is known that the molecules tend to become entangled rather than remain as

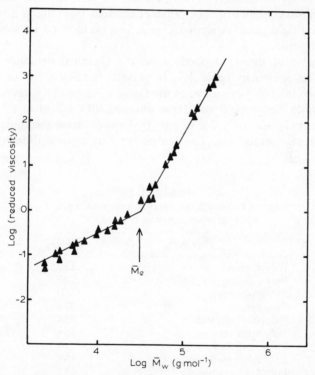

Fig. 1.6. Log–log plot of reduced melt viscosity as a function of $\bar{M}_w$ for polystyrene produced by anionic polymerisation (after Porter & Johnson[13]).

isolated coils. The effect is particularly apparent in polymer melts where it is found[13] that above a critical molar mass (for example, $\bar{M}_w = 35\,000$ for polystyrene) the dependence of the viscosity of the melt upon $\bar{M}_w$ changes from a power of 1 to a power of about 3·5 as shown in Fig. 1.6. This abrupt change has been interpreted[13] as being due to the onset of entanglements in the polymer melt at a critical molar mass, $\bar{M}_e$. The fracture behaviour of several polymers has also been found to undergo an abrupt transition at $\bar{M}_e$.[14]

1.3.2 The Glass Transition

The physical properties of amorphous polymers vary with temperature and rate but there is a very abrupt change in behaviour at a critical temperature known as the glass transition temperature, T_g. For example, when a polymer is cooled from the melt through the T_g there is an abrupt change in viscosity, Young's modulus, heat capacity and thermal expansion coefficient. The polymer changes from being a rubbery liquid to a rigid glass. A similar change can be induced by increasing the testing rate.

The value of the T_g depends upon the chemical structure of the polymer as shown in Table 1.2. In general it reflects the ease with which the molecules can move in the liquid state and so is increased if the polymer has a rigid backbone and/or bulky sidegroups.[1] For a particular polymer the value of the T_g depends upon the molar mass and degree of branching. The reason for this can be thought of in

TABLE 1.2

VALUES OF GLASS TRANSITION TEMPERATURE, T_g, FOR SOME COMMON POLYMERS

Polymer	$T_g(K)$
Polyethylene	~150
Poly(ethylene oxide)	206
Polypropylene	250
Polystyrene	373
Poly(vinyl chloride)	354
Poly(vinyl alcohol)	358
Poly(methyl methacrylate)	388
Poly(ethyl methacrylate)	335
Poly(1,4-butadiene)	172
Natural rubber	200

terms of the concept of 'free volume' whereby defects such as chain ends have extra volume associated with them. The free volume allows molecular motion to take place more easily and hence the T_g will increase as the molar mass of the polymer is increased and the amount of branching is reduced.

1.3.3 Crystalline Polymers

The ability of polymer molecules to crystallise has been recognised for many years but the detailed structure of semicrystalline polymers is still not yet fully understood.

The unit cell dimensions of a large number of polymer crystals are now known to a high degree of accuracy[15] and are not in dispute. However, there is a considerable amount of argument concerning the molecular arrangements in semicrystalline polymers. Isolated polymer crystals (Fig. 1.7(a)) can be grown by precipitation from dilute solution.[15,16] They are lamellar and are of microscopic dimensions with the molecules *folded* in a regular manner[16] with the top and bottom surfaces of the lamellae as fold surfaces. Melt-crystallised polymers are known to be spherulitic (Fig. 1.7(b)) and contain similar lamellar crystals separated by layers of amorphous polymer.[1] However, the source of contention is the way in which the molecules are incorporated in the structure. There is strong evidence that *tie molecules*[17] pass from one crystal to another throughout the amorphous layers and, indeed, they are necessary to hold the structure together. It is also thought[16] that the molecules are folded in the crystals in semicrystalline polymers. Further evidence has been obtained from small-angle neutron scattering of mixtures of protonated and deuterated molecules[18,19] where it has been shown that the conformations of the molecules are not greatly different from those of the molecules in a polymer melt. The neutron scattering data have been interpreted in terms of various models and the most widely accepted one is shown in Fig. 1.7(c) where the molecules have two or three adjacent folds and are shared between at least two crystals. This model is consistent with most of the experimental observations.[16–19]

1.3.4 Crystallisation and Melting

As with other crystalline solids, at a sufficiently high temperature polymer crystals melt. The melting temperature, T_m, is of importance as it limits the temperature at which the polymer can be used and it also controls the temperature at which the polymer can be moulded.

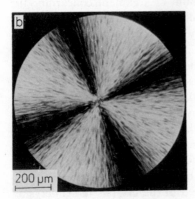

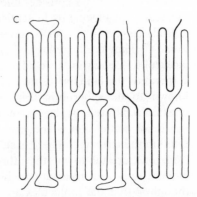

Fig. 1.7. (a) Electron micrograph of a solution-grown polyethylene lamellar single crystal (courtesy of Dr P. Allan); (b) Optical micrograph of a single spherulite growing in isotactic polystyrene (courtesy of Dr D. Tod); and (c) Schematic representation of a possible model for the conformation of a particular molecule (heavy line) in a polymer crystal (after Stamm et al.[19]).

Polymers are often chosen because they can be fabricated at relatively low temperatures but this also means that their high-temperature performance is often rather poor.

The value of T_m is controlled by the structure of the polymer and there is now considerable interest in preparing polymers for high-temperature applications. The effect of chemical structure upon the value of T_m is shown in Table 1.3. The T_m is increased by the incorporation of rigid units into the polymer chain or by having

TABLE 1.3
VALUES OF MELTING TEMPERATURE, T_m,
FOR SOME COMMON POLYMERS

Polymer	$T_m(K)$
Polyethylene	415
Poly(ethylene oxide)	340
Polypropylene	460
Polystyrene	450
Nylon 3	603
Nylon 4	533
Nylon 5	531
Nylon 6	498
Natural rubber	310

interchain hydrogen-bonding as in polyamides (nylons). T_m is also higher in polymers which have bulky rather than long side-groups. These factors are similar to the ones which control the value of the T_g (Section 1.3.2) and so it is perhaps not surprising that there is a relationship between the values of T_m and T_g for polymers which exhibit both types of transition. It is found[20] that the value of T_g is generally between 0·5 and 0·8 T_m and this means that it is not possible to control T_g and T_m independently for homopolymers. There is not a strong dependence of T_m upon molar mass but branching has an important effect. For example, branched polyethylene (LDPE) melts at about 100°C whereas the linear polymer (HPDE) has a much higher melting temperature of 140°C. Branches reduce both the degree of crystallinity and the crystal perfection and so the branched polymer is more flexible and melts at a lower temperature.

For many materials the value of T_m is unique and is the same as the crystallisation temperature, T_c. However, polymers are unusual in that $T_m > T_c$ and T_m depends upon several factors such as the value of T_c, the degree of crystallinity, the crystal size and the heating rate. Because of this an 'equilibrium melting temperature', T_m^0, has to be defined for a particular type of polymer.[1] This can be defined in several ways but can be thought of as the temperature at which a crystal of the polymer of infinite size, heated infinitely slowly, melts. The value of T_m^0 is normally determined by an extrapolation procedure.[1]

The crystallisation of a polymer is a slow process because of the kinetics of incorporating long entangled molecules into crystals. Hence, the structure of semicrystalline polymers is strongly affected by the crystallisation conditions such as cooling rate, T_c and time of crystallisation. For example, many polymers can be cooled so rapidly from the melt to below T_g that they do not crystallise at all. Some polymers, such as polypropylene, crystallise partly when moulded but continue to crystallise slowly over many months when aged at room temperature. This has repercussions since the physical properties of such materials will also vary as the crystallinity changes with ageing.

1.4 STRESS AND STRAIN

The increasing use of polymers in advanced engineering applications means that they are now being subjected to appreciable stresses and strains. Hence rigorous definitions of stress and strain are required.

1.4.1 Stress
In simple terms it is possible to define stress as force per unit area but in general it is necessary to resolve the stresses on a body into nine components, as shown in Fig. 1.8, and describe the stress state in terms of a stress tensor, σ_{ij}

$$\sigma_{ij} = \begin{pmatrix} \sigma_{11} & \sigma_{12} & \sigma_{13} \\ \sigma_{21} & \sigma_{22} & \sigma_{23} \\ \sigma_{31} & \sigma_{32} & \sigma_{33} \end{pmatrix} \tag{1.3}$$

The first subscript gives the normal to the plane on which the stress acts and the second subscript defines the direction of the stress. The components σ_{11}, σ_{22} and σ_{33} are known as normal or direct stresses since they are perpendicular to the plane on which they act, and the other components are shear stresses. The sign convention which is normally used for the normal stresses is that tensile ones are positive and compressive ones are negative. These nine components are not all independent of each other and in order to stop the body rotating it is necessary for the shear stresses to be related by

$$\sigma_{12} = \sigma_{21}, \quad \sigma_{23} = \sigma_{32}, \quad \sigma_{31} = \sigma_{13}$$

Knowledge of the stress tensor allows the stresses acting on any plane within the body to be determined.

It is always possible to express the stress acting at a point in terms of *principal stresses* acting along principal axes. In this case the shear

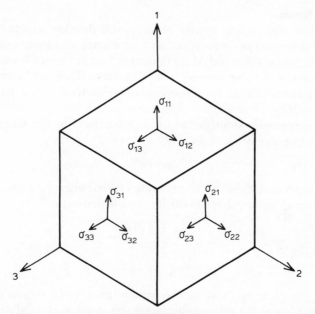

Fig. 1.8. Schematic illustration of the nine stress components for a rectangular coordinate system.

stresses $(i \neq j)$ are all zero and the only terms remaining in the tensor are σ_{11}, σ_{22} and σ_{33}, normally termed σ_1, σ_2 and σ_3, respectively. It is often possible to determine the principal axes from simple inspection of the body as two principal axes always lie in the plane of a free surface.

In consideration of the mechanical properties of polymers it is often useful to divide the stress tensor into a hydrostatic or dilatational component which causes a volume change and into a deviatoric or pure shear component which causes a change in shape. The hydrostatic component, p, of the stress tensor is given by

$$p = \tfrac{1}{3}(\sigma_{11} + \sigma_{22} + \sigma_{33}) \qquad (1.4)$$

and the deviatoric stress tensor, σ'_{ij}, is found by subtracting the hydrostatic stress components from the overall tensor such that

$$\sigma'_{ij} = \begin{pmatrix} (\sigma_{11}-p) & \sigma_{12} & \sigma_{13} \\ \sigma_{21} & (\sigma_{22}-p) & \sigma_{23} \\ \sigma_{31} & \sigma_{32} & (\sigma_{33}-p) \end{pmatrix} \qquad (1.5)$$

1.4.2 Strain

Any body subjected to a state of stress will develop strains although the full definition of strain is not an easy matter. A simple example of strain would be a thin rod of continuum of length l which is extended a small amount δl by an externally applied stress. There are several ways in which the strain can be defined, all of which treat it as a dimensionless quantity.

The *engineering strain*, e, which is often used in the linear-elastic analysis of polymers is defined as

$$e = \delta l/l \tag{1.6}$$

The *extension ratio*, λ, is sometimes used when large strains are encountered, as in rubber elasticity, and is defined as

$$\lambda = (l + \delta l)/l \tag{1.7}$$

and clearly

$$\lambda = 1 + e \tag{1.8}$$

The complete analysis of the strains in a body requires careful consideration of the relative displacements in the body under stress. It can be shown[21] that it is possible to describe the state of strain in terms of a strain tensor e_{ij} (cf., the stress tensor, σ_{ij}) such that

$$e_{ij} = \begin{pmatrix} e_{11} & e_{12} & e_{13} \\ e_{21} & e_{22} & e_{23} \\ e_{31} & e_{32} & e_{33} \end{pmatrix} \tag{1.9}$$

and, as in the case of stresses, it is possible to define principal strains e_1, e_2 and e_3.

1.4.3 Plane Stress and Plane Strain

There are several special states of stress particularly relevant to the fracture of materials. One is *plane stress* which is obtained in deformed thin sheets[21] as shown in Fig. 1.9(a). Since the stresses normal to free surfaces are zero then the stresses on planes parallel to the surface of a thin sheet will be very small. As the stresses on planes normal to the surface are finite then the two principal stresses acting in the plane of the sheet, σ_1 and σ_2, will be also finite and the third stress normal to the plane, σ_3, will tend to zero.

Another important situation is the case where one of the three principal strains, e_3, is equal to zero. This is often encountered in the

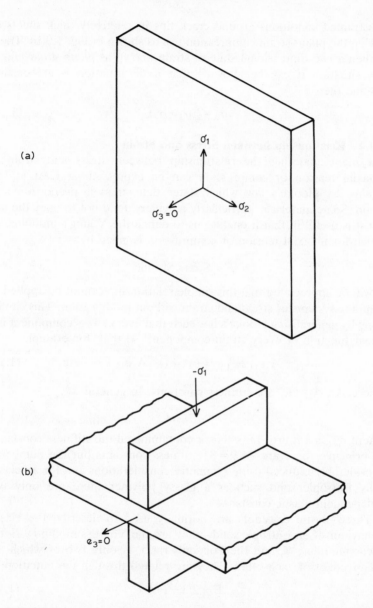

Fig. 1.9. (a) Schematic representation of plane stress in a thin sheet of material ($\sigma_3 = 0$); and (b) Schematic representation of a plane-strain compression test ($e_3 = 0$).

constrained conditions around crack tips in relatively thick sheets or during the plane-strain compression test as shown in Fig. 1.9(b). There is then a two-dimensional state of strain known as *plane strain* and in this situation it can be shown[21] that if deformation is at constant volume then

$$\sigma_3 = \tfrac{1}{2}(\sigma_1 + \sigma_2) \tag{1.10}$$

1.4.4 Relationship between Stress and Strain

For many materials the relationship between stress and strain in uniaxial tension or compression can be expressed, at least at low strains, by Hooke's law which states that stress is proportional to strain. Some materials, particularly polymers, tend not to obey the law but it is useful in that it enables us to define the Young's modulus, E, which for uniaxial tension or compression is given by

$$E = \text{Stress/Strain}$$

It will be appreciated that this simple relationship cannot be applied to complex systems of stress and strain without modification. This can be done by generalising Hooke's law such that every stress component is a linear function of every strain component[1] so that, for example

$$\sigma_{11} = A_1 e_{11} + A_2 e_{22} + A_3 e_{33} + A_4 e_{12} + \cdots \text{ etc.} \tag{1.11}$$

where A_1, A_2, etc. are stiffness constants. In general

$$\sigma_{ij} = c_{ijkl} e_{ij} \tag{1.12}$$

where c_{ijkl} is a fourth-rank tensor containing all the stiffness constants. In principle there are $9 \times 9 = 81$ stiffness constants but the number is considerably reduced using symmetry considerations and for an elastically isotropic solid such as a glassy polymer there are only two independent elastic constants.[1]

Three elastic constants are normally used to describe the elastic behaviour of an isotropic solid—they are the Young's modulus, E, the shear modulus, $\mathscr{G}$, and the Poisson's ratio, ν, only two of which are independent of each other. They are related through the equation

$$E = 2(1 + \nu)\mathscr{G} \tag{1.13}$$

Hence although the relationship between stress and strain is potentially highly complex the elastic behaviour of isotropic solids can be described through a small number of elastic constants.

The Young's modulus, E, relates the stress to the strain for uniaxial tensile or compressive loading and the shear modulus, $\mathcal{G}$, relates the shear stress to the shear strain. The Poisson's ratio, ν, accounts for the lateral contraction during unaxial tension and can be thought of as the ratio of the lateral to the longitudinal strain for a bar deformed in uniaxial tension. For a constant volume process $\nu = 0\cdot5$ but for most materials there is a volume expansion or dilatation during tensile loading and ν is usually of the order of $0\cdot3$. It should be pointed out, however, that the lateral strains are due to the longitudinal stress and occur without any lateral stresses being applied or present.

The elastic constants E and ν can be used to show how a body will respond to a set of principal stresses σ_{11}, σ_{22} and σ_{33}. A stress of σ_{11} will cause a strain of σ_{11}/E along the 1 direction, but will also lead to strains of $-\nu\sigma_{11}/E$ along the 2 and 3 directions (Fig. 1.8). Similarly a stress of σ_{22} will cause strains of σ_{22}/E along 2 and of $-\nu\sigma_{22}/E$ in the other directions. If it is assumed that the strains due to the different stresses are additive then it follows that

$$e_{11} = \frac{\sigma_{11}}{E} - \frac{\nu}{E}(\sigma_{22} + \sigma_{33}) \qquad (1.14)$$

$$e_{22} = \frac{\sigma_{22}}{E} - \frac{\nu}{E}(\sigma_{33} + \sigma_{11}) \qquad (1.15)$$

$$e_{33} = \frac{\sigma_{33}}{E} - \frac{\nu}{E}(\sigma_{11} + \sigma_{22}) \qquad (1.16)$$

1.5 DEFORMATION OF POLYMERS

1.5.1 Elastic Deformation

Polymers exhibit a wide range of elastic properties depending upon their structure and the testing conditions. Figure 1.10 shows the variation of E with temperature for an amorphous polymer. At low temperatures the polymer is glassy with a relatively high modulus ($\sim 10^9\,\mathrm{N\,m^{-2}}$). The modulus falls rapidly through the region of the T_g where the polymer is viscoelastic and the modulus is very rate- and temperature-dependent. At a sufficiently high temperature the polymer becomes rubbery. If the polymer is cross-linked then the modulus remains approximately constant with increasing temperature at $\sim 10^6\,\mathrm{N\,m^{-2}}$ otherwise it flows like a viscous liquid.

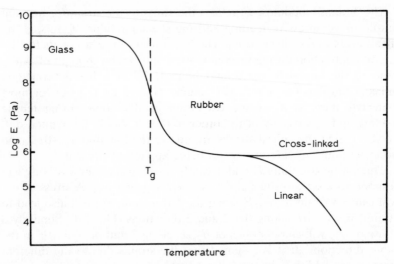

Fig. 1.10. Typical variation of Young's modulus, E, with temperature for a polymer showing the effect of cross-linking upon E in the rubbery state (after Young[1]).

Semicrystalline polymers behave like amorphous polymers below the T_g of the non-crystalline phase. However, they have interesting and useful properties between T_g and T_m where the structure consists of crystals in a rubbery matrix. The modulus of the material depends upon the degree of crystallinity ranging from $\sim 10^7\,\mathrm{N\,m^{-2}}$ for 5 % crystallinity to $E > 10^9\,\mathrm{N\,m^{-2}}$ for isotropic polymers which are >70 % crystalline. The elastic properties of polymers also depend upon the degree of orientation. In highly oriented polymer fibres or polymer single crystal fibres the modulus can be in excess of $10^{11}\,\mathrm{N\,m^{-2}}$. The modulus values for different types of polymer are summarised in Table 1.4.

The elastic behaviour of polymers reflects the deformation of the structure on a molecular level. In the high-modulus polymer fibres and crystals the deformation takes place essentially through bending and stretching of the aligned polymer backbone bonds which requires high forces.[22] In an isotropic polymer glass the molecules are frozen in the structure, coiled and randomly oriented and so elastic deformation induces the relatively easier bond rotation[23] which requires lower forces.

TABLE 1.4

TYPICAL VALUES OF YOUNG'S MODULUS, E, AND FRACTURE STRENGTH, σ_f, FOR DIFFERENT TYPES OF POLYMER MEASURED AT ROOM TEMPERATURE AND MODERATE TESTING RATES

Type of polymer	Modulus $E(Pa)$	Fracture strength $\sigma_f(MPa)$
Rubber	$\sim 10^6$	~ 10
Semicrystalline polymer (above T_g)	$\sim 10^8$	~ 30
Semicrystalline polymer (below T_g)	$\sim 10^9$	~ 50
Glassy polymer	$\sim 10^9$	~ 70
Semicrystalline polymer fibre	$\sim 10^{10}$	~ 500
Polymer single crystal fibre	$\sim 10^{11}$	$\sim 2\,000$

Elastic deformation in the rubbery state has received a great deal of interest.[24] The coiled polymer chains are able to translate past each other reversibly when deformed. The behaviour can be readily analysed using statistical thermodynamics and it is envisaged that deformation reduces the conformational entropy of the polymer molecules. Stressing causes the chains to uncoil and since a stretched chain has less conformations available to it, its entropy is reduced. Removal of the applied stress allows the chains to increase their entropy by readopting randomly coiled conformations. It can be readily shown[24] that the equilibrium modulus of a rubber is given by an equation of the form

$$\mathscr{G} = \rho_d \mathbf{R} T / \bar{M}_c \qquad (1.17)$$

where ρ_d is the density of the rubber, $\mathbf{R}$ is the molar gas constant and $\bar{M}_c$ is the average molar mass between cross-links. Hence the modulus of a rubber will increase as the cross-link density increases. A perhaps more unexpected implication is that the equilibrium modulus will increase as the temperature increases, a direct consequence of the deformation of rubbers being controlled by changes in entropy rather than internal energy.

1.5.2 Viscoelasticity

A distinctive feature of the mechanical behaviour of polymers is the way in which their response to an applied stress or strain depends upon the rate or time period of loading. Elastic materials obey Hooke's law whereby the stress is proportional to strain whereas viscous materials, such as liquids, tend to obey Newton's law whereby the stress is proportional to strain-rate and independent of the strain. The behaviour of many polymers can be thought of as being somewhere between that of elastic solids and liquids. At low temperatures and high rates of strain they display elastic behaviour whereas at high temperatures and low rates of strain they behave in a viscous manner flowing like a liquid. Polymers are therefore termed *viscoelastic* as they display both viscous and elastic types of behaviour. The subject of viscoelasticity is covered in several textbooks[1,25-7] and so only a brief review will be given here.

An example of viscoelastic behaviour is given in Fig. 1.11 for the variation of stress, σ, and strain, e, with time, t, for a simple polymer specimen subjected to four different deformation histories. The examples given are for creep, stress relaxation, constant stress-rate and constant strain-rate. In each case the response of the stress or strain is indicated for the applied strain or stress and the behaviour of an elastic material is indicated by dashed lines. The situation can often be simplified by assuming that a polymer behaves in a *linear viscoelastic* manner and the deformation is represented using mechanical models.[1,25-7] These models are combinations of elastic springs and viscous dashpots such as the Maxwell model (spring and dashpot in series) or the Voigt model (spring and dashpot in parallel). More complex combinations of the two components are often used to model the behaviour more accurately but it must be remembered that they are only mathematical models and give no idea of the molecular mechanisms involved. A useful way of predicting the behaviour of viscoelastic materials is to use the *Boltzmann superposition principle*.[25] This assumes that if the applied stress is varied with time the overall deformation can be determined from the algebraic sum of the strains due to each loading step.

The viscoelastic behaviour of polymers is often examined using dynamic mechanical testing[1,25,26] where the polymer is subjected to an oscillating sinusoidal stress. Unlike an elastic material the strain lags somewhat behind the stress and so the variation of stress and strain

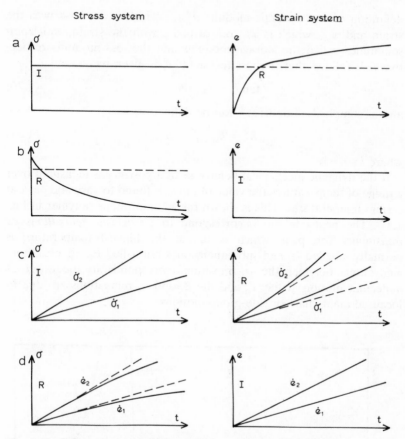

Fig. 1.11. Schematic representation of the variation of stress and strain with time indicating the input (I) and responses (R) for different types of loading. (a) Creep; (b) relaxation; (c) constant stress-rate; and (d) constant strain-rate. The dashed lines are for elastic materials and the solid lines for viscoelastic ones (after Williams[21]).

with time can be given by expressions of the type

$$e = e_a \sin \nu_d t \tag{1.18}$$

$$\sigma = \sigma_a \sin (\nu_d t + \delta_r) \tag{1.19}$$

where e_a and σ_a are the strain and stress amplitude, ν_d is the frequency and δ_r is the phase angle or phase lag.[1] This approach leads to the definition of two dynamic moduli, $\mathscr{G}_{storage}$ which is in-phase with the strain and $\mathscr{G}_{loss}$ which is $\pi/2$ out-of-phase with the strain, which are sometimes called the storage modulus and the loss modulus respectively. It follows that the loss factor tan δ_r is given by

$$\tan \delta_r = \mathscr{G}_{loss}/\mathscr{G}_{storage} \qquad (1.20)$$

and a 'complex' modulus $\mathscr{G}^*$ can be defined as

$$\mathscr{G}^* = \mathscr{G}_{storage} + i\mathscr{G}_{loss} \qquad (1.21)$$

where $i = \sqrt{-1}$.

If the dynamic mechanical behaviour of a polymer is measured over a range of temperatures the value of tan δ_r is found to vary and peak at certain temperatures. This is shown for an amorphous polymer in Fig. 1.12. The peaks in tan δ_r correspond to *viscoelastic relaxations* or *transitions*. The peak which occurs at the highest temperature is normally labelled α_r and subsequent ones are called β_r, γ_r, etc. In an amorphous polymer the α_r-transition corresponds to the onset of molecular motion at the T_g and the β_r and γ_r relaxations are due to localised main-chain or side-group motions.

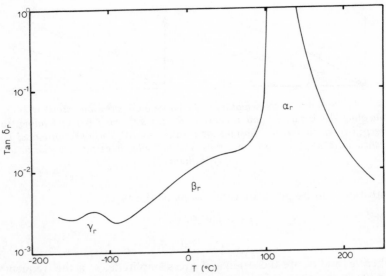

Fig. 1.12. Variation of tan δ_r with temperature for amorphous polystyrene (after McCrum et al.[26]).

The mechanical behaviour of polymers depends upon testing rate as well as temperature and it is found that there is a general equivalence between time and temperature. For example, glass to rubber transitions can be induced by either increasing the temperature or reducing the rate.[1] The behaviour can be represented in a procedure known as *time–temperature superposition*. For example, if a series of mechanical measurements are made over a range of temperatures at different testing frequencies the data can be put onto a simple 'master curve' by shifting the data measured at one temperature along the frequency axis by a factor which is a function only of the test temperature. Much of the early work on the time–temperature superposition was done by Ferry[27] and co-workers who proposed that the shift factor, a_T, could be given by an equation of the form

$$\log a_T = \frac{-C_1(T - T_r)}{C_2 + (T - T_r)} \tag{1.22}$$

where C_1 and C_2 are constants and T_r is a reference temperature. This equation is normally termed the *WLF* (*Williams–Landel–Ferry*) *equation*. It was originally developed empirically but has since been justified from consideration of the effect of 'free volume' in polymers.[1]

1.5.3 Hysteresis and Plastic Flow

It has been pointed out already that polymers only tend to obey Hooke's law at vanishingly small strains and at high strains their behaviour is non-Hookean. The relationship between stress and strain for some polymers does not follow a straight line. An example of this is given in Fig. 1.13(a). Another type of non-Hookean behaviour is shown in Fig. 1.13(b) where a rubber is stretched to a high strain and then unloaded. As the unloading path is below the loading path, energy will be dissipated in the strain cycle.[28] This phenomenon is known as *hysteresis* but the term can only be applied strictly when the deformed material returns to its original shape (i.e. zero strain). For filled rubbers and many plastics there is a 'permanent set' following a deformation cycle, with a small amount of residual deformation, even when the maximum strain is below the yield strain.

Hysteresis is of particular importance during crack propagation in polymers since when a crack moves through a body elements close to the crack tip will experience a full deformation cycle. Theoretical analysis of the fracture of ductile polymers has suggested that mechanical hysteresis will undoubtedly affect crack propagation.[29]

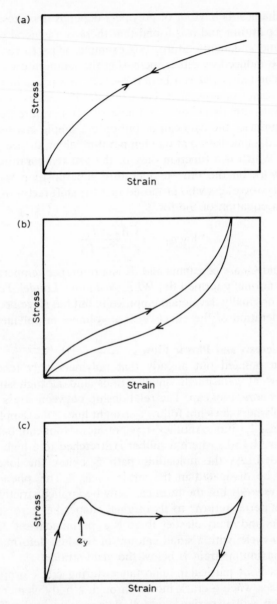

Fig. 1.13. Schematic representation of different types of non-Hookean deformation. (a) Non-linear elastic deformation; (b) mechanical hysteresis; and (c)
yield and plastic deformation.

Ductile plastics tend to have a fairly well-defined yield point as shown in Fig. 1.13(c) with the value of yield strain typically of the order of 5–10 %—much higher than the value for metals or ceramics. Some semicrystalline polymers can be cold-drawn to extension ratios in excess of 20 during which a stable neck extends along the specimen. Most amorphous glassy polymers are brittle in tension but yield and flow to high strains in compression or pure shear when there is no overall hydrostatic tensile stress.[30] Even cross-linked epoxy resins which are normally thought to be very brittle show a high degree of ductility in compression.[31]

In practice it is often difficult to differentiate between true mechanical hysteresis and the dissipation of energy due to plastic deformation. However, this is not particularly important as both processes lead to a dissipation of energy which is similar for both mechanisms.

1.5.4 Shear Yielding

One important mechanism which can lead to plastic deformation in polymers is *shear yielding*.[30] It takes place essentially at *constant volume* and leads to a permanent change in specimen shape. There is obviously a translation of molecules past each other during shear yielding but on annealing a deformed glassy polymer above its T_g it often completely recovers its original shape. The molecules are well anchored at entanglements in the structure and are not broken to any great extent during deformation. They return to their original conformations when they have sufficient mobility above the T_g.

The micromechanisms involved in shear yielding are discussed in detail in Chapter 4 and so only a brief account will be given here. Shear yielding in semicrystalline polymers takes place through slip, twinning and martensitic transformations[32] as with other crystalline solids. Shear yielding in glassy polymers is rather more unusual and can take place either through highly localised shear bands or diffuse shear deformation zones.[30] The deformation of glassy polymers has been interpreted on a molecular level through the theoretical approaches of Bowden & Raha[33] and Argon.[34] As will become evident later, shear yielding is not only an interesting phenomenon in its own right but is of particular importance in fracture.

1.5.5 Crazing

The second important deformation mechanism in polymers is *crazing*.[35] It is possible to consider crazes as microcracks bridged by fibrils and their formation is accompanied by an *increase* in specimen volume. Crazing is discussed in detail in Chapter 5 and so only a brief review will be given here.

It is known that there is an intimate relationship between crazing and the fracture of amorphous thermoplastics. There is very strong evidence that cracks propagate in these materials with crazes at their tips.[35] The nucleation of crazes, for example, in active environments[36] can lead to both a deterioration in specimen appearance and ultimate failure. There has been a great deal of progress over recent years concerning the molecular mechanisms involved in crazing and it is now well established that molecular entanglements play an important role in controlling craze geometry.

Crazes are generally nucleated at imperfections in polymer specimens such as surface flaws or dust particles and crazing generally requires the presence of a hydrostatic or dilatational component of the stress tensor. The phenomenon is sometimes referred to as craze yielding although it normally leads to brittle fracture through craze breakdown. Nevertheless, *multiple* crazing can lead to general yielding and act as a toughening mechanism in polymers, and polymers containing a second phase have been specifically prepared where the multiphase polymer (Chapter 11) can take full advantage of this toughening mechanism.

1.6 FRACTURE OF POLYMERS

In the final section of this chapter we will introduce the concept of fracture in polymers and so set the scene for the rest of the book.

1.6.1 General Approaches
There have, in the main, been three general approaches to the study of fracture in polymers. They are:

1. Continuum;
2. Molecular; and
3. Statistical approaches.

The main emphasis in this book is upon the continuum approach where a polymer is considered as a continuum with particular physical properties but for which the molecular structure is mainly ignored. However, to gain a full idea of the fracture of polymers their molecular structure must be taken into account and so the molecular approach is also discussed where it is relevant. The statistical approach sees the fracture process as being due to a series of events which can be predicted using statistical arguments. Over the years this has been ignored but it is now assuming more significance and is probably an area where there will be important future developments. Clearly to fully understand the fracture process all three approaches need to be followed simultaneously and in this book we try as far as is possible to draw together the different areas and to highlight work which has used an integrated approach.

1.6.2 General Behaviour

Polymers tend to have rather lower fracture strengths than other materials such as metals or ceramics and typical values of fracture stress, σ_f, for different plastics and rubbers are given in Table 1.4. As with the values of Young's modulus there is a wide variation. Also when the relatively low density of polymers is taken into account their *specific strengths* (σ_f divided by density) compare rather better with other materials. Hence they are tending to replace metallic components when weight-saving is at a premium.

A major problem with ductile polymers is their tendency to undergo transitions to brittle behaviour when modifying the polymer or changing the testing conditions and *ductile/brittle* transitions are dealt with at great length in this book. In general, this transition can be considered as being due to a competition between a brittle fracture mechanism such as crazing and a ductile mechanism such as bulk shear yielding. The brittle mechanism tends to be favoured by reducing the test temperature, increasing the strain-rate or specimen thickness, having sharp notches or annealing the polymer.

1.6.3 Stresses at Crack Tips

In most practical situations a fracture originates from local concentrations of stress at flaws, scratches or notches. Because of this it is essential to have a knowledge of the local state of stress at these defects. The situation is most easily analysed for materials which deform in a linear elastic manner. Time dependence, viscoelasticity and plastic deformation are more difficult to cope with and the approach that is generally used is to follow a linear elastic analysis and then modify it to account for added complications. The analysis of stresses at notches and cracks[21,28,37] is dealt with in later chapters and so only a brief introduction will be given here.

One of the simplest cases to analyse concerns the stresses around an elliptical hole in a thin sheet under an applied stress, σ_0, as shown in Fig. 1.14. In this case the stress at the end of the major axis, σ_t, is given by[21]

$$\sigma_t = \sigma_0(1 + 2\sqrt{a/\rho}) \qquad (1.23)$$

where ρ is the radius of curvature of the tip and $2a$ is the major axis. It can be shown[37] that equations of a form similar to eqn. (1.23) describe the concentration of stress at surface notches and steps as well as for

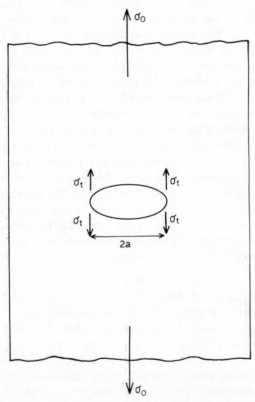

Fig. 1.14. *Model of an elliptical crack of length 2a subjected to a uniform stress σ_0 in an infinite plate.*

elliptical holes. Clearly failure occurs where the concentration of stress is the highest and the stress concentration (σ_t/σ_0) will increase with an increase in a and a decrease in ρ. However, as $\rho \to 0$ the elliptical hole becomes a crack, the stress concentration becomes infinite and so a modified approach is needed. One way of overcoming this problem is to use the classical analysis of Griffith (Section 1.6.4) or the stress-intensity factor approach outlined in Section 3.3.

1.6.4 Griffith Fracture

Griffith[38] overcame the problem of the infinite stress concentration at a crack tip by using an energy balance approach to model the fracture process. He calculated the energy released by putting a sharp crack into a plate and related this to the energy required to create a new surface and obtained an equation relating the fracture stress, σ_f, to the ellipse semiaxis or crack length, a, such that

$$\sigma_f = \left(\frac{2E\gamma}{\pi a}\right)^{\frac{1}{2}} \qquad (1.24)$$

where E is the Young's modulus and γ is the surface free-energy of the material. Andrews[28] has shown that it is also possible to derive a similar equation from an atomistic viewpoint, clearly establishing the link between the continuum and atomic or molecular approaches.

Measurements of σ_f as a function of a have clearly established that the Griffith equation holds for brittle materials such as glassy polymers.[39] However, the value of the parameter γ derived from such measurements is much higher than the surface free-energy. This is because there is invariably a high degree of local plastic deformation at the crack tip. The energy dissipated by such processes swamps the surface energy term and the Griffith equation has to be modified to account for this by replacing 2γ with the *fracture energy*, G_c, such that

$$\sigma_f = \left(\frac{EG_c}{\pi a}\right)^{\frac{1}{2}} \qquad \text{(Plane stress)} \qquad (1.25)$$

or

$$\sigma_f = \left(\frac{EG_c}{\pi(1-\nu^2)a}\right)^{\frac{1}{2}} \quad \text{(Plane strain)} \qquad (1.26)$$

where ν is Poisson's ratio. The fracture energy is then the total amount of energy dissipated during crack growth.

Although the fracture strength, σ_f, is a parameter which is easy to define unambiguously the same cannot be said for the fracture energy, G_c. Different workers use different definitions and a variety of symbols. We have tried to unify the definition of fracture energy as 'the energy required to form a unit area of crack', with units in the S.I. system of $J m^{-2}$. We also do not differentiate between G_c for brittle or ductile fracture.

One useful aspect of the Griffith approach is that the effect of *flaws* present in a specimen can be readily appreciated. Since E and G_c can be treated as material constants for a given set of testing conditions, the fracture strength will be controlled principally by the size of the largest cracks or flaws in the structure. Hence, if the flaw dimensions are known, σ_f can be predicted. Several brittle polymers behave as if they contain flaws of a particular size even when the specimens are carefully polished to remove any superficial scratches or flaws. This gives rise to the concept of an 'inherent flaw size', a_0. It is thought that these flaws are formed by the nucleation, growth and breakdown of crazes during loading. Hence polystyrene with large crazes has a higher value of a_0 than poly(methyl methacrylate) which has smaller crazes.[39]

1.6.5   Toughening Mechanisms

A great deal of effort has been expended into methods of toughening polymers and increasing the fracture energy, G_c. Much of this book is concerned with such problems. From considerations in the previous section it is obvious that increasing the amount of plastic deformation at the crack tip will have the required effect.

Even in brittle materials, such as glassy polymers, there is a limited amount of plastic deformation at the crack tip. For example, *localised crazing* normally takes place at the tips of cracks in brittle thermoplastics and *localised shear yielding* occurs at crack tips in brittle epoxy resins. Both of these localised processes tend to be favoured by plane-strain conditions, as found, for example, in thick fracture specimens. More extensive plastic deformation will take place in thinner specimens where plane-stress conditions prevail and most brittle polymers undergo a brittle/ductile transition on reducing the specimen thickness.[40] There is less constraint in the thin sheets and extensive shear yielding rather than localised shear yielding or crazing takes place. The opposite of this behaviour is also found. Ductile polymers can undergo a ductile/brittle transition on increasing specimen thickness and this can be a major problem in using polymers in practical situations. More constraint is also induced by having sharp cracks rather than blunt notches leading to the phenomenon of 'notch brittle-ness'.

It is possible to increase the toughness of polymers by modifying the material rather than by changing specimen geometry. For example, polycarbonate *quenched* from the T_g is relatively tough whereas it can be embrittled by prolonged annealing. This is thought[41] to be due to annealing increasing the yield stress but leaving the craze stress rela-tively unaffected. Hence the annealed polymer is brittle because it tends to undergo localised crazing rather than extensive shear yielding. Another important method of toughening polymers is by incorporating a soft rubbery phase into a brittle polymer matrix—a technique known as *rubber toughening* (Chapter 11). High-impact polystyrene is toughened by multiple crazing whereas polymers such as rubber-modified epoxy resins and poly(vinyl chloride) mainly undergo multiple shear yielding. Both of these mechanisms cause extensive plastic deformation at crack tips and lead to a considerable increase in G_c over the unmodified polymers.

1.7 CONCLUDING REMARKS

In this chapter an attempt has been made to introduce concepts and ideas which will be needed and referred to later. The synthesis and structure of polymers have been described briefly. Stress and strain have been defined carefully as they are used constantly throughout the book. The deformation of polymers is of particular relevance to fracture and so the unusual, and in some ways unique, deformation behaviour has been discussed in detail. Finally, polymer fracture has been discussed briefly and basic concepts such as stress concentrations, Griffith fracture, inherent flaws, and fracture energy have been intro-duced.

REFERENCES

1. Young, R. J. (1981). *Introduction to polymers*, Chapman and Hall, London.
2. Odian, G. (1970). *Principles of polymerization*, McGraw-Hill Inc., New York.
3. Lenz, R. W. (1967). *Organic chemistry of high polymers*, Interscience, New York.
4. Wegner, G. (1977). *Pure Appl. Chem.*, **49**, 443.

5. Zbinden, R. (1964). *Infrared spectroscopy of high polymers*, Academic Press, New York.
6. Ouano, A. C. (1981). *Rubber. Chem. Tech.*, **54**, 535.
7. Morawetz, H. (1975). *Macromolecules in solution*, Wiley-Interscience, New York.
8. Yeh, G. S. Y. (1972). *Crit. Rev. Macromol. Chem.*, **1**, 173.
9. Uhlmann, D. R. (1979). *Farad. Disc.*, **68**, 87.
10. Thomas, E. L. In: *Structure of crystalline polymers*, Ed. by I. H. Hall, Applied Science Publishers Ltd., London, to be published.
11. Flory, P. J. (1953). *Principles of polymer chemistry*, Cornell University Press, Ithaca, New York, p. 602.
12. Wignall, G., Ballard, D. G. H. & Schelten, J. (1976). *J. Macromol. Sci.-Phys.*, **B12**, 75.
13. Porter, R. S. & Johnson, J. F. (1966). *Chem. Rev.*, **66**, 1.
14. Gent, A. N. & Thomas, A. G. (1972). *J. Polym. Sci.*, *A2* **10**, 571.
15. Wunderlich, B. (1973, 1976). *Macromolecular physics*, Vols 1 and 2, Academic Press, New York.
16. Keller, A. (1968). *Rep. Prog. Phys.*, **31**, 623.
17. Keith, H. D., Padden, F. J. & Vadimsky, R. G. (1971). *J. Appl. Phys.*, **42**, 192.
18. Schelten, J., Wignall, G. D., Ballard, D. G. H. & Longman, G. W. (1977). *Polymer*, **18**, 1111.
19. Stamm, M., Fischer, E. W. & Dettenmaier, M. (1979). *Farad. Disc.*, **68**, 263.
20. Boyer, R. (1963). *Rubber. Chem. Tech.*, **36**, 1303.
21. Williams, J. G. (1973). *Stress analysis of polymers*, Longman, London.
22. Crist, B., Ratner, M. A., Brower, A. L. & Savin, J. R. (1979). *J. Appl. Phys.*, **50**, 6047.
23. Bowden, P. B. (1968). *Polymer*, **9**, 449.
24. Treloar, L. R. G. (1958). *The physics of rubber elasticity*, Clarendon Press, Oxford.
25. Ward, I. M. (1971). *Mechanical properties of solid polymers*, Wiley-Interscience, London.
26. McCrum, N. G., Reed, B. E. & Williams, G. (1967). *Anelastic and dielectric effects in polymeric solids*, John Wiley, London.
27. Ferry, J. D. (1970). *Viscoelastic properties of polymers*, John Wiley, New York.
28. Andrews, E. H. (1968). *Fracture in polymers*, Oliver and Boyd, London.
29. Andrews, E. H. (1974). *J. Mater. Sci.*, **9**, 887.
30. Bowden, P. B. (1973). In: *The physics of glassy polymers*, Ed. by R. N. Haward, Applied Science Publishers Ltd., London, p. 279.
31. Yamini, S. & Young, R. J. (1980). *J. Mater. Sci.*, **15**, 1814.
32. Bowden, P. B. & Young, R. J. (1974). *J. Mater. Sci.*, **9**, 2034.
33. Bowden, P. B. & Raha, S. (1974). *Phil. Mag.*, **29**, 149.
34. Argon, A. (1977). *Phil. Mag.*, **35**, 917.
35. Kambour, R. P. (1973). *J. Polym. Sci., Macromol. Rev.*, **7**, 1.
36. Kramer, E. J. (1979). In: *Developments in polymer fracture*—1, Ed. by E. H. Andrews, Applied Science Publishers Ltd., London, p. 55.

37. Kelly, A. (1966). *Strong solids*, Clarendon Press, Oxford.
38. Griffith, A. A. (1920). *Phil. Trans. Roy. Soc.*, **A221,** 163.
39. Berry, J. P. (1972). In: *Fracture VII*, Ed. by H. Liebowitz, Academic Press, New York.
40. Brown, H. R. (1982). *J. Mater. Sci.*, **17,** 469.
41. Pitman, G. L., Ward, I. M. & Duckett, R. A. (1978). *J. Mater. Sci.*, **13,** 2092.

Part I

MECHANICS AND MECHANISMS

Chapter 2

Molecular Aspects

2.1 INTRODUCTION

It is possible to consider a solid polymer as either a uniform mechanical continuum which responds in a predictable way to stress and strain or as a macromolecular solid made up of long molecules for which deformation causes a disturbance of the inter- and intra-molecular bonding. For many engineering applications the continuum approach is the most useful and the discipline of fracture mechanics outlined in Chapter 3 is based upon the assumption that the material undergoing fracture may be assumed to be a continuum. The reason that this assumption holds and that continuum mechanics appears to work for atomic and molecular solids is due to the fact that variations in the deformation and orientation of the individual bonds tend to be 'averaged-out' since objects of macroscopic proportions contain a vast number of atoms or molecules. Hence continuum mechanics can be applied to solids as they respond on a macroscopic level in a uniform way to stress and strain even though deformation at the atomic or molecular level may be highly inhomogeneous. In fact, it is now well established that in deformed polymer samples some molecules are much more highly stressed than others and only a minute fraction of the molecules are involved in the fracture event.

Some important developments in the area of polymer fracture have been concerned with using ideas and experimental techniques which examine deformation and fracture on the molecular level. The developments have been assisted both by a better understanding of both the nature of chemical bonds and the structure and morphology of

43

polymeric solids that has taken place over the years and by the use of sophisticated spectroscopic techniques (e.g. infra-red, electron spin resonance) which have enabled the deformation and fracture of covalent bonds to be detected.

In this chapter the general phenomenon of molecular fracture is discussed first and, in particular, the factors which control the strength of macromolecular solids. The kinetic theories of fracture are then discussed and it is shown how fracture may be considered as an activated-rate process. The techniques for studying molecular deformation and fracture are then described and this is followed by a discussion of the micromechanisms involved, with particular reference to crystalline polymer fibres and glassy polymers.

2.2 FRACTURE ON THE MOLECULAR LEVEL

When a polymeric sample undergoes fracture there must clearly be a creation of new surface which can only occur by the severance of either primary (covalent) or secondary (e.g. van der Waals or hydrogen) bonds or both. In this section the theoretical strength of a general solid is estimated. The analysis is then extended to the case of a polymeric solid and the extent to which different types of bond are broken during crack growth is considered.

2.2.1 Theoretical Strength of a Solid

It is of considerable interest to obtain an estimate of the theoretical strength of a solid since when this is compared with experimentally determined values of strength it gives a valuable insight into the failure processes that occur in such materials. The calculation of theoretical strength is relatively simple when the material is assumed to be a perfectly elastic isotropic solid and a specimen of such a material under stress is shown schematically in Fig. 2.1(a). The application of a tensile stress, σ_0, to the body will cause an increase in the interatomic separation. The variation of interatomic potential energy with the separation of the atoms is shown schematically in Fig. 2.1(b) and it is clear that the stress will cause an increase in the energy of the system. The force required to cause bond separation is the first derivative of the potential energy with respect to the separation. It will increase as the bonds are stretched until it reaches a maximum at the point of inflexion in the curve in Fig. 2.1(b). It has been suggested[1,2] that the

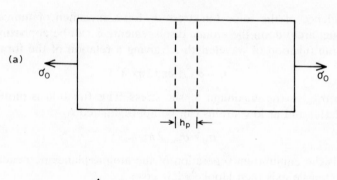

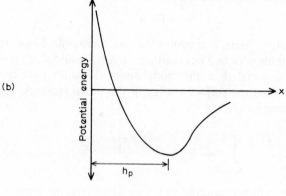

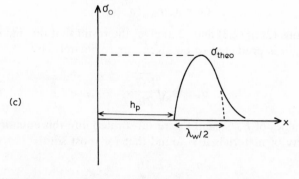

Fig. 2.1. Deformation of an elastically isotropic solid. (a) Body under an applied stress σ_0 with atomic planes of equilibrium separation h_p; (b) Interatomic potential energy as a function of separation, x; and (c) Dependence of σ_0 upon x.

dependence of the force (or stress σ_0 for a specimen of unit cross-sectional area) upon the atomic displacement, x, can be approximated to a sine function of wavelength λ_w giving a relation of the form

$$\sigma_0 = \sigma_{theo} \sin (2\pi x/\lambda_w) \qquad (2.1)$$

where σ_{theo} is the maximum tensile stress. This function is plotted in Fig. 2.1(c) and at low strains can be approximated to

$$\sigma_0 = \sigma_{theo} 2\pi x/\lambda_w \qquad (2.2)$$

If h_p is the equilibrium separation of the atomic planes perpendicular to the tensile axis then Hooke's law gives

$$\sigma_0 = Ex/h_p \qquad (2.3)$$

where E is the Young's modulus of the material. Since fracture involves the creation of two new surfaces in a body and work is done in stressing the material then thermodynamics demands that the work cannot be less than the surface energy of these two surfaces. Equating these two quantities gives

$$\int_0^{\lambda_w/2} \sigma_{theo} \sin (2\pi x/\lambda_w) \, dx = G_0 \qquad (2.4)$$

where G_0 is the energy required to create new surfaces (Section 3.2.1). Evaluation of the integral gives

$$G_0 = \lambda_w \sigma_{theo}/\pi \qquad (2.5)$$

combining eqns (2.2), (2.3) and (2.5) gives the result that the maximum tensile strength is predicted to be given, approximately, by

$$\sigma_{theo} = \sqrt{\frac{EG_0}{2h_p}} \qquad (2.6)$$

If different values of E, G_0 and h_p are substituted into this equation for a large variety of materials it is found that for most solids

$$\sigma_{theo} \approx E/10 \qquad (2.7)$$

The measured values of tensile strength, σ_f, are invariably much less than $E/10$ for most materials because of the presence of flaws.[2-5] They are typically of the order of $E/50$ to $E/100$ for isotropic polymers as shown in Table 2.1. However, there are certain materials such as fine

TABLE 2.1

COMPARISON OF THE VALUES OF MEASURED TENSILE STRENGTH, σ_f,[*] WITH THE VALUE OF THEORETICAL TENSILE STRENGTH, σ_{theo}, CALCULATED USING EQN. (2.7)

Material	E (MPa)	σ_{theo} (MPa)	σ_f (MPa)
Typical glassy polymer (PMMA)	3 000	300	50
Typical semicrystalline polymer (HDPE)	~2 000	~200	20
Typical thermo-setting polymer (epoxy resin)	3 500	350	70
Typical polymer fibre (nylon 6)	6 000	600	500
Polydiacetylene single crystal fibre	60 000	6 000	2 000

[*] Measured at room temperature and a moderate strain rate.

whiskers of glass or silica[3] and oriented polymer fibres or polymer single crystal fibres (Section 9.3.1) that do not contain many flaws and are not capable of undergoing plastic deformation, which have values of σ_f approaching the theoretical value.

2.2.2 Molecular Fracture in Polymers

The mechanical properties of a material are a manifestation of the way in which the individual bonds in the material respond to an applied stress. When a solid is fractured it is necessary that this may involve the severing of either primary or secondary bonds, or both. In atomic solids such as metals it is clear that fracture must involve the breaking of primary bonds and the same will be true for covalently bonded network materials such as diamond where cracks can only form and grow by the breaking of covalent bonds. However, in another form of carbon (graphite) cleavage can occur along the basal planes by breaking the relatively weak van der Waals bonds which hold the covalently bonded layers together.

The situation is more complex in the case of polymers since fracture can occur by breaking either primary covalent bonds or secondary van der Waals bonds through molecular 'pull-out'. It is thought[6-9] that both types of process can take place but the extent to which each one occurs depends upon the type of polymer undergoing fracture and the testing conditions. Clearly network polymers such as thermosetting resins will act like diamond and covalent bonds must be severed, whereas in thermoplastics it may be possible for fracture to occur by molecules sliding past each other with no molecular fracture. In high-molar-mass thermoplastics chain entanglements may act as cross-links, preventing molecular pull-out and the crystals in a semicrystalline polymer may act as similar anchorage points for the molecules. Regardless of the actual mechanism of failure it is likely that the strength of a polymer will be affected by the density of main-chain bonds crossing the fracture plane.

Vincent[7] attempted to quantify this effect for a series of different polymers and in order to ensure that the polymers were subjected to similar experimental conditions he measured the critical tensile strength, σ_{fc}, at the ductile/brittle transition for each polymer. He then related this to the number of backbone bonds per unit area, N_a, and found that by using data for several polymers there was a linear relationship between σ_{fc} and N_a with a slope of 37 when σ_{fc} is in $MN\,m^{-2}$ and N_a is the number of bonds nm^{-2}, as shown in Fig. 2.2. The breaking force for each of the covalent backbone C—C bonds in thermoplastics is thought to be of the order of 3 nN by Kausch[9] and 6 nN by Kelly[3] and so the line should have a slope of the order of 3000–6000 for fracture by bond breaking only. This means that in the polymers studied by Vincent[7] less than 1 % of the main-chain bonds were fully deformed during fracture. The measured slope is considerably larger for oriented polymers and fibres and for high-strength fibres can reach over 500.[9] In high-modulus-polymer single-crystal fibres (Section 9.3.1) for which a bond breaking force of up to 3 nN has been measured[10] the figure is well over 1000. Clearly as very few main-chain bonds are fully strained during fracture in isotropic polymers it is probable that the strength of these materials may be controlled more by intermolecular forces than by the strength of the main-chain covalent bonds.[8,9]

It is also of interest to consider how molecular fracture affects the measured values of fracture energy for polymers. It is found that for most materials, even though $\sigma_f \ll \sigma_{theo}$, the measured value of fracture energy is very much greater than the energy, G_0, required solely to break bonds (primary or secondary). This may seem something of a

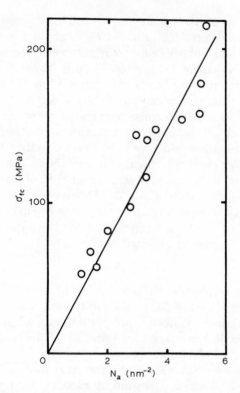

Fig. 2.2. Variation of critical tensile strength, σ_{fc}, at the ductile/brittle transition with the number of backbone bonds per unit area, N_a, for thirteen different polymers (after Reference 7).

paradox, but σ_f is reduced by the presence of flaws whereas the fracture energy is increased by the simultaneous occurrence of other energy absorbing processes, such as plastic deformation, which take place during fracture.

It is sometimes possible to take these other dissipative processes into account and evaluate the intrinsic energy of fracture, G_0. The question that arises is that of how this value of G_0 relates to the energy required to break bonds or pull molecules out. Clearly for network polymers such as thermosets or rubbers G_0 should be related to the energy needed to break primary bonds. It has been possible to measure G_0 for some cross-linked rubbers. For example, Lake & Lindley[11] measured G_0 by evaluating the fatigue limit of a series of vulcanised rubbers and found it to be of the order of 40–$100\,\mathrm{J\,m^{-2}}$, and Andrews & Fukahori[12] have determined values of G_0 of about $130\,\mathrm{J\,m^{-2}}$ for both a styrene–butadiene rubber and an ethylene–propylene rubber (Section 10.3.3). These values of G_0 are considerably higher than the energy required to break primary bonds (typically $0{\cdot}5\,\mathrm{J\,m^{-2}}$) and the discrepancy has been explained theoretically by Lake & Thomas.[13] They suggested that in order to cause a crack to grow in a cross-linked polymer network all the bonds of a chain lying between its junction points in the network would have to be stressed to their breaking point before the chain eventually breaks. If each bond has a dissociation energy of U_b and if there is an average number $\bar{n}_b$ of main-chain bonds between cross-links then Lake & Thomas[13] predicted that the minimum energy to cause a crack to propagate by chain rupture would be $\bar{n}_b \times U_b$. They went on to show that for this type of process an expression for G_0 can be obtained as

$$G_0 = \tfrac{1}{2}\bar{L}N_b\bar{n}_bU_b \qquad\qquad (2.8)$$

where N_b is the number of chains per unit volume and $\bar{L}$ is the average distance between cross-links in the unstrained state. When typical values of the various parameters are put into eqn. (2.8) a value of G_0 between 20 and $40\,\mathrm{J\,m^{-2}}$ is obtained which is of the same order as the measured values discussed above.

To summarise the situation then, it is clear that in many types of polymeric solids, such as cross-linked rubbers, high-molar-mass or oriented polymers, the fracture of primary bonds will be a major factor controlling the failure process and determining the value of G_0. In other cases, however, where chain pull-out is a relatively easy process intermolecular forces may play a larger role in controlling the fracture behaviour.

2.3 KINETIC APPROACH TO FRACTURE

Some of the earliest attempts to explain the fracture behaviour of polymers involved theories which considered fracture as a kinetic phenomenon. This concept was developed in the 1950s and 1960s simultaneously by Zhurkov and co-workers[14,15] in the USSR, and Bueche & Halpin[16–19] in the USA. The kinetic theories of polymer fracture have been reviewed extensively by several authors[6,9,20,21] and only the principal features of the approach will be discussed.

Most of the kinetic theories can be considered together as they have a main common feature which is that the basic fracture event is assumed to be bond rupture and it is the accumulation of rupture events which leads to eventual failure of the body. The rate at which the fractures accumulate is assumed to be controlled by chemical rate kinetics. The energetics of the process are represented schematically in Fig. 2.3. The body is stable in the unstressed state since the breaking of bonds can only take place through an increase in free energy of ΔG_f

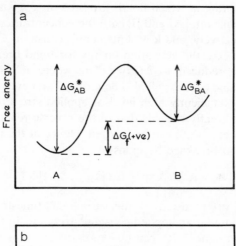

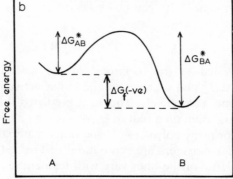

Fig. 2.3. Schematic representation of the free energy change. ΔG_f, for bond rupture. State A represents the intact bond and State B the broken bond. (a) Situation with no applied stress (ΔG_f increases); and (b) Situation with a high applied stress (ΔG_f decreases).

(Fig. 2.3(a)). When a stress is applied to the body the curve becomes modified (Fig. 2.3(b)) and, at a sufficiently high level of applied stress, ΔG_f becomes negative and hence fracture through bond rupture is more likely. Moreover, the height of the activation energy barrier, ΔG_{AB}^* for chain scission is also reduced and since this will control the *rate* of bond rupture the forward reaction will again be favoured. The mathematical formulation of the kinetic theory of fracture is usually expressed in terms of an equation of the form[6,20]

$$\nu_r = \nu_{r0}\{[A] \exp(-\Delta G_{AB}^*/\mathbf{k}T) - [B] \exp(-\Delta G_{BA}^*/\mathbf{k}T)\} \qquad (2.9)$$

where ν_r is the rate at which bonds are broken, ν_{r0} is a temperature-independent constant, [A] and [B] are the concentrations of the states A and B, respectively, and $\mathbf{k}$ is Boltzmann's constant. On the application of a stress, σ_0, the activation energy for bond breakage rupture, ΔG_{AB}^*, will be reduced to $\Delta G_{AB}^* - v^*\sigma_0$ where v^* is an activation volume. The value of ΔG_f will also be reduced and eventually becomes negative. At a sufficiently high level of applied stress, σ_c, the rate of bond breakage greatly exceeds that of the reverse reaction and so the second term in eqn. (2.9) can be ignored. Hence at the point of failure the rate of bond breakage becomes

$$\nu_r = \nu_{r0}[A] \exp[-(\Delta G_{AB}^* - v^*\sigma_c)]/\mathbf{k}T\} \qquad (2.10)$$

The theory is often tested by measuring the time-to-failure, t_f, of specimens held under an applied constant stress, σ_c. In this case, it can be shown[15] that eqn. (2.10) can be expressed in terms of an equation of the form

$$t_f = t_0 \exp[(\Delta G^* - v^*\sigma_c)/\mathbf{R}T] \qquad (2.11)$$

where t_0 is related to the reciprocal of the molecular oscillation frequency and ΔG^* and v^* are now the molar activation energy and activation volume, respectively. Thus it is predicted that there should be a linear relationship on a plot of σ_c versus $\log t_f$, and indeed this is what is found for many polymers[14,15] and other materials. Some of the reported data for polymers are reproduced in Fig. 2.4 and it can be seen that the slopes of the lines vary with temperature in accordance with eqn. (2.11). In addition it is found that the values of ΔG^* determined by this analysis agree closely with the values determined for the rupture of covalent bonds from independent experiments, as can be seen from Table 2.2.[14]

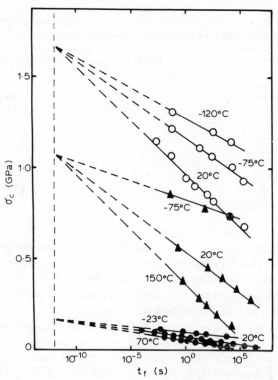

Fig. 2.4. *Dependence of time-to-failure, t_f, upon applied constant stress, σ_c, for three polymers at different temperatures:* [15] ●, *PMMA,* ▲, *viscose·fibres,* ○, *nylon 6 fibres.*

More recent developments in the kinetics approach to fracture have concentrated upon considerations of the failure process on a microscopic level. Kausch & Hsiao[22,23] have taken into account the microscopic stresses acting upon the elements in a polymer structure and have been able to account for the increase in strength of polymer fibres with increasing orientation. Another factor not properly considered by the early theories is that the fracture of bonds will not be a truly random event because the presence of ruptured bonds in the vicinity of a stressed bond will increase the likelihood of that particular bond breaking. Hence there will be a tendency for defects to accumulate preferentially at one site[24] and for cracks to propagate from these sites when rapid crack growth takes place.[9] It has been suggested[24] that

TABLE 2.2

COMPARISON OF THE ACTIVATION ENERGIES FOR BOND DISSOCIATION DETER-
MINED FROM FATIGUE FRACTURE TESTS AND THERMAL DEGRADATION[14]

Polymer	Fracture, ΔG^* $(kJ\,mol^{-1})$	Thermal degradation, ΔU^* $(kJ\,mol^{-1})$
Poly(vinyl chloride)	147	134
Polystyrene	227	231
Poly(methyl methacrylate)	227	218–222
Polypropylene	235	231–243
Polytetrafluoro-ethylene	315	319–336
Nylon 6	189	181

the most likely sites for chain scission will be tie-chains between
crystallites in semicrystalline polymer fibres or crystalline rubbers.
Other sites might be connecting molecules between cross-links or filler
particles with activated surfaces, and molecules in amorphous polymers
which happen to be in extended conformations.

To conclude this discussion of the kinetic theories of polymer
fracture it must be emphasised that such approaches offer a good
explanation of the initiation phase but are not so useful in accounting
for propagation especially in materials which are not completely brittle
and are capable of undergoing inelastic or plastic deformation. It
therefore tends to complement the fracture mechanics approach
(Chapter 3) which is concerned principally with the processes which
occur during propagation. However, fracture mechanics offers very
little towards an explanation of the initiation phase which can often be
important in controlling the lifetimes of specimens subjected to a
constant load.

2.4 TECHNIQUES FOR STUDYING MOLECULAR DEFORMATION AND FRACTURE

The theories of molecular fracture were originally developed without
any direct evidence that molecular fracture actually occurs and it is
only relatively recently that techniques have become available to study
molecular fracture directly. It has been suggested[24] that the polymer

fracture process can be broken down into three distinct steps:

1. The excitation of bonds under the action of an applied stress;
2. The scission of the excited over-stressed bonds by thermal fluctuations; and
3. The formation of small submicrocracks or crazes which coalesce to form larger cracks.

Experimental techniques are now available to study all of these phases of fracture. The most widely employed technique has been electron spin resonance spectroscopy (ESR) which can be used to follow Step 2. It allows the direct observation of the free radicals which are produced when covalent bonds are broken. It is an extremely powerful technique which allows the number and the chemical nature of the radicals produced to be determined. Other experimental techniques have included infra-red and Raman spectroscopy, small-angle X-ray scattering, and the measurement of molar mass variations—these techniques are all discussed in this section.

2.4.1 Techniques for Studying Bond Straining

The response of the chemical bonds within a polymer to mechanical stress is of interest since it acts as a precursor to molecular fracture. The main technique that has been used to monitor this type of deformation has been infra-red (IR) spectroscopy[6,9,21,25-8] although recently the technique of resonant Raman scattering (RRS) has been used[29,30] to follow the deformation of molecules in polymer crystals up to fracture. The two techniques are related in that they both involve monitoring the shift in the frequencies of the main-chain vibration modes with stress or strain. It has been found that for IR and RRS there is an approximately linear variation of the vibration frequencies with stress and strain respectively as shown in Fig. 2.5. For the infra-red data in Fig. 2.5(a) the relationship between vibration frequency, ν_σ, and stress

$$\nu_\sigma = \nu_0 - A_I \sigma_0 \qquad (2.12)$$

holds, whereas for the Raman data in Fig. 2.5(b) the equivalent relationship between vibration frequency, ν_e, and strain is

$$\nu_e = \nu_0 - A_R e_0 \qquad (2.13)$$

where σ_0 and e_0 are the applied stress and strain respectively, ν_0 is the vibration frequency in the undeformed state, and A_I and A_R are

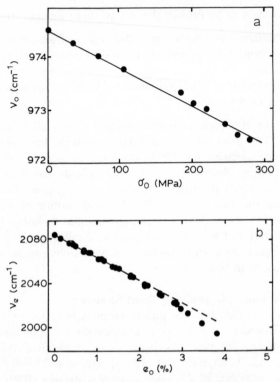

Fig. 2.5. (a) Shift in frequency of the 974·5 cm^{-1} band in oriented PP film due to applied stress;[26] and (b) Shift in frequency of the triple bond stretching mode in a polydiacetylene single crystal as a function of applied strain.[29]

constants. Since at low strains polymers tend to obey Hooke's law the difference between eqns (2.12) and (2.13) may be more apparent than real.

In the RRS studies of the deformation of polymer single crystal fibres it is found that the RRS spectra do not change shape on straining but only shift in frequency.[29,30] This indicates that in single crystals the strain is distributed uniformly over the main-chain bonds. This is not found to be the case with the amorphous and semicrystalline polymers that have been used in the IR studies where it is found that the absorption bands shift and change shape[26,28] indicating that the distribution of stress is not uniform and that some bonds are more highly stressed than others. For example, it has been shown[28] that although over half of the bonds are uniformly stressed in a deformed specimen of polypropylene a small number are over-stressed by more than 10-times the mean stress.

This distribution of stress in the bonds of deformed polymers will clearly depend critically upon the morphology and structure of the material. It is of particular significance because it is the highly stressed bonds which are likely to be the first to break and go on to nucleate crazes and cracks.

2.4.2 Study of Bond Breakage

The techniques that can be used to monitor main-chain bond breakage in polymers fall into two categories: *direct* methods, such as electron spin resonance (ESR) spectroscopy, which measure directly the number of free radicals formed when bonds are broken, and *indirect* methods, such as the measurement of the reduction in molar mass due to bond breakage or the use of IR spectroscopy to detect new groups at the ends of severed polymer chains.

2.4.2.1 Direct Methods (ESR)

The application of ESR to the study of the deformation and fracture of polymers is now a well-established technique. ESR is used to study atoms or molecules which have a net magnetic moment because of unpaired electrons. When molecular orbitals are fully occupied there are usually no unpaired electrons because of the Pauli exclusion principle but, if a covalent bond is broken by homolytic fission, free radicals with unpaired electron spins are formed and these may be detected using ESR. There have been several reviews of the application of ESR to polymer fracture[6,9,24] and the reader is directed towards these and other texts[31,32] to cover the principles behind the ESR technique. Only a very brief review will be given here.

The magnetic moment of a free electron is given by

$$\mu_{mag} = g_e \beta s_e \qquad (2.14)$$

where g_e is the spectroscopic splitting factor, β is the Bohr magneton and s_e is the spin vector. When a specimen is subjected to a magnetic field, H, the spin quantum numbers may take one of two values (either $+\frac{1}{2}$ or $-\frac{1}{2}$) and these two states will have different energies, the energy difference being ΔE which is given by[6,9]

$$\Delta E = g_e \beta H \qquad (2.15)$$

At equilibrium it can be shown from Boltzmann statistics that a majority of the free electrons will populate the ground state but transitions between the two energy levels can be induced using electromagnetic radiation of frequency ν_{em} such that

$$\Delta E = \mathbf{h}\nu_{em} = g_e \boldsymbol{\beta} H \tag{2.16}$$

where $\mathbf{h}$ is Planck's constant. For free electrons g_e is normally of the order of 2 and as most spectrometers employ H of about 3200 gauss the resonant condition can be satisfied with microwave radiation of the order of 9·5 GHz.

Although ESR is a powerful technique for the study of molecular fracture during polymer deformation it does suffer from several limitations[6] such as:

1. The lack of sensitivity in spectrometers that are currently available;
2. The instability of the free radicals produced during deformation; and
3. The size of the spectrometer cavity limiting the volume of specimen that can be studied.

The levels of sensitivity in most ESR spectrometers mean that spin concentrations must normally be of the order of at least 10^{14}–10^{16} spins kg^{-1}. This necessitates the use of ground or milled samples where the area of the fracture surface is large or there are highly oriented fibres which when deformed in tension produce a high density of free radicals. Since the free radicals are highly reactive it is normally necessary to work in inert environments and at temperatures below the T_g of the polymer. Consequently, a great deal of work has been done in liquid nitrogen at 77 K. Finally, since the working region within the cavity of ESR spectrometers is generally small, the possibility of using large amounts of material and the scope for *in situ* experiments is limited especially when glassware is employed to ensure low temperatures.

A few attempts have been made to study the production of radicals in deformed polymers using non-spectroscopic techniques. For example, Salloum & Eckert[33] measured the concentrations of free radicals produced when polymers were drilled in a solution of a free-radical scavenger, diphenylpicrylhydrazal (DPPH). The free radicals could be detected by the change in concentration of DPPH but the technique is not particularly reliable because of the possibility of side reactions occurring and detection being limited to radicals produced on free surfaces.

2.4.2.2 Indirect Methods

There are several techniques which can be used to follow molecular fracture which do not detect radicals directly but rely upon following structural changes in the polymer which take place as a result of molecular fracture events. Free radicals are unstable, reactive species and once produced will normally react to try to form stable groups at the end of the fractured molecules. Both the reduction in average molar mass[34-6] and the increase in concentration of end-groups[37,38] can be used to follow the fracture process indirectly. The change in the number of end-groups enables the number of fracture events to be estimated. The concentration of end-groups can be determined using infra-red spectroscopy and some results obtained by Zhurkov & Korsukov[38] from polyethylene are given in Table 2.3. There is clearly an increase in the concentration of end-groups following deformation and for oriented polymers subjected to a constant load the concentration of the end-groups is found to increase with time.[37]

Although IR end-group analysis, molar-mass measurements and ESR all show that molecular rupture occurs during the deformation and fracture of polymers there is not always good agreement between the concentrations of chain ends measured by the different techniques. IR measurements often give values 100 to 1000 times higher than ESR measurements because, it is thought,[6] ESR detects only a fraction of the primary radicals produced. Further support for this can be obtained from the studies of Stoeckel et al.[35] who showed from measurements of the reduction in molar mass for deformed semicrystalline polymer fibres that there appeared to be approximately 10-times more

TABLE 2.3
CHANGE IN CONCENTRATION OF END GROUPS IN POLYETHYLENE UPON LOADING
(AFTER ZHURKOV & KORSUKOV[38])

IR frequency (cm^{-1})	Terminal group	Concentration $(10^{-24}\ m^{-3})$	
		Before loading	After loading
910	—HC=CH$_2$	18·8	25·6
1 379	—CH$_3$	40·0	60·0
1 710	—COOH	2·2	3·4
1 735	—COH	13·4	20·6

chain rupture than was measured by using ESR. Hence it seems that the indirect methods may be more accurate techniques of determining the absolute numbers of severed molecules.

2.4.3 Void Formation and Growth

The final phase of the initiation of polymer fracture involves the formation and growth of microvoids from accumulations of chain ends and the coalescence of these voids into crazes and microcracks. One of the most convenient ways of following this process is small-angle X-ray scattering.[21,39,40] A polymer containing voids of the order of 20–1000 Å in size will give rise to strong scattering of X-rays at small angles (i.e. up to 2° with Cu Kα radiation of wavelength $\lambda_w = 1 \cdot 54$ Å) because of the large electron-density difference between bulk polymer and voids. This technique is similar to that used to measure the long period and lamellar thickness for semicrystalline polymers.[41] However, for analysis of the growth of cavities in polymers under stress the

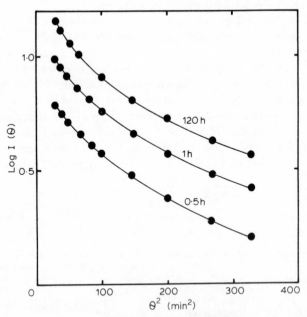

Fig. 2.6. *Small-angle X-ray scattering intensity distribution for nylon 6 held under load for different periods of time.*[56]

Guinier formula is normally employed. The intensity of scattering $I(\theta)$ at the scattering angle θ is given by[6]

$$I(\theta) \simeq Z_g N_m v^2 \exp\left[-(4\pi^2/3\lambda_w^2)L_m^2\theta^2\right] \qquad (2.17)$$

where Z_g is a factor related to the cavity geometry, N_m is the number of cavities per unit volume, v is the cavity volume, L_m is the dimension of the cavity in the scattering direction, and λ_w is the electron wavelength. The data are normally presented in the form of a Guinier plot of $\log I(\theta)$ versus θ^2 as is shown in Fig. 2.6 for nylon 6. The size of the cavities, L_m, can be determined from the slope of such a plot and the number per unit volume, N_m, from the intercept at $\theta = 0$. However, this may not in practice be very simple because, as can be seen from Fig. 2.6, the slope of the curves normally varies continuously because of a distribution of void sizes in the samples. When this happens the data must be fitted to suitable distribution functions in order to determine the average cavity sizes.

2.5 MICROMECHANISMS OF POLYMER FRACTURE

In the previous section the techniques used to follow the process of molecular deformation and fracture and subsequent void growth were discussed and in this section the failure mechanisms which occur on a microscopic scale will be considered. The details of the failure process are highly complex and depend upon many factors such as polymer structure, environment, stress and strain, and time. It is clear that molecular fracture does not occur to the same extent for all polymers and that the micromechanisms are different for different types of polymer.

When a solid polymer is deformed the molecules slide past each other and tend to uncoil, breaking secondary (e.g. van der Waals) bonds. Molecular fracture through the scission of primary bonds will take place if, for any reason, the flow of molecules past each other is restricted due to the nature of the polymer structure. For example, in a semicrystalline polymer the crystals can act as anchorage points and restrict flow. Alternatively in cross-linked polymers the chemical cross-link points can make flow more difficult and in high-molar-mass amorphous polymers physical entanglements will restrict flow especially at high extensions. Flow will also be difficult in structures in which the molecules are aligned such as polymer fibres or fully extended rubbers. Hence, as might be expected, the majority of studies of molecular fracture in polymers have been confined to semi-crystalline fibres and cross-linked materials.

2.5.1 Molecular Fracture During Deformation

There is a great deal of evidence now available showing that during the deformation and fracture of polymers molecular fracture takes place and free radicals are formed. The most direct evidence has been obtained from ESR studies. A typical ESR spectrum from a stressed polymer is shown in Fig. 2.7 in the form of a first-derivative spectrum.

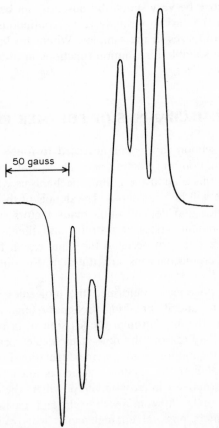

Fig. 2.7. ESR spectrum of secondary free radicals formed in stressed nylon 6 fibres.[24]

(For experimental reasons[6] ESR spectra tend to be presented as the first derivative of the absorption with respect to the magnetic-field strength rather than as simple absorption spectra.)

It is not a trivial matter to identify the radical species responsible for particular ESR signals. Methods of doing this have been discussed elsewhere.[6,9] One problem that arises is that because of the high reactivity and mobility of the radicals the primary radical that is formed can change either by rearrangement along the polymer chain or reaction with its environment. In particular free radicals often react with oxygen necessitating experiments to be undertaken in oxygen-free environments. The energy levels are frequently split because the free electrons are attached to molecules and have interactions with the nuclei of the surrounding atoms as well as with the externally applied magnetic field. However, the hyperfine structure can be used to advantage to identify the particular types of radical giving rise to the spectra.[6,9]

The results of some of the numerous experiments upon free-radical formation in polymers during deformation are summarised in Table 2.4 for grinding and milling and in Table 2.5 for polymer samples deformed in tension. Some of the strongest signals have been obtained by grinding and milling because of the large area of fracture surface

TABLE 2.4

FORMATION OF FREE RADICALS DURING THE MECHANICAL DEGRADATION OF VARIOUS POLYMERS. THE SAMPLES WERE DEGRADED AND THE SPECTRA WERE OBTAINED IN INERT ENVIRONMENTS AT 77 K (AFTER REFERENCES 6 AND 9)

Degraded polymer	Primary radicals	Secondary radicals
Polyethylene $(-CH_2-CH_2-)_n$	$-CH_2-\dot{C}H_2$	None
Polypropylene $(-CH_2-(CH_3)CH-)_n$	$-CH_2-(CH_3)\dot{C}H$	$-CH_2-(CH_3)\dot{C}-CH_2-$
Polystyrene $(-CH_2-(C_6H_5)CH-)_n$	$-CH_2-(C_6H_5)\dot{C}H$	$-CH_2-(\dot{C}_6H_4)CH_2$
Poly(methyl methacrylate) $(-CH_2-(COOCH_3)(CH_3)C-)_n$	$-CH_2-(COOCH_3)CH_3\dot{C}$	None
Polymethacrylate $(-CH_2-(COOCH_3)CH-)_n$	$-CH_2-(COOCH_3)\dot{C}H$	None
Poly(vinyl acetate) $(-CH_2-(OCOCH_3)CH-)_n$	$-CH_2-(OCOCH_3)\dot{C}H$	None

TABLE 2.5

FORMATION OF FREE RADICALS DURING THE TENSILE DEFORMATION OF VARI-
OUS POLYMERS

Polymer	Observed radical	Concentration (spins m^{-3})	Reference
Polyethylene	Peroxide	5×10^{22}	15
	Peroxide	$\sim 10^{22}$	42
Polypropylene	Not identified	$< 10^{20}$ [a]	43
Polystyrene	Not identified	$< 10^{20}$ [a]	15
Poly(methyl methacrylate)	Not identified	$< 10^{20}$ [a]	15
cis-1,4-Polyisoprene	$-CH_2-C(CH_3)=CH-\dot{C}H_2$ and $-CH_2-CH=C(CH_3)-\dot{C}H_2$	$\sim 10^{22}$	44–46
Polycaprolactam (nylon 6)	$-CO-NH-\dot{C}H-CH_2-$	5×10^{23}	15
Poly(ethylene terephthalate)	Peroxide	$\sim 10^{22}$	15

[a] Any spin concentration below the sensitivity of the apparatus.

produced. However, there can be problems in relating the ESR signal from mechanical degradation experiments quantitatively to the deformation experienced by the polymer. In contrast, the signals obtained from tensile deformation tend to be rather weak but they can often be related quantitatively to the applied deformation.

In discussing the features of radical formation during the deformation of polymers it is convenient to examine the behaviour of different types of polymer separately since it is found that the extent to which molecular fracture takes place varies with the polymer structure and morphology.

2.5.1.1 Crystalline Polymer Fibres

Many of the studies of radical production during the deformation of polymers have been concerned with the deformation of oriented fibres of crystalline polymers such as nylon 6[24,47–9] and this approach has been reviewed in detail by Kausch & DeVries.[24] Polymer fibres are particularly amenable to analysis using ESR because the oriented structures tend to have molecules in extended conformation which are prone to fracture during deformation. Experimentally, in order to obtain strong signals, yarns made up of many filaments rather than individual fibres are subjected to deformation.

The production of radicals during the deformation of nylon 6 at a constant loading-rate is shown in Fig. 2.8. There are very few radicals produced until the strain reaches about 8 %—above this there is a

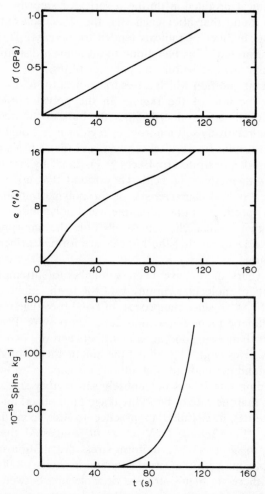

Fig. 2.8. Production of free radicals during a constant loading-rate test upon nylon 6 fibres.[24]

rapid increase in the rate of radical production with applied strain. Similarly during a constant applied-stress test, where the strain is held above 8 % (Fig. 2.9), there is a rapid increase in the number of radicals formed when the load is first applied and eventually an equilibrium radical concentration is achieved. If in this type of experiment the stress is increased further the number of radicals will again increase. To look at this behaviour in more detail several workers[43,47] have examined radical production during a series of stepwise increases in strain. They found that after each step the stress relaxed but at the same time the number of radicals tended to increase. This behaviour has been interpreted[9,24] as being due to an uneven distribution of the local molecular stresses within the polymer fibres.

An important question which arises for radical formation in polymer fibres is the location of the regions in the polymer microstructure where the radicals are produced. Since the bulk of the deformation is carried by the relatively soft amorphous regions it is thought that this is where the molecular fracture takes place and the radicals are formed. This has been demonstrated by Becht & Fischer[50] by swelling samples of nylon 6 with methacrylic acid. They found that upon subsequent deformation a radical characteristic of the polymerisation of methacrylic acid was produced rather than the usual polyamide radical. Since it is known that methacrylic acid swells only the amorphous regions this was taken as proof that the radicals are formed principally in the amorphous areas.

Over the years there have been a number of attempts to relate measurements of molecular rupture by ESR to the kinetic theories of fracture[15,38,48,49,51,52] since the process of bond breakage is an essential part of the kinetic theories (Section 2.3). Zhurkov & Tomashevsky[15] reported that there was good agreement between the two approaches. However, DeVries et al.[49] examined the kinetic theory of Zhurkov[14,15] more closely and pointed out that although it appears to be valid for a constant loading-rate it was not entirely satisfactory since it predicts, for example, that the rate of bond breakage under fixed load should be constant whereas it is found in practice to vary considerably with loading time (Fig. 2.9(c)). DeVries et al. suggested that since the Zhurkov approach assumes a uniform stress distribution in the specimen it cannot cope with the actual situation in semicrystalline polymer fibres where there are highly strained tie molecules between crystalline regions. Under fixed loading the most highly strained tie molecules will break first of all, spreading the load to other less strained molecules

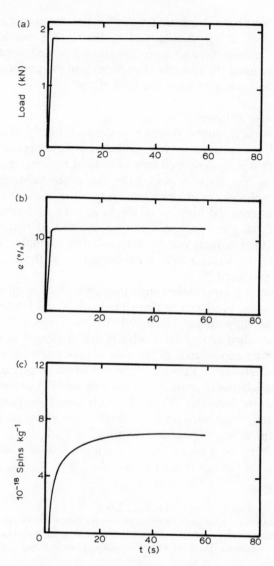

Fig. 2.9. Production of free radicals during a constant load test upon nylon 6 fibres.[24]

thus giving rise to the decreasing rate of molecular rupture with time apparent in Fig. 2.9(c). Similarly, Peterlin[51,52] has emphasised the effect of the unique fibrillar morphology of oriented semicrystalline polymer fibres upon their fracture behaviour and the importance of the severing of tie molecules upon the ESR signal.

2.5.1.2 Glassy Polymers

When an isotropic glassy polymer undergoes brittle fracture in a conventional tensile test very few radicals can be detected[6,9] because the deformation is concentrated into a localised region (e.g. a craze) in the vicinity of the fracture plane. On the other hand, grinding or milling such polymers produces a large number of radicals (Table 2.4) which can be detected because of the large area of fracture surface produced. If the glassy polymer can be induced to undergo plastic deformation then radicals can be detected. For example, when polycarbonate is cold-drawn a radical concentration of the order of 10^{22} spins m^{-3} is produced.[53]

If the polymer is cross-linked then there is a much greater tendency for radicals to be produced during deformation and fracture, clearly indicating the importance of molecular anchorage. It has been found[6,44] that when cross-linked rubbers are deformed below the T_g there is a strong dependence of the radical concentration upon crosslink density as shown in Table 2.6. The cross-link density increases as the molar mass between cross-links decreases and the concentration of spins at fracture increases. Even relatively small degrees of crosslinking produce much stronger ESR signals than when uncross-linked versions of the same polymer are deformed. Clearly the cross-linking makes flow between adjacent molecules more difficult and increases the tendency for molecular fracture to take place.

TABLE 2.6

VARIATION OF SPIN CONCENTRATIONS PRIOR TO FRAC
TURE WITH MOLAR MASS BETWEEN CROSS-LINKS, $\bar{M}_c$,
FOR NATURAL RUBBER (AFTER REFERENCE 44)

$\bar{M}_c$ $(g\ mol^{-1})$	Spin concentration prior to fracture $(spins\ kg^{-1})$
11 158	$4 \cdot 0 \times 10^{20}$
6 082	$8 \cdot 9 \times 10^{20}$
4 385	$9 \cdot 5 \times 10^{20}$
3 364	$11 \cdot 1 \times 10^{20}$

Recently Wool & Rockhill[36] have measured the changes in molar mass during the microtoming of thin slices (1–2 μm thick) from polystyrene rods. They found that there was a reduction in molar mass which depended upon the square root of the initial molar mass of the polymer. In addition they showed that there was no reduction below an initial molar mass of $30\,000\,\mathrm{g\,mol^{-1}}$, the critical entanglement molar mass,[54] and so the clear indication is that entanglements provide anchorage points and without them there would be little molecular fracture in a glassy polymer.

2.5.2 Microvoid Formation and Craze Growth

It is clear that following chain scission several other processes must occur before a polymer eventually undergoes macroscopic fracture. It is known that microvoids form in the polymer during deformation[21]

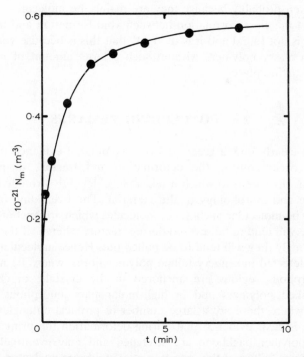

Fig. 2.10. *Increase in the number of microvoids per unit volume, N_m, with time for a sample of poly(vinyl chloride) held under a tensile stress of 60 MPa (after Reference 56).*

and that they can grow and coalesce to form larger cavities and crazes which can be observed with the naked eye.[55] Eventually fracture will occur, at least in a glassy polymer, by the breakdown of crazes into a crack (Chapter 5).

The formation and growth of microvoids can best be followed using small-angle X-ray scattering as described in Section 2.4.3. It is found[21,56] that if a polymer is held under a constant stress the concentration of microvoids increases with time as shown in Fig. 2.10. Concentrations of up to 10^{21}–10^{22} m^{-3} have been reported with void sizes of the order of several tens of nanometres. It has been found[40] that for certain oriented crystalline polymer fibres the concentrations of free radicals and voids are the same, clearly implying that voiding and radical formation are related to each other, for example by voids being nucleated at the ends of broken chains.

Also when a cavity grows in the amorphous areas of a crystalline polymer fibre most of the molecules passing through the void regions are broken probably because they are mainly tie molecules. In glassy polymers the close correlation between void formation and molecular fracture is not found and it is thought[6] that this is because voiding can occur in glassy polymers without such a large amount of molecular fracture taking place.

2.6   CONCLUDING REMARKS

There is clearly now a great deal of accumulated evidence that chain scission occurs during the deformation and fracture of polymers. However, the extent to which it takes place depends strongly upon the structure and morphology of the material. The overriding factor appears to be molecular anchorage; molecules which are anchored in the structure will tend to be severed during fracture whereas if they are not held strongly they will tend to be pulled out. Hence molecular fracture can be detected in semicrystalline polymer fibres, where tie molecules in amorphous regions are anchored in the crystals, in chemically cross-linked polymers and in high-molar-mass amorphous thermoplastics where there are a large number of physical entanglements.

There is clear evidence that during deformation the primary bonds of the polymer backbone are stretched and may eventually break. Before gross failure of the specimen microvoids are nucleated probably where the most highly strained molecules are broken and these voids increase in both size and number with increasing strain until crazes and/or macrocracks are produced.

In conjunction with experimental measurements of bond breaking and void formation, theories have been developed which view the fracture process as a kinetic phenomenon. It is envisaged that the activation energy for bond breakage is reduced under the action of an applied stress. This approach has been found to be consistent with many of the experimental observations although it is thought to be most useful in accounting for the initiation rather than the propagation phase of fracture. In Chapter 3 the use of fracture mechanics is discussed—this has had the most success in explaining *crack propagation* in polymers.

REFERENCES

1. Cottrell, A. (1953). *Dislocations and plastic flow in crystals*, Clarendon Press, Oxford.
2. Young, R. J. (1981). *Introduction to polymers*, Chapman and Hall, London.
3. Kelly, A. (1966). *Strong solids*, Clarendon Press, Oxford.
4. Berry, J. P. (1961). *J. Polym. Sci.*, **50**, 107.
5. Berry, J. P. (1972). In: *Fracture VII*, Ed. by H. Liebowitz, Academic Press, New York.
6. Andrews, E. H. & Reed, P. E. (1978). In: *Advances in polymer science*, Vol. 27, Ed. by J. D. Ferry, Springer-Verlag, New York, p. 1.
7. Vincent, P. I. (1972). *Polymer*, **13**, 557.
8. Williams, J. G. (1980). *Metal Science*, **14**, 344.
9. Kausch, H. H. (1978). *Polymer fracture*, Springer-Verlag, Berlin, Heidelberg.
10. Galiotis, C. & Young, R. J. Unpublished results.
11. Lake, G. J. & Lindley, P. B. (1965). *J. Appl. Polym. Sci.*, **9**, 1233.
12. Andrews, E. H. & Fukahori, Y. (1977). *J. Mater. Sci.*, **12**, 1307.
13. Lake, G. J. & Thomas, A. G. (1967). *Proc. Roy. Soc. A*, **300**, 108.
14. Zhurkov, S. N. (1965). *Int. J. Fract. Mech.*, **1**, 210.
15. Zhurkov, S. N. & Tomashevsky, E. E. (1966). *Physical basis of yield and fracture*, Conf. Proc., Institute of Physics, London, p. 200.
16. Bueche, F. (1957). *J. Appl. Phys.*, **28**, 784.
17. Bueche, F. (1958). *J. Appl. Phys.*, **29**, 1231.
18. Bueche, F. & Halpin, J. C. (1964). *J. Appl. Phys.*, **35**, 36.
19. Halpin, J. C. (1964). *J. Appl. Phys.*, **35**, 3133.
20. Andrews, E. H. (1979). In: *Developments in polymer fracture—I*, Ed. by E. H. Andrews, Applied Science Publishers Ltd., London, p. 1.
21. Kuksenko, V. S. & Tamuzs, V. P. (1981). *Fracture micromechanics of polymer materials*, Martinus Nijhoff, The Hague.
22. Kausch, H. H. & Hsiao, C. C. (1968). *J. Appl. Phys.*, **39**, 4915.

23. Kausch, H. H. (1970). *Kolloid-Z. u.Z-Polymere*, **236**, 48.
24. Kausch, H. H. & DeVries, K. L. (1975). *Int. J. Fract.*, **11**, 727.
25. Zhurkov, S. N., Vettegren, V. I., Korsukov, V. E. & Novak, I. I. (1969). *2nd International conference on fracture*, Conf. Proc., Chapman and Hall, London, p. 545.
26. Roylance, D. K. & DeVries, K. L. (1971). *J. Polym. Sci., Polym. Lett.*, **9**, 443.
27. Wool, R. P. (1975). *J. Polym. Sci., Polym. Phys. Ed.*, **18**, 1795.
28. Vettegren, V. I., Novak, I. I. & Friedland, K. J. (1975). *Int. J. Fract.*, **11**, 789.
29. Batchelder, D. N. & Bloor, D. (1979). *J. Polym. Sci., Polym. Phys. Ed.*, **17**, 569.
30. Galiotis, C. (1982). *Polydiacetylene single crystal fibres*, PhD Thesis, Queen Mary College, London.
31. Poole, C. P. (1967). *Electron spin resonance*, John Wiley and Sons, New York.
32. Ayscough, P. (1967). *Electron spin resonance in chemistry*, Methuen, London.
33. Salloum, R. J. & Eckert, R. E. (1973). *J. Appl. Polym. Sci.*, **17**, 509.
34. Casale, A., Porter, R. S. & Johnson, J. F. (1971). *Rubber Chem. and Tech.*, **44**, 534.
35. Stoeckel, T. M., Blasius, J. & Crist, B. (1978). *J. Polym. Sci., Polym. Phys. Ed.*, **16**, 485.
36. Wool, R. P. & Rockhill, A. T. (1981). *J. Macromol. Sci.*, **B20**, 85.
37. Tomashevsky, E. E., Zakrevskii, V. A., Novak, I. I., Korsukov, V. E., Regel, V. R., Pozdnyakov, O. F., Slutsker, A. I. & Kuksenko, V. S. (1975). *Int. J. Fract.*, **11**, 803.
38. Zhurkov, S. N. & Korsukov, V. E. (1974). *J. Polym. Sci., Polym. Phys. Ed.*, **12**, 385.
39. Guinier, A. & Fornet, A. (1955). *Small-angle scattering of X-rays*, John Wiley and Sons, New York.
40. Zhurkov, S. N., Zakrevskii, V. A., Korsukov, V. E. & Kuksenko, V. S. (1972). *J. Polym. Sci., A-2*, **10**, 1509.
41. Schultz, J. M. (1974). *Polymer materials science*, Prentice Hall, New Jersey.
42. Davis, L. A., Pampillo, C. A. & Chiang, T. C. (1973). *J. Polym. Sci., Polym. Phys. Ed.*, **11**, 841.
43. Becht, J. & Fischer, H. (1972). *Kolloid-Z. u.Z-Polymere*, **250**, 1048.
44. Natarajan, R. & Reed, P. E. (1972). *J. Polym. Sci., A-2*, **10**, 585.
45. Mead, W. T. (1975). *Molecular fracture in mechanically deformed polymers*, PhD Thesis, Queen Mary College, London.
46. Mead, W. T., Porter, R. S. & Reed, P. E. (1978). *Macromolecules*, **11**, 56.
47. Kausch, H. H. & Becht, J. (1970). *Rheologica Acta*, **9**, 137.
48. Lloyd, B. A., DeVries, K. L. & Williams, M. L. (1972). *J. Polym. Sci., A-2*, **10**, 1415.
49. DeVries, K. L., Roylance, D. K. & Williams, M. L. (1971). *Int. J. Fract. Mech.*, **7**, 197.
50. Becht, J. & Fischer, H. (1969). *Kolloid-Z. u.Z-Polymere*, **229**, 167.

51. Peterlin, A. (1969). *J. Polym. Sci.*, *A-2*, **7**, 1151.
52. Peterlin, A. (1972). *J. Macromol. Sci.-Phys.*, **B6**, 583.
53. Zaks, B. Yu., Lebedinskaya, L. & Chalidze, V. N. (1971). *Polym. Sci. (USSR)*, **12**, 3025.
54. Gent, A. N. & Thomas, A. G. (1972). *J. Polym. Sci.*, *A-2*, **10**, 571.
55. Regel, V. R. (1956). *Sov. Phys. Tech. Phys.*, **1**, 353.
56. Zhurkov, S. N., Kuksenko, V. S. & Slutsker, A. I. (1969). *2nd International conference on fracture*, Conf. Proc., Chapman and Hall, London, p. 531.

Chapter 3

Fracture Mechanics

3.1 INTRODUCTION

It has been shown (see Chapter 2 and reference 1) that the theoretical stress to cause cleavage fracture in a brittle solid is of the order of $E/10$; that is, one-tenth of the Young's modulus. The modulus of a brittle polymer is typically 3 GPa and so the theoretical strength of such a material should be 300 MPa. The measured fracture strengths of polymers are well below the theoretical value (typically 10–100 MPa), as is the case for many other materials. This shortfall in strength was recognised many years ago by Griffith[2] who showed that the relatively low strength of a brittle solid could be explained by the presence of flaws which act as stress concentrators. This hypothesis has led to the development of a large body of experimental and theoretical work which is now termed fracture mechanics.

The basic tenet of fracture mechanics is, therefore, that the strength of most real solids is governed by the presence of flaws and, since the various theories enable the manner in which they propagate under stress to be analysed mathematically, the application of fracture mechanics to crack growth in polymers has received considerable attention. Two main, interrelatable, conditions for fracture are proposed. Firstly, the energy criterion arising from Griffith's,[2] and later Orowan's,[3] work which supposes that fracture occurs when sufficient energy is released (from the stress field) by growth of the crack to supply the requirements of the new fracture surfaces. The energy released comes from stored elastic or potential energy of the loading system and can, in principle, be calculated for any type of test piece.

This approach, therefore, provides a measure of the energy required to extend a crack over unit area and this is termed the fracture energy or critical strain-energy release rate and is denoted as G_c. Secondly, Irwin[4] found that the stress field around a sharp crack in a linear elastic material could be uniquely defined by a parameter named the stress-intensity factor, K, and stated that fracture occurs when the value of K exceeds some critical value, K_c. Thus, K is a stress field parameter independent of the material whereas K_c, often referred to as the fracture toughness, is a measure of a material property.

A basic aim of fracture mechanics is to identify fracture criteria such as G_c and K_c and others discussed later, which are independent of the geometry of the cracked body and, ideally, even of the test conditions, e.g. test temperature. Thus fracture mechanics parameters should greatly assist in developing a more fundamental understanding of the fracture process and should be of considerable use in the practical areas of data specification and engineering design.

This chapter aims to outline theoretical and experimental aspects of fracture mechanics, with particular relevance to polymeric materials. More detailed treatises, with the emphasis on metals, have been published by Knott[5] and Broek.[6]

3.2 ENERGY BALANCE APPROACH

3.2.1 Basic Principles
The energy criterion for fracture is simply an extension of Griffith's hypothesis which describes quasi-static crack propagation as the conversion of the work done, F, by the external force and the available elastic energy, stored in the bulk of the sample, U, into surface free-energy, γ. It may be written

$$\frac{\partial}{\partial a}(F-U) \geqslant \gamma \frac{\partial A}{\partial a} \qquad (3.1)$$

where ∂A is the increase in surface area associated with an increment of crack growth ∂a. For a crack propagating in a lamina of thickness b, the criterion becomes

$$\frac{1}{b}\frac{\partial}{\partial a}(F-U) \geqslant 2\gamma \qquad (3.2)$$

TABLE 3.1

VALUES OF 2γ, G_0 AND G_c FOR PMMA AND NATURAL RUBBER

Polymer	$2\gamma\ (J\,m^{-2})$	$G_0\ (J\,m^{-2})$	$G_c\ (J\,m^{-2})^a$	Reference
PMMA	0·078	0·5	500	7, 9
Cross-linked natural rubber	0·072	40	13 000	8, 10

^{a} Values of G_c were taken at room temperature in air and at a moderate rate-of-test.

since

$$\partial A = 2b\,\partial a \qquad (3.3)$$

However, initial measurements on poly(methyl methacrylate) (PMMA)[7] and cross-linked rubbers[8] revealed that the energy required to cause crack growth was more than twice the surface free-energy, 2γ, as may be seen from Table 3.1. There are two main reasons for this discrepancy. Firstly, the value of 2γ only reflects the energy required to rupture secondary bonds, e.g. van der Waals forces, while crack growth in polymers generally necessitates the rupture of stronger, covalent bonds. The energy required solely for bond rupture has been termed the intrinsic fracture energy—this will be denoted by the symbol G_0; when only secondary bonds are present $G_0 = 2\gamma$ but if stronger bonds are involved $G_0 > 2\gamma$. If the material is perfectly elastic then G_0 is the appropriate energy requirement. However, secondly, fracture in even the most brittle of polymers invariably involves localised viscoelastic and/or plastic energy dissipative processes occuring under the high strains experienced in the vicinity of the crack tip or, indeed, elsewhere in the specimen. Such micromechanisms usually represent the main source of energy absorption in the material and are discussed in detail in later chapters.

Now, if it is assumed that energy dissipation around the crack tip occurs in a manner independent of both the test geometry and the way in which forces are applied to the specimen then 2γ may be replaced in eqn. (3.2) by the symbol G_c. The value of G_c encompasses all the energy losses incurred around the crack tip and is, therefore, the energy required to increase the crack by unit length in a specimen of unit width. Hence, the fracture criterion becomes

$$\frac{1}{b}\frac{\partial}{\partial a}(F - U) \geqslant G_c \qquad (3.4)$$

and from the first law of thermodynamics (ignoring dynamic effects such as energy radiation by stress waves)

$$G_c = G_0 + \psi \qquad (3.5)$$

where ψ is the energy dissipated in viscoelastic and plastic deformations at the crack tip. As mentioned above, and illustrated in Table 3.1, the value of ψ is usually the major contribution to the value of G_c and this frequently results in the measured value of G_c being highly dependent upon the rate and temperature of testing.

The application of fracture mechanics to the failure of cross-linked rubbery adhesives bonded to various substrates led Gent & Kinloch,[11] Andrews & Kinloch[12,13] and Gent & Schultz[14] to propose, from dimensional and intuitive arguments, the following simple relationship, which was later derived more rigorously by Andrews (Section 3.2.4)

$$\psi = G_0 f(\dot{a}, T, e) \qquad (3.6)$$

where f is a function the value of which depends upon the crack growth rate $\dot{a}$, the temperature T and the strain level e. Now let

$$\Phi(\dot{a}, T, e) = 1 + f(\dot{a}, T, e) \qquad (3.7)$$

then, combining eqns (3.5) to (3.7)

$$G_c = G_0 \Phi(\dot{a}, T, e) \qquad (3.8)$$

where Φ is a loss function. The dependence of the energy loss term, ψ, upon the intrinsic failure energy, G_0, is particularly intriguing. This dependence arises because material around the crack tip can only be subjected to stress, and hence energy losses, whilst the chemical and physical bonds acting ahead of the crack tip remain unbroken. An important aspect of eqn. (3.8) is that when viscoelastic and plastic energy losses are negligible, i.e. $\Phi(\dot{a}, T, e) \to 1$ and $f(\dot{a}, T, e) \to 0$, then the measured value of the fracture energy is equal to G_0. Thus, a direct measure of the inter- and intra-molecular bonding across the fracture plane may be obtained.

The next aspect to consider is the evaluation of G_c and this requires a solution for the left-hand side of eqn. (3.4). This is best discussed by examining the various types of material behaviour that one may encounter.

3.2.2 Linear Elastic Fracture Mechanics
The concepts of linear elastic fracture mechanics (LEFM) may strictly only be applied to those materials which obey Hooke's law so that

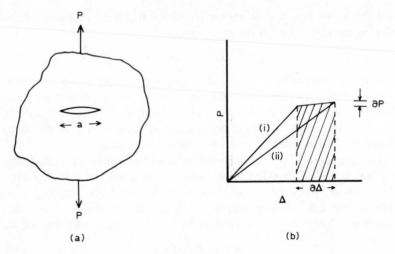

Fig. 3.1. Generalised loading of a cracked body which exhibits bulk linear elastic behaviour.

stress is proportional to infinitesimal strains. Thus, for any loaded body a linear load–deflection relationship results. However, the basic LEFM analyses, albeit with minor modifications in some instances, may also be applied to materials which exhibit inelastic deformations around the crack tip provided that such deformations are confined to the immediate vicinity of the tip. Hence, the bulk of the body will still exhibit linear elastic properties.

Thus, considering an energy balance argument for a cracked body of thickness b, subjected to a generalised load P (Fig. 3.1(a)) then the linear load–deflection curve is as shown in Fig. 3.1(b), line (i). The stored elastic energy, U_1, is given by the area under the curve[4,15]

$$U_1 = \tfrac{1}{2}P\Delta \tag{3.9}$$

where Δ is the displacement. If the crack grows by an increment ∂a then the stiffness of the body decreases and causes a change in load of ∂P and in deflection of $\partial \Delta$ and, since the material exhibits bulk linear elastic behaviour, unloading would give line (ii) in Fig. 3.1(b). Thus the stored elastic energy is given by

$$U_2 = \tfrac{1}{2}(P + \partial P)(\Delta + \partial \Delta) \tag{3.10}$$

and the change in stored elastic energy is

$$\partial U = U_2 - U_1 \tag{3.11}$$

There is also external work done, shown as the hatched area in Fig. 3.1(b), so

$$\partial F = P \, \partial \Delta + \tfrac{1}{2} \partial P \, \partial \Delta \tag{3.12}$$

$$= \left(P + \frac{\partial P}{2} \right) \partial \Delta \tag{3.13}$$

Therefore, substituting from eqns (3.9) and (3.10) into eqn. (3.11) and combining with eqn. (3.13) yields

$$\partial(F - U) = \tfrac{1}{2}(P \, \partial \Delta - \Delta \, \partial P) \tag{3.14}$$

and now putting eqn. (3.14) into eqn. (3.4) reveals that for crack growth to occur

$$G_c = \frac{1}{2b} \left(\frac{P \, \partial \Delta}{\partial a} - \frac{\Delta \, \partial P}{\partial a} \right) \tag{3.15}$$

It is useful to consider the compliance, C, of the cracked body which may be defined by

$$C = \frac{\Delta}{P} \tag{3.16}$$

so that

$$\partial \Delta = P \, \partial C + C \, \partial P \tag{3.17}$$

and substituting into eqn. (3.15), taking the load at the onset of crack propagation to be P_c, yields

$$G_c = \frac{P_c^2}{2b} \frac{\partial C}{\partial a} \tag{3.18}$$

This equation is the foundation for many calculations of G_c since if C is determined as a function of a, either analytically or experimentally, then $\partial C / \partial a$ may be found. Thus, if P_c is measured the value of G_c may be deduced.

3.2.3 Bulk Non-Linear Elastic Behaviour

The earliest application of fracture mechanics to polymers was the work reported in 1953 by Rivlin & Thomas[8] on crack growth in cross-linked rubbers. These materials generally show a high degree of hysteresis in the immediate vicinity of the crack tip, where large strains are experienced, but away from these regions possess non-linear, but elastically reversible, behaviour.

If we consider eqn. (3.4) but carry out the differentiation at a constant overall length, l, of the test piece or, more precisely, if the external forces do no work since their points of application do not move, then the criterion becomes

$$-\frac{1}{b}\left(\frac{\partial U}{\partial a}\right)_l \geqslant G_c \qquad (3.19)$$

Rivlin & Thomas[8] next deduced solutions for the left-hand side of this equation for several different test pieces so as to determine the value of G_c (or T for tearing energy as they named this quantity) and hence establish its invariance with loading conditions and geometry. Some of the test pieces they considered are discussed in detail later (Section 3.6) but the essential features of the analysis may be illustrated by reference to the single-edge crack specimen shown in Fig. 3.2.

The single-edge crack specimen consists of a parallel-sided sheet of material loaded in tension containing a short edge-crack. A similar specimen containing no crack possesses a uniform strain-energy density (i.e. strain-energy per unit volume) of W_0. The insertion of the crack reduces this to zero over the shaded area shown in Fig. 3.2 which dimensional considerations and experimental evidence[16] suggests will be $k_1 a^2$, where k_1 is a proportionality constant. Further, since the material is elastically reversible, except at points very close to the crack tip, the value of W_0 may be taken simply as the integral of the stress/strain curve up to the required strain level in the bulk of the specimen. Thus, the loss of elastic energy caused by introducing the crack is

$$-U = k_1 a^2 b W_0 \qquad (3.20)$$

Therefore, upon differentiation

$$-\left(\frac{\partial U}{\partial a}\right)_l = 2 k_1 a b W_0 \qquad (3.21)$$

Hence crack growth will commence at some critical value, W_c, of the elastic stored energy density in the bulk material and from eqn. (3.4)

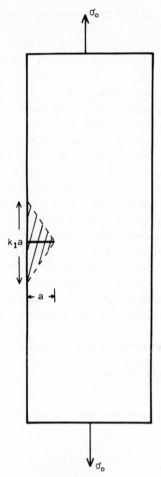

Fig. 3.2. Single-edge crack test specimen.

the value of G_c is given by

$$G_c = 2k_1 a W_c \qquad (3.22)$$

where it can be shown that[16,17]

$$k_1 \simeq \frac{\pi}{\lambda_c^{\frac{1}{2}}} \qquad (3.23)$$

where λ_c is the extension ratio (final length/original length; $\lambda_c = e_c + 1$)

of the sheet at the onset of crack propagation. Equation (3.22) thus applies to both bulk linear and non-linear elastic materials.†

An approach to the problem of identifying a unique parameter to characterise the failure of bodies which exhibit non-linear elastic behaviour because of extensive crack tip plasticity has been developed principally by Rice[18] and applied by workers, such as Turner,[19] Chell[20] and Landes & Begley,[21] to crack growth in metals. Rice[18] showed that a certain integral, now commonly called the J-contour integral, described the flow of energy into the crack tip region and that the dominant term in the description of the stress and strain singularities at the crack tip could also be written in terms of J. He demonstrated that the value of J was independent of the integration path. However, it should be noted that the derivation of J is strictly only valid for linear and non-linear elastic materials where unloading occurs down the same path as the initial loading. After plastic deformation real materials unload down a different path to the loading one. Nevertheless, in practice, the use of J for materials which show this type of plasticity has been supported by direct experimentation, as recently reviewed by Landes & Begley[21] and by the rather indirect analysis, outlined by Turner.[19] For bulk non-linear elastic materials Rice[18] found that J may

---

† It may readily be shown that for a linear elastic material in the form of a single-edge crack specimen eqn. (3.22) reduces to the well-known Griffith equation. Since, for linear elasticity

$$W_c = \tfrac{1}{2}\sigma_c e_c \tag{3.24}$$

where σ_c and e_c are the stress and strain, respectively, at crack propagation. Now

$$\frac{\sigma_c}{e_c} = E \tag{3.25}$$

and therefore

$$W_c = \frac{1}{2}\frac{\sigma_c^2}{E} \tag{3.26}$$

Substituting eqns (3.23) and (3.26) into eqn. (3.22), and for $\lambda_c \to 1$, yields the Griffith equation

$$G_c = \frac{\pi \sigma_c^2 a}{E} \tag{3.27}$$

as a special case of eqn. (3.22) for those materials which obey the assumptions of LEFM.

be simply defined in terms of energy as the rate of decrease of potential energy, U, with crack length and Fig. 3.3 shows schematic non-linear loading curves corresponding to specimens with crack lengths a and $(a + \partial a)$ under displacement control. The hatched area represents the energy change $Jb\,\partial a$, thus

$$J = -\frac{1}{b}\left(\frac{\partial U}{\partial a}\right)_l \qquad (3.28)$$

and the criterion for the onset of crack growth is

$$J \geqslant J_c \qquad (3.29)$$

where J_c is a material property independent of crack length and specimen geometry. However, despite its increasing popularity in the metals field, the use of the J-contour integral for characterising the onset of crack growth in plastics has only been employed by a few workers.[22-4]

The Rice[18] contour integral and the Rivlin & Thomas[8] approaches are extremely similar and for bulk non-linear elastic materials the parameter J_c is directly equivalent to the fracture energy, G_c, determined by the Rivlin & Thomas method, i.e. eqn. (3.22) in the case of

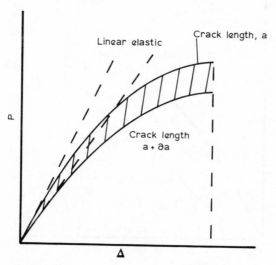

Fig. 3.3. The J-integral (displacement control). The hatched area represents $Jb\,\partial a$.

the single-edge crack specimen. In practice, although not demanded on theoretical grounds, the former approach has been adopted for ductile plastics while the latter has been used in connection with cross-linked rubbers. Obviously, in the case of materials obeying the assumptions of LEFM, both the above approaches are exactly equivalent to the equations formulated in Section 3.2.2, as illustrated by eqns (3.24) to (3.27).

3.2.4 Bulk Inelastic Behaviour

Recently Ahagon et al.,[25] Thomas & Kadir[26] and Mohamed[27] have suggested that for rubbers which exhibit significant internal energy dissipation outside of the immediate crack tip regions eqns (3.19) and (3.22) may still be employed. However, the stored strain-energy available for crack propagation should not now be taken as the input energy but rather as that deduced from the stress/strain relation upon retraction from the deformed state—that is, the input energy minus the hysteresis (loss) energy as indicated in Fig. 3.4 by the hatched area. Thomas & Kadir[26] and Mohamed[27] employed different geometries and established the validity of this argument from the independence of G_c on test geometry.

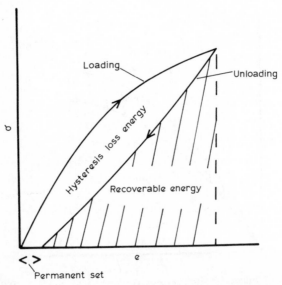

Fig. 3.4. Stress/strain curve of a polymer exhibiting bulk inelastic behaviour.

These approaches assume that there is a region surrounding the crack tip where the local energy dissipation, arising from both viscoelastic and bond-rupture mechanisms, may be considered to be characteristic of the fracture process. They allow for bulk hysteresis, away from this region, and therefore obtain a value of G_c which, as in the case of bulk linear and non-linear but elastic materials, is taken to be a characteristic measure of this localised energy dissipation and hence independent of geometrical considerations.

Andrews and co-workers[28-31] have taken a somewhat different approach to the problem of bulk inelastic behaviour and have proposed a generalised theory of fracture mechanics. This theory embodies, and more rigorously derives, eqn. (3.8)

$$G_c = G_0 \Phi(\dot{a}, T, e)$$

and Andrews then proceeded to explicitly derive the loss function, Φ, as

$$\Phi = \frac{k_2(e)}{k_2(e) - \sum_{PU} h_r g \, \delta v} \tag{3.30}$$

where, h_r is the hysteresis ratio, i.e. the fractional energy loss in a stress cycle at a point in the stress field. For elastic materials $h_r = 0$ and for perfectly plastic solids $h_r = 1$;

δv is a volume element;

g is a distribution function of the energy density W throughout the specimen;

PU denotes summation only over points which unload as the crack propagates, i.e. where $\partial W / \partial a$ is negative; and

k_2 is an explicit function.

Andrews & Fukahori[30] and Andrews[31] examined the validity of the generalised theory by calculating values of the intrinsic fracture energy, G_0 for a range of materials and comparing these values to theoretical estimates and values obtained by other experimental methods. For cross-linked rubbers the agreement was good but for plasticised-PVC and polyethylene the correlation was less satisfactory and for polycarbonate a value of G_0 in the order of many kJ m^{-2} was obtained which was clearly too high (cf., Table 3.1). Andrews[31] commented that in many polymers the elements in which the majority of the viscoelastic and plastic energy losses occur are small and close to the crack tip.

Thus it is difficult experimentally to take account of the very high energy density gradients encountered in these microscopic regions and hence the value of G_0 deduced does not solely reflect that required for bond breakage, as ideally expressed in the theory. Andrews[31] concluded that for polycarbonate the value of G_0 obtained was the craze formation energy, which included a major contribution from viscoelastic and plastic deformations (see Chapter 5). It should also be noted that in the generalised theory it is the value of G_0 which is truly characteristic and geometry independent; the value of Φ, and hence G_c, will be a function of the test geometry. The power of this approach is that it enables the macroscopic fracture mechanics to be related to the microscopic physical processes of energy loss (via h_r) and to bond failure (via G_0).

3.3 STRESS-INTENSITY FACTOR APPROACH

3.3.1 Basic Principles

Figure 3.5 shows a sharp crack in a uniformly stressed, infinite lamina and, assuming Hookean behaviour and infinitesimal strains, Westergaard[32] has developed certain stress-function solutions which relate the local concentration of stresses at the crack tip to the applied stress σ_0. For regions close to the crack tip the solutions take the form

$$\sigma_{ij} = \sigma_0 \left(\frac{a}{2r}\right)^{\frac{1}{2}} f_{ij}(\theta) \qquad (3.31)$$

where σ_{ij} are the components of the stress tensor at a point, r and θ are the polar coordinates of the point, taking the crack tip as the origin, and $2a$ is the length of the crack.

Irwin[4] modified this solution to give

$$\sigma_{ij} = \frac{K}{(2\pi r)^{\frac{1}{2}}} f_{ij}(\theta) \qquad (3.32)$$

The parameter K is the stress-intensity factor and relates the magnitude of the stress-intensity local to the crack in terms of the applied loadings and geometry of the structure in which the crack is located.

A crack in a solid may be stressed in three different modes, denoted I, II and III, as depicted in Fig. 3.6—superposition of the three modes constitutes the general case of crack loading. The cleavage or tensile-opening mode, Mode I, is technically the most important since it is the

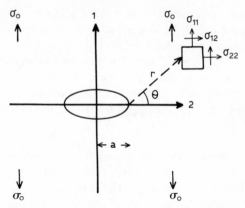

Fig. 3.5. Sharp crack in a uniformly stressed, infinite lamina.

most commonly encountered and usually the one which most often results in failure. The following discussions will therefore mainly be confined to this situation, although analogous arguments may be developed for the other two modes, i.e. Mode II, the inplane-shear mode, and Mode III, the antiplane-shear mode.

For the Mode I case, the crack tip stresses may be developed from eqn. (3.32) to yield[18]

$$\begin{Bmatrix} \sigma_{11} \\ \sigma_{12} \\ \sigma_{22} \end{Bmatrix} = \frac{K_I}{(2\pi r)^{\frac{1}{2}}} \cos (\theta/2) \begin{Bmatrix} 1 + \sin (\theta/2) \sin (3\theta/2) \\ \sin (\theta/2) \cos (3\theta/2) \\ 1 - \sin (\theta/2) \sin (3\theta/2) \end{Bmatrix} \quad (3.33)$$

and

$$\sigma_{33} = 0 \qquad \text{(Plane stress), or} \qquad (3.34)$$

$$\sigma_{33} = \nu(\sigma_{11} + \sigma_{22}) \qquad \text{(Plane strain), and} \qquad (3.35)$$

$$\sigma_{23} = \sigma_{13} = 0 \qquad (3.36)$$

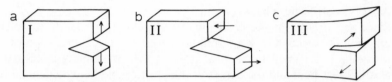

Fig. 3.6. Modes of loading. (a) Cleavage or tensile-opening mode: Mode I; (b) inplane-shear mode: Mode II; and (c) antiplane-shear mode: Mode III.

where ν is Poisson's ratio. Note that in the plane $\theta = 0°$ the shear stress is zero hence for $\theta = 0°$ the stresses σ_{11}, σ_{22} and σ_{33} are the principal stresses σ_1, σ_2 and σ_3, respectively.

From eqn. (3.33) it is evident that as $r \to 0$ then the stress $\sigma_{ij} \to \infty$ and hence stress alone does not make a reasonable local fracture criterion. Therefore, since the level of K_I uniquely defines the stress field around the crack, Irwin[4] postulated that the condition

$$K_I \geqslant K_{Ic} \qquad (3.37)$$

represented a fracture criterion, where K_{Ic} is a critical value for crack growth in the material and, as such, is a material property and often termed the fracture toughness. The units of K are $MN\,m^{-\frac{3}{2}}$ (or psi in$^{\frac{1}{2}}$) and it should be emphasised that it is a factor which characterises the *intensity* of the stress field ahead of a crack. It is not a stress concentration, η, which may be defined as σ_{ij}/σ_0.

The power of the stress-intensity factor approach is that for any Mode I problem K_I may always be expressed in the form

$$K_I = Q\sigma_0 a^{\frac{1}{2}} \qquad (3.38)$$

and, hence, K_{Ic} by

$$K_{Ic} = Q\sigma_c a^{\frac{1}{2}} \qquad (3.39)$$

where σ_c is the applied stress at the onset of crack growth and Q is the geometry parameter. Thus, the solution to eqns (3.38) and (3.39), and hence the examination of the fracture criterion as embodied in eqn. (3.37), depends upon finding an expression for the parameter Q. This parameter is a non-dimensional function of crack size and structural geometry and in its usual form is given by a series expansion. For the infinite plate the value of Q is $\pi^{\frac{1}{2}}$ and thus Q may be considered as a suitable function chosen to make the appropriate surface forces zero. Handbooks[33-5] provide expressions for Q for many standard geometries containing cracks.

3.3.2 Small Scale Yielding
Since the stresses at the crack tip are singular then clearly the yield criterion is exceeded in some zone in the crack tip region. However, if this zone is assumed to be small then it will not greatly disturb the elastic stress field and the extent of the plastic zone may be defined by the elastic stresses. Thus again we return to the assumption of LEFM.

Irwin[4] suggested that if a material is considered which is elastic up to

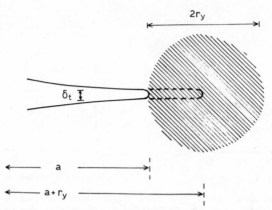

Fig. 3.7. *Irwin model of the plastic zone at a crack tip.*

the uniaxial tensile yield stress, σ_y, and then becomes plastic, then the extent of crack tip plasticity is, to a first approximation, as shown in Fig. 3.7. Here δ_t is the crack tip opening displacement and r_y is the radius of a circular plastic zone at the tip of a 'notional' crack. The tip of this notional crack is thus at the centre of the plastic zone so that its length is $(a + r_y)$. The elastic stress field ahead of this notional crack may therefore be regarded as identical to the stress distribution of a real crack of length a with the extent of the plastic zone $2r_y$. For $r_y \ll a$ eqns (3.38) and (3.39) have been shown to be still valid, although a small correction to the crack length may occasionally be employed in order to improve the accuracy of the calculation. This correction simply consists of using $(a + r_y)$ instead of a in these equations.

The size of the plastic zone radius, r_y, is given by

$$r_y = \frac{1}{2\pi}\left(\frac{K_I}{m_p \sigma_y}\right)^2 \tag{3.40}$$

where m_p is the plastic constraint factor. This factor reflects the amount of constraint on the developing plastic zone, created by the surrounding elastic material. This increases the stress necessary for yield to occur above that needed in uniaxial tension, i.e.

$$m_p = \frac{\text{Effective yield stress}}{\sigma_y} \tag{3.41}$$

The value of m_p is dependent upon the stress state around the crack tip

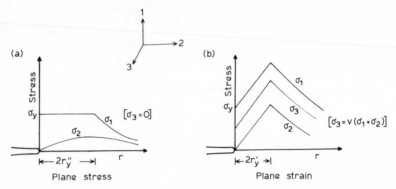

Fig. 3.8. *Schematic variation of elastic/plastic stresses ahead of a crack as a function of distance, r (for $\theta = 0°$). (a) In plane stress ($\sigma_3 = 0$); and (b) in plane strain ($e_3 = 0$).*

and Knott[5] has considered the stress distribution ahead of a crack around which localised plastic yielding has occurred. The stress distribution obtained is shown in Fig. 3.8 for plane-stress ($\sigma_3 = 0$) and plane-strain ($e_3 = 0$) conditions. It was derived from considering the stress distribution in the 1 direction, caused by the applied load, and the resulting stress distribution in the 2 direction created by the accompanying lateral Poisson ratio contractions of small elements ahead of the crack along the 2 axis. It is only approximate and semiquantitative but is, nevertheless, a useful model for illustrating the effect of plastic constraint. If, for example, we employ the Tresca yield criterion (Section 4.2.4) then the stress in the plastic zone under plane-stress conditions is the uniaxial yield stress, σ_y, since in eqn. (4.6) the value of σ_3 will be zero under plane-stress conditions. However, under plane-strain conditions the stress σ_1 required for yielding is given by ($\sigma_y + \sigma_2$), since σ_2 is the smallest principal stress. Thus, the increased constraint introduced under the influence of plane-strain conditions has elevated the level of tensile stress, σ_1, which must be attained for yielding to occur. Therefore, in plane stress the plastic constraint factor, m_p, has a value of unity and the plastic zone radius in plane stress, r_y'', is given by

$$r_y'' = \frac{1}{2\pi}\left(\frac{K_I}{\sigma_y}\right)^2 \qquad \text{for plane stress} \qquad (3.42)$$

To a first approximation the increased constraint in plane strain may be represented by assuming[36] that m_p takes the value $\sqrt{3}$, thus

$$\sigma_y \text{ (plane strain)} \simeq \sqrt{3}\,\sigma_y \qquad (3.43)$$

The higher stress in the plastic zone in plane strain means that the plastic zone radius, r_y', in plane strain is smaller and is given by

$$r_y' = \frac{1}{6\pi}\left(\frac{K_I}{\sigma_y}\right)^2 \qquad \text{for plane strain} \qquad (3.44)$$

The corresponding crack-opening displacements at the crack tip, δ_t, are[36,37]

$$\delta_t = \frac{K_I^{\,2}}{E\sigma_y} \qquad \text{for plane stress} \qquad (3.45)$$

and

$$\delta_t = \frac{K_I^{\,2}}{E\sigma_y}(1-\nu^2) \qquad \text{for plane strain} \qquad (3.46)$$

where E is Young's modulus.

However, in many polymers the plasticity ahead of a crack tip is not even approximately circular in shape but is better modelled as a line zone, as shown in Fig. 3.9. This may be described by using the Dugdale analysis,[38] which has many similarities to ideas put forward by Barenblatt.[39] It is assumed that yielding of the material at the crack tip makes the crack longer by the length of the plastic zone, R. The stress singularity at the crack tip is exactly cancelled out by a series of internal stresses of magnitude σ_p which act on the boundary of the plastic zone. The value of σ_p is usually taken to be the yield stress, σ_y,

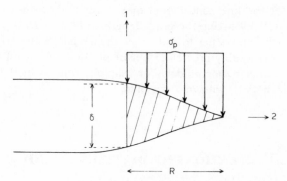

Fig. 3.9. The Dugdale line plastic-zone model.

when modelling shear zones and the craze surface stress, σ_{cs}, when modelling craze zones; these aspects are considered in Chapters 4 and 5. The length of the plastic zone, R, ahead of the crack is related to K_I, for $\sigma_0 \ll \sigma_p$, by[15,40]

$$R = \frac{\pi}{8}\left(\frac{K_I}{\sigma_p}\right)^2$$ (3.47)

and the thickness, $\delta(r)$, of the plastic zone at any distance, r ($\theta = 0°$), is given by[18]

$$\delta(r) = \frac{8}{\pi E^*}\sigma_p R\left[\xi - \frac{r}{2R}\log\left(\frac{1+\xi}{1-\xi}\right)\right]$$ (3.48)

where

$$\xi = \left(1 - \frac{r}{R}\right)^{\frac{1}{2}}$$ (3.49)

and E^* is the modulus which is equal to Young's modulus, E, in plane stress and $E/(1-\nu^2)$ in plane strain. The crack-opening displacement, δ, at the crack tip ($r = 0$, $\delta(r) = \delta_t$) is given by

$$\delta_t = \frac{8\sigma_p R}{\pi E^*}$$ (3.50)

$$= \frac{K_I^2}{E^*\sigma_p}$$ (3.51)

When $\sigma_p \equiv \sigma_y$ then eqn. (3.51) is equivalent to either eqn. (3.45) or eqn. (3.46).

For values of $\sigma_0/\sigma_p > 0.5$ substantial deviations from the above equations for the line zone model may occur and again a correction may be made[11] by taking the crack length to be ($a + R/2$).

Finally, it is interesting to note that the Dugdale line zone model predicts a considerably greater extent of plasticity ahead of the crack tip than the circular zone models; for example, comparing the Dugdale and circular models, with $\sigma_p = \sigma_y$, then

$$R \simeq 2.5 r_y''$$ (3.52)

3.4 RELATIONSHIP BETWEEN G AND K

In the case of LEFM a simple relationship exists between G and K, and for a crack in a homogeneous material, under plane-strain conditions, this relationship is given by[4,41]

$$G_c = \left(\frac{1-\nu^2}{E}\right)K_{Ic}^2 + \left(\frac{1-\nu^2}{E}\right)K_{IIc}^2 + \left(\frac{1+\nu}{E}\right)K_{IIIc}^2 \quad (3.53)$$

or equivalently

$$G_c = G_{Ic} + G_{IIc} + G_{IIIc} \quad (3.54)$$

where, for Mode I

$$G_{Ic} = \frac{K_{Ic}^2}{E} \qquad \text{for plane stress} \quad (3.55)$$

$$G_{Ic} = \left(\frac{K_{Ic}^2}{E}\right)(1-\nu^2) \qquad \text{for plane strain} \quad (3.56)$$

Thus, for LEFM, a critical G_{Ic} criterion is identical to a critical K_{Ic} criterion and K_{Ic} combines both material properties, i.e. G_{Ic} and E.

It should be noted that the factor $(1-\nu^2)$ arises because when the body is wholly elastic the strains are reduced by this factor in passing from plane stress to plane strain. This change is not great. However, because some degree of local plasticity accompanies crack growth, the change of conditions may have a considerable effect on the actual value of K_{Ic}, as discussed in Section 3.5. Thus a switch between plane-stress and plane-strain conditions cannot be regarded simply as a matter of applying the $(1-\nu^2)$ factor.

For non-LEFM the concept of G is, of course, still valid and of practical benefit but the interpretation of stress-intensity factors is not clear and eqns (3.53) to (3.56) are inapplicable.

3.5 THICKNESS EFFECTS

It is sometimes found in practice that the measured value of K_{Ic}, or G_{Ic}, for some materials varies with the specimen thickness, over a particular range of thicknesses. A typical form of the relationship between K_{Ic} and specimen thickness, b, is shown in Fig. 3.10 where K_{Ic}' is the value for fracture under plane-strain conditions and K_{Ic}'' that for full plane-stress conditions. (It should be noted that K_{Ic} is often referred to as the plane-strain fracture toughness, e.g. ASTM-E 399[42]—however, in the present text the term K_{Ic} will simply refer to the measured value of the stress-intensity factor at failure in Mode I, since in much of the published work, especially in the field of polymer

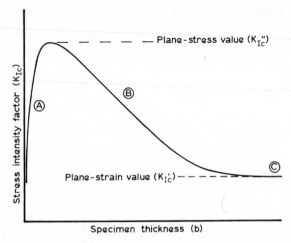

Fig. 3.10. *Variation of the measured stress-intensity factor, K_{Ic}, at failure as a function of specimen thickness, b.*

fracture, it is not possible to determine whether the quoted values of K_{Ic} are truly plane-strain values.)

The thickness effect arises because the state of stress near the crack tip varies from plane stress in the surface regions of a relatively thin plate, or throughout the thickness of a thin plate, to plane strain in the centre of a thick plate. Now, as discussed in Section 3.3.2, the stress at which a material yields is greater in a triaxial stress field (plane strain) than in a biaxial one (plane stress). Thus in the former more constrained case a less extensive degree of plasticity develops at the crack tip. A more accurate impression of the shapes of the plastic zone ahead of the crack than that modelled in Fig. 3.7 may be derived by considering in detail the complex stress state that exists around the crack tip together with an appropriate yield criterion. Either the Tresca or the von Mises criterion (see Chapter 4) is usually applied and hence the shape and the size of the plastic zone may then be obtained from the stresses given in eqn. (3.33). (It is noteworthy that along the $\theta = 0°$ plane the radius of the plastic zone in plane stress is independent of whether an Irwin model or Tresca or von Mises criterion is employed; in all cases r_y'' is given by $K_I^2/2\pi\sigma_y^2$. In plane strain somewhat different values of r_y' $(\theta = 0°)$ are obtained from the various models. This essentially arises because the different models have different expressions for the plastic constraint factor, m_p; see References 6 and 40 for detailed discussion on this point.) Using a von Mises criterion the resulting[40] model is shown schematically in Fig. 3.11. The far more limited degree of plasticity which develops at the crack tip under plane-strain conditions, due to the effective yield stress being greater under these constrained conditions, is evident. This limited degree of plastic deformation means that the strain gradient immediately ahead of the crack tip is steeper, that strain is more concentrated and that the associated energy losses are smaller. These effects are reflected in a lower value of K'_{Ic}, or G'_{Ic}, compared to K''_{Ic} or G''_{Ic}.

Considering the regions A, B and C indicated on Fig. 3.10 in detail, then in region C the value of $K_{Ic} \rightarrow K'_{Ic}$. For this to occur a sufficiently thick sample is required to enable plane strain to dominate and the thickness, b, necessary to achieve this is usually taken to be

$$b \geqslant 2 \cdot 5 \left(\frac{K'_{Ic}}{\sigma_y} \right)^2 \qquad (3.57)$$

and hence from eqn. (3.44)

$$b \geqslant 47 r'_{yc} \qquad (3.58)$$

where the subscript 'c' again indicates the value at fracture.

In region B a mixture of plane-strain and plane-stress conditions influence the failure of the specimen. Williams & Parvin[43,44] have assumed that the plane-stress contribution is effective over a surface

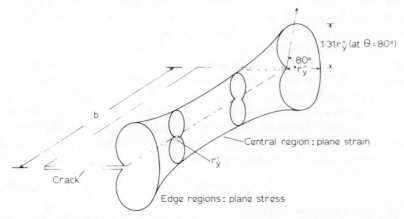

Fig. 3.11. Shape of plastic zone at crack tip, according to a von Mises yield criterion, shown schematically as a function of specimen thickness, b.

skin of depth r''_{yc} and plane strain prevails over the remaining central portion, $(b - 2r''_{yc})$. Thus they suggested that

$$K_{Ic} = \left(\frac{b - 2r''_{yc}}{b}\right)K'_{Ic} + \left(\frac{2r''_{yc}}{b}\right)K''_{Ic} \qquad (3.59)$$

where

$$r''_{yc} = \frac{1}{2\pi}\left(\frac{K''_{Ic}}{\sigma_y}\right)^2 \qquad (3.60)$$

Various workers[43–8] have adopted this approach to describe thickness effects in a wide range of polymers such as polycarbonate, nylon 6.6, polypropylene, poly(butylene terephthalate) and even nitroglycerine/nitrocellulose-based propellants. However, it should be recognised that there is no theoretical justification for eqn. (3.59). Indeed, Ward and co-workers[49–51] have proposed a similar model but have summed contributions from G'_{Ic} and G''_{Ic}. A further difference in the work of Ward and colleagues was that they actually observed shear yield lips at the edges of the polycarbonate and poly(ethersulphone) samples they studied. They therefore proposed that

$$G_{Ic} = \left(\frac{b - 2w_{sl}}{b}\right)G'_{Ic} + \frac{2\phi w_{sl}^2}{b} \qquad (3.61)$$

where w_{sl} is the width of the shear lip and ϕ is the energy to fracture per unit volume of shear lip estimated from separate uniaxial tensile tests. The two models are not interchangeable since K is proportional to $\sqrt{G}$ not G, but it is interesting to note that whichever model was selected by an author the data were adequately described. This suggests that the models are only approximations to the behaviour of the material and that the experimental results so far obtained cannot be used to establish which model, if either, is the more valid.

As the thickness of the sample is decreased further, the plane-strain central region completely disappears and full through-thickness yielding occurs and hence $K_{Ic} \rightarrow K''_{Ic}$. Equation (3.59) predicts that complete plane-stress behaviour occurs at

$$b = 2r''_{yc} \qquad (3.62)$$

but other conditions such as

$$b = 4r''_{yc} \qquad (3.63)$$

and

$$b = 2r'_{yc} \qquad (3.64)$$

have also been proposed.[6,43] The value of $2r''_{yc}$ is, of course, larger than $2r'_{yc}$ by a factor of at least three. For very thin sheets, in region A, K_{Ic} is proportional to $\sqrt{b}$, as discussed by Knott.[5]

Finally, it may be noted that models proposed by Williams & Parvin[43,44] and Fraser & Ward[49] are both essentially extensions of one proposed by Bluhm[52] to explain the behaviour of metals. Other models have been proposed, as reviewed by Broek,[6] but have not as yet been employed in the fracture of polymers.

3.6 EXPERIMENTAL CONSIDERATIONS

A basic aim of fracture mechanics is to provide a parameter for characterising crack growth which is independent of test geometry. In order to validate this requirement experimentally a wide range of different geometries have been developed. Sketches of some of the various fracture mechanics specimens that have been used with flexible and rigid polymers are shown in Figs 3.12 and 3.13, respectively.

3.6.1 Flexible Polymers

As discussed in Section 3.2.3 Thomas and co-workers[8,53,54] studied crack growth in cross-linked rubbers, which exhibited bulk non-linear but elastic behaviour, and deduced solutions for the left-hand side of eqn. (3.19)

$$-\frac{1}{b}\left(\frac{\partial U}{\partial a}\right)_l \geqslant G_c$$

for several different geometries. The resulting formulae for determining values of G_c are shown in Table 3.2 for those geometries sketched in Fig. 3.12.

3.6.2 Rigid Polymers

Some of the geometries which have been used to study the fracture of rigid, usually brittle, polymers are shown in Fig. 3.13. All of the specimens measure K_{Ic} and G_{Ic} for the tensile-opening mode of fracture (Mode I).

As discussed in Section 3.3 the value of K_I is normally obtained

TABLE 3.2

EXPRESSIONS FOR G_c FOR FRACTURE MECHANICS SPECIMENS USED TO STUDY CRACK GROWTH IN FLEXIBLE POLYMERS

Geometry (see Fig. 3.12)	Expression for G_c	Comments	References
Single-edge crack	$G_c = 2k_1 a W_c$ $\quad k_1 \simeq \pi/\lambda_c^{\frac{1}{2}}$	λ_c = Extension ratio at onset of crack growth W_c = Critical stored elastic strain-energy density	8, 16, 17
Pure-shear	$G_c = l W_c$	l = Initial length	8
Trouser-tear	$G_c = \dfrac{2P_c \lambda_c}{b} - 2wW_c$ if $\lambda_c \approx 1$, $G_c = \dfrac{2P_c}{b}$	P_c = Load at onset of crack growth w = Width of specimen arms λ_c = Critical extension ratio in arms W_c = Strain-energy density in arms b = Specimen thickness	8
Split-tear	$G_c = \dfrac{(\lambda_c^{A} + \lambda_c^{B})}{2b}(\sqrt{P_{1c}^{2} + P_{2c}^{2}} - P_{2c})$	λ_c^{A} and λ_c^{B} are critical extension ratios in regions A and B respectively	53
Angled-tear	$G_c = \dfrac{2P_c}{b} \sin \alpha/2$		54

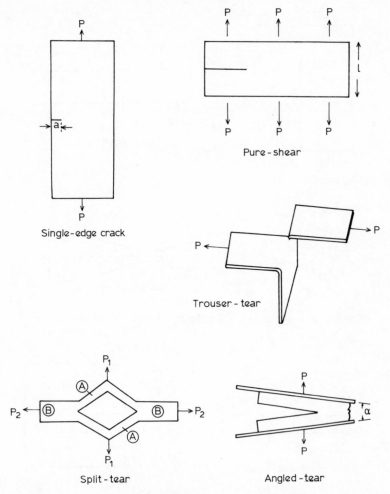

Fig. 3.12. Sketches of various fracture mechanics specimens employed with flexible polymers.

from an expression which has been obtained either analytically or numerically for the particular specimen geometry. It is a function of the applied stress, σ_0, or load, P, crack length, a, and a non-dimensional function of the specimen dimensions. The expressions for K_I for the geometries illustrated in Fig. 3.13 are given in Table 3.3. These expressions for K_I are often only strictly applicable to certain

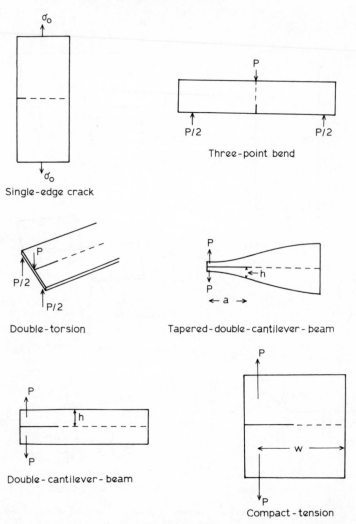

Fig. 3.13. Sketches of various fracture mechanics specimens employed with rigid polymers.

specimen dimensions and crack lengths and so care must be taken to ensure that particular specimens comply with these requirements before a valid K_I value may be quoted. This should be done by checking the original references. Also, of course, these expressions are only strictly applicable to materials which obey the assumptions of LEFM.

Considering the test geometries in Table 3.3, then if the single-edge crack and three-point bend specimens are used a problem that immediately arises is the method for inserting the edge cracks. The measured value of K_{Ic}, or G_{Ic}, is dependent upon the sharpness of the crack employed and an essential requirement of fracture mechanics testing is that a 'naturally' sharp crack is used for the experimental determination of K_{Ic} or G_{Ic}. If a relatively blunt crack is used an optimistically high value of K_{Ic} or G_{Ic} may be recorded. Suitable techniques include slow, controlled pressure applied to a razor blade, possibly having pre-cooled the specimen in liquid nitrogen, and fatigue crack growth. The other specimens listed in Table 3.3 overcome to some extent the problem of introducing a sharp crack since their geometries are such that the crack from which measurements are taken may often be formed by controlled propagation of an initially inserted blunt crack.

Another problem with the single-edge crack and three-point bend specimens is that if they are tested at a constant displacement rate, even in a hard testing machine, a crack once it starts to propagate at a particular load may quickly become unstable and accelerate until it reaches the end of the specimen. This results from the relatively small specimen displacements required to cause crack propagation and it means that with these specimens it may be difficult to monitor K_{Ic} or G_{Ic} with crack velocity. Again the other specimens listed in Table 3.3 are far better in this respect.

Finally, the double-torsion and tapered-double-cantilever-beam specimens may be designed so that the compliance changes linearly with crack length, and hence they are often referred to as linear-compliance variation specimens. Thus $\partial C/\partial a$ is constant with crack length and, as may be seen from Table 3.3, for both specimens K_I is therefore independent of crack length, a. Thus, these specimens are well suited to experiments where it is intended to relate K_{Ic}, or G_{Ic}, to crack velocity or when the value of crack length is difficult to ascertain, for example, when the specimen is opaque or is immersed in a liquid.

3.6.3 Value of G_{Ic} and K_{Ic}

It is obvious from the above discussions that it is difficult to state exact values of G_{Ic} and K_{Ic} for a polymer without defining the material, e.g. molar mass, degree of crystallinity, etc., and the test conditions, e.g. temperature, rate and environment. However, representative values[5,8,15,59-61] for a range of materials at room temperature in air are

TABLE 3.3

EXPRESSIONS FOR K_I FOR FRACTURE MECHANICS SPECIMENS USED TO STUDY CRACK GROWTH IN RIGID POLYMERS

Geometry (see Fig. 3.13)	Expression for K_I	Comments	References
Single-edge crack	$K_I = Q\sigma_0 a^{\frac{1}{2}}$ $Q = \left[1{\cdot}99 - 0{\cdot}41\left(\frac{a}{w}\right) + 18{\cdot}70\left(\frac{a}{w}\right)^2 - 38{\cdot}48\left(\frac{a}{w}\right)^3 + 53{\cdot}85\left(\frac{a}{w}\right)^4\right]$	(see eqn. 3.38) w = Width of specimen	55
Three-point bend	$K_I = \frac{Ps}{bw^{\frac{3}{2}}}\left[2{\cdot}9\left(\frac{a}{w}\right)^{\frac{1}{2}} - 4{\cdot}6\left(\frac{a}{w}\right)^{\frac{3}{2}} + 21{\cdot}8\left(\frac{a}{w}\right)^{\frac{5}{2}} - 37{\cdot}6\left(\frac{a}{w}\right)^{\frac{7}{2}} + 38{\cdot}7\left(\frac{a}{w}\right)^{\frac{9}{2}}\right]$	P = Applied load s = Span between supports $= 4w$ b = Sheet thickness	42
Double-torsion	$K_I = Pl_m\left[\frac{3(1+\nu)}{lb^3 b_n}\right]^{\frac{1}{2}}$ (Plane stress) $K_I = Pl_m\left[\frac{3}{lb^3 b_n(1-\nu)}\right]^{\frac{1}{2}}$ (Plane strain) $(l/2 > 6)$	l_m = Length of moment arm b_n = Sheet thickness in plane of crack, i.e. for grooved specimen ν = Poisson's ratio	56

Tapered-double-cantilever beam	$K_I = 2P\left(\dfrac{m_1}{bb_n}\right)^{\frac{1}{2}}$	$m_1 = \dfrac{3a^2}{h^3} + \dfrac{1}{h}$ specimen is contoured such that m_1 is constant h = Height of specimen edge from fracture plane	57, 58
Double-cantilever beam	$K_I = \dfrac{2P}{(bb_n)^{\frac{1}{2}}}\left[\dfrac{3a^2}{h^3} + \dfrac{1}{h}\right]^{\frac{1}{2}}$		57, 58
Compact-tension	$K_I = \dfrac{P}{bw^{\frac{1}{2}}}\left[29{\cdot}6\left(\dfrac{a}{w}\right)^{\frac{1}{2}} - 185{\cdot}5\left(\dfrac{a}{w}\right)^{\frac{3}{2}} + 655{\cdot}7\left(\dfrac{a}{w}\right)^{\frac{5}{2}} - 1017\left(\dfrac{a}{w}\right)^{\frac{7}{2}} + 638{\cdot}9\left(\dfrac{a}{w}\right)^{\frac{9}{2}}\right]$		42

TABLE 3.4
TYPICAL VALUES OF G_{Ic} AND K_{Ic} FOR VARIOUS MATERIALS

Material	Young's modulus, E (GPa)	$G_{Ic}\,(kJ\,m^{-2})$	$K_{Ic}\,(MN\,m^{-\frac{3}{2}})$
Rubber	0·001	13	—
Polyethylene	0·15	20 (J_{Ic})	—
Polystyrene	3	0·4	1·1
High-impact polystyrene	2·1	15·8 (J_{Ic})	—
PMMA	2·5	0·5	1·1
Epoxy	2·8	0·1	0·5
Rubber-toughened epoxy	2·4	2	2·2
Glass-reinforced thermoset	7	7	7
Glass	70	0·007	0·7
Wood	2·1	0·12	0·5
Aluminium—alloy	69	20	37
Steel—mild	210	12	50
Steel—alloy	210	107	150

given in Table 3.4 with the aim of imparting to the reader the typical values obtained for polymers and their positions relative to other materials.

3.7 CONCLUDING REMARKS

This chapter has reviewed the basic principles of continuum fracture mechanics with a particular emphasis on those aspects which have been employed in studying the fracture of polymers. Many of the concepts and models which have been described will be used and further developed in later chapters when specific mechanisms and materials are considered.

REFERENCES

1. Kelly, A. (1966). *Strong solids*, Clarendon Press, Oxford.
2. Griffith, A. A. (1920). *Phil. Trans. Roy. Soc.*, **A221**, 163.
3. Orowan, E. (1948). *Repts. Prog. Phys.*, **12**, 185.
4. Irwin, G. R. (1964). *Appl. Mats. Res.*, **3**, 65.
5. Knott, J. F. (1973). *Fundamentals of fracture mechanics*, Butterworths, London.

6. Broek, D. (1974). *Elementary engineering fracture mechanics*, Noordhoff, Leyden.
7. Berry, J. P. (1961). *J. Polym. Sci.*, **50**, 107.
8. Rivlin, R. S. & Thomas, A. G. (1953). *J. Polym. Sci.*, **10**, 291.
9. Shafrin, E. G. (1976). In: *Handbook of adhesives*, Ed. by I. Skeist, Van Nostrand, New York, p. 67.
10. Lake, G. J. & Thomas, A. G. (1967). *Proc. Roy. Soc.*, **A300**, 108.
11. Gent, A. N. & Kinloch, A. J. (1971). *J. Polym. Sci.*, *A2*, **9**, 659.
12. Andrews, E. H. & Kinloch, A. J. (1973). *Proc. R. Soc.*, **A332**, 385.
13. Andrews, E. H. & Kinloch, A. J. (1973). *Proc. R. Soc.*, **A332**, 401.
14. Gent, A. N. & Schultz, J. (1972). *J. Adhesion*, **3**, 281.
15. Williams, J. G. (1978). *Adv. Polym. Sci.*, **27**, 67.
16. Greensmith, H. W. (1963). *J. Appl. Polym. Sci.*, **7**, 993.
17. Lake, G. J. (1970). *Yield, deformation and fracture of polymers*, Conf. Proc., Phys. Institute, London, p. 5.3.
18. Rice, J. R. (1968). In: *Fracture, an advanced treatise*, Vol. 2, Ed. by H. Liebowitz, Academic Press, New York, p. 192.
19. Turner, C. E. (1979). In: *Post-yield fracture mechanics*, Ed. by D. G. H. Latzko, Applied Science Publishers Ltd., London, p. 23.
20. Chell, G. G. (1979). In: *Developments in fracture mechanics—1*, Ed. by G. G. Chell, Applied Science Publishers Ltd., London, p. 67.
21. Landes, J. D. & Begley, J. A. (1979). In: *Post-yield fracture mechanics*, Ed. by D. G. H. Latzko, Applied Science Publishers Ltd., London, p. 211.
22. Plati, E. & Williams, J. G. (1975). *Polym. Eng. Sci.*, **15**, 470.
23. Sridharan, N. S. & Broutman, L. J. (1978). *Toughening of plastics*, Conf. Proc., Plastics and Rubber Inst., London, p. 19.1.
24. Hodgkinson, J. M. & Williams, J. G. (1981). *J. Mater. Sci.*, **16**, 50.
25. Ahagon, A., Gent, A. N., Kim, H. J. & Kumagi, Y. (1975). *Rubber Chem. Technol.*, **48**, 896.
26. Thomas, A. G. & Kadir, A. (1983). *J. Polym. Sci. Polym. Phys. Ed.*
27. Mohamed (Kadir), A. K. B. (1980). *Crack propagation in rubbers*, PhD Thesis, Queen Mary College, London, p. 116.
28. Andrews, E. H. (1974). *J. Mater. Sci.*, **9**, 887.
29. Andrews, E. H. & Billington, E. W. (1976). *J. Mater. Sci.*, **11**, 1354.
30. Andrews, E. H. & Fukahori, Y. (1977). *J. Mater. Sci.*, **12**, 1307.
31. Andrews, E. H. (1979). *Makromol. Chem. Suppl.*, **2**, 189.
32. Westergaard, H. M. (1939). *J. Appl. Mech.* **A** June, 46.
33. Sih, G. C. (1973). *Handbook of stress-intensity factors for researchers and engineers*, Lehigh Univ., Bethlehem, USA.
34. Tada, H., Paris, P. & Irwin, G. R. (1973). *The stress analysis of cracks handbook*, Del Research Corp., Hellertown, USA.
35. Rooke, D. P. & Cartwright, D. J. (1976). *Compendium of stress-intensity factors*, HMSO, London.
36. Irwin, G. R. & Paris, P. C. (1971). In: *Fracture, an advanced treatise—Vol. 3*, Ed. by H. Liebowitz, Academic Press, New York, p. 13.
37. Wells, A. A. (1963). *Brit. Welding J.*, **10**, 563.
38. Dugdale, D. S. (1960). *J. Mech. Phys. Solids*, **8**, 100.
39. Barenblatt, G. I. (1962). *Adv. Appl. Mechs.*, **7**, 56.

40. Williams, J. G. (1980). *Stress analysis of polymers*, Ellis Horwood, Chichester.
41. Corten, H. T. (1972). In: *Fracture, an advanced treatise—Vol. 7*, Ed. by H. Liebowitz, Academic Press, New York, p. 675.
42. ASTM-E 399-78, *Plane-strain fracture toughness of metallic materials*.
43. Williams, J. G. & Parvin, M. (1975). *Int. J. Fract.*, **11**, 963.
44. Williams, J. G. & Parvin, M. (1975). *J. Mater. Sci.*, **10**, 1883.
45. Mai, Y. W. & Williams, J. G. (1977). *J. Mater. Sci.*, **12**, 1376.
46. Gledhill, R. A. & Kinloch, A. J. (1979). *Prop. Explos.*, **4**, 73.
47. Hobbs, S. Y. & Bopp, R. C. (1980). *Polymer*, **21**, 559.
48. Gledhill, R. A. & Kinloch, A. J. (1981). *J. Spacecraft Rockets*, **18**, 333.
49. Fraser, R. A. W. & Ward, I. M. (1978). *Polymer*, **19**, 220.
50. Pitman, G. L. & Ward, I. M. (1979). *Polymer*, **20**, 895.
51. Hine, P. J., Duckett, R. A. & Ward, I. M. (1981). *Polymer*, **22**, 1745.
52. Bluhm, J. I. (1961). *ASTM Proc.*, **61**, 1325.
53. Lake, G. J., Lindley, P. B. & Thomas, A. G. (1979). In: *Fracture*, Ed. by L. Averbach, Chapman-Hall, London, p. 493.
54. Thomas, A. G. (1960). *J. Appl. Polym. Sci.*, **3**, 168.
55. Brown, W. F. & Srawley, J. E. (1966). *Plane-strain crack toughness testing of high strength metallic materials*, ASTM, STP 410, p. 12.
56. Young, R. J. & Beaumont, P. W. R. (1976). *J. Mater. Sci.*, **11**, 1113.
57. Mostovoy, S., Crosley, P. B. & Ripling, E. J. (1967). *J. Mater.*, **2**, 661.
58. Crosley, P. B., Mostovoy, S. & Ripling, E. J. (1971). *Eng. Fract. Mechs.*, **3**, 421.
59. Young, R. J. (1979). In: *Developments in polymer fracture—1*, Ed. by E. H. Andrews, Applied Science Publishers Ltd., London, p. 183.
60. Kinloch, A. J. & Shaw, S. J. (1981). In: *Developments in adhesives—2*, Ed. by A. J. Kinloch, Applied Science Publishers Ltd., London, p. 83.
61. Williams, J. G. (1981). *Phil. Trans. R. Soc. London*, **A299**, 59.

Chapter 4

Shear Yielding

4.1 INTRODUCTION

When a polymer starts to deform plastically under an applied stress it is said to have yielded. Shear deformation consists of a change of shape without significant change in volume and the shear yielding of polymers is highly relevant to the mechanics and mechanisms of polymer fracture.

Shear yielding is important; firstly, it is the factor which limits the strength of the polymer if brittle fracture can be suppressed. A polymer must have a high yield stress in order to be strong and if bulk, homogeneous yielding does occur the polymer is likely to be tough. Secondly, recent evidence suggests that shear yielding, in the form of microshear bands, plays a key role in the initiation of cracks. Thirdly, as is evident from Chapters 2 and 3, even brittle crack propagation in polymers usually involves localised viscoelastic and plastic energy dissipative processes occurring in the vicinity of the crack tip. Indeed, such micromechanisms usually represent the main source of energy absorption in the material and two of major importance are shear yielding and crazing. Both involve localised, or inhomogeneous, plastic deformation of the material which arises from strain softening and geometric considerations. The difference between the mechanisms is that shear yielding occurs essentially at constant volume whereas crazing occurs with an increase in volume. Thus, unlike shear yielding, crazing is a cavitation process in which the initiation step requires the presence of a dilatational component to the stress tensor.

The essential features of shear yielding and crazing, and particularly

107

those relevant to polymer fracture, will be considered in this chapter and in Chapter 5, respectively.

4.2 GENERAL ASPECTS OF YIELD BEHAVIOUR

This section will briefly review some general aspects of the yield behaviour of polymers and for further information the reader is referred to more extensive reviews of the subject which have been published by Bowden[1] and Ward.[2,3]

4.2.1 Definitions

Figure 4.1 shows two schematic curves of true-stress/nominal-strain which might be obtained from load/elongation measurements on polymeric specimens. In the elastic region the material is deforming elastically or viscoelastically and the deformation is essentially recoverable on unloading. At some point beyond this it yields and as the deformation proceeds further the sample may or may not exhibit strain softening. At greater strains many polymers exhibit orientation hardening. At the yield point the deformation ceases to be entirely elastic and the material starts to deform plastically. However, this concept is

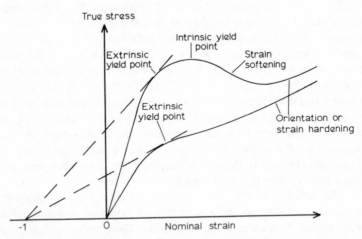

Fig. 4.1. Schematic true-stress versus nominal-strain curves. A tangent to the curve through the point on the abscissa $e = -1$ is Considères construction and defines the extrinsic yield point of a sample tested in tension (after Bowden[1].)

difficult to apply precisely to polymers. Experimentally the distinction between elastic (recoverable) and plastic (permanent) deformation is not clear-cut and there may be no sharp distinction in mechanisms. For example, plastic deformation in glassy polymers is often almost completely recoverable if the material is heated to just above its glass transition temperature, T_g.

For polymers which exhibit a true-stress/strain curve with a maximum similar to that of the top curve in Fig. 4.1 the intrinsic yield point may conveniently be defined as the maximum point. The yield stress and yield strain then correspond to the values at this maximum. It is termed an 'intrinsic yield point' as it is intrinsic to the material and should not be a function of any of the geometrical features of the test. The minimum that occurs after this point is sometimes referred to as the lower yield stress and, when it is necessary to distinguish between the two, the yield stress at the maximum is termed the upper yield stress. For polymers which have a true-stress/strain curve that does not pass through a maximum, as shown in the bottom curve of Fig. 4.1, then this definition of the yield point does not work but an intrinsic yield point can generally be located in the region of a kink in the curve.

When a sample is tested in tension the deformation becomes unstable at a point defined by Considère's construction (see Fig. 4.1), and a neck develops. For a material which has a yield stress independent of strain-rate, the *load* carried by the specimen passes through a maximum at this point and the specimen as a whole can be said to have yielded. The point at which the *load* goes through a maximum is termed the 'extrinsic yield point' since it is related to the geometry of the deformation of the tensile specimen and only indirectly to the intrinsic material properties. In a strain-rate sensitive material, such as a polymer, the extrinsic yield point may occur at a later point on the true-stress/strain curve than that indicated by Considère's construction and so can approach the intrinsic yield point.[1] However, from the geometry of Considère's construction it is never possible for the extrinsic yield stress to be very much less than the intrinsic yield stress. The extrinsic yield point is the one generally referred to as the yield point in most of the literature on polymers.

Strain softening may be defined as a fall in the *true* stress as deformation takes place at yield and has been considered in detail by Haward.[4] Unlike most other materials, such softening is often an intrinsic property of polymers and evidence for its existence may be obtained from several different types of experiment. However, because of the geometrical features which occur in a tensile test which tend to promote extrinsic instabilities, e.g. necking, results from compression[5-12] or shear[13,14] tests provide the most positive evidence. All isotropic amorphous glassy polymers exhibit strain softening although some that orientate and harden rapidly, e.g. cellulose nitrate, may show only a small amount. The lower curve in Fig. 4.1, where no strain softening is present, appears to be given only by some crystalline polymers or fibre-forming glassy polymers which crystallise on drawing. With these polymers rapid orientation hardening masks any possible strain softening.

The orientation or strain hardening referred to above may be observed in many polymers and describes the region of the true stress versus strain curve where the true stress rises after yield and after any strain softening has occurred. The fact that this rise occurs at large strains, when the polymer chains have undoubtedly become oriented to some extent, led Vincent[15] to describe it as 'orientation hardening'. The strain at which this phenomenon sets in is very dependent upon the actual polymer being studied.[4]

4.2.2 Mechanical Tests

The various common types of mechanical test which have been used to determine the yield behaviour of polymers are shown schematically in Fig. 4.2 and have been discussed in detail by Bowden.[1]

The tensile test is the most widely used but suffers from two main disadvantages—namely, in many polymers the applied tensile stress may lead to fracture before yield occurs and, even if this does not occur, it is only the extrinsic yield point that can be readily investigated.

The uniaxial-compression test overcomes both of these disadvantages. Firstly, because the stress is compressive, brittle tensile fracture is suppressed and plastic yielding may be observed in materials that under most other conditions are brittle, e.g. thermosetting polymers. Secondly, the measured yield stress is the intrinsic yield stress since there is no geometrical reason for the deformation to become unstable, as there is, for example, in the tensile test. A practical difficulty with the compression test is that if the diameter-to-height ratio is too small the sample is liable to buckle while if it is too large friction between the dies and the sample will introduce a constraint. An initial diameter-to-height ratio of about 0·5 is a good compromise.[16] Finally, it should be

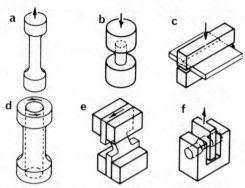

Fig. 4.2. *Mechanical tests used to study yield in polymers: (a) tensile test; (b) uniaxial-compression test; (c) plane-strain compression test; (d), (e) and (f) tests in simple shear (after Bowden[1]).*

noted that since the cross-sectional area of the specimen increases as the test proceeds, the true stress in a compression test is always less than the nominal or engineering stress; in a tensile test the true stress is always greater.

The plane-strain compression test is shown in Fig. 4.2(c) and has been employed by several workers.[9,10,17,18] The same general comments may be made as for the uniaxial-compression test but the problem of frictional constraint at large strains is not quite so serious.

Three different methods that may be employed to obtain a simple shear deformation are shown in Figs. 4.2(d)–(f). In Fig. 4.2(d) a torsion test is shown and although the stress and strain may be accurately determined, the samples are difficult to prepare. Shearing an initially symmetrical waisted specimen clamped between steel blocks is illustrated in Fig. 4.2(e) but an experimental difficulty is that the blocks have to be constrained to move parallel to each other, and the shear strain in the waisted region is not always uniform. The method shown in Fig. 4.2(f) is the symmetric shearing of a cylinder of the material and is a quick and convenient test. However, it is not amenable to precise analysis since even if the dies are accurately made the thickness of the regions being sheared is not well defined and so it is difficult to specify the shear strain.

4.2.3 Viscoelastic Nature of Yield Behaviour

The yield behaviour of polymers is very dependent upon the temperature and the rate of testing. Generally, the yield stress increases as the

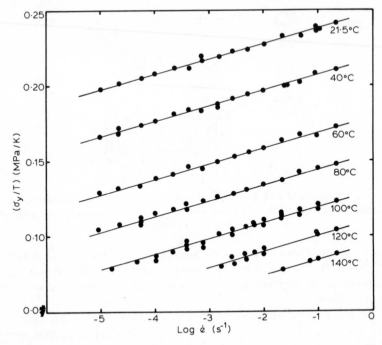

Fig. 4.3. *Measured ratio of yield stress, σ_y, to temperature, T, as a function of the logarithm of strain-rate, $\dot{e}$, for polycarbonate (after Bauwens-Crowet et al.[19]).*

temperature, T, is decreased or the strain-rate, $\dot{e}$, increased. This effect is shown in Fig. 4.3 for polycarbonate and is taken from the work of Bauwens-Crowet *et al.*[19] These investigations, and many others,[20-3] have modelled this dependence using the Eyring theory of viscosity. The Eyring theory[24,25] assumes an activated-rate process, i.e. one involving the surmounting of a potential energy barrier of height ΔE^*. The energy barrier may be surmounted because random thermal fluctuations ensure that the thermal or kinetic energy of an atom or molecular segment varies in time with a finite possibility of exceeding the potential barrier. The model envisages that the effect of an applied stress is to reduce the height of the barrier for a jump in the forward direction and to increase it for a jump in the reverse direction. It is further assumed that the macroscopic strain-rate of the sample is proportional to the net jump-rate of the segments in the forward direction. Thus, in the high-stress region where yield occurs, the Eyring theory gives the relationship between strain-rate, $\dot{e}$, and applied stress, σ_0, as

$$\dot{e} = A_E \exp\left\{ -\frac{(\Delta E^* - v^* |\sigma_0|)}{RT} \right\} \qquad (4.1)$$

where A_E is a constant, R is the gas constant and v^* is the activation volume. This equation may be rearranged to give the yield stress, σ_y, in terms of the strain-rate

$$\frac{|\sigma_y|}{T} = \frac{\Delta E^*}{v^* T} + \left(\frac{R}{v^*}\right) \ln (\dot{e}/A_E) \qquad (4.2)$$

This suggests that a plot of σ_y/T versus $\log \dot{e}$ should give a set of parallel lines for different temperatures, as was indeed found by Bauwens-Crowet et al.[19] and is shown in Fig. 4.3 for polycarbonate. The solid lines in Fig. 4.3 are calculated from eqn. (4.2) with values of ΔE^* and v^* of 335 kJ mol^{-1} and 2·8 nm^3 per molecule respectively.

The physical significance, if any, of both these parameters is obscure. The value of ΔE^* cannot usually be directly correlated to any molecular relaxation process, although near the T_g it may approach the activation energy of the α_r molecular relaxation. The value of v^* is much greater than the volume of a statistical random link (e.g. about 0·5 nm^3 for polycarbonate[26]). Haward & Thackray[26] discussed the interpretation of the activation volume and suggested that it may represent the volume of the polymer segment which has to move as a whole in order for flow to occur. They found that the values of v^* for most polymers were considerably greater than the volume of the statistical random link in the polymer chain in dilute solution; v^* being larger by a factor of about 2–10 depending upon the polymer. This result was very much expected since it would appear reasonable to suppose that yielding involves the cooperative movement of a larger number of chain segments than would be required for a molecular conformation change in dilute solution. However, Bowden[1] considered that although v^* has the dimensions of volume it is not in fact a volume; the quantity $v^* \sigma_0$ has the dimensions of energy and is the work done on a mobile segment during a jump. To resolve this point a clear correlation needs to be established between v^* and the volume of the statistical random link.

The stress-activated rate mechanism of the type described by Eyring has also been successfully employed to model the time-dependent yielding of polymers subjected to a constant applied stress.[22,27–32] In particular the delay time may be predicted—the delay time being the time between application of the load and the onset of yielding.

However, when the yield behaviour of several polymers was examined over a wider range of temperatures than that indicated in Fig. 4.3 it was found that eqn. (4.1) was inadequate to fully describe the yield behaviour. This has led[33-6] to a modification of the theory where the deformation is suggested to involve two different flow processes which possess different values of ΔE^* and v^*. For example, in polycarbonate above $-50°C$ eqn. (4.2) fitted the data adequately, with a ΔE^* value of $335\ kJ\ mol^{-1}$, as described above, but below $-50°C$ it was found necessary to follow the Ree–Eyring model[25] and assume two activated-flow processes. The two values of ΔE^* required were 335 and $42\cdot6\ kJ\ mol^{-1}$ and it was proposed that the similarity of the latter activation energy with that for the secondary (β_r) molecular-relaxation (determined from dielectric measurements) indicated that the molecular mechanism was the same for this second type of flow process as for the molecular-relaxation behaviour.

Finally, Ward and co-workers[2,3,37] have suggested a simple modification to the Eyring equation to include the effect of the hydrostatic component of stress, p (see Section 4.2.4). They proposed that

$$\dot{e} = A_E \exp \left\{ -\frac{(\Delta E^* - v^* |\sigma_0| - p\Omega)}{RT} \right\} \tag{4.3}$$

where

$$p = \frac{(\sigma_{11} + \sigma_{22} + \sigma_{33})}{3} = \frac{I_1}{3} \tag{4.4}$$

and I_1 is the first stress invariant and Ω is the pressure activation volume. This modification can bring consistency to yield data in tension and compression, and can model the effect of hydrostatic pressure.

4.2.4 Criteria for Shear Yielding

A yield criterion is a critical condition that must be satisfied by the applied stress tensor for yield to occur. The simplest criterion is due to Tresca and states that yield will occur when the maximum shear stress on any plane in the material reaches a critical value. It may be written as

$$|\sigma_1 - \sigma_3| = 2\tau_T \tag{4.5}$$

where, $\sigma_1 > \sigma_2 > \sigma_3$, and σ_1, σ_2 and σ_3 are the principal stresses. The value of τ_T is usually taken to be the yield stress of the material in pure shear, i.e. τ_y, thus

$$|\sigma_1 - \sigma_3| = 2\tau_y = \sigma_y \qquad (4.6)$$

where σ_y is the uniaxial tensile yield stress. The Tresca yield criterion was originally developed for metals but, except for mild steel, most metals obey the von Mises criterion better.

The von Mises criterion may be stated as

$$(\sigma_1 - \sigma_2)^2 + (\sigma_2 - \sigma_3)^2 + (\sigma_3 - \sigma_1)^2 = 6\tau_M^2 \qquad (4.7)$$

where the constant τ_M is the shear stress for flow in pure shear, i.e. τ_y. Hence it may be rewritten as

$$(\sigma_1 - \sigma_2)^2 + (\sigma_2 - \sigma_3)^2 + (\sigma_3 - \sigma_1)^2 = 6\tau_y^2 \qquad (4.8)$$

Alternatively, it may be expressed in terms of the octahedral shear stress, τ_{oct}, as

$$\tfrac{1}{3}\sqrt{(\sigma_1 - \sigma_2)^2 + (\sigma_2 - \sigma_3)^2 + (\sigma_3 - \sigma_1)^2} = \tau_{oct} \qquad (4.9)$$

where τ_{oct} is a constant and related to τ_M by

$$9\tau_{oct}^2 = 6\tau_M^2 = 6\tau_y^2 \qquad (4.10)$$

This criterion, for a Hookean material, is equivalent to stating that yield will occur when the elastic shear strain-energy density reaches a critical value. It is obeyed fairly well for most metals.

Experiments have shown that neither the Tresca nor the von Mises criterion adequately describes the shear yield behaviour of polymers. For example, the true yield stress is invariably higher in uniaxial compression than in tension, and uniaxial-tensile tests conducted in a pressure chamber show that yield stresses of polymers increase significantly with hydrostatic pressure.[38-48] In both the Tresca and von Mises criteria the yield stress is independent of the hydrostatic component of the stress tensor so that they cannot be used to describe the above behaviour.

To overcome this problem several solutions have been suggested. The first is to use the Mohr–Coulomb yield criterion which states that failure will occur when the shear stress on any plane in the material reaches a critical value which varies linearly with the stress normal to that plane. This criterion is similar to the Tresca criterion with τ now given by

$$\tau_C = \tau_C^0 - \mu_C \sigma_n \qquad (4.11)$$

The quantity σ_n is the stress acting normal to the plane on which failure is occurring, μ_C is a constant analogous to a coefficient of friction and τ_C^0 is also a material constant and is the 'cohesion' of the material. Bowden[1] has discussed the theoretical difficulties in applying the Mohr–Coulomb criterion to polymeric materials and proposed[1,18] a modified form of the Tresca criterion which is pressure dependent.

This modified Tresca criterion envisages the quantity τ_T in eqn. (4.5) being dependent upon the hydrostatic component of the stress tensor, p, such that

$$\tau_T = \tau_T^0 - \mu_T p \tag{4.12}$$

and (eqn. (4.4))

$$p = \frac{(\sigma_{11} + \sigma_{22} + \sigma_{33})}{3} = \frac{I_1}{3}$$

where μ_T and τ_T^0 are material constants. The constant τ_T^0 is the yield stress in pure shear, i.e. τ_y, since under this stress state the value of p is zero. The value of μ_T now describes the effect of pressure.

The von Mises criterion may also be modified[43-5] to incorporate the effect of pressure by substituting into eqns (4.7) and (4.9) a value of τ_M or τ_{oct} that varies linearly with the hydrostatic component of the stress tensor. Thus

$$\tau_M = \tau_M^0 - \mu_M p \tag{4.13}$$

and

$$\tau_{oct} = \tau_{oct}^0 - \left(\frac{2}{3}\right)^{\frac{1}{2}} \mu_M p \tag{4.14}$$

As in the case of the constant τ_T^0 in eqn. (4.12), the constant τ_M^0 is still the yield stress in pure shear.

Some values of τ_y and μ, which hold approximately for all three criteria, i.e. eqns (4.11), (4.12) and (4.13), are shown[10] in Table 4.1.

Raghava et al.[46,47] have suggested a more complex modification to the von Mises criterion where the dependence of τ_{oct} upon p is not simply linear. There is no fundamental reason why this dependence should be linear and, indeed, there is evidence[45,47] that it is not always linear. However, the differences between the linear and non-linear modification to the von Mises criterion are small until high pressures are involved.

Finally, it should be noted that the viscoelastic nature of the yield

TABLE 4.1

VALUES OF τ_y AND μ FOR VARIOUS POLYMERS[a]

Polymer	$\tau_y(MN\,m^{-2})$	μ
PMMA	47·4	0·158±0·02
Polystyrene	40·0	0·25 ±0·05
Poly(ethylene terephthalate)	31·0	0·09 ±0·02
PVC	42·0	0·11 ±0·02
Plasticised, anhydride-cured epoxy	49·0	0·09 ±0·03
Highly plasticised, anhydride-cured epoxy	42·0	0·19 ±0·03
High-density polyethylene	17·4	<0·05

[a] Test temperature, 22°C; strain rate, approximately $2 \times 10^{-3}\,s^{-1}$

behaviour will result in parameters such as τ_y and μ being dependent upon the temperature and rate of testing.

4.2.5 Molecular Theories

4.2.5.1 Glassy Polymers

Bowden[1] has reviewed the molecular theories of yielding in glassy polymers in detail and considers that any molecular theory of yielding must relate the observed yield behaviour to the detailed molecular structure of the polymer and to the local changes in molecular conformation that occur at yield.

One of the earlier suggestions[49,50] was that the applied stress reduced the glass transition temperature, T_g, until at yield the T_g was equivalent to the test temperature. Thus the mobility of the molecular segments would increase until, at yield, they were fully mobile hence permitting plastic flow to occur. Many authors[51-4] have considered that this increase in molecular mobility may arise from an increase in free volume brought about by the dilatational hydrostatic tensile component of the stress tensor. However, a problem with this argument is that shear yielding occurs in response to the deviatoric component of the stress tensor, i.e. no elastic volume change. Indeed work[55-7] on amorphous polymers indicates that a small volume *decrease* actually occurs upon yielding and that plastic flow after yield occurs at essentially constant volume, although further experimental work is needed to resolve this issue.

The Eyring theory was one of the first models to quantitatively describe the flow of polymers and this theory has been discussed in

Section 4.2.3. Robertson[58] and Kambour & Robertson[59] have extended the Eyring approach by attempting to incorporate a molecular explanation, rather than leaving the discussion at a purely phenomenological level. They assumed that the polymer molecules had two rotational states per bond: a *cis* (high energy) and a *trans* (low energy) state. Above the T_g the molecules are in equilibrium with respect to rotational conformations and the distribution between the *cis* and *trans* states is given by the Boltzmann distribution. The higher the temperature the more *cis* conformations are present but at the T_g the conformation populations become frozen and for all temperatures below T_g remain unaltered, in the absence of stress. However, when a shear stress is applied to the system of molecules the energy difference between the *cis* and *trans* states is lowered. This causes certain segments to change over from the *trans* to the *cis* conformation, increasing the population of *cis* states sufficiently for yield to occur. For yielding to occur at temperatures below T_g the model is such that the population of *cis* states has to be increased by the applied stress to a value considerably greater than that appropriate at the T_g.

Two important theories, based upon physical descriptions of plastic flow at the molecular level, have been recently developed by Bowden and co-workers[1,60,61] and Argon & Bessonov.[62,63] These theories, although different from each other, do not use the Eyring model but are both concerned with the thermal activation of the molecular displacements that take place during plastic flow. Bowden's model envisages the critical step in the yield process as being the thermally activated nucleation under stress of small disc-shaped sheared regions in the polymer. The strain fields of the sheared regions are assumed to be analogous to those of dislocation loops with a Burgers vector equal to the shear displacements. Bowden stressed, however, that the dislocation concept is only an analogy in the case of glassy polymers. It was introduced because solutions for the energies of and stresses in dislocation loops are readily available and at no time is it suggested that dislocations are present in such materials. Argon & Bessonov's theory of yielding proposes that yield occurs by the thermally activated production of local molecular kinks which they modelled by the formation of wedge disclinations. The mathematical analysis is somewhat complex but the final equations predicting the relationship between the shear yield stress and shear modulus are relatively simple. These two theories have been tested by their proponents on a variety of glassy thermoplastic polymers with a considerable degree of success.

Recently Yamini & Young[64] have shown that the plastic deformation of a series of glassy thermosetting polymers could also be explained by these yield theories.

4.2.5.2 Crystalline Polymers

Considering crystalline polymers, then most such polymers are two-phase materials consisting of a non-crystalline amorphous component (normally rubbery) and crystals typically of the order of 10 to 20 nm thick.[65] Above the glass transition temperature, T_g, of the amorphous phase the non-crystalline material behaves approximately as a rubber and does not undergo shear yielding. Below T_g it deforms as a polymer glass. On the other hand it is thought that the crystalline regions are capable of undergoing shear yielding, as other crystalline solids, through processes such as slip, twinning and martensitic transformations.[66,67]

The temperature dependence of slip in directions parallel to the chain direction in polyethylene crystals has been examined by Young.[68] It was found that, because of the relative thinness of polymer crystals due to chain folding and the low shear modulus in the chain direction, deformation could take place by the thermal activation of screw dislocations with Burgers vectors parallel to the chain direction. The theory of Young[68] is similar to that used by Bowden and co-workers[60,61] for glassy polymers but in the case of polyethylene there is clear evidence that such dislocations exist[69] whereas dislocations cannot exist in glassy polymers and Bowden used the dislocation approach simply as an analogy.

4.3 INHOMOGENEOUS DEFORMATION

In many materials plastic deformation does not occur in a homogeneous manner but, instead, the plastic strain in some local regions increases more rapidly than in the body as a whole. Indeed, in the limiting case plastic strain may occur only in certain localised regions. This inhomogeneous flow, leading to a localisation of plastic strain, occurs because homogeneous deformation has become unstable. There are two reasons for this instability: the first arises from geometrical considerations, and the second from the material's intrinsic properties. They may both act simultaneously to create the instability.

4.3.1 Causes

A common example of a geometrical instability is the neck which may develop in a specimen upon being stressed in uniaxial tension. The theory of neck formation, based upon Considère's construction, has been considered by Nadai[70] and Vincent,[71] and has been reviewed by Haward.[4] The instability occurs because the stress and strain are often highest at one point on the specimen, owing to, for example, slight variations in the cross-sectional area. This results in the stress required for plastic yielding being attained at this point before the rest of the sample. Further plastic deformation then occurs more readily at this point, while in other parts of the specimen the stress is not high enough to pass over the yield point. At the location where the plastic deformation is occurring the cross-sectional area is reduced preferentially, causing a neck to develop. As the neck develops molecular orientation occurs in this region and this may result in strain hardening (see Fig. 4.1) thereby enabling the neck to stabilise and extend throughout the specimen. Thermal effects may aid neck formation since the viscous and entropic components of the deformation energy may result in appreciable heat evolution. If this heat is not removed the temperature will rise and cause the yield stress locally to fall so that any tendency for necking will increase.

A second, and more fundamental, reason for inhomogeneous plastic deformation is strain softening which may occur after the yield point. Strain softening is an intrinsic property of the material and is illustrated in Fig. 4.1. In such a material once the yield point is reached the resistance to further plastic deformation falls with shear strain. Thus if any small region should deform to a slightly higher strain than the rest of the material it will become softer locally and so will deform more easily and attain an even higher strain than elsewhere. Again this process may eventually be halted by strain hardening.

4.3.2 Types of Inhomogeneous Deformation

The types of strain inhomogeneity that may develop are governed by the constraint imposed on the deforming region by the surrounding material. Bowden[1] has examined this relationship for isotropic materials. He identified the criterion that if the geometry of the formation of a strain inhomogeneity involves a restraint in any direction then the extension rate must be zero in that direction for the inhomogeneity to initiate at a stress equal or less than the stress required for bulk yielding. This criterion is applied to the three examples shown in Fig. 4.4, all of which are loaded in tension.

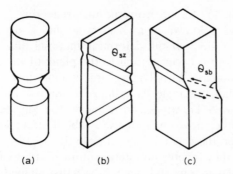

(a)   (b)   (c)

Fig. 4.4. Types of inhomogeneous deformation (tensile loadings). (a) Formation of a neck in a cylindrical test specimen; (b) Formation of an inclined neck in a flat strip tensile specimen; and (c) Formation of a shear band (after Bowden[1].)

In Fig. 4.4(a) a cylindrical tensile test specimen is shown; there is no restraint and the only possible form of strain inhomogeneity is a symmetrically necked region. It is possible for a similar form of inhomogeneity to develop in a compression test, where a bulge would form rather than a neck. However, the basic reason for the instability would then have to be strain softening, rather than the geometrical effect discussed in Section 4.3.1.

The only form of strain inhomogeneity that it is possible to form with restraint in one direction is the locally thinned zone of material, known as the inclined neck, that can form in a flat specimen tested in uniaxial tension as shown in Fig. 4.4(b). For such a zone there is restraint in the direction along the length of the zone and the material relaxes inwards in the region of the neck. Indeed, for its formation the zone width must be comparable with or greater than the thickness of the strip so that local thinning is possible. It should also be noted that there is no shear off-set of the upper half of the specimen with respect to the bottom half, cf., Figs. 4.4(b) and 4.4(c). If no volume change occurs then the aforementioned criterion leads to an angle θ_{sz} of 54·7° but this increases if the material should dilate during plastic deformation.

The third case is where the volume of deforming material is restrained in two directions—this is of considerable interest in a discussion of polymer fracture since within the body of a solid specimen, including the vicinity of crack tips, the material is often restrained in two dimensions. The deformation occurs in plane strain and if it is at constant volume then it will be a simple shear deformation of a band at an angle θ_{sb} of 45° for an isotropic material—this is shown in Fig. 4.4(c); the band is known as a shear band and is discussed in more detail in Section 4.3.3. If the deforming material dilates, so enabling volume expansion to occur normal to the plane of the band, then the angle θ_{sb} will increase. In polymers large volume increases may occur to the extent that the angle θ_{sb} attains its limiting value of 90°. The resulting structure is known as a craze and will be considered in Chapter 5. There are other noteworthy features about strain inhomogeneities that form under these conditions of restraint in two directions. For example, since they involve no lateral contraction they may be limited to a very thin planar zone and can exist as a disc-shaped region entirely inside the material. Also, if the deformation of the specimen is uniaxial tension or compression these inhomogeneities can only be nucleated if there is a local stress concentration sufficiently large to raise the stress to the appropriate value for the deformation to occur under plane-strain conditions. Finally, since there is no change in the cross-sectional area that can lead to a geometrical instability, such inhomogeneities can only form if the material is strain softening.

4.3.3 Shear Bands in Glassy Polymers

As discussed above, shear bands may form in a material which exhibits strain softening and all amorphous glassy polymers show this be-haviour to some degree. Hence, when the conditions which favour crazing are suppressed, all such polymers will possess a tendency to form shear bands. Indeed, shear bands have been observed[1,9,10,18,72–82] in many different glassy polymers, particularly when they have been loaded in compression. (Compressive stresses obviously inhibit craze formation which involves volume expansion.)

Figure 4.5(a) shows a section cut from a sample of polystyrene that has been deformed just past yield at room temperature under plane-strain compression and viewed between cross polars. The shear bands are sharply defined and have been termed 'microshear bands'. The shear strain in them is about 2·5. On the other hand, Fig. 4.5(b) shows a section from PMMA in which the shear bands are broad diffuse zones. The strain in them is only a few percent above that in the rest of the material. Amorphous polyethylene terephthalate, epoxy resins and PVC tend to form shear bands intermediate in character between these extremes. However, even for a particular polymer the appearance of the shear bands does depend upon other factors such as test tempera-ture, strain-rate and whether the specimen is quenched, slow-cooled or

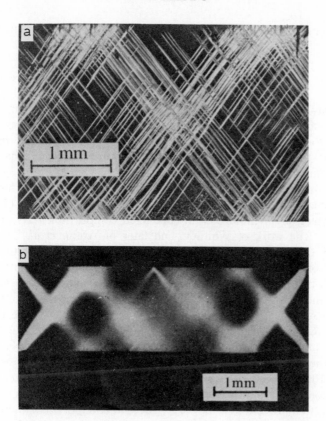

Fig. 4.5. Sections cut from specimens that have been deformed just past yield at 22°C in a plane-strain compression test viewed between crossed polars. Strong shear bands have been nucleated at the corners of the dies. (a) Polystyrene showing microshear bands; (b) PMMA showing broad, diffuse zones (after Bowden[83]).

annealed. Bowden[83] has suggested that the difference in character of the bands arises from the differing rates at which they propagate, which is largely controlled by the rate of strain softening and strain-rate sensitivity of the yield stress. Microshear bands tend to develop if the variation of the yield stress with strain-rate $[d\sigma/d(\ln \dot{e})]$ is small, if the negative slope of the true stress/strain curve, $(-d\sigma_y/de)_{\dot{e}}$ after the yield point is large and if the material contains large local in-homogeneities to begin with. Bowden quantified this statement by proposing a material parameter, e_{sb}, with the dimensions of strain such that

$$e_{sb} = -\frac{[d\sigma/d(\ln \dot{e})]_e}{(d\sigma_y/de)_{\dot{e}}} \qquad (4.15)$$

The parameter e_{sb} has a value of $0 \cdot 11$ for PMMA at room temperature and a value of $0 \cdot 2$ for polystyrene at 80°C and in both cases diffuse shear zones were formed. At about 70°C the value of e_{sb} had decreased to $0 \cdot 016$ and the shear bands were relatively sharp and well defined.

The most detailed work on the structure of shear bands has been conducted using polystyrene. Indeed, shear bands were first observed in polymers by Whitney[72] who conducted compression tests on polystyrene. The work of Whitney, and later of Argon et al.,[73] demonstrated that shear bands in polystyrene at room temperature may consist of microshear bands about $0 \cdot 5$ to $1 \mu m$ thick and that packets of such microshear bands propagate across the sample at an angle of 38° to the compression direction. It was also reported that the strain in the microshear bands was recoverable upon heating above the T_g. Brady & Yeh[55,74] have obtained replica transmission electron micrographs of internal surfaces of polystyrene samples loaded in compression. They found that the bands possessed a fine structure consisting of a 20–100 nm diameter fibrous morphology. Several workers[10,75,76] have confirmed that the angle the microshear bands make to the compression direction is not 45° (the direction of maximum shear stress) but about 38°. Bowden & Jukes[10] have suggested that this is due to a small transitory volume increase as yield occurs. Kramer[76] considers this explanation unlikely, especially since Brady & Yeh[55] measured a small permanent density increase. Kramer reviewed other explanations but concluded that current explanations could not quantitatively explain such relatively large deviations.

Apart from the microshear bands a second form of shear band has been observed in polystyrene and other polymers, namely the diffuse shear zones mentioned earlier. Kramer[75,76] studied the diffuse shear zones generated in notched bars of polystyrene subjected to uniaxial compression. He reported that the diffuse shear zones were viscoelastic, rather than plastic, in character and the strain in them was relatively low. However, their contribution to the total strain-rate was relatively large when compared to the microshear bands; a small strain over a large area had a greater effect than a large strain over a very small area. Also, the diffuse shear zones propagated along the maximum shear stress direction (i.e. ±45° to the compression direction). Wu & Li[77] examined in detail the structure of the diffuse shear zones formed in compression tests. They found that the diffuse shear zones consisted of very fine deformation bands about 50 nm in width and that they were not as continuous as the coarser microshear bands. These features may be seen from the replica transmission electron micrograph shown in Fig. 4.6. The shear strain in the very fine deformation bands, which make up the diffuse shear zone, was about the same as that in the microshear bands. As might be expected, the fine deformation bands and microshear bands were not independent but were interconvertible during deformation. In agreement with Bowden & Raha,[9] Wu & Li found that the formation of the microshear bands was favoured by high strain-rates and slow cooling of the specimen from the polymer melt. Finally, they noted that when a packet of microshear bands propagated across the specimen it produced a shear fracture but the overall plastic strain was small and the failure was essentially brittle. Alternatively, when the conditions favoured a diffuse shear zone, comprising of fine deformation bands, propagating across the specimen then a large overall plastic strain

Fig. 4.6. Microshear bands and fine deformation bands (the latter comprise the diffuse shear zone) in polystyrene (after Wu & Li[77]).

resulted, producing a large kink, and hence a ductile mode of fracture was recorded. Li & Wu[78] subsequently developed a generalised Tresca yield criterion to describe the contribution of these two different shear mechanisms.

The kinetics of shear band propagation have been studied in polystyrene by Argon *et al.*[73] and Kramer.[76] Kramer studied the effects of applied stress and temperature—the relationship between the velocity of microshear band propagation and temperature, at a nominal compressive stress of 90 MPa, is shown in Fig. 4.7. Kramer used an Eyring activated-rate equation to model the results and found good agreement with experimental measurements. An activation energy of

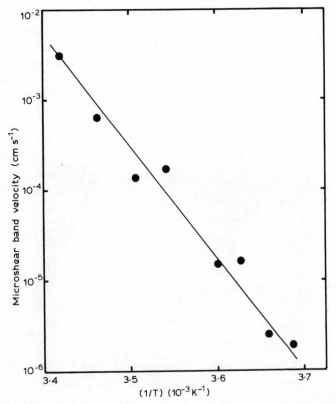

Fig. 4.7. Microshear band velocity in polystyrene (under a compressive stress of 90 MPa) (after Kramer[76]).

270 kJ mol^{-1} was deduced and this is in good agreement with a value of 251 kJ mol^{-1} obtained for bulk yielding by Brady & Yeh.[55] This led Kramer to suggest that the propagation of microshear bands was controlled by the plastic strain-rate of the polymer immediately ahead of the tip of the band.

4.3.4 Crystalline Polymers

The plastic deformation of crystalline polymers invariably takes place in an inhomogeneous manner especially at the microscopic level. The two-phase amorphous/crystalline nature of semicrystalline polymers means that because of their differences in physical properties the two phases will respond differently to an applied stress. When the amorphous phase is rubbery it will readily undergo shear deformation. In contrast the crystals will be more resistant to deformation and when they do deform the deformation will be anisotropic taking place in certain crystallographic directions on particular crystallographic planes such that molecules remain unbroken.[66]

The formation of shear bands does not normally occur when isotropic samples of crystalline polymers are deformed, unlike glassy polymers. However, when oriented samples of crystalline polymers are deformed, kink bands are often generated.[84-6] These are regions of sheared material in the form of localised bands which lie at an inclined angle to the direction of orientation (normally the chain direction) in the sample. It is thought that the kink bands form by a combination of slip in the crystals and deformation of the amorphous regions. They are called 'kink bands' because the direction of chain orientation is changed sharply by the presence of the band. The angle through which the chain direction is kinked varies from material to material and depends upon the testing conditions[86] for a particular sample. Zaukelies[86] was able to show from the measurement of the kink angles in filaments of nylon that the kink bands in this material were due to slip on hydrogen-bonded planes in the chain direction.

One of the clearest examples of inhomogeneous deformation in crystalline polymers is the formation of twins[67,87,88] in macroscopic polydiacetylene single crystals. For these materials the crystals are 100 % crystalline and the molecules are in extended-chain conformations. The molecules bend sharply at angles up to 40° across a well-defined boundary such that the crystal orientation on one side of the boundary is a mirror image of that on the other. It has also been found that cracks may be initiated where twins interact.[88]

4.4   SHEAR YIELDING AND CRACK INITIATION

Several authors[77,79,83,89,90] have considered the possibility that cracks may be initiated from microvoids which form at the intersection points of shear bands. Essentially it is suggested that defects in the polymer, such as flaws, air bubbles or molecular inhomogeneities, act as stress concentrations and enable microshear bands to be initiated by the shear stress and thermal motions at an applied load below that required for bulk yielding. The highly strained polymer fibrils in a shear band will then be further stretched when sheared by another shear band. This is illustrated in the electron micrographs of the intersection of microshear bands in polystyrene shown in Fig. 4.8. In the very highly strained material at the intersection points, chain disentanglement/scission will preferentially occur and will generate microvoids which act as nuclei for crack formation.

Chau & Li[91] have recently reported an interesting series of experiments where they examined crack initiation arising from the tensile fracture of coarse microshear bands in polystyrene. They generated coarse microshear bands in a notched specimen of polystyrene by subjecting the specimen to a compressive stress, removing the notch by polishing the specimen's surface and then fracturing the specimen in tension. This sequence of events is illustrated in Fig. 4.9(a). The mechanism of tensile fracture was via crack initiation and propagation either at the shear band/bulk (undeformed) material interface or between strands of fibres comprising the shear band. The morphology of the fracture surface from optical microscopy, shown in Fig. 4.9(b), indicates that strands of fibres were pulled apart and elongated by the tensile loads. A more detailed micrograph of the fracture surface is shown in Fig. 4.9(c), a scanning electron micrograph, where it may be seen that the strands of fibres which are visible in the optical micrograph are really fibrous sheets which extend all the way through the thickness of the specimen. The mechanism of formation of such fibrous sheets is shown in Fig. 4.10. In this figure part a represents undeformed material and part b represents the formation of strands of fibres in a shear band. The situation after some tensile deformation but before fracture is shown in part c; partial fracture at both of the shear band surfaces and relative shear between strands of fibres is indicated. Further deformation and final fracture at one of the shear band surfaces is shown in Fig. 4.10(d), with the formation of a fibrous sheet.

However, in many instances rather than localised shear yield bands

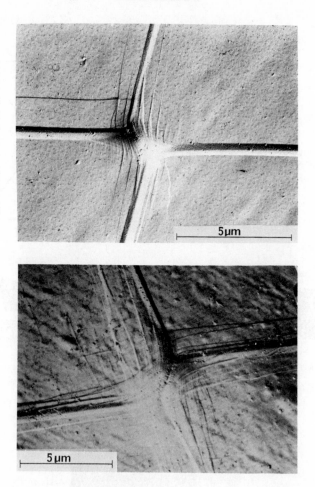

Fig. 4.8. Replica transmission electron micrographs of the intersection of micro-shear bands formed in polystyrene in notched compression tests (after Wu & Li[77]).

leading directly to crack initiation, the microvoids which are nucleated at the intersection of shear bands plastically expand and groups of them stabilise to form a craze structure. The craze plane is orientated normal to the maximum principal tensile stress direction and crack formation now results from the subsequent growth and breakdown of the craze. Wellinghoff & Baer[92] have employed transmission electron

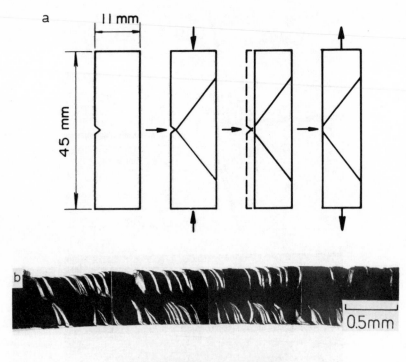

Fig. 4.9. (a) Experimental procedure for producing tensile fracture of coarse microshear bands; (b) Optical micrograph of the fracture surface of a coarse microshear band after being fractured in tension; and (c) Scanning electron micrograph of tensile fractured coarse microshear band (side view) (after Chau & Li[91]).

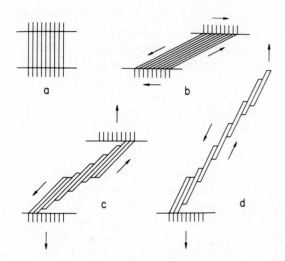

Fig. 4.10. Schematic drawing of the formation of fibrous sheets during tensile fracture of a coarse microshear band (after Chau & Li[91]).

microscopy to study the nucleation of microvoids and their subsequent coalescence to form a craze. They found that the surface microstructure of thin films of polystyrene was sufficiently heterogeneous to initiate localised microvoids of about 10–30 nm in diameter. Also, in several instances, the nucleation of the microvoids was clearly associated with the close proximity of localised plastic deformations. These microvoids were found even at the T_g, where the predominant mode of deformation was a bulk shear mechanism. However, at lower temperatures these microvoids grew into more elliptical shapes and induced a stress concentration in the surrounding matrix that was sufficient to initiate additional nuclei nearby. This is an essential step in the initiation of a craze and the detailed micromechanisms will be considered in Chapter 5.

Further evidence for the role of shear bands in craze initiation comes from the work of Camwell & Hull,[93] Mills[94] and Narisawa et al.[95] Camwell & Hull examined polystyrene subjected to compression, Mills studied the tensile impact of notched polycarbonate and Narisawa et al. examined notched bars of PMMA, PVC and polycarbonate subjected to three-point bending over a range of low strain-rates from

10^{-1} to $10^{-4}\,\text{s}^{-1}$; all tests were conducted under plane-strain conditions. They all found that internal crazes initiated at the intersection of shear bands. The fracture mechanism that therefore emerges is: (1) strain softening in plane-strain deformation causing strain inhomogeneities (shear bands); (2) the intersection of shear bands causing a stress concentration; (3) an internal craze initiating at the maximum stress concentration (which will be a shear band intersection at the tip of the plastic zone); and (4) craze breakdown and *crack* initiation and growth. This brittle crazing mechanism is favoured by plane-strain conditions (i.e. sharp cracks/thick specimens), low temperatures, high strain-rates and annealing the material. These conditions result in the stress for bulk shear yielding being relatively high but intense localised shear bands being formed (see Section 4.3.3), the intersections of which give high stress concentrations leading to ready craze initiation and breakdown. Finally, Narisawa et al.[95] and Mills[94] used the slip-line field analysis to estimate the stresses in the plastic shear yield zone in polycarbonate. Narisawa et al. reported that the greatest hydrostatic tensile stress, p (which was at the tip of the plastic zone where the craze initiated) was about 70–100 MPa, whilst Mills calculated a somewhat higher value of 150 MPa for impact fracture.

In conclusion, the role of localised shear in the nucleation of microvoids which may lead to crack initiation is only poorly understood—it is a difficult area to explore but undoubtedly one where further work is needed.

4.5 SHEAR YIELDING AND CRACK PROPAGATION

4.5.1 Mechanisms
Apart from possibly playing an important role in crack initiation, shear yielding mechanisms are also frequently involved in the subsequent growth of cracks in polymers. The shear yielding may be highly localised about the crack tip, involving relatively little viscoelastic and plastic energy dissipation, and hence may result in brittle fracture. However, the mode of crack propagation will become increasingly ductile in nature as the extent of shear deformation increases. As the amount of energy dissipated around the crack tip increases, effectively blunting the crack tip, then the toughness of the material generally rises. Obviously, the limiting factor is when bulk yielding occurs and fully ductile failure occurs.

4.5.1.1 Brittle Fracture

Considering firstly essentially tensile brittle fracture, then localised shear yielding and crazing are competing mechanisms, although crazing is generally the more favoured precursor to brittle fracture. Both are obviously favoured by a high degree of localisation of plastic strain, and hence by the polymer exhibiting strain-softening behaviour. However, the fundamental reasons why some polymers exhibit brittle fracture via a crazing mechanism, whilst in others a localised shear yielding micromechanism is involved, are not understood. Nevertheless, it has been observed that cross-linking the macromolecules appears to inhibit crazing and leads to brittle fracture via a localised shear yielding mechanism.

In cross-linked plastics the macromolecules are usually connected to each other by primary covalent bonds to give a class of materials known as thermosetting polymers. These are discussed in detail in Chapter 8 and examples include epoxy, unsaturated polyester, phenol-formaldehyde and amino resins. Such materials are usually cross-linked during the fabrication process and once cured possess a relatively high modulus and do not melt and flow at high temperatures. Many years ago it was reported[96,97] that cross-linking of polymers eventually led to the disappearance of crazing. These observations have been confirmed by van den Boogaart[98] who found that crazes did form at crack tips in lightly cross-linked epoxy materials but when the material was cured to give the usual high degree of cross-linking no crazes were formed—instead shear bands at the crack tip were visible. More recently craze-like structures have been reported[99-101] in highly cross-linked, simple epoxy materials but the present evidence is not convincing and certainly no structures even approaching the appearance of the crazes shown in Chapter 5 have yet been observed. On the other hand, fractographic studies[102-6] have clearly confirmed that plastic deformation occurs at the crack tip and have strongly suggested that this arises from highly localised shear deformations at the crack tip rather than craze formation. Thus, there appears to be a certain molar mass between cross-links below which the development of crazes is unlikely and localised shear yielding dominates.

It should be noted that crazing and localised shear yielding are not mutually exclusive micromechanisms—in many polymers both may be observed simultaneously and interactions occur between them.[107-12] This is illustrated in Fig. 4.11, which shows the possible interactions between shear bands and crazes. Bucknall et al.[110] have proposed that

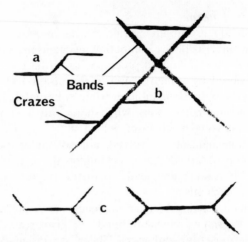

Fig. 4.11. Interactions of crazes and microshear bands in PMMA and polycarbonate as suggested by Kambour,[107] Newman & Wolock[108] and Jacoby & Cramer.[109] a—Microshear band growth between craze tips; b—Crazes terminated at pre-existing bands; and c—Isolated crazes terminated by self-generated bands (after Kambour[107]).

such interactions may be extremely important in imparting a high toughness to multiphase polymers (see Chapter 11). However, more recently, Donald and co-workers[111,112] have investigated the interactions between crazes and shear bands in considerable detail. Their observations indicate that shear bands may only act as craze terminators when they grow at a craze tip and so effectively blunt the craze, e.g. region c in Fig. 4.11. On the other hand, when a growing craze meets a pre-existent shear band the stresses at the craze tip cannot be relieved since the shear band was already formed; indeed the pre-orientation in the shear band is such as to cause premature craze breakdown and crack nucleation (see also Section 5.7.3). Thus region b in Fig. 4.11 would not, according to these workers, lead to craze termination but to premature craze breakdown and crack nucleation.

4.5.1.2 Ductile Fracture
Ductile fracture is usually associated with extensive shear yielding mechanisms. The precise features of the polymer's chemical and physical structure which favour ductile, as opposed to brittle, fracture are

far from being well understood but are considered in Chapter 5 and Part II. Typical test variables which favour ductile crack growth are plane-stress, as opposed to plane-strain, conditions, elevated test temperatures, relatively low rates of test and an absence of aggressive environments.

However, before considering the detailed micromechanics and mechanisms of ductile crack-growth via shear yielding, it should be noted that crazing, via a multiple crazing mechanism, is also a possible mechanism which may lead to ductile, tough polymers. Multiple crazing may accompany gross shear yielding, as discussed below, or may even be the dominant mechanism, as considered in Chapter 11, since this is observed in some toughened multiphase polymers.

Returning to ductile crack-propagation via shear yielding, then Mills,[113] Brinson[114] and Donald & Kramer[115-17] have studied the formation of shear yield zones ahead of cracks in thin sheets (i.e. tensile plane-stress conditions) in polymers such as polycarbonate, polysulphone and poly(2,6-dimethyl 1,4-phenylene oxide). It was generally observed that considerable lateral contraction occurred and that the shape of the zone was of the Dugdale line-zone type, rather than inclined shear bands, as may be seen from Fig. 4.12. Mills[113] and Brinson[114] found that the experimentally determined size and shape of the zone were in good agreement with the predictions from the Dugdale model, i.e. eqn. (3.48), and that the maximum displacement in the Dugdale zone was equal to or greater than the thickness of the polymer sheet, in agreement with the criterion discussed in Section 4.3.2 for the formation of this type of plastic inhomogeneity. Donald & Kramer[115-117] found that the shear yield zones ahead of cracks in these materials became less diffuse and more localised if the polymer was annealed just below T_g, possibly because of an increase in the yield stress and degree of strain softening. They characterised the structure of the zones (e.g. Fig. 4.12) using transmission electron microscopy followed by microdensitometry of the electron image plate to obtain an average value of the extension ratio, λ_{sz}, of the material within the shear deformation zone. Typical values of λ_{sz} lay between about 1·5 and 2·5 for a wide range of polymers. Donald & Kramer also found that

$$\lambda_{sz} = 0·6\lambda_{max} \qquad (4.16)$$

where λ_{max} is a theoretically predicted maximum extension ratio derived from a simple model in which the entanglement points are

Fig. 4.12. Transmission electron micrograph of a shear yield zone ahead of a crack loaded in tension (plane-stress conditions) in annealed poly(2,6-dimethyl 1,4-phenylene oxide) (after Donald & Kramer[115]).

assumed to act as permanent cross-links, with no chain slippage or scission occurring. Thus

$$\lambda_{\max} = \frac{l_e}{\langle \bar{R}_{\text{rms}}^2 \rangle_e^{\frac{1}{2}}} \tag{4.17}$$

where l_e is the chain contour length between entanglements (obtained from melt elasticity measurements) and $\langle \bar{R}_{\text{rms}}^2 \rangle_e^{\frac{1}{2}}$ is the root mean square end-to-end distance of a chain of molar mass $\bar{M}_e$, the entanglement molar mass (determined from neutron or light-scattering experiments). Thus, the extension ratio within the shear yield zone appears to be largely governed by the maximum extension ratio achievable by the entanglement network of the polymer.

In PVC inclined localised shear bands, at an angle of ± 55–$64°$ to the tensile direction, have been observed both in the unmodified material[113] and in PVC which has been toughened by the inclusion of discrete rubber particles.[118] In the latter multiphase material, the rubber particles act as stress concentrators and initiate many such localised shear bands. Thus a much greater volume of material is involved in energy dissipating plastic deformations than solely that encompassed by the immediate crack tip and this multiple-deformation mechanism results in a relatively tough polymer, as discussed in detail in Chapter 11.

Haward and co-workers[119-24] have conducted extensive investigations on the post-yield fracture of polymers, i.e. crack propagation in materials which have undergone tensile loading past their yield point. The post-yield fracture occurs under tensile plane-stress conditions and is initiated by cavities which grow from defects such as scratches or crazes on the surface of the drawn material. The cavities generally have four roughly equal straight sides which form a rhombus, the long and short diagonals of which lie perpendicular and parallel to the direction of drawing respectively. The cavities have been termed 'diamonds' and have been observed under plane-stress conditions in PVC, ultra-high-molar-mass polyethylene, poly(ethylene terephthalate), plasticised cellulose acetate, and at elevated temperatures in polycarbonate, PMMA, poly(ethersulphone) and polystyrene. In a typical tensile test of these polymers, under these conditions, a neck propagates down the specimen under a constant drawing load. As the neck propagates, diamond cavities are initiated in the drawn material from surface defects or the multiple crazes which may be generated in some polymers under these conditions. At low strain-rates the diamonds grow in a slow, stable manner until one reaches a critical size and initiates a rapid failure. This may occur before or after the neck has propagated along the whole length of the specimen; the initiation of a diamond cavity from a craze generated in highly drawn polycarbonate, obtained by deforming a thin sheet at 70°C, is shown in Fig. 4.13(a). However, in specimens with a rectangular cross-section, diamonds may also grow from defects on the corner and the scanning electron

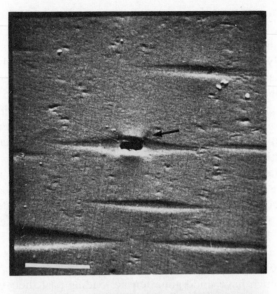

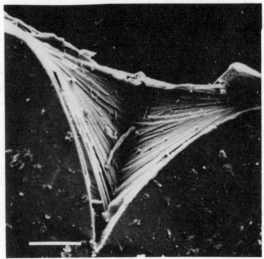

Fig. 4.13. (a) Scanning electron micrograph showing a diamond cavity originating in a craze formed in highly drawn polycarbonate. The polycarbonate was deformed in tension at 70°C and was in the form of a thin sheet (i.e. plane-stress conditions). (Bar indicates 50 μm) (after Cornes et al.[120]); and (b) Scanning electron micrograph showing the onset of fracture in drawn PVC by growth of a corner diamond. (Bar indicates 200 μm) (after Cornes & Haward[119]).

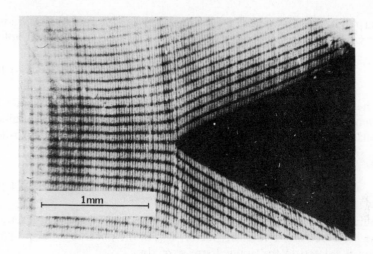

Fig. 4.14. *Large edge diamond in drawn PVC showing that the deformation is almost exclusively in the simple shear mode (after Walker et al.[121]).*

micrograph shown in Fig. 4.13(b) illustrates the onset of fracture by growth of such a corner diamond in drawn PVC. Walker *et al.*[121] have demonstrated that the characteristic shape of diamond cavities is produced by material adjacent to the diamond tip deforming plastically in simple shear parallel to the draw direction. This is clearly shown in Fig. 4.14 for a drawn PVC specimen which contains an edge diamond, i.e. a corner diamond which has penetrated the full thickness of the specimen, onto the surface of which has been evaporated a metal grid in order to observe the associated strain field. Each element deforms in simple shear to a maximum shear strain which constrains the faces of the diamond to be linear at a constant angle to each other.

4.5.2 Criteria

The plastic deformation that occurs around the crack effectively blunts the crack tip; the degree of crack tip blunting that is incurred largely controls the measured toughness and mode of crack growth. Thus, in considering possible criteria for crack propagation, it is of interest to know the stress distribution around a blunt crack.

An estimate of this effect may be made[125] by considering the elastic stress, σ_{11}, at a small distance, r, ahead of the tip of an elliptical crack of minor axis $2y$, and major axis $2a$, in an infinite sheet. When the crack is sharp but the tip radius, ρ, is finite then $y \ll a$ and the tip radius $\rho = y^2/a$. By using the solution for stresses around an elliptical hole

$$\sigma_{11} = \sigma_0 \left(\frac{a}{2r}\right)^{\frac{1}{2}} \frac{(1+\rho/r)}{(1+\rho/2r)^{\frac{3}{2}}} \tag{4.18}$$

It has been proposed by Kinloch & Williams[126] and by Yamini & Young[127] that fracture occurs when a critical stress, σ_{tc}, is attained which acts over a certain distance, c, ahead of the crack tip, then $\sigma_{11} = \sigma_{tc}$ and $r = c$ and eqn. (4.18) becomes

$$\sigma_{tc} = \sigma_c \left(\frac{a}{2c}\right)^{\frac{1}{2}} \frac{(1+\rho_c/c)}{(1+\rho_c/2c)^{\frac{3}{2}}} \tag{4.19}$$

where ρ_c is the crack tip radius and σ_c is the applied stress at fracture. The measured stress-intensity factor, K_{Ic}, at the onset of crack propagation is related to the applied stress, σ_c, by

$$K_{Ic} = \sigma_c(\pi a)^{\frac{1}{2}} \tag{4.20}$$

and the criterion for the propagation of a 'sharp' crack at a value of K_{Ics} may be interpreted as requiring the critical stress, σ_{tc}, to be attained at the distance c such that from eqn. (3.33)

$$K_{Ics} = \sigma_{tc}(2\pi c)^{\frac{1}{2}} \tag{4.21}$$

Thus, by rearranging eqn. (4.19) so that

$$\frac{\sigma_c(\pi a)^{\frac{1}{2}}}{\sigma_{tc}(2\pi c)^{\frac{1}{2}}} = \frac{(1+\rho_c/2c)^{\frac{3}{2}}}{(1+\rho_c/c)} \tag{4.22}$$

and substituting for eqns (4.20) and (4.21) yields

$$\frac{K_{Ic}}{K_{Ics}} = \frac{(1+\rho_c/2c)^{\frac{3}{2}}}{(1+\rho_c/c)} \tag{4.23}$$

Alternatively, from Section 3.4, if the modulus is assumed to be a constant, then this equation may be rewritten in terms of the fracture energy, such that

$$\frac{G_{Ic}}{G_{Ics}} = \frac{(1+\rho_c/2c)^3}{(1+\rho_c/c)^2} \tag{4.24}$$

The relationship between K_{Ic}/K_{Ics} as a function of $(\rho_c/c)^{\frac{1}{2}}$ is shown in Fig. 4.15, and it may be seen that there is a slight drop in K_{Ic}/K_{Ics} for $\rho_c/c < 3$ but for higher values of ρ_c the value of the measured stress-

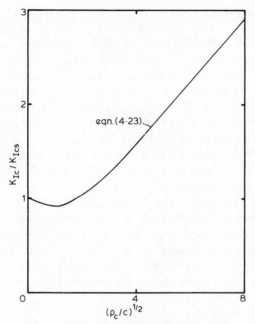

Fig. 4.15. Relationship between K_{Ic}/K_{Ics} as a function of the degree of crack tip blunting.

intensity factor, K_{Ic}, increases rapidly. This general form of behaviour modelled by eqn. (4.23) has been observed in polymers[126-30] and metals.[131,132] The model does not, however, specify the nature of the deformation which causes the crack blunting but the value of σ_{tc} should reflect the micromechanisms involved. The applicability of the above model and implicit fracture criteria will be discussed in later chapters. However, since this model has its foundations in LEFM it can only cope with those situations in which a relatively moderate extent of plasticity occurs and in such circumstances the values of crack tip stresses, σ_{tc}, deduced are eminently reasonable for the stresses to be expected in a plastic zone ahead of a crack tip. Indeed, this model is, in fact, surprisingly successful in providing a useful fracture criterion for even quite ductile crack-growth.

Considering highly ductile crack-growth, then Vincent,[133] Andrews & Fukahori[134] and Hodgkinson & Williams[135] have discussed the potential of different criteria. Vincent[133] has examined crack propagation in biaxially drawn and crystalline poly(ethylene terephthalate) film, about 25 μm thick. No strain softening was observed in the material's stress/strain curve and no crazes or shear bands were formed in the specimen. The curve was non-linear and a high degree of hysteresis was recorded. Vincent concluded that the techniques of LEFM were invalid since, for example, the measured value of K_{Ic} was dependent upon the crack length. He suggested a criterion for crack extension, based on an earlier idea by McClintock & Irwin,[136] namely that it is necessary for the strain to attain a critical value at a certain distance ahead of the crack tip. His experimental results were inadequate to verify fully the suggested criterion but its similarity to the model discussed above is striking.

Andrews & Fukahori[134] and Hodgkinson & Williams[135] have both considered ductile crack-growth in low-density polyethylene. The former workers analysed their data using the generalised fracture mechanics approach (Section 3.2.4) while the latter employed the J-contour integral method (Section 3.2.3). Both approaches met with reasonable success and the details are discussed in Chapter 9.

4.6 CONCLUDING REMARKS

It has been shown that shear yielding in polymers is a complex mechanism, difficult to interpret in molecular terms and to define, even at a phenomenological level. Nevertheless, plastic deformation plays a crucial role in the initiation and growth of cracks in polymers. When relatively homogeneous shear yielding occurs the polymer exhibits a ductile failure mode and is usually tough since it is able to absorb considerable energy by deforming plastically prior to fracture. At the other extreme, shear yielding may occur in the form of highly localised plastic deformations due to local stress concentrations and the strain-softening characteristics of the polymer. Such deformations may readily lead to crack initiation since the intersection of shear bands generates an area of highly strained material where preferential chain disentanglement/scission may occur leading to the formation of a crack. Further, if upon crack extension only highly localised shear yielding occurs around the crack tip then the material will generally exhibit brittle fracture at a low value of G_{Ic} or K_{Ic}, since plastic deformation is now confined to only a comparatively small volume of polymer.

There is another type of plastic inhomogeneity which is of key importance in polymer fracture and has been briefly referred to in this chapter. This is the structure known as a craze and it will be discussed in detail in Chapter 5.

REFERENCES

1. Bowden, P. B. (1973). In: *The physics of glassy polymers*, Ed. by R. N. Haward, Applied Science Publishers, Ltd., London, p. 279.
2. Ward, I. M. (1971). *The mechanical properties of solid polymers*, Wiley, London, p. 270.
3. Ward, I. M. (1971). *J. Mater. Sci.*, **6**, 1397.
4. Haward, R. N. (1973). *The physics of glassy polymers*, Applied Science Publishers Ltd., London, p. 340.
5. Binder, G. & Muller, F. H. (1961). *Koll. Zeit.*, **177**, 129.
6. Lazurkin, Yu. S. & Fogelson, R. A. (1951). *Zur. Tech. Phys.*, USSR, **21**, 267.
7. Haward, R. N. & Thackray, G. (1968). *Proc. Roy. Soc.*, **A302**, 453.
8. Murphy, B. M., Haward, R. N. & White, E. F. T. (1971). *J. Polym. Sci.*, A2, **9**, 801.
9. Bowden, P. B. & Raha, S. (1970). *Phil. Mag.*, **22**, 463.
10. Bowden, P. B. & Jukes, J. A. (1972). *J. Mater. Sci.*, **7**, 52.
11. Gledhill, R. A., Kinloch, A. J., Yamini, S. & Young, R. J. (1978). *Polymer*, **19**, 574.
12. Gledhill, R. A. & Kinloch, A. J. (1979). *Polym. Eng. Sci.*, **19**, 82.
13. Sternstein, S. S., Ongchin, L. & Silverman, A. (1968). *Applied Polymer Sympos.*, **7**, 175.
14. Brown, N. & Ward, I. M. (1968). *J. Polym. Sci.*, A2, **6**, 607.
15. Vincent, P. I. (1966). *Proc. Conf. Physical Basis of Yield and Fracture, Oxford*, Inst. Physics, London, p. 155.
16. ASTM-0695-69, *Compressive properties of rigid plastics*.
17. Williams, J. G. & Ford, H. (1964). *J. Mech. Eng. Sci.*, **6**, 405.
18. Bowden, P. B. & Jukes, J. A. (1968). *J. Mater. Sci.*, **3**, 183.
19. Bauwens-Crowet, C., Bauwens, J. C. & Homès, G. (1969). *J. Polym. Sci.*, A2, **7**, 735.
20. Roetling, J. A. (1965). *Polymer*, **6**, 311.
21. Holt, D. L. (1968). *J. Appl. Polym. Sci.*, **12**, 1653.
22. Robertson, R. E. (1963). *J. Appl. Polym. Sci.*, **7**, 443.
23. Bauwens-Crowet, C., Ots, J. M. & Bauwens, J. C. (1974). *J. Mater. Sci.*, **1**, 1197.
24. Eyring, H. (1936). *J. Chem. Phys.*, **4**, 283.
25. Ree, T. & Eyring, H. (1958). In: *Rheology*, Ed. by F. R. Eirich, Vol. II, Academic Press, New York, p. 83.
26. Haward, R. N. & Thackray, G. (1968). *Proc. Roy. Soc.*, **A302**, 453.
27. Lazurkin, Yu. S. (1958). *J. Polym. Sci.*, **30**, 595.

28. Coleman, B. D. & Knox, A. G. (1957). *Text. Res. J.*, **27**, 393.
29. Kramer, E. J. (1970). *J. Appl. Phys.*, **41**, 4327.
30. Ishai, O. (1967). *J. Appl. Polym. Sci.*, **11**, 1863.
31. Matz, D. J., Guldemond, W. G. & Cooper, S. L. (1972). *J. Polym. Sci., Polym. Phys. Ed.*, **10**, 1917.
32. Narisawa, I., Ishikawa, M. & Ogawa, H. (1978). *J. Polym. Sci., Polym. Phys. Ed.*, **16**, 1459.
33. Bauwens, J. C. (1971). *J. Polym. Sci., C*, **33**, 123.
34. Bauwens-Crowet, C., Bauwens, J. C. & Homès, G. (1972). *J. Mater. Sci.*, **7**, 176.
35. Bauwens, J. C. (1972). *J. Mater. Sci.*, **7**, 577.
36. Bauwens-Crowet, C. (1973). *J. Mater. Sci.*, **8**, 968.
37. Duckett, R. A., Rabinowitz, S. & Ward, I. M. (1970). *J. Mater. Sci.*, **5**, 909.
38. Ainbinder, S. R., Laka, M. G. & Maiors, I. Yu. (1965). *Meck. Polimerov*, **1**, 65.
39. Holliday, L., Mann, J., Pogany, G., Pugh, H. D. & Gunn, D. A. (1964). *Nature*, **202**, 381.
40. Rabinowitz, S., Ward, I. M. & Parry, J. S. C. (1970). *J. Mater. Sci.*, **5**, 29.
41. Christiansen, A. W., Baer, E. & Radcliffe, S. V. (1971). *Phil. Mag.*, **24**, 451.
42. Matsushige, K., Radcliffe, S. V. & Baer, E. (1975). *J. Mater. Sci.*, **10**, 833.
43. Bauwens, J. C. (1967). *J. Polym. Sci., A2*, **5**, 1145.
44. Bauwens, J. C. (1970). *J. Polym. Sci., A2*, **8**, 893.
45. Sternstein, S. S. & Ongchin, L. (1969). *Polym. Preprints, Amer. Chem. Soc.*, **10**(2), 1117.
46. Raghava, R., Caddell, R. M. & Yeh, G. S. (1973). *J. Mater. Sci.*, **8**, 225.
47. Raghava, R., Caddell, R. M. & Atkins, A. G. (1974). *Mater. Sci. Eng.*, **13**, 113.
48. Sardar, D., Radcliffe, S. V. & Baer, E. (1968). *Polym. Eng. Sci.*, **8**, 290.
49. Bryant, G. M. (1961). *Text. Res. J.*, **31**, 399.
50. Andrews, R. D. & Kazama, Y. (1967). *J. Appl. Phys.*, **38**, 4118.
51. Newman, S. & Strella, S. (1965). *J. Appl. Polym. Sci.*, **9**, 2297.
52. Eirich, F. R. (1965). *Appl. Polym. Symp.*, **1**, 271.
53. Nielsen, L. E. (1965). *Trans. Soc. Rheol.*, **9**, 243.
54. Rusch, K. C. & Beck, R. H. (1969). *J. Macromol. Sci.*, **B3**, 365.
55. Brady, T. E. & Yeh, G. S. Y. (1971). *J. Appl. Phys.*, **42**, 4622.
56. Pampillo, C. A. & Davis, L. A. (1971). *J. Appl. Phys.*, **42**, 4674.
57. Whitney, W. & Andrews, R. D. (1967). *J. Polym. Sci.*, **C16**, 2981.
58. Robertson, R. E. (1968). *Appl. Polym. Sympos.*, **7**, 201.
59. Kambour, R. P. & Robertson, R. E. (1972). In: *Polymer science*, Ed. by A. D. Jenkins, North-Holland, London, p. 688.
60. Bowden, P. B. & Raha, S. (1974). *Phil. Mag.*, **29**, 149.
61. Thierry, A., Oxborough, R. J. & Bowden, P. B. (1974). *Phil. Mag.*, **30**, 527.
62. Argon, A. S. & Bessonov, M. I. (1977). *Polym. Eng. Sci.*, **17**, 174.
63. Argon, A. S. & Bessonov, M. I. (1977). *Phil. Mag.*, **35**, 917.
64. Yamini, S. & Young, R. J. (1980). *J. Mater. Sci.*, **15**, 1814.

65. Keller, A. (1968). *Rep. Prog. Phys.*, **31**, 623.
66. Bowden, P. B. & Young, R. J. (1974). *J. Mater. Sci.*, **9**, 2034.
67. Young, R. J. (1979). In: *Developments in polymer fracture*, Ed. by E. H. Andrews, Applied Science Publishers Ltd., London, p. 223.
68. Young, R. J. (1974). *Phil. Mag.*, **30**, 85.
69. Petermann, J. & Gleiter, H. (1973). *J. Mater. Sci.*, **8**, 673.
70. Nadai, A. (1950). *Theory of flow and fracture of solids*, McGraw-Hill, New York, p. 71.
71. Vincent, P. I. (1960). *Polymer*, **1**, 7.
72. Whitney, W. (1963). *J. Appl. Phys.*, **34**, 3633.
73. Argon, A. S., Andrews, R. D., Godrick, J. A. & Whitney, W. (1968). *J. Appl. Phys.*, **39**, 1899.
74. Brady, T. E. & Yeh, G. S. Y. (1973). *J. Mater. Sci.*, **8**, 1083.
75. Kramer, E. J. (1974). *J. Macromol. Sci.*, **B10**, 191.
76. Kramer, E. J. (1975). *J. Polym. Sci.*, *Polym. Phys. Ed.*, **13**, 509.
77. Wu, J. B. C. & Li, J. C. M. (1976). *J. Mater. Sci.*, **11**, 434.
78. Li, J. C. M. & Wu, J. B. C. (1976). *J. Mater. Sci.*, **11**, 445.
79. Friedrich, K. & Schafer, J. K. (1979). *J. Mater. Sci.*, **14**, 480.
80. Li, J. C. M. (1978). *Met. Trans.*, **9A**, 1353.
81. Chau, C. C. & Li, J. C. M. (1979). *J. Mater. Sci.*, **14**, 1593.
82. Chau, C. C. & Li, J. C. M. (1979). *J. Mater. Sci.*, **14**, 2172.
83. Bowden, P. B. (1970). *Phil Mag.*, **22**, 455.
84. Kurokawa, M. & Ban, T. (1964). *J. Appl. Phys.*, **8**, 971.
85. Robertson, R. E. (1969). *J. Polym. Sci.*, *A-2*, **7**, 1315.
86. Zaukelies, D. A. (1962). *J. Appl. Phys.*, **33**, 2797.
87. Young, R. J., Bloor, D., Batchelder, D. N. & Hubble, C. L. (1978). *J. Mater. Sci.*, **13**, 62.
88. Young, R. J., Dulniak, R., Batchelder, D. N. & Bloor, D. (1979). *J. Polym. Sci.*, *Polym. Phys. Ed.*, **17**, 1325.
89. Argon, A. S. (1975). *Pure and Appl. Chem.*, **43**, 247.
90. Argon, A. S. & Hannoosh, J. G. (1977). *Phil. Mag.*, **36**, 1195.
91. Chau, C. C. & Li, J. C. M. (1981). *J. Mater. Sci.*, **16**, 1858.
92. Wellinghoff, S. & Baer, E. (1977). *J. Macromol. Sci.*, **B4**(3), 1195.
93. Camwell, L. & Hull, D. (1973). *Phil. Mag.*, **27**, 1135.
94. Mills, N. J. (1976). *J. Mater. Sci.*, **11**, 363.
95. Narisawa, I., Ishikawa, M. & Ogawa, H. (1980). *J. Mater. Sci.*, **15**, 2059.
96. Berry, J. P. (1963). *J. Polym. Sci.*, **A1**, 993.
97. Broutman, L. J. & McGarry, F. J. (1965). *J. Appl. Polym. Sci.*, **9**, 585.
98. van den Boogaart, A. (1966). *Physical basis of yield and fracture*, Inst. Phys., London, p. 167.
99. Theocaris, P. S., Paipetis, S. A. & Tsangaris, J. M. (1974). *Polymer*, **15**, 441.
100. Lilley, J. & Holloway, D. G. (1973). *Phil. Mag.*, **28**, 215.
101. Morgan, R. J. & O'Neal, J. E. (1977). *J. Mater. Sci.*, **12**, 1966.
102. Owen, M. J. & Rose, R. G. (1975). *J. Mater. Sci.*, **10**, 1711.
103. Christiansen, A. & Shorthall, J. B. (1976). *J. Mater. Sci.*, **11**, 1113.
104. Sultan, J. N. & McGarry, F. J. (1973). *Polym. Eng. Sci.*, **13**, 29.
105. Broutman, L. J. & McGarry, F. J. (1965). *J. Appl. Polym. Sci.*, **9**, 609.

106. Young, R. J. (1974). In: *Developments in polymer fracture—1*, Ed. by E. H. Andrews, Applied Science Publishers Ltd., London, p. 183.
107. Kambour, R. P. (1973). *J. Polym. Sci., Macromol Rev.*, **7**, 1.
108. Newman, S. B. & Wolock, I. (1957). *J. Res. Natl. Bur. Stds.*, **58**(6), 339.
109. Jacoby, G. & Cramer, C. (1968). *Rheol. Acta*, **7**, 23.
110. Bucknall, C. B., Clayton, D. & Keast, W. E. (1972). *J. Mater. Sci.*, **7**, 1443.
111. Donald, A. M. & Kramer, E. J. (1982). *J. Mater. Sci.*, **17**, 1871.
112. Donald, A. M., Kramer, E. J. & Kambour, R. P. (1982). *J. Mater. Sci.*, **17**, 1739.
113. Mills, N. J. (1974). *Eng. Fract. Mechs.*, **6**, 537.
114. Brinson, H. F. (1970). *Expt. Mechs.*, **27**, 72.
115. Donald, A. M. & Kramer, E. J. (1982). *Polymer*, **23**, 1183.
116. Donald, A. M. & Kramer, E. J. (1982). *J. Polym. Sci., Polym. Phys. Ed.*, **20**, 899.
117. Donald, A. M. & Kramer, E. J. (1982). *J. Mater. Sci.*, **17**, 1765.
118. Breuer, H., Haaf, F. & Stabenow, J. (1977). *J. Macromol. Sci.*, **B14**(3), 387.
119. Cornes, P. L. & Haward, R. N. (1974). *Polymer*, **15**, 149.
120. Cornes, P. L., Smith, K. & Haward, R. N. (1977). *J. Polym. Sci., Polym. Phys. Ed.*, **15**, 955.
121. Walker, N., Haward, R. N. & Hay, J. N. (1979). *J. Mater. Sci.*, **14**, 1085.
122. Walker, N., Hay, J. N. & Haward, R. N. (1980). *J. Mater. Sci.*, **15**, 1059.
123. Walker, N., Haward, R. N. & Hay, J. N. (1981). *J. Mater. Sci.*, **16**, 817.
124. Walker, N., Hay, J. N. & Haward, R. N. (1979). *Polymer*, **20**, 1056.
125. Williams, J. G. (1980). *Stress analysis of polymers*, 2nd Edn., Ellis Horwood, Chichester, p. 350.
126. Kinloch, A. J. & Williams, J. G. (1980). *J. Mater. Sci.*, **15**, 987.
127. Yamini, S. & Young, R. J. (1980). *J. Mater. Sci.*, **15**, 1823.
128. Constable, I., Culver, L. E. & Williams, J. G. (1970). *Int. J. Fract. Mechs.*, **6**, 279.
129. Plati, E. & Williams, J. G. (1975). *Polym. Eng. Sci.*, **15**, 470.
130. Williams, J. G. & Hodgkinson, J. M. (1981). *Proc. R. Soc.*, **A375**, 231.
131. Irwin, G. R. (1964). *Appl. Mater. Res.*, **3**, 65.
132. Spink, G. M., Worthington, P. J. & Heald, P. T. (1973). *Mater. Sci. Eng.*, **11**, 113.
133. Vincent, P. I. (1971). *Polymer*, **12**, 534.
134. Andrews, E. H. & Fukahori, Y. (1977). *J. Mater. Sci.*, **12**, 1307.
135. Hodgkinson, J. M. & Williams, J. G. (1981). *J. Mater. Sci.*, **16**, 50.
136. McClintock, F. A. & Irwin, G. R. (1965). *Fracture toughness testing and its applications*, ASTM STP 381, p. 95.

Chapter 5

Crazing

5.1 INTRODUCTION

A craze is initiated when an applied tensile stress causes microvoids to nucleate at points of high stress concentrations in the polymer created by scratches, flaws, cracks, dust particles, molecular heterogeneities, etc. The microvoids develop in a plane perpendicular to the maximum principal stress but do not coalesce to form a true crack since they become stabilised by fibrils of plastically deformed, oriented polymeric material spanning the craze. The resulting localised yielded region therefore consists of an interpenetrating system of voids and polymer fibrils and is known as a craze. Unlike a crack, it is capable of transmitting loads across its faces. However, when cracks do initiate and grow they do so by means of the breakdown of the fibrillar structure in a craze. This typically results in slow cavity expansion followed by crack extension through the craze, and finally crack propagation preceded by a craze or crazes at the crack tip through the remainder of the material.

The importance of crazing is that it is frequently a precursor to brittle fracture. This is because, although considerable plastic deformation and local energy adsorption are involved in craze initiation, growth and breakdown, this micromechanism is often highly localised and confined to a very small volume of the material. However, it should be recognised that if stable crazes can be initiated in a comparatively large volume of the polymer, i.e. a multiple deformation mechanism, then such multiple crazing may lead to a tough, and possibly even a ductile, material response. This has been discussed in

147

Section 4.5.1 in connection with polymers tested under plane-stress conditions at elevated temperatures near the T_g but, more importantly, multiple crazing is a major mechanism in some tough multiphase polymers, as discussed in detail in Chapter 11.

Crazing, like the formation of shear bands or zones, involves localised or inhomogeneous plastic deformation of the material which arises from strain softening. However, whereas shear yielding occurs essentially at constant volume, crazing is a cavitation process and hence occurs with an increase in volume. Craze initiation therefore usually requires the presence of a dilatational component to the stress tensor and may be inhibited by applying hydrostatic pressure but enhanced by the presence of triaxial tensile stresses. The latter stress state exists ahead of flaws in relatively thick specimens in plane strain, as was discussed in Sections 3.3.2 and 3.5. Also, under such conditions crazing is additionally favoured since the applied tensile stress necessary for shear yielding is high, due to the constraint (eqns (3.41) and (3.43)), whilst the cavitation involved in crazing relieves the plane-strain constraint and so enables the material to undergo plastic deformation more readily. Thus, the presence of sharp cracks or defects in thick specimens, or in thick sections of manufactured components, will favour craze initiation leading to a brittle fracture, as opposed to a bulk shear yielding mechanism leading to ductile failure.

As mentioned above, the importance of crazing is that crazes may initiate, grow and break down to give cracks at stresses below those necessary to cause bulk shear yielding and so lead to brittle fracture requiring only a relatively low value of fracture energy, G_{Ic}, or stress-intensity factor, K_{Ic}. The various stress levels for polystyrene as a function of temperature are illustrated in Fig. 5.1. As may be seen, both the crazing stress and the yield stress rise with decreasing temperature but the latter parameter rises more rapidly and, except at high temperatures, is usually considerably greater than the crazing stress. Thus, except at high temperatures near the glass transition temperature (~90°C), crazing which results in a brittle fracture mode will be the dominant micromechanism. Apart from low temperatures, high strain-rates, aggressive liquid environments and, as discussed above, a plane-strain stress state, also favour a brittle crazing mechanism. At temperatures near the T_g, the stresses necessary for shear yielding and crazing are relatively low and approach one another and hence both extensive shear yielding and crazing leading to a ductile fracture mode may be observed, as was mentioned above.

Unfortunately, the initiation, growth and breakdown of isolated

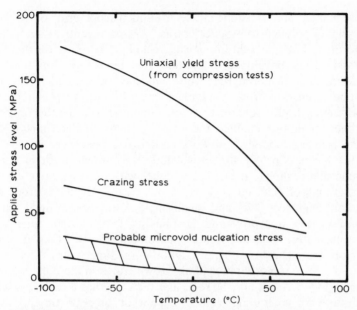

*Fig. 5.1. Relationship between yield stress, crazing stress and microvoid nuclea-
tion stress in polystyrene (after Haward[1]).*

crazes not only result in most of the glassy thermoplastic polymers
behaving in a brittle manner but is often the dominant micromechanism when many polymers which are generally thought of as
being tough ductile materials are subjected to the test conditions listed
above. Thus, a ductile/brittle transition may be induced which obviously has important consequences for the design- or materials-
engineer.

In the following sections general features of the microstructure and
micromechanics of crazes will be considered first. Aspects of the
fracture process involving craze initiation, growth and breakdown and
the influence of polymer structure will then be discussed.

5.2 MICROSTRUCTURE

The microstructure of crazes has been examined in detail by several
groups of workers.[2-9] Transmission electron micrographs have provided the most information concerning craze microstructure and early
techniques for preparing specimens included microtoming sections of
the bulk polymer after the crazes had been reinforced with various

impregnants[6,7] and straining an electron microscope grid coated with a thin film of polymer to produce crazes.[2-4] More recently, Lauterwasser & Kramer[5] have devised an elegant technique based upon this latter method. They developed a method for depositing thin, uniform-thickness films of polystyrene onto a *ductile* copper grid which could then be strained to produce a known state of uniform stress in the film overlying each grid square; the earlier method gave neither uniform-thickness films nor enabled the stress level to be determined, since electron microscope grids of work-hardened copper were used.

The thickness profile for an isolated craze grown in air in a polystyrene film is shown in Fig. 5.2 together with representative electron micrographs of selected regions of the craze.[5] Evidence from both electron microscopy[4,8,9] and small-angle X-ray scattering[10] experiments suggests that providing the films used for electron microscopy are sufficiently thick, i.e. greater than about 150 nm, then the craze microstructure shown in Fig. 5.2, and the micromechanics discussed in Section 5.3 are representative of air-grown crazes in the bulk polymer.

From Fig. 5.2(a) it may be seen that the craze has a thickness which tapers to very small dimensions (<2·5 nm) at the craze tip and, as the craze grows, the thickness at any particular point along the craze increases. The very sharp nature of the craze/bulk polymer interface should also be noted. The dense interconnected network of polymer fibrils, typical of an air-grown craze, is clearly evident, especially in Fig. 5.2(b). The fibrils have diameters of about 5–20 nm and the fibril diameter appears to be approximately constant along the length of the craze. Earlier work[2] had indicated that different craze fibril structures existed in different regions along the craze, but this observation is now thought to be due to a film of non-uniform thickness having been employed.[8]

Kramer,[11] in an excellent review, has pointed out that the mechanism of thickening is important in determining the microstructure of the craze. Two mechanisms are possible:

1. By new fibrillar material being drawn in from bulk unoriented polymer at the craze/bulk polymer interface; and
2. By creep of the existing fibrils in which the thickening occurs by further straining of the existing fibrils.

In crazes grown in air the surface-drawing mechanism predominates but in environmentally induced crazes the fibril creep mechanism is often the major one. Also, apart from any thickening process, fibril

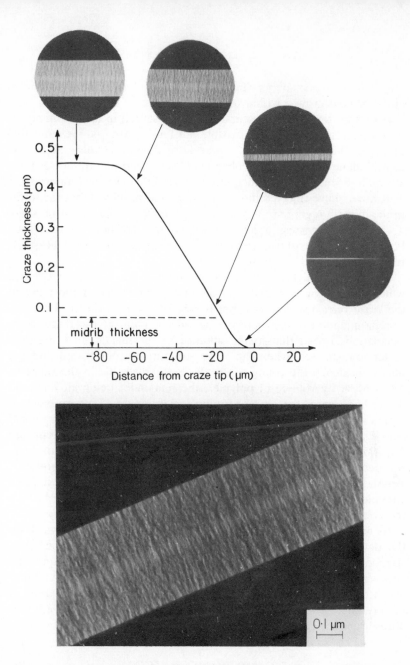

Fig. 5.2. (a) Thickness profile for an isolated air-grown craze in polystyrene, together with representative electron micrographs of selective regions of the craze; (b) Transmission electron micrograph of a region near the centre of the craze showing the distinctive mid-rib and the very sharp nature of the craze/bulk polymer interface (after Lauterwasser & Kramer[5]).

creep is an important mechanism of craze failure and of subcritical crack or void growth within the craze.

An interesting microstructural feature observed in air-grown crazes in polystyrene, and clearly visible in Fig. 5.2(b), is the so-called mid-rib. This is a region of lower fibril density running along the central plane of the craze. Beahan et al.[4] suggested that this arises from extra-large voids being formed at the craze tip. However, Lauterwasser & Kramer[5] have rejected this explanation and proposed that the fibrils in the mid-rib region are subjected to a relatively high extension ratio, λ, and hence possess a lower fibril volume fraction, v_f ($v_f = 1/\lambda$), because they are drawn from the craze surfaces in the high-stress region just behind the craze tip.

The craze is highly light reflecting since it has a refractive index which is much lower than that of the bulk polymer. The importance of the craze refractive index is that it may be used[12] with the Lorentz–Lorenz equation to calculate the polymer content of the craze. Such calculations reveal that in the absence of residual applied stress or under low stresses, when the craze structure is compressed and the fibrils buckled,[10] the compositions of 'fresh crazes' lie in the range of 40 to 60 % by volume of polymer, the remainder being air or liquid depending upon the craze-forming environment. Lauterwasser & Kramer[5] have determined the polymer volume fraction from optical densitometry measurements of transmission electron micrographs and for a *loaded* air-grown craze in polystyrene an average value of 27 % was deduced which is in good agreement with other measurements.[13,14] Apart from the value obviously being dependent upon the applied stress level, other factors, such as a thickening with age, may influence the craze density which is not, therefore, a fixed quantity.

As may be inferred from the above discussion most of the work on the detailed microstructure of crazes has been conducted on polystyrene. The microstructure will obviously differ depending upon the chemical and physical structure of the polymer and the environment in which the craze is grown. For example, crazes grown in polystyrene in the presence of n-heptane, as compared to air, exhibit no mid-rib, the fibrils are much coarser and the fibril volume fraction is much lower.[11]

5.3 MICROMECHANICS

5.3.1 Mechanical Properties of Crazes and Craze Fibrils

As would be expected the mechanical properties of the craze differ considerably from those of the bulk polymer. Kambour & Kopp[15] grew

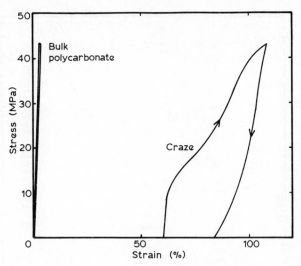

Fig. 5.3. *Cyclic stress/strain loops for bulk polycarbonate and a polycarbonate craze (after Kambour & Kopp[15]). (The bulk polymer is the reference state for calculating strain.)*

thick crazes completely through a polycarbonate bar and measured the stress/strain properties of the craze matter. The results are shown in Fig. 5.3 where, for comparison, the cyclic stress/strain behaviour of bulk isotropic polycarbonate is also illustrated. The initial modulus of the craze material is similar to that of the bulk polymer but yielding of the craze matter occurs at a relatively low stress, followed by strain hardening at higher strains and, upon returning the stress to zero, a large hysteresis loop is evident. Hoare & Hull[16] have reported that the stress/strain characteristics of polystyrene crazes are similar to those described above for polycarbonate.

These experiments do not, however, impart any direct information as to the mechanical behaviour of the craze fibrils and these are the microstructural elements whose failure precedes crack extension. These data have recently been reported by Kramer and co-workers[5,17] for crazes grown in PMMA exposed to methanol and for air-grown crazes in polystyrene. For the latter a true stress/strain curve for the craze fibrils is shown in Fig. 5.4. It is evident that fibrils in all regions of the craze have experienced severe strain hardening and that the greatest strain and greatest hardening occurred in the region just behind the craze tip. This confirms that the craze thickening mechanism for air-grown crazes in polystyrene is by surface drawing because if

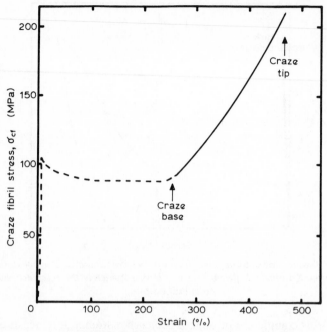

Fig. 5.4. *Craze fibril true stress/strain curve for fibrils in an air-grown craze in polystyrene (after Lauterwasser & Kramer[5]).*

it were by fibril creep the highest fibril strain would have been across the craze base. In solvent-grown crazes, where fibril creep is a main craze-thickening mechanism, the strain in the fibrils increases from the craze tip to a maximum at the craze base.[17]

The severe strain-hardening that may be observed in Figs 5.3 and 5.4 arises from the polymer chains in the fibrils undergoing molecular orientation.[18,19] The ability of the fibrils to undergo strain hardening greatly enhances the strength and stability of the craze structure. At the molecular level, Lauterwasser & Kramer[5] have shown, from using the dimensions of polystyrene molecules in the glass as measured by neutron diffraction, that complete extension of a polymer chain gives the same value of strain as the greatest strain measured in the fibrils, i.e. in those at the craze tip. Further deformation of these fibrils must involve disentanglement of the molecular network in the fibrils and Lauterwasser & Kramer suggested that this process is probably the important step in fibril failure and slow crack growth in the craze. This is discussed further in Section 5.7.2.

5.3.2 Models of Craze Shape and Stress Distribution

Modelling the shape of a craze and its associated stress field is more complex than for a crack since the walls of a craze are connected by load-bearing fibrils and are not, therefore, stress free. In one of the first papers on this topic Knight[20] assumed that the shape of a craze could be represented by a long section of uniform thickness tapering at the tip according to a unique relationship. He then employed the Fourier transform method of Sneddon[21] to deduce the associated stress distribution. Kambour[22] has remarked that from Knight's result the microscopic stress in the craze is approximately equal to the applied stress and this is significant for several aspects of craze behaviour. Firstly, it gives rise to additional lateral tensile stresses at the craze/bulk polymer boundary. The resultant complex tensile stresses result in further cavitation and so explain the gradual thickening of the mature part of the craze with time. Secondly, it is responsible for the important fact that a number of crazes may grow close together and parallel to each other under load. This is a vital mechanism in many tough, multiphase polymers, as discussed in Chapter 11. Knight's analysis has recently been re-examined[23] and the requirement for a unique tip profile found to be unnecessary; any profile which does not produce a singularity in σ_{11} is acceptable.

The general shape of the craze zone has led many workers[24–36] to suggest that it may be modelled using the Dugdale line plastic-zone model which was discussed in Section 3.3.2. If the craze surface stress is denoted by σ_{cs} then from eqn. (3.48) the thickness, $\delta(r)$, of the craze at any distance, r ($\theta = 0°$) is given by

$$\delta(r) = \frac{8}{\pi E^*} \sigma_{cs} R\left[\xi - \frac{r}{2R} \log\left(\frac{1+\xi}{1-\xi}\right)\right] \qquad (5.1)$$

where, $\xi = [1-(r/R)]^{\frac{1}{2}}$ (eqn. (3.49)).

In optically transparent materials it is possible to measure the crack-opening displacement, $\delta(r)$, close to the crack tip and in the craze zone ahead of the crack tip using optical interference microscopy.[37,38] The configuration of the loaded crack tip and craze in PMMA, deduced[29] from the optical interference patterns, is shown in Fig. 5.5. Also plotted is the predicted craze shape from the Dugdale model which assumes a craze surface stress, σ_{cs}, of 80 MPa. This is

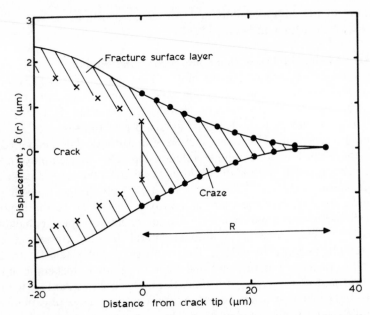

Fig. 5.5. Comparison of measured displacements of craze zone (points) and crack boundaries (crosses) with those calculated (solid curve) from the Dugdale model for PMMA (after Weidmann & Döll[29]). (Note the different horizontal and vertical scales.)

similar in magnitude to the polymer's predicted uniaxial tensile yield stress, σ_y, and this is, of course, not too surprising since crazing involves considerable plastic deformation under relatively unconstrained conditions. The value of σ_{cs} is considerably lower than the craze fibril stress, σ_{cf}, the relationship between σ_{cs} and σ_{cf} being[5,20]

$$\sigma_{cs} = v_f \sigma_{cf} \tag{5.2}$$

where v_f is the volume fraction of polymer matter.

The susceptibility of polymers to fracture at relatively low stresses via a crazing mechanism upon exposure to certain environments has been examined using a Dugdale model by several authors.[11,17,35,39] Graham et al.[39] have calculated values of the craze surface stress, σ_{cs}, for PMMA in a variety of liquid environments. All of the environments, and in particular immersion in alcohols, resulted in drastic decreases in the value of σ_{cs} compared to the value in air. For example, in ethanol the value of σ_{cs} was only of the order of 5 MPa. This

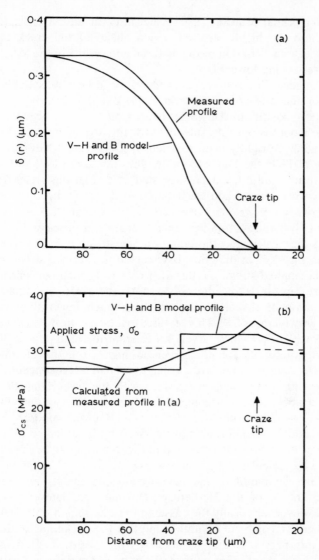

Fig. 5.6. (a) Comparison of measured opening displacement profile with that calculated from the Verheulpen-Heymans–Bauwens model; (b) Craze surface stress profiles calculated from the displacement profile shown in (a) and from the Verheulpen-Heymans–Bauwens model (after Lauterwasser & Kramer[5]).

reduction primarily arises[11,17,40,41] because the liquid is rapidly absorbed into the highly stressed region ahead of the crack tip. This causes local plasticisation of the material and results in the local T_g and yield stress being lowered.

The Dugdale line zone appears therefore to be a reasonable model for describing the craze shape in PMMA and polycarbonate under plane-strain conditions. However, Israel et al.[42,43] have argued that the Dugdale model is not fully adequate for the former polymer but their arguments have rightly been rejected by Döll et al.[44] Nevertheless, in the case of PVC the Dugdale model does not agree well with experimental results and it has been suggested[32,36,45] that this arises from the co-existence of crazes and shear bands at the crack tip.

Lauterwasser & Kramer[5] deduced the craze shape for an air-grown craze in polystyrene from direct measurements, as discussed in Section 5.2, and then calculated the craze surface stress, σ_{cs}. The results are shown in Fig. 5.6. In the craze base region the surface stress, σ_{cs}, lies below the applied stress, σ_0, but then rises to a small concentration at the craze tip. It is of interest to note the relatively small stress concentration at the craze tip, which is much lower than that for solvent-grown crazes.[17,46] This feature, together with the high strength of the craze fibrils (which largely arises from the high degree of strain hardening) accounts for the observed high strengths of air-grown crazes. The feature of the stress rising to a small stress concentration at the craze tip is obviously at variance with the basic Dugdale model described above but is accounted for by either a modified Dugdale model[47-50] or the Verheulpen-Heymans & Bauwens model.[51] In both of these models a small region at the craze tip is subjected to a higher stress than the rest of the craze and in Fig. 5.6 predicted displacements and stresses, calculated by Lauterwasser & Kramer[5] using the latter model, are compared to the measured displacements and resulting stresses. The fit of the Verheulpen-Heymans & Bauwens model is good. However, physically they assume that the region of higher stress is a region of incomplete cavitation and that the thickening of the craze behind this region is due to creep of the fibrils. Lauterwasser & Kramer[5] have shown that neither of these assumptions is correct.

5.4 CRAZE INITIATION

5.4.1 Mechanisms and Criteria

In single-phase polymers crazes are usually initiated either at surface imperfections such as flaws, cracks or scratches, or at internal defects such as air bubbles, dust particles or molecular inhomogeneities. These defects provide the stress concentrations necessary for the formation of the initial microvoids and their role has recently been examined[52-5] in detail. Turning to the criteria which have been proposed for craze initiation, then the earliest and simplest criteria were those which invoked a critical applied stress or strain requirement for craze initiation.[22,56] However, since craze formation is a dilatational process, and thus aided by hydrostatic tension and retarded by hydrostatic compression, many subsequent workers have suggested criteria which possess a dilatational stress component.

Argon[53] has proposed that craze initiation occurs in two stages. In the first stage microvoids form at stress concentrations produced when microshear bands, initiated by the shear stress and thermal motions, are arrested at molecular-level plastic heterogeneities. Thus at an applied load, below bulk yield, the polymer undergoes a stable thermally activated cavitation in regions of stress concentrations and this produces microvoids of about 10 nm in diameter. This stage of the proposed mechanism has been discussed in Section 4.4. In the second stage visible craze nuclei form during a comparatively short time governed by the rate of plastic expansion of the microvoids. This occurs when the local porosity reaches a critical level, which is dependent upon the hydrostatic tensile stress available to produce plastic void interaction, so that plastic cavitation becomes possible by unloading the elastically strained surroundings. This produces a craze nucleus that reflects light. Argon[53] has suggested that homogenising the material at a molecular level and preventing strain softening, which tend to make plastic deformation inhomogeneous, would suppress premature cavitation and void formation. More recently, Argon & Hannoosh[54] have developed a theoretical model describing the above mechanism. It accounts for the statistical nature of the craze initiation process, i.e. under an imposed stress or strain crazes are initiated over a range of times and, for craze initiation, under a multi-axial state of stress. The model requires a considerable number of molecular and microstructural details of the polymer to be known, in addition to some bulk material properties, and some of the parameters could not be directly determined. However, by fitting the model to the experimental results it was found that the model predicted the time-dependent behaviour reasonably well. Both experiments and theory showed, for example, that the induction time for craze initiation decreased, and the saturation craze-density increased, with increasing deviatoric stress or hydrostatic tensile stress.

Haward and co-workers[1,55,57] and Andrews and co-workers[40,58,59] have commented that the local stress must be sufficient to provide the surface free-energy to nucleate the void when it is small and must also be sufficient to provide for the nucleated centre to grow effectively in the elastic-plastic material. They considered this mathematically by deriving an equation relating the hydrostatic tensile stress, p_c, needed to form a microvoid of radius a, in an elastic-plastic material, and proposed that

$$p_c = \frac{2\gamma_{SL}}{a} + \frac{2\sigma_y}{3}\left[1 + \ln\left(\frac{E}{3\sigma_y(1-\nu)}\right)\right] \qquad (5.3)$$

where γ_{SL} is the interfacial tension of the void. The second term in the equation represents the stress necessary to expand the void against the resistance to plastic flow and it was concluded that this term was generally the more important. However, the authors recognised that if p_c is the hydrostatic cavitation stress then a problem exists and is highlighted by eqn. (5.3); this equation reveals that typically the value of p_c will be about two to three times that of σ_y and hence a shear yielding mechanism might well be expected rather than a cavitation process. To explain this apparent problem, Haward & Owen[57] calculated the stress and displacements suffered by a two-dimensional array of cylindrical voids in a sheet of uniform thickness when subjected to both uniaxial and biaxial loading conditions. From a finite-element analysis they concluded that when voids grow in a group the energy requirement for the formation of a void is reduced, since the zones of plastic deformation overlap and there is no energy requirement in the volume occupied by another void. Thus the effective yield stress is considerably *lower* than the value of the uniaxial tensile yield stress, σ_y, of the bulk material and the value of the effective yield stress should be used in eqn. (5.3), thereby reducing the value of p_c required.

An alternative mechanism and criterion has been proposed by Gent[60,61] which is that the hydrostatic tensile stress at the tip of a chance flaw or scratch increases the local free-volume to the extent that the T_g of the zone at the flaw tip is lowered to that of the test temperature. Once the material at the flaw tip is rubber-like, and its yield stress is negligible, then void formation through cavitation follows inevitably. The stress concentration at the newly formed craze tip allows the sequence to be repeated and the craze to advance. This mechanism readily explains several aspects of craze initiation—firstly, the retardation of crazing by a superimposed pressure since this will have to be compensated for by the local hydrostatic tension; secondly, the marked reduction in the craze initiation stress (or strain) in the presence of certain liquids,[11,22,39,56,62] which was accounted for by calculating the liquid absorption in the flaw tip region, increased by the local dilatational stress operating there; the associated decrease in T_g due to plasticisation was considered to aid the transformation of the tip material to a rubber-like polymer; thirdly, the craze initiation stress decreases as the test temperature is increased towards the bulk material's T_g (see Fig. 5.1); the closer the test temperature is to T_g then the less free-volume will need to be generated by the dilatational stress component. Gent[60,61] expressed these ideas in the following criteria for the formation of a narrow band of rubber-like material

$$\sigma_c = \frac{[\beta_g(T_g - T) - p]}{\eta} \qquad (5.4)$$

where σ_c is the critical applied tensile stress, η is the stress concentration at the crack tip, $-p$ is any externally applied hydrostatic compression, and β_g is a coefficient related to the pressure dependence of T_g, and is about 5 MPa °C^{-1}. From studies on crazing in polypropylene at low temperatures and in gaseous environments Olf & Peterlin[63] have suggested that it is not necessary to reduce the local T_g as far as the test temperature but only sufficiently to ease the plastic flow involved in crazing. However, Lauterwasser & Kramer[5] have calculated that the hydrostatic tensile stress at a craze tip can only produce about a 3°C decrease in the local T_g. A decrease in T_g of this small amount would not generally decrease the T_g to the test temperature, typically room temperature, and would only produce a minor decrease in the yield stress. Gent's model also predicts an atypical microstructure for a craze, as discussed later in Section 5.5.1, and thus does not appear to really offer a viable mechanism or criterion.

Considering phenomenologically based criteria, then the first such criterion to include the dilatational stress component to the stress tensor was proposed by Sternstein & Ongchin[64] to fit their experimental data for surface craze initiation in PMMA when the polymer was subjected to biaxial tension. The criterion is expressed in terms of the stress bias, σ_b, such that

$$\sigma_b = |\sigma_1 - \sigma_2| = A_1 + \frac{B_1}{I_1} \qquad (5.5)$$

where σ_1 and σ_2 are the principal stresses and I_1 is the first stress invariant of the stress tensor

$$I_1 = \sigma_1 + \sigma_2 + \sigma_3 \qquad (5.6)$$

and represents the dilatational component ($\sigma_{33} = 0$ in their experiments); A_1 and B_1 are time–temperature-dependent material parameters. Several authors[22,65] have questioned the physical interpretation of this empirical relationship and have commented that the evaluation of σ_b for a general triaxial state of stress is difficult. A more understandable criterion has been suggested by Bowden & Oxborough[65] which is that crazing occurs when the strain in any direction attains a critical value and that this critical value depends upon the hydrostatic component of the stress tensor. Their criterion may be expressed as

$$e_c = Y_1 + \frac{X_1}{I_1} \qquad (5.7)$$

where Y_1 and X_1 are again time–temperature-dependent parameters and e_c is the critical strain for craze initiation. Now

$$e_1 = \frac{1}{E}(\sigma_1 - \nu\sigma_2 - \nu\sigma_3) \qquad (5.8)$$

and eqn. (5.7) may therefore be rewritten so as to define the criteria in terms of the principal stress

$$\sigma_1 - \nu\sigma_2 - \nu\sigma_3 = Y + \frac{X}{\sigma_1 + \sigma_2 + \sigma_3} \qquad (5.9)$$

where $X = EX_1$ and $Y = EY_1$. Bowden & Oxborough[65] commented that, while for plane stress this equation is very similar to the criterion proposed by Sternstein & Ongchin (eqn. (5.5)), there are now no difficulties either in physical interpretation or in applying the criteria to a triaxial stress state. The variation of the critical tensile strain, e_c, for craze initiation as a function of the hydrostatic tensile component, p, of the applied stress tensor is shown in Fig. 5.7 for air-grown crazes in polystyrene; the continuous curves were calculated from eqn. (5.7) using experimentally determined values of X and Y. It is evident that the tensile strain required for craze initiation decreases rapidly as the hydrostatic tensile component of the stress tensor increases.

Having now considered the criteria for both shear yielding (Section 4.2.4) and crazing it is of interest to compare them. Figure 5.8 comes from the work of Sternstein & Ongchin[64] on PMMA and shows the

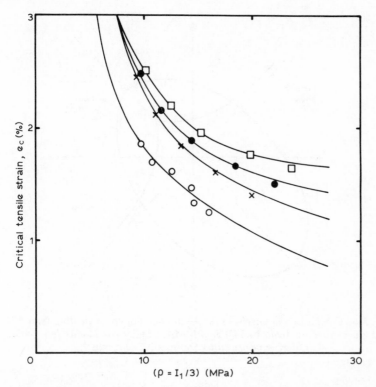

Fig. 5.7. *Critical tensile strain, e_c, for craze initiation as a function of the hydrostatic tensile component of the applied stress tensor for polystyrene in air. Points are for different load hold times and represent experimental results; the solid curves represent eqn. (5.7).* □, *1 s test, $E = 3·22$ GPa;* ●, *10 s test, $E = 3·20$ GPa;* ×, *100 s test, $E = 3·07$ GPa;* ○, *1000 s test, $E = 2·92$ GPa (after Bowden & Oxborough[65]).*

biaxial stress (plane stress) envelopes for craze initiation and shear yielding predicted from the stress-bias (eqn. (5.5)) and pressure-modified von Mises (eqn. (4.13) or (4.14)) criteria, respectively. In the first quadrant of stress space the crazing envelope is everywhere inside the shear yielding envelope. This implies that for PMMA all combinations of tensile biaxial stress produce crazes prior to shear yielding. However, the second and fourth quadrants show different behaviour, due to the significant increase in stress bias required to initiate a craze as the pure shear condition, which is a non-dilatational stress state, is

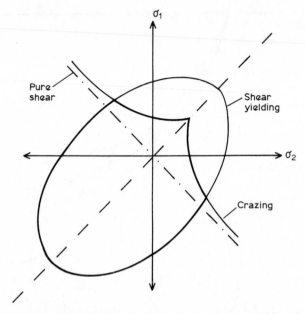

Fig. 5.8. Comparison of envelopes for the initiation of craze yielding (eqn. (5.5)) and shear yielding (eqn. (4.14)) in PMMA. Heavy continuous line indicates failure envelope (after Sternstein & Ongchin[64]).

reached. Shear yielding is of course possible in a non-dilatational stress field and thus at a particular combination of stresses, the two envelopes intersect each other. For all stress fields having I_1 less than the value of I_1 at which this intersection occurs, then the preferred mode of plastic deformation is shear yielding rather than crazing. The envelopes in Fig. 5.8 clearly illustrate that the dilatational stress component has a far greater effect on the stress required for craze initiation than for shear yielding but that both mechanisms co-exist and which one is predisposed to occur first depends upon, amongst other factors, the particular stress state.

Finally, Kramer[11] has noted that environmental craze initiation differs in several respects from craze initiation in air. For example, there appears to be no induction time[66] and the stress criterion[67-9] for environmental crazing seems to be simply that the largest principal stress exceeds a critical value which does not depend upon the value of I_1.

5.4.2 Kinetics

There is an obvious difficulty in observing the microscopic defects which are the sites for craze initiation and in defining the exact moment of initiation. This difficulty is compounded by the effect of various external parameters such as level and type of applied stress or strain, time, temperature, environment, etc. Indeed for crazing in air, an induction time (the time between applying the stress or strain level and first observing crazes) has often been recorded,[22,54,70-3] as mentioned above, and this may be due to a slow initiation step or simply the slow accumulation of cavities large enough in number and size to be observable.

Many, but not all, workers have found that the relationship between rate of craze initiation, temperature, and applied stress may be described by an activated-rate process. Bucknall[74] has used this model to analyse data obtained by Maxwell & Rahm[75] for craze initiation in polystyrene. This yielded an activation energy of about 175 kJ mol^{-1} which was compared with the activation energy of thermal bond rupture in polystyrene, namely 230 kJ mol^{-1}. This suggests that stress-activated chain scission may be the rate-determining step in craze initiation.

5.5 CRAZE GROWTH

5.5.1 Mechanisms

The growth of the craze is obviously an important step in the failure process and several aspects, including craze thickening, have already been discussed. The details of the mechanisms of craze advance are not well established and various explanations have been offered by Gent[60,61] (see Section 5.4.1) and by Argon & Salama.[76]

Argon & Salama[76] rejected the hypothesis that crazes grow by the repeated nucleation of microvoids ahead of the main craze, arising from the same inhomogeneous plastic flow processes that are responsible for the craze initiation process. They claimed that this was inconsistent with both the relatively low stress concentration at the craze tip (see Fig. 5.6) and the craze microstructure. In the case of the microstructure such a mechanism would result in a closed-cellular craze structure that is topologically different from the most widely observed one in which the air gaps of the craze are continuously interconnected and can transmit fluids and gases. They suggested that craze growth occurs by the mechanism of 'meniscus instability'[77] in which the yielded polymer at the concave air/polymer interface at the craze tip breaks up and produces new craze matter by repeated convolutions. This is shown schematically in Fig. 5.9. Such convolution of the yielded polymer at the craze tip results from the basic instability of all fluid menisci advancing under the action of a suction gradient (negative pressure-gradient) created in the fluid. This is because such interfaces are unstable to perturbations above a certain wavelength, which decreases with increasing suction gradient, and break up into a series of fingers.

Donald & Kramer[78] have recently obtained stereo-pairs of transmission electron micrographs of polystyrene and conclusively demonstrated that crazes grow via the meniscus instability mechanism. They found that the critical wavelength, λ_{wc}, of this instability was in the range of 16 to 33 nm—these values are in agreement with the observed interfibrillar spacing along the craze of 20 to 30 nm. However, at very high stresses nearing general yield, or in very thin films less than about 150 nm thick, a mechanism based upon independent cavity formation at the craze tip was considered to be the more likely one.[8,76]

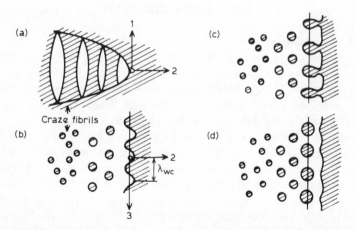

Fig. 5.9. Craze growth by meniscus instability. (a) Side view of craze tip; (b)–(d) Sections through the mid-line of the craze viewed from above, illustrating the advance of the craze-tip and fibril formation by the meniscus instability mechanism (after Argon & Salama[76]).

5.5.2 Kinetics and Criteria

The work of Argon & Salama[76] also showed that, whilst craze initiation obeyed a complex criterion involving both the deviatoric and dilatational components of the stress tensor, the craze growth rate via the meniscus instability mechanism was theoretically and experimentally governed *only* by the value of the maximum principal tensile stress. Indeed, it was demonstrated that crazes could *grow* in a state of pure shear stress without any assistance from a hydrostatic tensile stress.

Apart from the work of Argon & Salama, some of the most extensive studies of craze growth in air have been conducted by Williams & Marshall.[35] They employed single-edge cracked specimens subjected to a constant tensile stress and measured craze length, R, as a function of time for polycarbonate, PMMA and rubber-modified polystyrene. The resulting data are shown on a logarithmic plot in Fig. 5.10; the higher the initial stress-intensity factor, K_I, the faster and further the crazes grow. Williams & Marshall analysed these data using the Dugdale analysis but allowed the craze stress to be time dependent since polymers are viscoelastic materials. Thus

$$R = \frac{\pi}{8}\left(\frac{K_I^2}{\sigma_{cs}^2}\right) \tag{5.10}$$

They then assumed the time dependence could be expressed by a power law such that

$$\sigma_{cs} = e_y E_0 t^{-n} \tag{5.11}$$

where e_y is the yield strain, E_0 is the unit time Young's modulus, t is the time scale and $n = d \ln E / d \ln t$ and is assumed to be approximately constant for a given material. Combining eqns (5.10) and (5.11) gives

$$R = \frac{\pi}{8}\left(\frac{K_I^2}{(e_y E_0)^2}\right)t^{2n} \tag{5.12}$$

The linear relation predicted from this equation for $\log R$ versus $\log t$ obviously coincides with the experimental data. The values of n obtained from the slopes of the plots agreed with the modulus against time exponents obtained from separate deformation tests. Further, n may be related approximately to the loss factor, $\tan \delta_r$, obtained from molecular-relaxation studies, and for a constant n[48]

$$\tan \delta_r = \tan \frac{\pi n}{2} \tag{5.13}$$

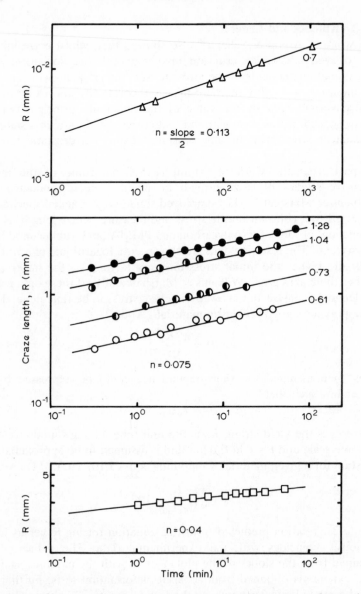

Fig. 5.10. Craze growth curves for air-grown crazes for various polymers (after Williams & Marshall[35]). △, PMMA; ●, ◑, ◐, ○, rubber-modified polystyrene; □, polycarbonate. Numbers on lines are K_I values, $MN\,m^{-3/2}$.

Therefore it appears that craze growth in polymers in air is a relaxation-controlled process and the proposed model is applicable. This model has been extended to environmental crazing. At low growth speeds, where there are no problems of fluid transportation, the growth characteristics are again controlled by relaxation processes in the craze zone. A transition from relaxation to fluid-flow control occurs when the fluids are unable to flow into the tip zone at a rate commensurate with the tip velocity. Indeed, Kramer *et al.*[79] have suggested that a craze grown in a liquid environment may be preceded by a very short length of 'dry' craze, which is necessary to achieve mechanical equilibrium. The craze stops when the fibril volume fraction in the solvent craze (just behind the short air-craze tip) becomes so large that fluid transport through this zone becomes negligibly small.

5.6 CRAZE BREAKDOWN

5.6.1 Mechanisms
Craze breakdown which leads to crack extension is obviously of vital importance to the failure process but surprisingly little is known about the detailed mechanisms involved. Models have been suggested[2,5,80–3] for polystyrene and have been largely evolved from fractographic evidence. The breakdown of the craze starts gradually as voids coalesce to produce a cavity equal in thickness to the craze itself. This cavity then propagates slowly through the highly extended mid-rib craze fibrils. When the propagating crack interacts with other large voids which have formed this generates secondary parabolic fracture markings on the surface.

If a low crack velocity is maintained then the growing crack is preceded by a wedge-shaped layer of craze; the tip of the craze is very sharp while that of the crack which propagates within the craze is blunt, as shown[83] in Fig. 5.11. The fracture surface for this slow centre-of-craze propagation has a smooth appearance apart from 'brushmarks' formed as the fibril bundles are laid down at the crack tip. At lower temperatures the stress required to rupture the craze at the crack tip increases and subsidiary or satellite crazes may be initiated in the high-stress regions ahead of the advancing crack tip, above and below the single craze in which fracture occurs. This is shown in Fig. 5.12. Again, if a low crack growth rate is maintained the fracture surfaces are relatively smooth but appear iridescent due to

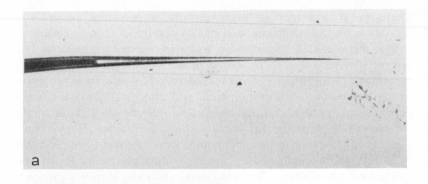

Fig. 5.11. (a) Surface of polystyrene sheet, side view of craze and craze wedge advancing slowly from left to right; reflected light ×300; (b) Crack tip region; Nomarski interference ×1250 (after Doyle[83]).

the increased reflection of light from the many parallel crazes below the fracture surfaces.

However, the test conditions are usually such that after a comparatively short period of slow crack extension the crack accelerates and the failure site now oscillates between the two craze/bulk polymer interfaces giving rise to banded markings on the fracture surfaces known as 'mackerel' or 'patch' patterns depending upon whether they are regular or irregular. The exact mechanism which creates these banded markings is disputed.[2,5,82–5] The formation of a bundle of crazes rather than a single craze at the crack tip, with subsequent crack growth occurring in many different craze sites at crazes at different levels, and a change of stress distribution in the craze during crack extension appear to be important factors.

Doyle *et al.*[82] have suggested that the very low toughness of polystyrene compared to PMMA reflects the lower craze/bulk polymer

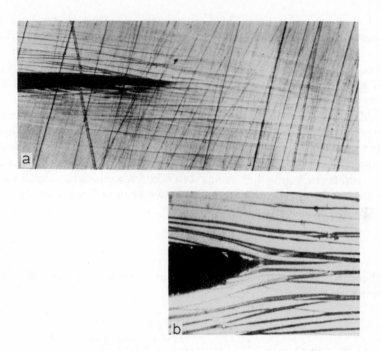

Fig. 5.12. (a) *Surface of polystyrene sheet, side view of crack and satellite crazes* (horizontal lines) *propagating slowly from left to right; reflected light ×115;* (b) *Crack tip and satellite crazes; reflected light ×750 (after Doyle[83]).*

interface strength of the former compared to the higher interfacial strength of the latter.

5.6.2 Kinetics

Many workers[35,48,86-8] have found that, for a crack growing relatively slowly in a stable manner and preceded by a craze, then the relation between K_{Ic} and crack velocity, $\dot{a}$, may be described by an equation of the form

$$K_{Ic} \propto \dot{a}^n \qquad (5.14)$$

Hence a plot of log K_{Ic} versus log $\dot{a}$ is linear with a slope of value n. This behaviour largely occurs in the time–temperature regime of the polymer's relaxation behaviour where there is a β_r-molecular relaxation and the value of n is generally in good agreement with the tan δ_r

value of this relaxation. Thus, viscoelastic processes at the crack tip appear to assist in stabilising crack growth until at high crack velocities an isothermal–adiabatic transition occurs in the craze region at the crack tip which results in thermal softening with a consequent decrease in K_{Ic} and a resulting instability. This is discussed in greater detail in Chapter 7.

Marshall et al.[34] have developed a theoretical model to describe the experimental relationship stated in eqn. (5.14). They first considered that when crack growth occurs the time-scale in the craze zone changes from t, the elapsed time, to that determined by the speed of crack growth. If crack growth is assumed to occur at a constant, critical value of the crack-opening displacement, δ_{tc} (see Section 5.6.3) then the time taken for δ_t to increase from zero to δ_{tc} is

$$t = \frac{R_c}{\dot{a}} \qquad (5.15)$$

where R_c is the length of the Dugdale zone at the onset of crack propagation

$$R_c = \frac{\pi}{8}\left(\frac{K_{Ic}^2}{\sigma_{cs}^2}\right) \qquad (5.16)$$

and

$$\delta_{tc} = \frac{K_{Ic}^2}{\sigma_{cs}E} \qquad (5.17)$$

If a power-law dependence is again assumed and σ_{cs} again implicitly taken to be equivalent to σ_y, then (eqn. (5.11))

$$\sigma_{cs} = e_y E_0 t^{-n}$$

Where, of course

$$E = E_0 t^{-n} \qquad (5.18)$$

Combining the above equations yields

$$K_{Ic} = (\delta_{tc}e_y)^{\frac{1}{2}}\left(\frac{8e_y}{\pi\delta_{tc}}\right)^n E_0\dot{a}^n \qquad (5.19)$$

This equation was shown to model the experimental observations and has also been successfully extended to include temperature effects, as discussed in Chapter 7.

On a molecular level, Zhurkov and colleagues have made extensive studies of the combined craze initiation, growth and breakdown processes and deduced the activation energies for these combined events for many polymers, as discussed in Chapter 2. The values were in excellent agreement with energies for chemical-bond rupture by thermal degradation. This evidence, together with the more direct experimental results obtained using infra-red, electron spin resonance, etc., provides support for main-chain bond scission as the rate-determining step in the failure process. This does not imply that bond rupture is the principal mechanism. However, once a few highly stressed bonds have broken at local stress-concentrations then the viscoelastic and plastic deformations involved in craze initiation, growth and breakdown may follow. Indeed, Haward et al.[89] have suggested that, if the majority of chain ends of the polymer molecules passing through the craze/bulk polymer interface terminate within the craze, then the craze may fracture by a largely viscous flow mechanism, which is a molecular separation process involving the viscous and viscoelastic disentanglement of polymer chains, rather than the breaking of covalent bonds. They calculated the probability of a polystyrene macromolecule spanning a thin craze and showed that for the viscous flow mechanism to operate in a commercial molar-mass polystyrene, then a craze must be more than 40 nm thick, which it usually is. Experimental support[2] for this mechanism comes from micrographs of craze breakdown where long drawn-out filaments, which retract upon failure, span the craze. These filaments possess a roughly globular tip, consistent with a viscous or viscoelastic rupture hypothesis.

5.6.3 Criteria

As mentioned above, Williams and co-workers[35,48,86] have employed the Dugdale model and proposed that a critical crack-opening displacement, δ_{tc} (eqn. (5.17)) provides a useful, and often unique, fracture criterion for the onset of crack extension in many polymers. For example, for PMMA a value of δ_{tc} of $1 \cdot 6$ μm was deduced over the complete regimes where stable crack-growth was observed. Support for this model comes from the work of Morgan & Ward[25] and Weidmann & Döll[29] who measured the value of δ_{tc} in PMMA directly using optical interferometry. Good agreement with the value calculated was found and the value of δ_{tc} was generally independent of temperature, except that the experiments of the latter authors indicated a molar-mass dependence of δ_{tc} and, for the higher molar mass material, the value was temperature-dependent above about 45°C.

5.7 EFFECT OF POLYMER STRUCTURE

The effects of polymer structure are considered in detail in Part II, but a few general aspects will now be considered to introduce some of the more important features.

5.7.1 Molar Mass

The optical interferometry studies of Ward and co-workers[26,27,90] and Weidmann & Döll[28-31] on polycarbonate and PMMA, respectively, reveal that the value of δ_{tc} increases as the molar mass of the polymer increases. For example, Pitman & Ward[27] have reported that the value of δ_{tc} increased from about 1·5 to 11 μm as the weight-average molar mass, $\bar{M}_w$, of the polycarbonate increased from 1·3 to 2·0 × 10^4 g mol^{-1}. Over the same range of molar mass the craze surface stress, σ_{cs}, appropriate to the Dugdale model, also rose from 40 to 120 MPa. Further work[90] has shown that in polycarbonate a transition from a ductile shear yielding mode to a brittle craze mechanism may be produced either by annealing or by reducing the molar mass, and this transition arises from an increase in the yield stress or a reduction in the local craze stress, respectively. In the case of PMMA the value of δ_{tc} at 20°C increased from about 1·2 to 2·7 μm as $\bar{M}_w$ increased from 1·1 × 10^5 to 9 × 10^6 g mol^{-1}. The value of σ_{cs} was relatively unaffected. Thus, the effect of molar mass on the properties of PMMA is far less marked than for polycarbonate and this is discussed further in Chapter 7. Weidmann & Döll[30] have suggested that the value of δ_{tc} is essentially dependent upon the maximum extension which the fibril-bundle of molecular chains spanning the tip of the crack in the craze can withstand. The increasing value of δ_{tc} with increasing molar mass can be explained by demonstrating that in the higher molar mass polymers the mechanical properties of the craze fibrils were such that the fibrils could endure greater strains prior to failure. The studies of Weidmann & Döll on PMMA, and other work on polystyrene[91] have indicated that the local and applied stress necessary to initiate crazes is independent of molar mass above a certain minimum value.

Kramer[92] has examined failure mechanisms in low molar mass polystyrene, where the weight-average molar mass, $\bar{M}_w$, is below the entanglement molar mass, $\bar{M}_e$; i.e. less than about 3·5 × 10^4 g mol^{-1}. In such low molar mass material Kramer postulated that a small craze existed at the crack tip but since entanglements cannot occur single molecules must span this craze; if they do not, the craze becomes unstable and the crack advances. Under these conditions a critical value of δ_{tc} and G_{Ic} can be computed from molecular considerations

$$G_{Ic} = \sigma_{cs}(\lambda_{cf} - 1)\langle \bar{R}^2_{rms}\rangle^{\frac{1}{2}} \tag{5.20}$$

where σ_{cs} and λ_{cf} are the craze surface stress and the craze fibril extension ratio, respectively, and $\langle \bar{R}^2_{rms}\rangle^{\frac{1}{2}}$ is the root mean square end-to-end distance of the polystyrene molecule determined from neutron diffraction experiments. The fracture energy is predicted, at these low molar masses, to decrease as $\bar{M}_w^{\frac{1}{2}}$ and this prediction and the absolute magnitude of G_{Ic} were in excellent agreement with the earlier experimental observations of Robertson.[93]

5.7.2 The Role of Molecular Entanglements
The role of molecular entanglements has been briefly mentioned and, from detailed studies on the microstructure and micromechanics of crazes in many glassy polymers, Donald et al.[94,95] have suggested that molecular entanglements have a major effect on whether a polymer will typically undergo crazing, as opposed to shear yielding, and, if it crazes, will influence the micromechanical behaviour of the craze structure.

As discussed in Section 4.5.1, the theoretically predicted maximum extension ratio, λ_{max}, derived from a simple model in which the entanglement points are assumed to act as permanent cross-links, with no chain slippage or chain scission occurring is (eqn. (4.17))

$$\lambda_{max} = \frac{l_e}{\langle \bar{R}^2_{rms}\rangle_e^{\frac{1}{2}}}$$

where l_e is the chain contour length between entanglements and $\langle \bar{R}^2_{rms}\rangle_e^{\frac{1}{2}}$ is the root mean square end-to-end distance of a chain of molar mass $\bar{M}_e$, the entanglement molar mass. Several interesting correlations between the fracture behaviour and the above molecular parameters were identified. Firstly, unlike the extension ratio in shear yield zones (see Section 4.5.1), the average extension ratio, λ_{cf}, of the craze fibrils was not always directly proportional to a fixed fraction of λ_{max}. Indeed, for some polymers λ_{cf} was greater than λ_{max}; for example, values of 7·2 and 4·8, respectively, were found for poly(tert-butyl-styrene). This was ascribed to the higher stresses in such crazes causing chain scission or disentanglements to occur which led to values of λ_{cf} greater than the theoretical λ_{max} value. Secondly, there was, however, a good correlation between λ_{cf} and the chain contour length, l_e, between entanglements; values of l_e varied between 11 nm (for polycarbonate) and 60 nm (for poly(tert-butylstyrene)) and λ_{cf} increased steadily from 2 to 7·2. Thirdly, an increase in λ_{max} may lead to a greater tendency for strain localisation, since the extent of strain softening will probably be greater and the plastic instability may develop over a larger range of λ before strain hardening sets in. Such high values of λ_{max} will lead to high stresses in the plastic zone and hence chain scission and disentanglements will result and, consequently, crazing should be favoured relative to extensive shear yield deformations as λ_{max}, and hence as l_e, increases. Indeed, the results indicated that in the range of polymers studied those with the greatest chain contour lengths, l_e, between entanglements did tend to be those which underwent crazing most readily. However, it is not immediately obvious from this explanation why thermosetting polymers (with effectively a very low l_e value) should exhibit such a high degree of strain localisation at a crack tip nor why, when chain scission must usually occur, the highly localised zone formed is via shear yield deformations.

5.7.3 Orientation

If the applied stress is parallel to the orientation direction then craze initiation and growth, and subsequent craze breakdown and crack extension, are inhibited and occur at higher stress levels compared to the isotropic material. Conversely, if the applied stress is perpendicular to the orientation direction these events occur more readily.[22,96] Kambour[22] has offered an explanation of these observations essentially based on the argument that orientation parallel to the stress direction (and thus normal to the craze growth direction) has already caused the alignment of molecular chains and hence pre-empted the crazing process. Alternatively, Sternstein & Rosenthal[97] have proposed a flaw spectrum model where the orientation of the polymer chains changes the direction of the adventitious elliptical flaws which provide the stress concentration necessary for craze initiation, and thus the stress distribution pattern is altered.

More recently Farrar & Kramer[98] have investigated the microstructure and micromechanics of crazes formed in oriented polystyrene. Crazes formed by an applied stress parallel to the orientation direction are smaller, possess a higher fibril volume fraction, v_f, and have a lower stress concentration near the tip than crazes formed by a stress applied perpendicular to the orientation direction. Thus, the former are the stronger.

5.7.4 Chemical Structure

The influence of the chemical structure of the polymer upon the crazing process is not well understood. The correlations which have been established, largely from empirical observations, are discussed in detail in Part II. Glassy thermoplastics are considered in Chapter 7 and the effect of cross-linking, which usually reduces the crack propagation energy and eventually leads to the disappearance of all signs of crazing, is considered in Chapter 8.

5.8 CONCLUDING REMARKS

It is evident from the present and preceding chapters that crazing and localised shear yielding have much in common. Both involve inhomogeneous plastic yielding, which arises from local stress-concentrations and the strain-softening characteristics of the polymer, and when highly localised may lead to brittle fracture. The initiation of crazes, unlike that of shear zones or bands, is, however, a dilatational process. Thus, craze formation is the more greatly enhanced by the hydrostatic tensile component of the stress field and, indeed, the influence of the stress state in dictating which mechanism will be favoured is relatively well understood. Nevertheless, the respective criteria cannot as yet be formulated from molecular considerations and, indeed, the influence of the polymer's chemical and physical structure upon the type of micromechanism, and the stress (or strain) level at which it initiates, is only appreciated in a qualitative sense. Both crazes and shear yield deformation zones may, in certain circumstances, be modelled by the Dugdale line plastic-zone but the micromechanics of the elements, such as the polymer fibrils which form the craze structure, have only recently been investigated in detail. This information is obviously of vital importance to the fracture process since it is the breakdown of such elements that leads to crack initiation and growth.

Finally, it should be recognised that although crazes are a common precursor to brittle fracture they are not necessarily detrimental to the crack resistance of a polymer. Crazes, and also shear bands or zones, involve large plastic strains and considerable local energy adsorption by the material. This results in the measured value of G_c being appreciably greater than the intrinsic fracture energy, G_0; see, for example, the values of G_c and G_0 of PMMA in Table 3.1. On the other hand, such micromechanisms are often highly localised and confined to a very small volume compared to the total volume of the test specimen. Thus the *total* amount of plastic energy absorbed is often relatively low. This may be summarised by stating that, while these micromechanisms result in $G_c > G_0$, to obtain *very tough* polymers it is necessary to ensure that the volume in which such energy dissipative deformations occur is sufficiently large. This, in turn, may require invoking mechanisms to limit the growth of crazes in order to prevent premature craze breakdown and crack initiation. A particularly successful, and widely employed, technique to meet these requirements has been to initiate controlled crazing and/or shear yielding from many sites in the polymer. Hence, a much greater volume of the material is involved in energy dissipative deformations than solely that encompassed by the immediate crack tip. This multiple-deformation mechanism has been most effectively achieved by the incorporation of a second phase of dispersed rubber particles into the matrix polymer to produce, for example, high-impact polystyrene. Chapter 6 considers impact and dynamic behaviour in general terms and the tough, high-impact performance polymers are discussed in detail in later chapters.

REFERENCES

1. Haward, R. N. (1972). *Amorphous materials*, Ed. by R. W. Douglas & B. Ellis, Wiley, London, p. 513.
2. Beahan, P., Bevis, M. & Hull, D. (1975). *Proc. R. Soc.*, **A343**, 525.
3. Beahan, P., Bevis, M. & Hull, D. (1971). *Phil. Mag.*, **24**, 1267.
4. Beahan, P., Bevis, M. & Hull, D. (1972). *J. Mater. Sci.*, **7**, 162.
5. Lauterwasser, B. D. & Kramer, E. J. (1979). *Phil. Mag.*, **A39**, 369.
6. Kambour, R. P. & Holik, A. S. (1969). *J. Polym. Sci.*, A2, **7**, 1393.
7. Kambour, R. P. & Russell, D. R. (1971). *Polymer*, **12**, 237.
8. Donald, A. M., Chan, T. & Kramer, E. J. (1981). *J. Mater. Sci.*, **16**, 669.
9. Chan, T., Donald, A. M. & Kramer, E. J. (1981). *J. Mater. Sci.*, **16**, 676.
10. Brown, H. R. & Kramer, E. J. (1981). *J. Macromol. Sci. Phys.*, **B19**, 487.
11. Kramer, E. J. (1979). *Developments in polymer fracture—1*, Ed. by E. H. Andrews, Applied Science Publishers Ltd., London, p. 55.
12. Kambour, R. P. (1964). *J. Polym. Sci.*, **2**, 4159.
13. Brown, H. R. (1979). *J. Mater. Sci.*, **14**, 273.
14. Doyle, M. J. (1973). *J. Mater. Sci.*, **8**, 1185.
15. Kambour, R. P. & Kopp, R. W. (1969). *J. Polym. Sci.*, A2, **7**, 183.
16. Hoare, J. & Hull, D. (1972). *Phil. Mag.*, **26**, 443.
17. Kramer, E. J., Krenz, H. G. & Ast, D. G. (1978). *J. Polym. Sci., Polym. Phys. Ed.*, **16**, 349.
18. Brown, H. R. (1979). *J. Polym. Sci., Polym. Phys. Ed.*, **17**, 1417.
19. Brown, H. R. (1979). *J. Polym. Sci., Polym. Phys. Ed.*, **17**, 1431.

20. Knight, A. C. (1965). *J. Polym. Sci.*, **A3**, 1845.
21. Sneddon, I. N. (1951). *Fourier transforms*, McGraw-Hill, New York, p. 395.
22. Kambour, R. P. (1973). *Macromol. Rev.*, **7**, 1.
23. Verheulpen-Heymans, N. (1976). *J. Polym. Sci., Polym. Phys. Ed.*, **14**, 931.
24. Brown, H. R. & Ward, I. M. (1973). *Polymer*, **14**, 469.
25. Morgan, G. P. & Ward, I. M. (1977). *Polymer*, **18**, 87.
26. Fraser, R. A. & Ward, I. M. (1978). *Polymer*, **19**, 221.
27. Pitman, G. L. & Ward, I. M. (1979). *Polymer*, **20**, 895.
28. Weidmann, G. W. & Döll, W. (1976). *Colloid and Polym. Sci.*, **254**, 205.
29. Weidmann, G. W. & Döll, W. (1978). *Int. J. Fract.*, **14**, R189.
30. Weidmann, G. W. & Döll, W. (1978). *Proc. of Mechanisms of Deformation and Fracture*, University of Lulea, Sweden, p. 323.
31. Weidmann, G. W. & Döll, W. (1979). *Prog. Colloid and Polym. Sci.*, **66**, 291.
32. Mills, N. J. & Walker, N. (1976). *Polymer*, **17**, 335.
33. Gales, R. D. R. & Mills, N. J. (1974). *Eng. Fract. Mechs.*, **6**, 93.
34. Marshall, G. P., Coutts, L. H. & Williams, J. G. (1974). *J. Mater. Sci.*, **9**, 1409.
35. Williams, J. G. & Marshall, G. P. (1975). *Proc. R. Soc.*, **A342**, 55.
36. Brown, H. R. & Stevens, G. (1978). *J. Mater. Sci.*, **13**, 2373.
37. Kambour, R. P. (1966). *J. Polym. Sci.*, A2, **4**, 349.
38. Bessenov, M. I. & Kuvshinshi, E. V. (1961). *Soviet Phys. Solid State*, **3**, 950.
39. Graham, I. D., Williams, J. G. & Zichy, E. L. (1976). *Polymer*, **17**, 439.
40. Andrews, E. H., Levy, G. M. & Willis, J. (1973). *J. Mater. Sci.*, **8**, 1000.
41. Kambour, R. P., Gruner, C. L. & Romagosa, E. E. (1973). *J. Polym. Sci., Polym. Phys. Ed.*, **11**, 1879.
42. Israel, S. J., Thomas, E. L. & Gerberich, W. W. (1979). *J. Mater. Sci.*, **14**, 2128.
43. Israel, S. J., Thomas, E. L. & Gerberich, W. W. (1980). *J. Mater. Sci.*, **15**, 2394.
44. Döll, W., Seidelmann, U. & Konczol, L. (1980). *J. Mater. Sci.*, **15**, 2389.
45. Brown, H. R. & Chin, T. H. (1980). *J. Mater. Sci.*, **15**, 677.
46. Krenz, H., Ast, D. G. & Kramer, E. J. (1976). *J. Mater. Sci.*, **11**, 2198.
47. Marshall, G. P., Culver, L. E. & Williams, J. G. (1970). *Proc. R. Soc.*, **A319**, 165.
48. Williams, J. G. (1978). *Adv. Polym. Sci.*, **27**, 69.
49. Kramer, E. J. & Bubeck, R. A. (1978). *J. Polym. Sci., Polym. Phys. Ed.*, **16**, 1195.
50. Gerberich, W. W. (1977). *Int. J. Fract.*, **13**, 535.
51. Verheulpen-Heymans, V. & Bauwens, J. C. (1976). *J. Mater. Sci.*, **11**, 7.
52. Wellinghoff, S. & Baer, E. (1975). *J. Macromol. Sci.*, **B11**, 367.
53. Argon, A. S. (1975). *IUPAC, Pure and Appl. Chem.*, **43**, 247.
54. Argon, A. S. & Hannoosh, J. G. (1977). *Phil. Mag.*, **36**, 1195.
55. Haward, R. N. (Ed.) (1973). *The physics of glassy polymers*, Applied Science Publishers Ltd., London, p. 340.

56. Jaques, C. H. M. & Wysgoski, M. G. (1979). *J. Appl. Polym. Sci.*, **23**, 1135.
57. Haward, R. N. & Owen, D. R. J. (1973). *J. Mater. Sci.*, **8**, 1136.
58. Andrews, E. H. (1973). In: *The physics of glassy polymers*, Ed. by R. N. Haward, Applied Science Publishers Ltd., London, p. 394.
59. Andrews, E. H. & Bevan, L. (1972). *Polymer*, **13**, 337.
60. Gent, A. N. (1970). *J. Mater. Sci.*, **5**, 925.
61. Gent, A. N. (1973). *J. Macromol. Sci.*, **B8**, 597.
62. Bernier, G. A. & Kambour, R. P. (1968). *Macromol.*, **1**, 393.
63. Olf, H. G. & Peterlin, A. (1974). *J. Polym. Sci., Polym. Phys. Ed.*, **12**, 2209.
64. Sternstein, S. S. & Ongchin, L. (1969). *Polym. Pre-prints, Amer. Chem. Soc.*, **19**(2), 1117.
65. Bowden, P. B. & Oxborough, R. J. (1973). *Phil. Mag.*, **28**, 547.
66. Sternstein, S. S. & Sims, K. J. (1964). *Polym. Preprints, Amer. Chem. Soc.*, **5**, 422.
67. Matsushige, K., Radcliffe, S. V. & Baer, E. J. (1973). *J. Mater. Sci.*, **10**, 833.
68. Matsushige, K., Baer, E. J. & Radcliffe, S. V. (1975). *J. Macromol. Sci.*, **B11**, 565.
69. Kitagawa, M. (1976). *J. Polym. Sci., Polym. Phys. Ed.*, **14**, 2095.
70. Regel, V. R. (1956). *Sov. Tech. Phys.*, **1**, 353.
71. Ziegler, E. E. & Brown, W. E. (1955). *Plastics Technol.*, **1**, 341.
72. Ziegler, E. E. & Brown, W. E. (1955). *Plastics Technol.*, **1**, 409.
73. Verheulpen-Heymans, N. & Bauwens, J. C. (1976). *J. Mater. Sci.*, **11**, 1.
74. Bucknall, C. B. (1977). *Toughened plastics*, Applied Science Publishers Ltd., London, p. 163.
75. Maxwell, B. & Rahm, L. F. (1949). *Ind. Eng. Chem.*, **41**, 1988.
76. Argon, A. S. & Salama, M. M. (1977). *Phil. Mag.*, **35**, 1217.
77. Saffman, P. G. & Taylor, G. I. (1958). *Proc. Roy. Soc.*, **A245**, 312.
78. Donald, A. M. & Kramer, E. J. (1981). *Phil. Mag.*, **A43**, 857.
79. Kramer, E. J., Krenz, H. G. & Ast, D. G. (1978). *J. Mater. Sci.*, **13**, 1093.
80. Murray, J. & Hull, D. (1970). *J. Polym. Sci.*, *A2*, **8**, 583.
81. Murray, J. & Hull, D. (1969). *Polymer*, **10**, 451.
82. Doyle, M. J., Maranci, A., Orowan, E. & Stork, S. T. (1972). *Proc. R. Soc.*, **A329**, 137.
83. Doyle, M. J. (1975). *J. Mater. Sci.*, **10**, 159.
84. Hull, D. (1970). *J. Mater. Sci.*, **5**, 537.
85. Hoare, J. & Hull, D. (1975). *J. Mater. Sci.*, **10**, 1861.
86. Parvin, M. & Williams, J. G. (1975). *J. Mater. Sci.*, **10**, 1883.
87. Mai, Y. & Atkins, A. G. (1976). *J. Mater. Sci.*, **11**, 677.
88. Beaumont, P. W. R. & Young, R. J. (1975). *J. Mater. Sci.*, **10**, 1334.
89. Haward, R. N., Daniels, H. E. & Treloar, L. R. G. (1978). *J. Polym. Sci., Polym. Phys. Ed.*, **16**, 1169.
90. Pitman, G. L., Ward, I. M. & Duckett, R. L. (1978). *J. Mater. Sci.*, **13**, 2092.
91. Fellers, J. F. & Kee, B. F. (1974). *J. Appl. Polym. Sci.*, **18**, 2355.
92. Kramer, E. J. (1979). *J. Mater. Sci.*, **14**, 1381.

93. Robertson, R. E. (1976). *Toughness and brittleness of plastics*, Ed. by R. D. Deanin & A. M. Crugnola, ACS, Washington, p. 89.
94. Donald, A. M. & Kramer, E. J. (1982). *J. Polym. Sci., Polym. Phys. Ed.*, **20**, 899.
95. Donald, A. M., Kramer, E. J. & Bubeck, R. A. (1982). *J. Polym. Sci., Polym. Phys. Ed.*, **20**, 1129.
96. Beardmore, P. & Rabinowitz, S. (1975). *J. Mater. Sci.*, **10**, 1073.
97. Sternstein, S. S. & Rosenthal, J. (1976). *Toughness and brittleness of plastics*, Ed. by R. D. Deanin & A. M. Crugnola, ACS, Washington, p. 35.
98. Farrar, N. R. & Kramer, E. J. (1981). *Polymer*, **22**, 691.

Chapter 6

Impact and Fatigue

6.1 INTRODUCTION

In the previous chapters the theories and micromechanisms of crack initiation and propagation in polymers have been reviewed and discussed. A recurring theme has been the often dominating influence of the time–temperature-dependent behaviour of polymeric materials upon both the mechanics and mechanisms of fracture. This aspect is amplified in the present chapter which describes the general behaviour of polymers under three types of loading condition which embrace the complete spectrum of time-scales encountered in service applications, namely: impact, dynamic fatigue and static fatigue.

6.2 IMPACT TESTS

6.2.1 Introduction

Impact tests are employed to measure the ability of a specimen or a finished component to withstand a sudden blow. In many applications a satisfactory resistance to impact loading is an important performance requirement and, indeed, impact toughness is often the deciding factor in materials selection. Impact testing and the impact performance of plastics have therefore been the subject of several reviews.[1-5]

An initial point to clarify, as emphasised by Turner,[3] is that the commonly encountered term 'impact strength' is a loose misnomer since the usual practice is to record the energy absorbed by the specimen before it breaks. Thus the impact energy is actually determined which may then be expressed as the energy per unit area of the broken cross-section, the energy per unit length of notch, the energy per unit width of the specimen or the energy per unit volume of the test specimen. It is generally agreed that expressing the impact strength as the energy absorbed per unit area of the broken cross-section is the most satisfactory of these various definitions.

The importance of impact testing is that such tests frequently indicate that many polymers which appear to exhibit tough, ductile failures when tested by tensile loading at a low or moderate strain-rate may suffer brittle fracture under impact loading when the strain-rate is relatively high. Brittle fracture, which is accompanied by relatively low energy absorption by the material, is obviously a mode of failure which the design engineer generally wishes to avoid. A transition from ductile to brittle behaviour is particularly likely to be observed if the impact tests are conducted at relatively low temperatures or if the specimen, or manufactured component under test, contains a stress concentrator. The stress concentration may arise from a deliberately introduced notch in the specimen or a design feature, such as a sharp step or corner, in the finished component.

Over the years a large number of empirical impact tests have been devised to measure the impact strength of materials and components. However, the impact strength is not a fundamental material property—apart from depending upon the specimen geometry it also depends upon the particular test method employed. Thus, it is difficult to correlate the results obtained from different test techniques and extremely difficult to correlate the results from impact tests on specimens of the material to the impact performance of the manufactured article. This is the main reason why many investigators go to the expense of conducting impact tests on the finished component. An interesting development, therefore, is the application of fracture mechanics theories to impact tests, notably by Brown,[6] Marshall et al.[7] and Plati & Williams,[8] which has enabled two of the standard test methods to be directly correlated (Section 6.2.4).

The major reason for the difficulties of interpretation and correlation of impact strength measurements is that the energy measured is a composite term. Ireland,[9] for example, has suggested that in the case of flexed-beam pendulum impact tests, five causes of energy loss may be identified

$$U_H = U_{SD} + U_I + U_B + U_{MV} + U_{ME} \tag{6.1}$$

where, U_H = Loss in pendulum energy when the hammer strikes the
specimen;

U_{SD} = Total energy consumed by specimen deformation and
fracture, e.g. in bending, crack initiation and crack propagation;

U_I = Increment of energy required to accelerate the specimen
from rest to the velocity of the hammer;

U_B = Energy consumed by Brinell-type deformation at the
specimen load points;

U_{MV} = Energy absorbed by the impact machine through vibra-
tions after initial contact with the specimen; and

U_{ME} = Elastic energy stored by the machine.

For other types of impact test similar expressions may be developed
which contain alternative or additional energy terms; for example, in
the falling-weight impact test a frictional 'push-through' energy term
may be involved. Variations in specimen geometry and in the individual characteristics of different test machines, even if of the same
basic design, will alter the value of the different energy terms stated in
eqn. (6.1) and, unfortunately, it is very difficult to ascertain independently
any of the terms on the right-hand side of this equation. An exception
is the value of U_I, the energy consumed in tossing the broken specimen
out of the machine, which may represent about 30–80 % of the total
energy.[10] Furthermore, the energy absorbed by specimen deformation
and fracture, U_{SD}, arises from several different sources—for example,
from elastic and viscoelastic deformation of the specimen during the
initial impact, local plastic yielding before crack initiation and deformation of the material around the tip of the propagating crack. Thus,
the value of U_{SD} cannot be ascertained precisely and the energy
required for crack initiation and propagation cannot be isolated.

However, despite these problems, impact tests have the advantage of
being easily and rapidly performed and provide a relatively simple
means of observing fracture phenomena of considerable practical importance that cannot be readily studied by other means. Impact tests
are therefore best regarded as providing valuable information for
ranking materials in order of impact toughness, especially when the
tests are conducted with specimens containing no notch or notches of
various tip radii, and are performed over a range of test temperatures.
However, it must be recognised that the ranking order may change
with factors such as test method, specimen geometry and temperature.

6.2.2 Experimental Methods

Turner[3] has classified the experimental methods for measuring impact strength into three basic categories:

1. Flexed-beam impact;
2. Falling-weight impact; and
3. High-speed tensile impact.

This classification covers most of the experimental methods which have been employed as basic impact tests and includes all those called for in British Standards (BS) and American Society for Testing and Materials (ASTM) specifications[11–17] for material assessment. However, as pointed out by Reed,[5] it possibly excludes certain high-strain-rate tests, e.g. split Hopkinson bar,[18] shock-tube tests[19,20] and the use of explosive charges.[21] It is also of interest to note that, while impact tests are generally considered to cover the high-strain-rate end of the strain-rate spectrum, the data tabulated in Table 6.1 by Reed[5] indicate that flexed-beam and falling-weight impact tests do not necessarily provide particularly high strain-rates. In the *notched* beam tests, however, the strain-rate at the notch tip is considerably higher and has been estimated[22] to be of the order of $5 \times 10^3 \, \mathrm{s}^{-1}$. Apart from impact tests for material assessment there are, as mentioned previously, tests for examining manufactured components, e.g. pipes and blow-moulded containers. These also are covered in appropriate BS and ASTM specifications.[16,23–5]

Two flexed-beam impact tests, the Charpy and the Izod methods, are the most commonly used methods and a standard test procedure is described in both BS 2782 and ASTM-D 256. In both the Charpy and

TABLE 6.1

ORDER OF MAGNITUDE CHARACTERISTICS OF VARIOUS IMPACT TESTS[5]

Test method	Order of magnitude of strain rate (s^{-1})	Impact velocity $(m \, s^{-1})$
Flexed beam		
Charpy	10	3
Izod	60	2
Falling weight	10^{-1}–10	1–4
Conventional tensile	10^{-3}–10^{-1}	10^{-5}–10^{-1}
Pneumatic gun	10^2–10^4	20–240
Hydraulically operated	1–10^2	0·008–4

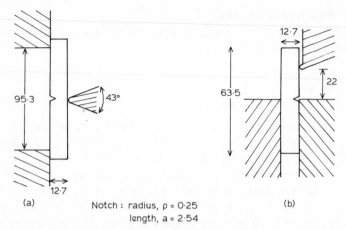

Notch : radius, ρ = 0·25
length, a = 2·54

*Fig. 6.1. Geometry of testing and specimen support arrangement for (a) Charpy;
and (b) Izod tests specified in ASTM-D 256 (all dimensions in mm).*

the Izod tests the specimen is usually notched and the specimen geometry and support arrangements are shown in Fig. 6.1. The specimen is struck, as indicated in Fig. 6.1, by a pendulum hammer at the bottom of its arc which then continues its swing to a measured maximum height. The pendulum is initially released from a fixed height and the energy absorbed from the pendulum is deduced from the difference between the release height and the maximum height at the end of its first half-oscillation. The basic difference between the Charpy and Izod tests is the manner in which the specimen is supported—held horizontally but not clamped in the former and clamped in a vertical position at its lower end in the latter (see Fig. 6.1). In the Izod test, variations in the clamping force may cause significant differences in the measured energy absorption but use of a standard clamping force may help in minimising this source of variability.

The flexed-beam impact tests are the most popular methods for determining impact strength but where these are inappropriate, because, for example, the specimen is too thin or too flexible, then the falling-weight tests are a useful alternative. The specifications for such tests are given in BS 2782,[11] ASTM-D 1709[13] and ASTM-D 3029.[16] Essentially, the specimen is a circular disc which is clamped around the periphery by one of several specified techniques and is struck by a hemispherically nosed metal dart of variable weight falling vertically. The speed of impact depends only upon the distance through which the mass falls but the associated energy and momentum depends also upon the mass. Thus, knowing the weight of the dart and the height through which it falls it is easy to calculate the energy available for fracturing the specimen. This experimental method is therefore an extremely simple one but, unlike the flexed-beam impact tests, the energy required for fracture has to be determined from a large number of tests, unless an instrumented test is employed, as discussed below. In the non-instrumented falling-weight impact test the weight of the striker is increased on successive drops, using a fresh specimen on each drop, until fracture occurs. The individual results are then combined, using one of two alternative statistical techniques, into a relationship between impact energy and failure probability. The statistical techniques are the Probit transformation or the staircase analysis. In the Probit transformation the percentage of failures of a relatively large number of specimen tests at a constant energy level are recorded and this procedure is repeated at different energy levels within the range bounded by the levels at which about 10 and 90 % failure probability occurs. The percentage of failures versus energy level relationship is then plotted on arithmetical probability paper. Thus the energy level required to produce a given percentage failure may be obtained and the slope of the curve gives an estimate of the variability and hence the likelihood of occasional failures occurring at low energy levels. The Probit transformation reveals several important aspects of impact behaviour which are not given by the more common staircase analysis. In the staircase technique the striker weight is progressively increased or decreased, depending upon whether non-failure or failure is observed, and the results tabulated showing the number of failures and non-failures at each energy level. The impact strength is then calculated from the interpolated impact energy required for a 50 % failure probability.

The high-speed tensile impact test is described in ASTM-D 1822.[15] The test essentially consists of a dumb-bell-shaped specimen with one end clamped to the pendulum hammer while a striker plate is attached to the other end. The pendulum is released from a fixed height and therefore swings through its arc trailing the specimen and attached striker plate behind. At the bottom of the swing of the pendulum the striker plate contacts a rigidly mounted anvil which causes the specimen to be rapidly strained in tension to failure. As with the Charpy and Izod tests, the impact energy absorbed is deduced from the difference between the release height and the maximum height at the end of its first half-oscillation. Turner[3] has commented that in the tensile-impact test the specimen is subjected to an approximately constant strain-rate while in the flexed-beam and falling-weight test methods the specimen is deformed at a strain-rate which decreases progressively, and rapidly.

As discussed previously, all three categories of test method result in values of impact strength which are basically only suitable for ranking materials. In an effort to obtain more scientifically based information, which might lead to a material parameter being deduced, the test methods described above have been instrumented by many investigators.[5,26,27] A number of instrumentation techniques have been employed including the use of strain gauges, piezoelectric crystal transducers, semiconductor photo cells, accelerometers and dynamic load cells, and several different types of instrumented impact test machine are now commercially available. Typically the load and associated displacement trace are obtained which may then be integrated to give the impact energy. Also several workers (e.g. References 28–33) have used instrumented notched-beam impact tests to obtain values of the dynamic fracture toughness, K_{Id}, for both metals[28–32] and plastics.[33] The value of K_{Id} represents the stress-intensity factor associated with a crack running at a given velocity. However, it has been argued[33,34] that the impact test on a stationary crack may give misleading information as to the true value of K_{Id} for a running crack, although the information may still serve as a useful guide. Finally, Reed[5] has discussed the factors which may cause artefacts in the output data from instrumented impact tests. Such artefacts may arise from inertial loading of the system, inadequacies of the electronics and the dynamic response of the system. Thus the data obtained from these tests are not always open to a clear interpretation. Nevertheless, instrumented impact tests are being increasingly used to assess the fracture behaviour of polymers at high rates of strain and the additional information such tests typically reveal about this poorly understood area will undoubtedly ensure that this trend continues.

6.2.3 Effect of Specimen Geometry

The impact strength and mode of failure are a function of specimen geometry. The specimen's length, width and thickness, and whether the specimen is unnotched or notched and, if notched, the depth and

sharpness of the notch, may all influence the observed impact behaviour. For example, increasing the length of a Charpy specimen
decreases the strain-rate and this may result in a somewhat higher
impact strength. Also, the thickness of the specimen in a flexed-beam
test may have a drastic effect on the impact strength.[35] Some polymers
exhibit a ductile failure and possess a high impact strength when the
specimen is relatively narrow but undergo a transition to brittle fracture, accompanied by a low impact strength, as the thickness is
increased. This arises from the state of stress in the specimen changing
from plane stress to plane strain as the thickness is increased, which
causes an increase in the stress necessary for shear yielding relative to
that necessary for crazing (see Chapters 4 and 5). Hence a reduction in
the extent of the energy dissipating mechanism accompanying failure,
or a change in the mechanism involved, e.g. extensive shear yielding to
localised crazing, is observed.

The notching of Izod and Charpy specimens is also an important
variable and one commonly studied. If unnotched then the measured
impact strength is influenced by the energy required for both crack
initiation and subsequent propagation but if the specimen contains a
sharp notch then the test places a greater emphasis on the material's
resistance to crack propagation. Testing of both unnotched and
notched specimens is frequently undertaken since it is a convenient
method for studying the important problem of notch sensitivity or
notch brittleness of some polymers; such materials possess a high
impact strength and exhibit a ductile mode of failure when unnotched
specimens are tested but if sharply notched specimens are employed
then they fail in a brittle manner at a low impact strength. This
transition is similar to the one described above in connection with
thickness effects but, in this case, arises from the sharp notch not only
creating a locally high triaxial stress concentration but also increasing
the local rate of strain at the notch tip. The effect of varying the notch
tip radius, in between the extremes of unnotched and sharply notched
specimens, is often explored to obtain more information concerning
the polymer's notch sensitivity. A blunt notch is also, of course,
employed in the BS or ASTM standard notched-beam test (see Fig.
6.1). Since blunt notches are not as effective as sharp notches in
producing plane-strain conditions[36] it is not surprising to find that
blunt notched specimens often exhibit intermediate behaviour, for
example, both crazing and shear yielding mechanisms may operate
simultaneously. Impact strengths as a function of notch tip radius are

shown in Fig. 6.2 for several different polymers. As may be clearly seen, changing the notch tip radius may drastically alter the ranking order. The effect of notch radius is further illustrated in Fig. 6.3. These data are for rigid PVC specimens, both unnotched and notched with different notch tip radii, and the impact strength has also been determined as a function of temperature. For this polymer the ductile-to-brittle transition temperature, T_b, is relatively easy to determine and is

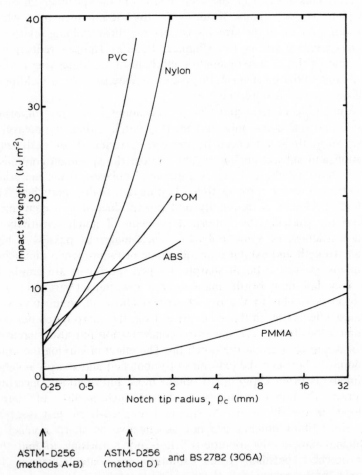

Fig. 6.2. *Impact strength as a function of notch tip radius for different polymers* (*after Vincent*[1]).

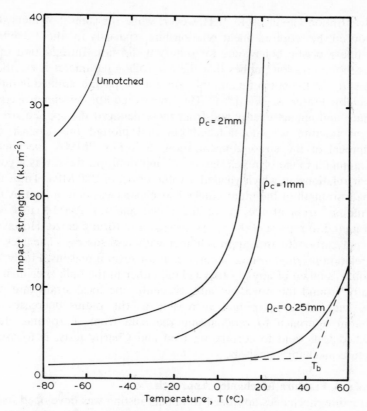

Fig. 6.3. Effect of test temperature on the impact strength of PVC specimens containing various notch radii, ρ_c (after Vincent[1]).

obviously a function of notch tip radius. As a sharper notch is employed, which favours a brittle fracture, then the higher is the temperature needed to ensure that ductile failure is the major fracture mechanism. The value of T_b is frequently more than 100°C higher for a sharply notched specimen than for an unnotched one.[2]

In an attempt to rationalise the effect of notch tip radius Vincent[1] suggested using the elastic stress concentration factor, η

$$\eta = \frac{\sigma_{tc}}{\sigma_c} = 1 + 2(a/\rho_c)^{\frac{1}{2}} \qquad (6.2)$$

He plotted the impact strength against the reciprocal of the stress concentration $(1+2(a/\rho_c)^{\frac{1}{2}})^{-1}$. However, while for some polymers this produced the required linear relationship, especially for those exhibiting linear elastic behaviour, for others it did not. Introduction of a stress concentration implies that the controlling parameter is a critical stress, σ_{tc}, at the notch tip and this concept has been examined in more detail by Fraser & Ward.[37,38] They measured the specimen's compliance and impact energy and from these deduced the applied stress, σ_c, at fracture for the notched bar and plotted this against the reciprocal of the stress concentration, η^{-1}. For PMMA specimens, containing a range of notch depths, a, and radii, ρ_c, there was a good linear relationship which yielded a value of σ_{tc} of 220 MPa. Thus, the impact strength of the blunt notched specimens was determined by the maximum stress at the tip of the notch and for PMMA this was considered to represent the stress necessary to form a craze. However, for polycarbonate this approach met with less success. The lack of correlation in some instances may occur for several reasons. Firstly, no account is taken of any plastic yielding, either in the bulk specimen or locally around the notch tip and, secondly, the local strain-rate will vary with notch tip radius, increasing as the radius decreases. A different approach to rationalising the data from sharp and blunt notched tests, and to correlating Izod and Charpy tests, is to use a fracture mechanics analysis.

6.2.4 A Fracture Mechanics Approach

A fracture mechanics approach to impact testing was developed independently by Brown[6] and by Marshall et al.[7] Essentially the Izod or Charpy specimen is assumed to exhibit bulk linear elastic behaviour and contain a sharp notch, i.e. LEFM assumptions. The elastic energy, U_c, absorbed as strain energy by the specimen at fracture is taken as

$$U_c = U_H - U_I \qquad (6.3)$$

where U_H is the energy lost by the pendulum, and U_I is the kinetic or tossing energy loss. The value of U_I may be estimated by lightly rejoining the broken pieces of the specimen and repeating the impact test. From eqn. (3.9) the value of U_c may be expressed by

$$U_c = \tfrac{1}{2}P_c\Delta_c \qquad (6.4)$$

and this may be expressed in terms of the compliance, C, of the specimen via eqn. (3.16) such that

$$U_c = \tfrac{1}{2}P_c^2 C \qquad (6.5)$$

Now in Chapter 3 it was shown (eqn. (3.18)) that the fracture energy, G_{Ic}, is given by

$$G_{Ic} = \frac{P_c^2}{2b} \frac{\partial C}{\partial a}$$ (6.6)

and expressing this relationship in terms of energy absorbed, rather than load at fracture, i.e. substituting eqn. (6.5) into eqn. (6.6) and rearranging

$$U_c = G_{Ic} b \frac{C}{\partial C/\partial a}$$ (6.7)

Introducing the specimen width, w, and the dimensionless geometry factor, Z

$$U_c = G_{Ic} bwZ$$ (6.8)

where Z is given by

$$Z = \frac{C}{\partial C/\partial(a/w)}$$ (6.9)

Hence the measured impact energy, U_H, may be directly related to the more fundamental material property G_{Ic} via eqns (6.3) and (6.8)

$$U_H = G_{Ic} bwZ - U_I$$ (6.10)

This analysis is applicable to those materials which exhibit small-scale yielding at the notch tip providing they still possess bulk linear elastic behaviour, as discussed in Section 3.3.2. However, as before, a small correction may sometimes be made to the crack length to improve the accuracy of the calculations by using $(a + r_y)$ instead of a.

Thus Z is a calibration factor for the particular geometry used and values of this parameter have been tabulated[8] for various Charpy and Izod specimen sizes. The effects of specimen geometry and of test method may therefore be eliminated and a value of G_{Ic} deduced from the impact tests. This analysis has been examined extensively by Williams and co-workers[7,8,39–42] and a typical plot of $(U_H - U_I)(\equiv U_c)$ against bwZ is shown in Fig. 6.4 for Charpy and Izod tests conducted on medium-density polyethylene, using a wide range of specimen sizes but all containing a sharp notch. (The sharp notch was obtained by the slow, controlled insertion of a razor blade, the initial crack propagating ahead of the blade as it was forced into the material.) A very good linear relationship exists which results in a constant value of G_{Ic} of $8·1 \text{ kJ m}^{-2}$, independent of specimen geometry and test method.

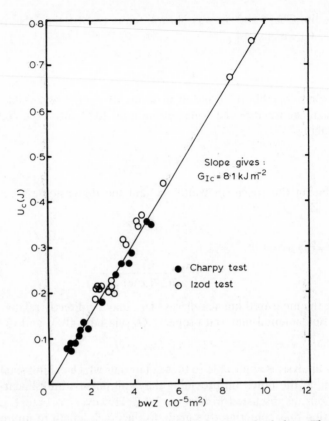

Fig. 6.4. Charpy and Izod data for a medium-density polyethylene. The elastic energy, U_c, absorbed by the specimen at impact fracture is plotted against bwZ (after Plati & Williams[8]). Slope gives: $G_{Ic} = 8.1$ kJ m^{-2}; ●, Charpy test; ○, Izod test.

Plati & Williams[8] have extended the above analysis to include tests where a blunt notch, as in the BS and ASTM standard tests, is employed. From the analysis outlined in Section 4.5.2 the following equation may be derived[8,42-4]

$$\frac{G_{Ib}}{G_{Ics}} = \frac{(1 + \rho_c/2c)^3}{(1 + \rho_c/c)^2}$$

(6.11)

where, G_{Ib} = The value of G_I calculated from a blunt-notched
specimen;

G_{Ics} = The value of G_I calculated from a specimen containing a
sharp crack;

ρ_c = Notch radius; and

c = Critical distance (see discussion in Section 4.5.2).

If $\rho_c \gg c$ then eqn. (6.11) reduces to

$$\frac{G_{Ib}}{G_{Ics}} = \frac{1}{2} + \frac{\rho_c}{8c} \qquad (6.12)$$

Plati & Williams[8] found that these equations modelled the experimental data extremely well for many polymers and some impact fracture energy values are given in Table 6.2. The problem of notch sensitivity, discussed earlier, is clearly evident; many polymers which are tough when they contain a blunt notch (or indeed are unnotched) exhibit only low impact resistance when they contain a sharp crack.

Now the LEFM approach discussed so far is no longer valid of course for polymers which exhibit gross yielding, but in these cases the J-contour integral technique (Section 3.2.3) may be appropriate. The term J may be expressed approximately by[45,46]

$$J_{Ic} = \delta_{tc}\sigma_y \qquad (6.13)$$

This same relation may be derived for G_{Ic} by combining eqns (3.45) and (3.55) but it would only be valid for the LEFM case, i.e. $J_{Ic} \equiv G_{Ic}$.

TABLE 6.2
FRACTURE MECHANICS PARAMETERS FROM IMPACT TESTS[8]

Polymer	Fracture energy from sharp crack ($kJ\,m^{-2}$)	Fracture energy from blunt notch ($\rho_c = 1\,mm$) ($kJ\,m^{-2}$)
PVC	1·4	7
Polycarbonate	4·9	62
PMMA	1·3	8·5
MDPE	8·1	62
HDPE	3·4	6·4
HIPS	~15 (J-value)	~15 (J-value)
ABS	~50 (J-value)	~80 (J-value)

However, the above expression for J_{Ic} is applicable for all degrees of plasticity. If full yielding is assumed in bending and the criterion in eqn. (6.13) is used then, assuming solid body rotations

$$U_c = \frac{\delta_{tc}\sigma_y}{2}[b(w-a)] \qquad (6.14)$$

If the ligament area, A_L, is introduced

$$A_L = b(w-a) \qquad (6.15)$$

then substituting from eqns (6.13) and (6.15) into eqn. (6.14) gives

$$J_{Ic} = \frac{2U_c}{A_L} \qquad (6.16)$$

There are several noteworthy points. Firstly, the energy absorbed, U_c, is that appropriate up to the *onset* of crack propagation which is not necessarily that under the complete load–deflection curve since this may represent extensive crack propagation. Secondly, the factor of 2 arises because the average displacement in bending is $\delta_{tc}/2$ compared with δ_{tc} in tension, and the factor of 2 must be included in bending if valid comparisons with G_{Ic} values are to be made. Thirdly, it will be recalled that one definition of impact strength given in Section 6.2.1 was the impact energy divided by ligament area but the use of eqn. (6.16) to determine *valid* J_{Ic} values is only appropriate for high-energy fractures accompanied by gross yielding.

Finally, the effect of temperature on the values of fracture energies determined from impact tests has been examined by Williams and co-workers.[41,47] They measured the fracture energy as a function of temperature and found peaks in these relations at particular temperatures and proposed that these impact data peaks coincided with molecular-relaxation loss peaks of the material. They suggested that such correlations were most likely when multiple crazing at the crack or notch tip was a major mechanism since the presence of a loss peak would be conducive to craze formation and the consequent energy absorption. A possible correlation between impact data and molecular relaxations, the latter usually being obtained from dynamic mechanical tests such as the torsion pendulum, has been argued for many years, as discussed in some detail by Heijboer.[48] However, he concluded that a dynamic mechanical damping, or loss, peak was not always accompanied by a peak or transition in the impact strength. These two viewpoints may be reconciled by the hypothesis that only if the molecular-relaxation peak originates from main-chain segmental motions is a correlation with impact behaviour likely; if it arises from the movement of side groups then no major effect on the impact strength may usually be expected. Correlations between fracture data and molecular-relaxation spectra are considered in detail in later chapters.

6.3 DYNAMIC FATIGUE

6.3.1 Introduction

Dynamic fatigue is the phenomenon of failure or fracture of a material or structure under repeated or oscillatory loading. The importance of dynamic fatigue is that under fluctuating loads materials will fail at stress levels much lower than they can withstand under monotonic loading. Also, for a given alternating stress amplitude, they will fail in a much shorter time than the static-fatigue time where a constant stress of the same magnitude has been applied. All types of material are liable to dynamic-fatigue failure and it accounts for a great number of service failures.

There is a large literature concerning the dynamic fatigue of polymeric materials and several excellent reviews[49-56] have been published. Therefore, only the major features of the mechanisms and mechanics of dynamic fatigue will be covered in the present text. Experimental aspects will be briefly considered before discussing the two main mechanisms of dynamic-fatigue failure: thermal and mechanical fatigue.

6.3.2 Experimental Considerations

When designing dynamic-fatigue tests the experimentalist has a wide range of variables to consider which contribute in different ways to the fatigue process. The following list is an extended version of that compiled by Andrews,[51] namely:

1. A periodically varying stress system having a characteristic stress amplitude, σ_a $[\sigma_a = \frac{1}{2}(\sigma_{max} - \sigma_{min})]$;
2. A corresponding fluctuating strain amplitude, e_a;
3. A mean stress level, σ_m;
4. A mean strain, e_m;
5. A stress ratio, $\sigma_{min}/\sigma_{max}$;

6. A strain ratio, e_{min}/e_{max};
7. A frequency, ν_d;
8. A characteristic wave-form (sinusoidal, square, etc.) for both the stress and strain;
9. The ambient and internal temperature of the specimen which in general will not be the same;
10. Environmental effects; and
11. The specimen geometry.

This list obviously presents the experimentalist with a formidable task if he wishes to study the fatigue behaviour in detail especially, since by their very nature, dynamic-fatigue tests often occupy expensive equipment for long periods of time. Thus, complex service-fatigue conditions are usually approximated by much simplified laboratory test programmes where many of the above parameters are held constant. This difficulty in reproducing expected service conditions emphasises the importance of understanding the mechanisms underlying fatigue fracture. If they can be identified then parameters affecting the service-life of components are unlikely to be neglected when designing laboratory tests for material selection and life prediction. Also, parameters which may be representative of a general type of failure may be isolated. A final comment on this list is that because most reports unfortunately do not detail the values of these experimental parameters it is extremely difficult to compare results from different groups of workers. This is undoubtedly one cause for the many different interpretations of the mechanisms and criteria of the dynamic-fatigue behaviour of polymers.

A number of different loading methods and specimen configurations have been devised, as discussed by several reviewers.[49,51,56] For example, loads may be applied by rotational bending, reciprocal bending, reciprocal torsion or by pulsating axial loads, and specimens may be in the form of rods or sheets, with or without an artificially introduced notch or crack. ASTM standard tests exist for assessing the fatigue behaviour of both rubbers[57,58] and plastics.[59]

The majority of the fatigue tests reported in the literature have been conducted by controlling the stress amplitude, although deflection- or strain-controlled testing may be undertaken when such tests are considered to be more appropriate to the expected service conditions. Of particular significance is that, unlike stress-controlled, neither deflection- nor strain-controlled tests lead to runaway creep or thermal failure of the specimen. Using strain-controlled testing Rabinowitz & Beardmore[60] have shown that many polymers undergo a decrease in deformation resistance prior to crack initiation and the detailed mechanism by which this softening develops can be related to the polymer's microstructure and thermal history. Essentially ductile polymers soften markedly while brittle polymers are not appreciably affected. Changes that may occur in the polymer's structure before and during crack initiation are discussed later. Beardmore & Rabinowitz[61] have compiled a useful review of the relatively few studies on deflection- and strain-controlled dynamic-fatigue testing of polymers.

From stress-controlled dynamic tests, generally using unnotched specimens, the classical fatigue curves, often referred to as 'S–N' curves, are obtained. (In the metals literature, from which this term is

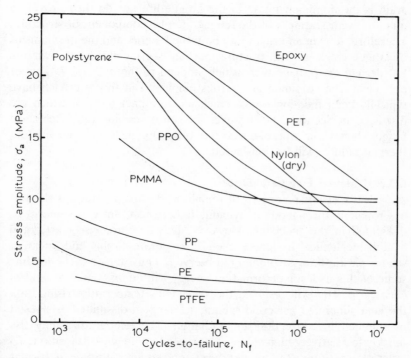

Fig. 6.5. Representative stress amplitude, σ_a, versus logarithm cycles-to-failure, N_f, curves for several polymers tested at a frequency, ν_d, of 30 Hz (after Riddell[62]).

derived, S and N refer to the stress and number of cycles to failure respectively; in the present text the symbols σ and N_f are employed.) Representative curves for a range of polymers[62] are shown in Fig. 6.5 and, as may be seen, they involve plotting the applied stress amplitude against the logarithm of the number of cycles to failure. These curves illustrate several now well-established features. Firstly, the cyclic life increases with decreasing stress amplitude and in the intermediate stress region there is an approximately linear relation between stress amplitude and $\log N_f$. Secondly, as the stress amplitude is further decreased the curve tends to become horizontal. Thus, below a certain stress level, the so-called endurance limit, some materials show no signs of fatigue failure, at least up to about 10^7 cycles.

However, such tests and resulting data do not generally provide much information concerning the mechanisms of the fatigue process. For example, they do not establish whether crack initiation or propagation is the dominant phase in the fatigue life nor do they provide a quantitative assessment of the fatigue life of a component or structure. Therefore, to gain an insight into both the kinetics and the mechanisms of fatigue crack growth, fracture mechanics principles have, over the last decade or so, been increasingly applied to the dynamic fatigue of polymers. The specimen geometries employed in this approach have typically been the single-edge crack and compact tension, which are discussed in Section 3.6. However, before describing the mechanical fatigue behaviour of polymers the other main failure mechanism, thermal failure, will be considered.

6.3.3 Thermal Fatigue Failure
A perfectly elastic material will remain at the temperature of the test environment throughout a dynamic-fatigue test, since no energy is dissipated in the specimen. However, polymers are viscoelastic and exhibit mechanical hysteresis even at moderate strains and at larger strains plastic flow is commonly observed. Thus, under cyclic loading some of this inelastic deformation energy will be dissipated as heat in each cycle. This will result in the specimen's temperature rising until the heat generated per cycle is equal to the heat dissipated as a result of conduction, convection and radiation. The temperature may rise quickly to relatively high values, e.g. exceeding the glass transition, T_g, or crystal melting, T_m, temperatures, or stabilise at some particular value. The temperature rise and rate of increase will depend upon the specimen's dimensions, the test temperature, the applied frequency

and the stress amplitude and on the internal friction, thermal conductivity and specific heat of the particular polymer. The energy dissipation rate may be described by[63]

$$\dot{U}_d = \pi \nu_d \mathcal{J}_{loss}(\nu_d, T, \sigma_{max})\sigma_{max}^2 \qquad (6.17)$$

where, ν_d is the applied frequency, $\mathcal{J}_{loss}$ the loss compliance and σ_{max} the maximum applied stress. The loss compliance is related to the phase angle, δ_r, by

$$\tan \delta_r = \frac{\mathcal{J}_{loss}}{\mathcal{J}_{storage}} \qquad (6.18)$$

where $\mathcal{J}_{storage}$ is the storage compliance. The loss compliance, $\mathcal{J}_{loss}$, is associated with the dissipation or loss of energy as heat. Thus, the resulting temperature increase will rise with increases in frequency, the maximum stress experienced on each cycle and internal friction, as measured by $\mathcal{J}_{loss}$. Hence, in polymers, unlike metals, thermal failure is a major potential mechanism of failure when conducting dynamic-fatigue experiments using a stress-controlled test. It should be noted that such failure may not necessarily involve fracture of the specimen into separate pieces, but may occur due to excessive plastic deformation.

Many workers[51,64–73] have considered the thermal effects associated with dynamic fatigue and different polymers exhibit vastly different susceptibilities to this mechanism of failure. For example, Sauer & Richardson[55] have noted that for polystyrene, which has a very low internal friction, it is possible to run fatigue tests at about 30 Hz and at maximum stresses of about 15 MPa with the accompanying temperature rise being less than 2K.[65] However, under these same conditions polyethylene samples would rapidly melt and PMMA, which has a viscoelastic damping maximum (the secondary (β_r) molecular-relaxation peak which arises from side-group motion) near room temperature, would fail by thermal rupture unless the applied stresses were maintained at a low level. Indeed, for PMMA tested at 50 Hz temperature rises of 80K have been reported as being induced.[72,73] The significant effect that frequency has upon the form of the applied stress amplitude, σ_a, versus number of cycles to failure, N_f, when a thermal fatigue mechanism is operating may be clearly seen from Fig. 6.6. These data also demonstrate that the thermal and mechanical fatigue mechanisms may be thought of as competing failure mechanisms and Crawford & Benham[70] described the transition from one

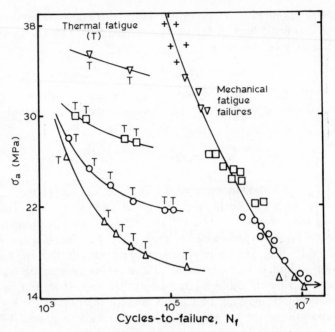

Fig. 6.6. Stress amplitude, σ_a, versus logarithm cycles-to-failure, N_f, for a polyacetal copolymer. $+$, $0 \cdot 167$; ∇, $0 \cdot 5$; $\square$, $1 \cdot 67$; $\bigcirc$, $5 \cdot 0$; $\triangle$, $10 \cdot 0$ Hz. (Note difference between thermal and mechanical fatigue failure mechanisms and their different dependencies upon frequency.) (After Crawford & Benham[70]).

mechanism to the other in terms of a critical value of applied stress amplitude. The critical value for the transition in mechanism is dependent upon mean stress, frequency, wave-form and specimen surface area-to-volume ratio, apart from obviously also being dependent upon the material.

Finally, it should also be noted that temperature increases upon dynamic fatigue will obviously affect the mechanical properties, such as modulus and yield stress, even if they are insufficient to cause thermal failure. Indeed, increases in the local temperature may cause blunting of a crack tip, due to the yield stress being lowered, and so improve the fatigue resistance as discussed in Section 6.3.4.

6.3.4 Mechanical Fatigue Failure

The other main mechanism of failure is mechanical fatigue which involves the initiation of a crack and its subsequent propagation. Most of the interest in both the metal and the polymer fields has focussed upon the growth of a crack which has macroscopic dimensions since it is this phase of the mechanical fatigue mechanism which often controls the fatigue life. However, this is not always the case and it is pertinent to consider first the initiation of a fatigue crack.

6.3.4.1 Crack Initiation

Crack initiation in metals upon fatigue cycling has been examined in some detail, as reviewed by Plumbridge.[74] Essentially it involves the production and movement of dislocations which form slip bands or slip lines where they intersect the surface of the specimen. Incomplete reversibility on repeated stressing leads to subsequent deformation being concentrated into certain of these slip steps which become broader and deeper until eventually a microcrack initiates. Tomkins[75] has suggested that a similar mechanism operates when crystalline polymers are subjected to dynamic fatigue but this was largely inferred and little is known in detail concerning the mechanisms of fatigue crack initiation in polymers.

Some workers[76-80] have studied the dynamic fatigue of polymers using the molecular theories of fracture (see Chapter 2). Leksovskii & Regel[79] reported that for cellulose acetate the activation energy, ΔG^*, had the same value of 188 kJ mol^{-1} in both static and dynamic fatigue but the activation volume, v^*, was about 15 % higher for the dynamic experiments. Thus, referring to eqn. (2.11) reveals that the energy barrier is therefore reduced and hence the time-to-failure is lower under the dynamic fatigue conditions. Indeed, for a wide range of polymers it was found[78] that the activation volume was greater for dynamic fatigue, resulting in a greater decrease of the energy barrier for bond rupture.

6.3.4.2 Crack Propagation

The kinetics and mechanisms of the propagation of cracks which are initially of macroscopic dimensions has been the aspect of mechanical fatigue which has received by far the most attention.

1. *Crack growth equations.* There have been a number of equations proposed to describe the fatigue crack growth rate (da/dN) as a function of applied stress level, crack length and material properties. These equations were largely developed from work on metals and have been reviewed by Plumbridge[74] and Erdogan.[81] The most popular

approach has been to employ growth equations embodying fracture mechanics parameters. Paris *et al.*[82,83] have suggested that the stress-intensity factor, K_I, is the major controlling factor in the growth process and proposed a simple functional relationship of the form

$$\frac{da}{dN} = A_f \, \Delta K_I{}^m \qquad (6.19)$$

where ΔK_I is the stress-intensity factor range ($\Delta K_I = K_{Imax} - K_{Imin}$) and A_f and m are constants but their values depend upon material variables, temperature, frequency, stress ratio and environment. For many polymers, as is the case for metals, the relationship between da/dN and ΔK_I is frequently linear on a log–log scale, as shown[84] for several polymers in Fig. 6.7, although it should be noted that the values of A_f and m are very dependent upon material parameters, such as molar mass, degree of crystallinity, etc., as discussed in Part II. However, in some instances the relationship may be sigmoidal in shape due to A_f and m not being truly constant. Crack growth rates are then found to decrease to very low values as ΔK_I approaches some limiting threshold value, ΔK_{Ith}, and to increase to very high values as K_{Imax} approaches the typical K_{Ic} values for crack growth under short-term monotonic loading conditions.

The above approach is obviously only valid for those materials which obey the assumptions of LEFM (Section 3.3). However, workers who have been concerned with bulk non-linear but elastic materials, e.g. cross-linked elastomers[85,86] and even inelastic materials, e.g. polyethylene[87-9] have found an analogous but more general form of eqn. (6.19) to be applicable. The crack growth rate is now expressed by

$$\frac{da}{dN} = B_f \, \Delta G^q \qquad (6.20)$$

where B_f and q are now the pre-exponential factor and exponent respectively. Obviously, for LEFM the values of ΔG, and ΔK_I may be directly equated via the modulus, E (Section 3.4) and thus eqns (6.19) and (6.20) are equivalent. The use of eqn. (6.20) in describing the fatigue behaviour of rubbers is discussed in detail in Chapter 10, Section 10.4.5.

2. Micromechanisms. The micromechanisms of crack extension under dynamic conditions involve a region ahead of the crack tip suffering some form of damage accumulation and in polymers this

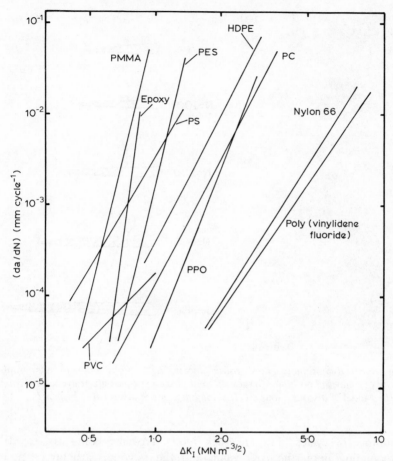

Fig. 6.7. Fatigue crack propagation behaviour in amorphous and crystalline polymers. The fatigue crack growth rate, da/dN, is plotted against $\Delta K_I (= K_{Imax} - K_{Imin})$ (after References 56 and 84).

region may be a localised shear yield zone, a single craze or a bunch of crazes.

Firstly, in glassy, and some semicrystalline, polymers the damage zone ahead of the crack is a single craze, or a few crazes at most, especially when they are tested at low ΔK_I values and high frequencies.[55,56,90-95] Under these conditions the craze develops continuously with cycling but the crack growth is discontinuous with the

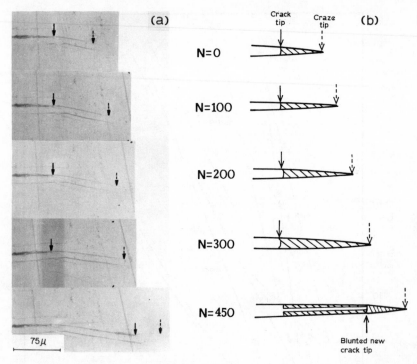

Fig. 6.8. Discontinuous crack growth process. (a) Composite optical micrograph of PVC showing position of crack (↓) and craze (↓) tip at given cyclic intervals; (b) Model of discontinuous crack propagation mechanism (after Skibo et al.[95]).

number of cycles between crack jumps typically being 10^2 to 10^3 depending upon the ΔK_I value and the polymer structure. These discontinuous crack growth bands are usually clearly visible as concentric bands on the fracture surface. Optical micrographs[95] of the crack tip in a PVC specimen are shown in Fig. 6.8(a) and illustrate this discontinuous crack propagation mechanism together with the proposed model which is outlined in Fig. 6.8(b). Note that the crack tip remained stationary until more than 300 load cycles were applied. Several authors[90-7] have used the Dugdale plastic-zone model (see Section 3.3.2) to describe the craze ahead of the fatigue crack tip. Skibo et al.[95] have determined the craze length, R_c, by measuring the band spacing and deduced the craze surface stress, σ_{cs}, using eqn. (5.16) and taking $K_{Ic} \equiv K_{Imax}$. For a range of polymers there was a reasonable correlation between the computed value of σ_{cs} and the measured plane-strain yield stress, as may be seen from Table 6.3. Williams[96] has commented that since cyclic fatigue crack growth occurs under stresses which would not induce fracture under static or monotonic loadings then it is necessary to introduce some form of either accumulation of damage or energy which arises from the 'continual loading/unloading process. He therefore employed the concept of a critical crack-opening displacement, δ_{tc}, for crack propagation but envisaged successive loading cycles resulting in the growth of the craze, with a corresponding increase in δ_t, until at the critical value, δ_{tc}, crack growth occurred. However, to allow for the damage, a two-stage Dugdale model was proposed where the stress in the forward region of the plastic zone was constant at σ_p (if crazing occurs $\sigma_p \equiv \sigma_{cs}$) but that in the rear portion, immediately ahead of the crack tip, was lower due to damage caused by the dynamic loading. The development[96,97] of this model led to the suggestion that the crack growth rate, da/dN, may be related to the applied stress-intensity factor, K_{Imax}, and the stress-intensity factor, K_{Ic}, applicable to monotonic loading, by

$$\frac{da}{dN} = \frac{\pi}{8(1-\alpha_f)^2} \frac{1}{\sigma_p^2} [K_{Imax}^2 - \alpha_f K_{Ic}^2] \qquad (6.21)$$

where the stress σ_p acts over the forward portion of the Dugdale zone but is reduced to $\alpha_f \sigma_p$ over the rear portion due to fatiguing and $\alpha_f < 1$ and is given by

$$\alpha_f = (1-f) + f s_f^2 \qquad (6.22)$$

where f is a damage function and s_f is the stress ratio ($s_f = \sigma_{min}/\sigma_{max} = K_{Imin}/K_{Imax}$). Thus, unlike eqn. (6.19) this model leads to da/dN being

TABLE 6.3

VALUES OF THE CRAZE SURFACE STRESS, σ_{cs}, DE-
DUCED FROM THE DUGDALE MODEL AND THE
PLANE-STRAIN YIELD STRESS, σ_y' [95]

Polymer	σ_{cs} (MPa)	σ_y' (MPa)
Polystyrene	38	38
PVC	51	47–65
Polysulphone	79	67–80
Polycarbonate	81	61–82

plotted against K_{Imax}^2. Williams[96] has applied this model to several polymers and found that it gives a good description of factors such as growth rate, stress ratio and frequency (see below). Values of σ_p and α_f were deduced and so enabled the value of δ_{tc} for crack growth under dynamic-fatigue conditions to be calculated. Values were found to be significantly lower than for monotonic loading; for example, for PMMA a value of δ_{tc} of $0.5\mu m$ was deduced for cyclic loading compared to $1.5\mu m$ for monotonic loading. Thus, basically, the loading and unloading cycles place the crack tip plastic zone, which may be a craze or a shear yield zone, in alternating tension and compression which results in a gradual weakening. Hence, compared to monotonic or static-fatigue loading conditions, a lower local strain is required to cause fracture of this plastically deformed region, and this is reflected by the lower values of δ_{tc}. However, recent measurements of δ_{tc} during dynamic-fatigue crack growth in PMMA by Döll et al.,[98,99] using a most elegant optical interferometry technique, have indicated that a constant δ_{tc} criterion is only really applicable at low fatigue crack growth rates; at moderate and high da/dN values the value of δ_{tc} increases as da/dN is increased. Obviously, structural features of the polymer which increase the strength of a craze, and so increase the resistance to craze breakdown, would be expected to increase the value of δ_{tc} for both dynamic and monotonic loading. The limited studies in this area support this observation. For example, increasing the molar mass increases δ_{tc} (see Section 5.7.1) and results in a marked improvement in fatigue resistance.[65,66,100-3] Conversely, environments such as alcohols which greatly assist craze breakdown (see Section 5.3.2) will reduce the fatigue resistance.[103,104]

Secondly, at high ΔK_I values and low frequencies most polymers, with the exception of PVC, experience incremental crack extension where the striation markings produced on the fracture surface correspond to successive positions of the advancing crack front as a result of individual load excursions.[56] Several authors[105,106] have described this mechanism using the crack tip blunting model proposed by Laird & Smith[107] where the crack tip is considered to be blunt and resharpens during loading and unloading portions of the stress cycle, respectively. The development of a bundle of crazes, rather than a single craze, has been suggested to be a possible crack tip blunting mechanism.[91] Also, of course, the Williams' model mentioned above may again be employed since it does not specify the micromechanism(s) described by the two-stage Dugdale plastic zone. As has been commented in previous chapters, this is both a strength and a weakness of such models.

Finally, in considering micromechanisms of dynamic-fatigue crack extension, it is noteworthy that if in crystalline polymers thermal failure can be avoided then such materials generally possess superior dynamic-fatigue characteristics compared to glassy polymers. It has been suggested[55] that this arises from their two-phase structure of a rigid crystalline phase embedded in a compliant amorphous phase offering greater resistance to crack propagation and the crystallite deformations dissipating energy around the propagating crack tip. Crack propagation both around and through the crystalline spherulitic microstructure has been recorded.[87,89,95]

3. *Experimental variables.* There are many experimental variables which affect the fatigue crack propagation, as discussed above. Considering the main variables of frequency, temperature and mean stress then firstly the influence of the test frequency depends greatly upon the viscoelastic nature of the polymer in the temperature range being investigated. For example, the fatigue crack growth rates for PMMA, polystyrene and PVC were found to decrease with increasing frequency over the range 0·1 to 100 Hz while those for polycarbonate, polysulphone, nylon 66 and poly(vinylidene fluoride) showed no change.[56] Williams[96] has explained this effect using his two-stage Dugdale model by assuming that the time dependence of the craze surface stress, σ_{cs}, may be described by a power-law relation, as stated in eqn. (5.11). This results in

$$\frac{da}{dN} \propto \nu_d^{-mn} \tag{6.23}$$

where m and n are defined in eqns (6.19) and (5.11), respectively, and have positive values. Thus, the fatigue crack growth rate is predicted to decrease as the frequency increases. However, Hertzberg and co-workers[56,108–10] have rejected this explanation and suggested that the attenuation of fatigue crack propagation rates occurs when the test frequency is similar to the frequency of the secondary (β_r) molecular-relaxation transition of the polymer. Their physical interpretation of this observation was that under these conditions maximum hysteresis and associated heating occur but that these effects are confined to the immediate vicinity of the crack tip. The local yield stress therefore falls causing a greater extent of plastic deformation and crack tip blunting. Thus, while hysteretic heating on a large scale may contribute to thermal failure, localised heating at the crack tip may result in lower fatigue crack growth rates.

Secondly, the effect of temperature on fatigue crack propagation rates is rather confusing. In some polymers, polystyrene and PMMA for example, the rates may decrease with decreasing temperature[97,111] while in others, such as polycarbonate and polysulphone, the rates may pass through maximum values at particular temperatures.[112,113] As might be expected other experimental variables, such as frequency, will influence the type of behaviour observed.[56]

Thirdly, in most cases fatigue testing involves stress cycling about a non-zero stationary stress and the magnitude of this stress would be expected to alter the fatigue crack propagation rate. In metals[74] an increase in the mean stress, or stress ratio, generally leads to an increase in growth rate. However, in polymers the effect of stress ratio is more complex and with some polymers the growth rate increases as the stress ratio increases while in others it decreases.[56] The surprising beneficial effect of relatively high stress ratios in some instances was attributed to the higher strains in the crack tip region leading to crack tip blunting and/or strain-induced orientation hardening. Both of these proposed mechanisms would enhance the fatigue resistance.

4. General correlations. Considering the large amount of data that has been reported on the fatigue crack growth behaviour of many different polymers, it is noteworthy that several authors[56,112,114] have reported a correlation between ΔK_{Ir} (the value of ΔK_I required to drive a crack at a constant value of the rate, da/dN) and the value of K_{Ic}, as measured by monotonic loading. This is shown in Fig. 6.9 for a wide range of polymers. The values of K_{Ic} are, in some cases, only approximate but, notwithstanding, the correlation is still relatively good. The fatigue resistance increases as one proceeds from the epoxy and PMMA materials through to poly(vinylidene fluoride). In engineering terms this arises from both the propagation of the fatigue crack requiring a greater ΔK_{Ir} value and the higher value of K_{Ic} resulting in a longer crack needing to be grown before relatively rapid fracture occurs. From the mechanistic viewpoint, the two-stage Dugdale model proposed by Williams[96] does in fact predict this form of dependence (see eqn. (6.21)).

If these data are used to predict the dynamic-fatigue life of components it must be remembered that the time required for crack initiation has been ignored and the thermal failure mechanism precluded. Indeed, it is probably these factors which largely account for the differences in ranking order that may be observed by comparing the data

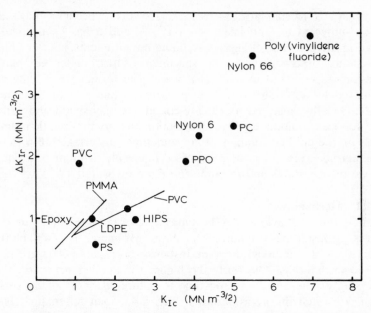

Fig. 6.9. Relationship between ΔK_{Ir} (at a constant value of da/dN of 7·5 × 10^{-4} mm cycle^{-1}) and K_{Ic} for fracture under monotonic loading conditions (after Hertzberg & Manson[56]).

shown in Fig. 6.5 (unnotched specimens) and Figs 6.7 and 6.9 (precracked specimens).

6.4 STATIC FATIGUE

6.4.1 Introduction

Static fatigue, or creep rupture, is the phenomenon of fracture which occurs some time after the application of a constant load. The applied stress is usually lower than that required to cause fracture under monotonic loading conditions but, as Andrews[115] has commented, there is no clear distinction between static fatigue and monotonic loading since in the latter the stress is continuously applied and a finite time must always elapse between application of the stress and fracture.

Turner[116] has considered the experimental aspects of static-fatigue tests, which are relatively straightforward compared to those involved in dynamic fatigue. Uniaxial tensile tests are usually conducted and a relevant ASTM standard test exists.[117] However, specimens have also been subjected to equibiaxial tension[118,119] and it has been noted[118] that, in the presence of aggressive liquid environments, shorter failure times are observed when the specimen is held under equibiaxial tension as compared to uniaxial tension. The former stress state was achieved by applying hydrostatic pressure to one side of a clamped sheet. Finally, since the processing conditions may significantly affect the surface condition, e.g. flaw distribution and orientation, then direct tests on the finished component are sometimes undertaken. For example, extruded pipes may be pressurised internally, with air or a liquid, at various pressures and the time-to-failure measured.[120-4]

6.4.2 Mechanisms
Static-fatigue behaviour may be typically characterised by a curve of stress against time-to-failure. The latter parameter is often plotted logarithmically, although in some instances both parameters are plotted logarithmically. Obviously the higher the applied stress, σ_c, then the shorter the corresponding time-to-failure, t_f. Plots of σ_c versus $\log t_f$ are often linear, as shown in Fig. 2.4, albeit approximately in some cases, and the interpretation of such data has been discussed in detail in Chapter 2 since it provides some of the main evidence for the molecular theories of fracture and the molecular models which have been proposed. However, static fatigue data may be more complex with different relationships existing between σ_c and t_f depending upon the time-scale involved in the fracture process—the different relationships reflecting different failure mechanisms.

In the static fatigue of PVC[120,121] and polyethylene,[119,122-5] both ductile and brittle failure mechanisms are frequently observed. Ductile fracture is generally dominant at high applied stresses/moderate failure times and brittle fracture at low applied stresses/long failure times, with the transition point being dependent upon other test factors, such as temperature and environment, and material parameters, such as microstructure, molar mass and molar-mass distribution. For example, the presence of an aggressive liquid environment favours a brittle fracture mechanism as does a polymer having a low molar mass and consisting of relatively large crystalline spherulites. These material aspects are discussed in more detail in later chapters in Part II.

Figure 6.10(a) shows static-fatigue data that were obtained[122,123] for high-density polyethylene (HDPE) pipes subjected to internal pressurisation at different stresses and temperatures. Two distinct regions

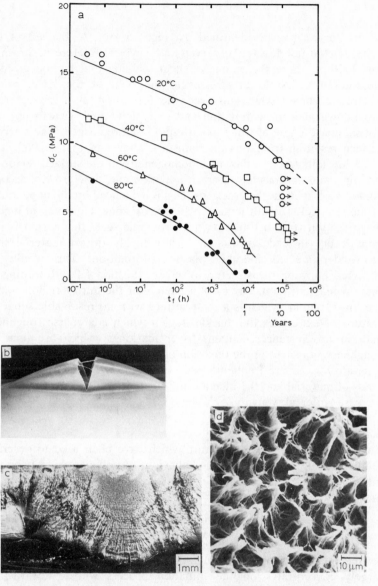

Fig. 6.10. (a) Applied hoop stress, σ_c, versus logarithm of time-to-failure, t_f, for high-density-polyethylene pipes under internal pressure at different temperatures—ductile failure to left of knee; brittle fracture to right of knee; (b) Typical ductile failure of pipe; (c) Typical fracture surface of brittle fracture; (d) Detail of the brittle fracture surface close to the upper centre of the mirror zone, the point of craze initiation (after Gaube & Kausch[122]).

213

of the curves may be identified. At high stresses, to the left of the knee, ductile fracture was observed and a typical fracture is shown in Fig. 6.10(b) where the extensive shear yielding that has occurred is clearly visible. At lower stresses to the right of the knee, brittle fracture occurred which involved the formation of a craze, craze breakdown and crack initiation and then slow crack growth up to a critical crack length at which point rapid fracture ensued. The fracture surface resulting from this mechanism is shown in Fig. 6.10(c). The craze has initiated at a flaw or inhomogeneity in the surface region of the pipe wall and has led to crack initiation and slow growth, accompanied by crazing at the crack tip. This is evidenced by the appearance of the relatively smooth semicircular 'mirror' zone. However, at higher magnification (Fig. 6.10(d)) on a microscopic scale this region is not smooth but instead consists of locally highly drawn material that has undergone considerable plastic deformation. This would be expected knowing the structure of crazes (Section 5.2). Returning to the low magnification, Fig. 6.10(c), then after the mirror region comes the 'mist' region, which is a matt surface with no resolvable separate features. Next comes the 'hackle' region which is a coarse roughness and, in this instance, contains 'river markings' which are lines of roughness elongated in the direction of crack propagation. These three separate regions are frequently seen on brittle fracture surfaces in all kinds of material and the increase in roughness can be associated with increases in crack velocity.[126,127]

6.4.3 Life-Prediction

The two main theories of fracture which have been used to describe mathematically the static-fatigue behaviour of polymers have been the molecular and fracture mechanics theories. The total time-to-failure, t_f, may be simply represented by

$$t_f = t_i + t_p \tag{6.24}$$

where t_i is the time required for crack initiation and t_p the time taken for the crack to propagate through the specimen. The molecular theory largely concentrates on the initiation process whilst the fracture mechanics arguments centre on the propagation of an existing flaw or defect which is in the form of a crack.

6.4.3.1 Molecular Theory

The molecular theory of fracture developed by Zhurkov and his colleagues, and discussed in Chapter 2, views fracture as an activated-rate process, i.e. one involving the surmounting of a potential energy barrier. The relationship between applied stress and time-to-failure is given by (eqn. (2.11))

$$t_f = t_0 \exp\left[(\Delta G^* - v^*\sigma_c)/\mathbf{R}T\right]$$

and thus successfully predicts the typical form of the experimental data, as shown in Figs 2.4 and 6.10(a), although in the latter case different values of the activation energy, ΔG^*, and activation volume, v^*, are needed for the two distinct linear relations. Values of these parameters for PVC and HDPE obtained from static-fatigue experiments on extruded pipes are shown in Table 6.4, together with the activation energy, ΔU^*, for thermal dissociation and ΔE^* for shear yielding (see Section 4.2.3). The activation energies, ΔG^*, for fracture do not appear to agree well with either ΔU^* or ΔE^* values. Also the values of the pre-exponential factor, t_0, cannot be readily interpreted in terms of any physical micromechanism. These observations are in direct contrast to those of Zhurkov and colleagues (Chapter 2) who found that values of ΔG^* and ΔU^* could be directly equated, indicating that the rupture of main-chain primary bonds was the rate-controlling step in the fracture process, and that the associated values of t_0, of the order of 10^{-12} to 10^{-14} s, could be assigned to longitudinal vibrational modes of the backbone chain. The lack of such close correlation of the fracture data shown in Table 6.4 to molecular

TABLE 6.4

VALUES OF ACTIVATION ENERGIES AND ACTIVATION VOLUMES FOR STATIC FATIGUE FRACTURE, THERMAL DEGRADATION AND YIELD

Material	Static-fatigue experiments[a]			Thermal dissociation	Yield experiments
	ΔG^* $(kJ\,mol^{-1})$	v^* (nm^3)	$t_0(s)$	ΔU^* $(kJ\,mol^{-1})$	ΔE^* $(kJ\,mol^{-1})$
PVC	397	2·9	$1\cdot7\times10^{-52}$	135^b	291^c
HDPE					
Ductile failure	307	7·3	3×10^{-40}	107^d	240^e
Brittle failure	181	6·0	8×10^{-20}		

[a] References 120–2, 128 and Fig. 6.10(a).
[b] Reference 129.
[c] Reference 130 and Section 4.2.3.
[d] Reference 131.
[e] Reference 132.

rupture or flow parameters may arise from either a combination of mechanisms comprising the rate-controlling step or, and possibly more likely, the molecular interpretation of eqn. (2.11) being somewhat limited in scope. This latter suggestion implies that values of ΔG^*, v^* and t_0 may simply be viewed as fitting parameters with the values of ΔG^* and v^* indicating the temperature and stress dependence of the fracture process.

Other theories have been proposed which may be classed as molecular although they are more statistical in nature and the parameters that appear in the mathematical relations cannot so readily be interpreted in terms of molecular features of the polymer. Coleman & Knox[133] developed an activated-rate model and obtained a similar relationship to that given in eqn. (2.9). Kawabata & Blatz[134] and Valanis & Yilmazer[135] have developed equations to describe the probability distribution function for the fracture event. The former authors studied the static fatigue of a cross-linked styrene–butadiene rubber and proposed a stochastic theory of failure. They assumed that their specimens contained a large number of defects, such as molecular inhomogeneities and voids, some of which became capable of initiating a crack after a constant load was applied, and they mathematically described the relation between applied stress and time-to-failure by considering the initiation event to be a stochastic process.

6.4.3.2 Fracture Mechanics Approach

Unlike the above approaches which consider static-fatigue failure to be controlled by crack initiation mechanisms, fracture mechanics describes the propagation of pre-existent flaws. A fracture mechanics approach has been used by many groups of workers to examine the static fatigue in glass,[136,137] ceramics,[138–42] and polymers such as cross-linked rubbers,[143] PMMA[144] and epoxy resins.[145–50] Evans[138,139] has proposed an analysis which essentially enables the static-fatigue life, t_f, to be predicted from short-time fracture mechanics experiments. It will be recalled from Section 5.6.2 (eqn. (5.14)) that for a crack growing relatively slowly and in a stable manner the relationship between K_{Ic} and the velocity of crack growth, $\dot{a}$, may be expressed by

$$K_{Ic} = A_v \dot{a}^n \qquad (6.25)$$

where A_v is a constant. A conservative static-fatigue lifetime may be predicted by ignoring the time for crack initiation, t_i, and equating t_f to the time for crack propagation, t_p. The value of t_p may be obtained by integration of the above expression. Thus

$$t_f = \int_{a_0}^{a_f} \frac{A_v^{1/n}}{K_{Ic}^{1/n}} \, da \tag{6.26}$$

where a_0 is the initial crack length (being the intrinsic flaw size if unnotched specimens are used) and a_f is the crack length at which propagation becomes relatively fast; hence the time occupied for propagation when $a > a_f$ is assumed to be negligible. Now, eqn. (3.39) stated

$$K_{Ic} = Q\sigma_c a^{\frac{1}{2}}$$

thus

$$da = \frac{2K_{Ic}}{Q^2 \sigma_c^2} \, dK_{Ic} \tag{6.27}$$

Substituting from eqn. (6.26) into eqn. (6.27) yields

$$t_f = \frac{2A_v^{1/n}}{Q^2 \sigma_c^2} \int_{K_{Ic}}^{K_{Icf}} K_{Ic}^{(n-1)/n} \, dK_{Ic} \tag{6.28}$$

where the limits are K_{Ic}, which is the applied stress-intensity factor, and K_{Icf}, which is the value at which relatively fast propagation ensues. In some instances the values of these integration limits are readily definable but in others a rather subjective interpretation is necessary. Equation (6.28) upon integration gives

$$t_f = \frac{2A_v^{1/n}}{Q^2 \sigma_c^2} \frac{n}{(1-2n)} [K_{Ic}^{(2n-1)/n} - K_{Icf}^{(2n-1)/n}] \tag{6.29}$$

If n is small and $K_{Ic} < 0.9 K_{Icf}$, eqn. (6.29) may be written approximately as

$$t_f \approx \frac{2n A_v^{1/n} K_{Ic}^{(2n-1)/n}}{Q^2 \sigma_c^2 (1-2n)} \tag{6.30}$$

Thus, from evaluating the value of A_v, experimentally or theoretically (eqn. (5.19)), a knowledge of the geometry constant, Q, the value of n (or $\tan \delta_r$, see eqn. (5.13)) and the values of K_{Ic} and K_{Icf} then the static-fatigue lifetime may be predicted for a given applied stress level, σ_c. This will be discussed further in Chapter 11. Also, Greensmith[143] has developed a similar expression for cross-linked rubbers but using, of course, the fracture energy approach rather than the stress-intensity approach; this is discussed in Chapter 10.

However, in some materials the expression for t_f stated in eqns (6.24), (6.29) and (6.30), may be somewhat misleading when interpreting static-fatigue behaviour. Essentially, in many relatively brittle materials, such as ceramics[141] and highly cross-linked thermosetting polymers[145,146,148–51] blunting of the crack tip may occur during the static-fatigue experiment. In the polymeric materials this results from a decrease in yield stress at long times which thus leads to greater plastic deformation and blunting at the crack tip. Indeed, in very brittle epoxy polymers this effect may be so severe that the stress concentration at the crack tip is reduced to such an extent that the tip stress level necessary for crack extension is not attained and thus this mechanism forestalls static-fatigue failure. However, in somewhat less brittle compositions, where the capacity for crack tip blunting during the static-fatigue test is limited, then delayed failure is still observed. In one such material Gledhill & Kinloch[145] found that a linear relationship existed between the applied fracture energy, G_{Ic}, and t_f; the failure time decreased as the value of G_{Ic} increased. However, the failure time represented an incubation period; the crack was not observed to propagate until the very end of the experiment, at the instant of fracture, when it propagated very rapidly. They suggested that crack propagation did not occur whilst $\delta_t < \delta_{tc}$, where δ_t is the crack-opening displacement at the crack tip and δ_{tc} the value at crack extension. By combining eqns (3.46) and (3.56) and using

$$\sigma_y = e_y E \tag{6.31}$$

they derived

$$\delta_{tc} = \frac{G_{Ic}}{E e_y} \tag{6.32}$$

where G_{Ic} is the time-dependent applied fracture energy, E the time-dependent modulus and e_y the yield strain which is approximately constant. Values of G_{Ic} and corresponding values of E are plotted in Fig. 6.11 and yield a linear relation over the entire time-scale of about seven decades over which the static-fatigue experiments were conducted. Thus, as time passes, the values of σ_y and E decrease because of the viscoelastic nature of the polymer, and fracture occurs when $\delta_t = \delta_{tc}$. The value of δ_{tc} is about 5μm and provides a unique failure criterion; until this critical value is attained no crack extension occurs.

Finally, an interesting development in the prediction of static-fatigue lifetimes of ceramics is the combination of a fracture mechanics approach with Weibull statistical methods. All brittle materials exhibit

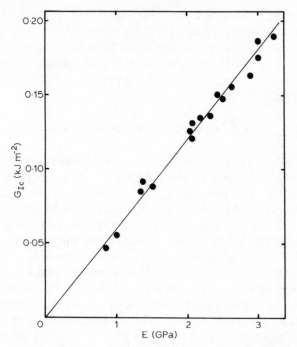

Fig. 6.11. Applied fracture energy, G_{Ic}, as a function of the corresponding modulus, E, for the static fatigue of an epoxy polymer (after Gledhill & Kinloch[145]).

a scatter in strength and this scatter is often best described by means of Weibull statistics in which a given strength-distribution function, p_f, permits the behaviour of the population to be predicted from the results obtained from a small sample. Unlike Gaussian statistics, the Weibull distribution is strongly skewed and a two-parameter Weibull distribution is given by[152,153]

$$p_f = 1 - e^{-(\sigma_c/\sigma_w)^{m_w}} \qquad (6.33)$$

where p_f is the failure probability, σ_c is taken as the fracture stress, σ_w is a normalising constant and m_w is known as the Weibull modulus— the value of m_w increases with decreasing scatter in strength. Davidge and co-workers[140-2,154] have combined fracture mechanics theories, such as those embodied in eqns (6.29) and (6.30), with the above Weibull distribution. This has enabled them to assign a probability level of failure to a value of t_f obtained from a given applied stress, σ_c. Obviously, a set of σ_c versus t_f relations representing various probability levels may be calculated and these have been termed strength–probability–time (SPT) diagrams. This concept, which is most useful for engineering design, has yet to be applied to polymers.

6.5 CONCLUDING REMARKS

The importance of understanding the failure behaviour of polymers under impact, dynamic-fatigue and static-fatigue loadings is self-evident and it has been clearly demonstrated that the associated mechanics and mechanisms of polymer fracture are highly dependent upon the manner in which stresses are applied to the material and the time-scale of the failure events. However, the micromechanisms and criteria of crack initiation and propagation under these conditions have only been identified in detail in a few instances, and even then the relationships between microstructure and fracture behaviour are only appreciated in a qualitative fashion. Nevertheless, the current level of knowledge may be used, often surprisingly successfully, in the development of polymers possessing improved properties and in the prediction of service performance and lifetimes. Such aspects will be considered further in the forthcoming chapters.

REFERENCES

1. Vincent, P. I. (1971). *Impact tests and service performance of thermoplastics*, Plastics Institute, London.
2. Bucknall, C. B., Gotham, K. V. & Vincent, P. I. (1972), In: *Polymer science*, Ed. by A. D. Jenkins, North-Holland, Amsterdam, p. 664.
3. Turner, S. (1973). *Mechanical testing of plastics*, Iliffe, London, p. 117.
4. Bucknall, C. B. (1977). *Toughened plastics*, Applied Science Publishers Ltd., London, p. 272.
5. Reed, P. E. (1979). In: *Developments in polymer fracture*, Ed. by E. H. Andrews, Applied Science Publishers Ltd., London, p. 121.
6. Brown, H. R. (1973). *J. Mater. Sci.*, **8**, 941.
7. Marshall, G. P., Williams, J. G. & Turner, C. E. (1973). *J. Mater. Sci.*, **8**, 949.
8. Plati, E. & Williams, J. G. (1975). *Polym. Eng. Sci.*, **15**, 470.
9. Ireland, D. R. (1974). In: *Instrumented impact testing*, ASTM STP 563, p. 3.

10. Spath, W. & Rosner, M. (1961). *Impact testing of materials*, Thames and Hudson, London, p. 133.
11. BS 2782 (1970). *Methods of testing plastics, Part 3: Mechanical properties.*
12. ASTM-D 256–73. *Impact resistance of plastics and electrical insulating materials.*
13. ASTM-D 1709–75. *Impact resistance of polyethylene film by the free falling dart method.*
14. ASTM-D 1790–62. *Brittleness temperature of plastic film by impact.*
15. ASTM-D 1822–68. *Tensile-impact energy to break plastics and electrical insulating materials.*
16. ASTM-D 3029–72. *Impact resistance of rigid plastic sheeting or parts by means of a tup (falling-weight).*
17. ASTM-D 3099–72. *Pneumatic ball impact resistance of plastic film and sheeting.*
18. Kolsky, H. (1963). *Stress waves in solids*, Dover, New York, p. 87.
19. Reed, P. E., Nurse, P. J. & Andrews, E. H. (1974). *J. Mater. Sci.*, **9**, 1977.
20. Reed, P. E. & Squires, H. V. (1974). *J. Mater. Sci.*, **9**, 129.
21. Abbott, B. W., Cornish, R. H. & Weil, N. A. (1964). *J. Appl. Polym. Sci.*, **8**, 151.
22. Furno, F. J., Webb, R. S. & Cook, N. P. (1964). *J. Appl. Polym. Sci.*, **8**, 101.
23. BS 4839 (1974). *Blow-moulded polyolefin containers.*
24. ASTM-D 2444–70. *Impact resistance of thermoplastic pipe and fittings by means of a tup (falling-weight).*
25. ASTM-D 2463–73. *Drop impact resistance of polyethylene blow-moulded containers.*
26. De Sisto, T. S. (Ed.) (1974). *Instrumented impact testing*, ASTM STP 563.
27. Driscoll, D. E. (Ed.) (1970). *Impact testing of metals*, ASTM STP 466.
28. Bush, A.J. (1970). *Impact testing of metals*, ASTM STP 466, p. 259.
29. Koppenaal, T. J. (1974). *Instrumented impact testing*, ASTM STP 563, p. 92.
30. Ewing, A. & Raymond, L. (1974). *Instrumented impact testing*, ASTM STP 563, p. 180.
31. Hoover, W. R. (1974). *Instrumented impact testing*, ASTM STP 563, p. 203.
32. Server, W. L. & Tetelman, A. S. (1972). *Eng. Fract. Mechs.*, **4**, 367.
33. Kalthoff, J. F., Winkler, S. & Beinert, J. (1977). *Int. J. Fracture*, **13**, 528.
34. Broek, D. (1978). *Elementary engineering fracture mechanics*, Sijthoff and Noordhoff, Netherlands, p. 161.
35. Wolstenholme, W. E., Pregan, S. E. & Stark, C. F. (1964). *J. Appl. Polym. Sci.*, **8**, 119.
36. Weiss, V. (1971). In: *Fracture, an advanced treatise, Vol. 3*, Ed. by H. Liebowitz, Academic Press, New York, p. 228.
37. Fraser, R. A. & Ward, I. M. (1974). *J. Mater. Sci.*, **9**, 1624.
38. Fraser, R. A. & Ward, I. M. (1977). *J. Mater. Sci.*, **12**, 459.

39. Nikpur, K. & Williams, J. G. (1978). *Plastics and Rubber: Mat. Appl.* **3**, 163.
40. Birch, M. W. & Williams, J. G. (1978). *Int. J. Fract.*, **14**, 69.
41. Kisbenyi, M., Birch, M. W., Hodgkinson, J. M. & Williams, J. G. (1979). *Polymer*, **20**, 1289.
42. Williams, J. G. & Hodgkinson, J. M. (1981). *Proc. R. Soc.*, **A357**, 231.
43. Williams, J. G. (1978). *Adv. Polym. Sci.*, **27**, 68.
44. Williams, J. G. (1980). *Metal Sci.*, **14**, 344.
45. Drucker, D. C. & Rice, J. R. (1970). *Eng. Fract. Mech.*, **1**, 577.
46. Rice, J. R., Paris, P. C. & Merkle, J. G. (1973). *Progress in flaw growth and fracture toughness testing*, ASTM STP 536, p. 231.
47. Plati, E. & Williams, J. G. (1975). *Polym. Eng. Sci.*, **16**, 915.
48. Heijboer, J. (1968). *J. Polym. Sci.*, **C16**, 3755.
49. Lake, G. J. & Lindley, P. B. (1966). In: *Physical basis of yield and fracture*, Conf. Proc., Institute of Physics, London, p. 176.
50. Andrews, E. H. (1968). *Fracture in polymers*, Oliver and Boyd, London.
51. Andrews, E. H. (1969). In: *Testing of polymers IV*, Ed. by W. Brown, Interscience, New York, p. 237.
52. Manson, J. A. & Hertzberg, R. W. (1973). *CRC Critical Rev. Macromol. Sci.*, **1**(4), 433.
53. Kambour, R. P. (1973). *J. Polym. Sci., Macromol. Rev.*, **7**, 1.
54. Andrews, E. H. (1973). In: *The physics of glassy polymers*, Ed. by R. N. Haward, Applied Science Publishers Ltd., London, p. 394.
55. Sauer, J. A. & Richardson, G. C. (1980). *Int. J. Fract.*, **16**, 499.
56. Hertzberg, R. W. & Manson, J. A. (1980). *Fatigue of engineering plastics*, Academic Press, New York.
57. ASTM-D 430–73 (1973). *Rubber deterioration—dynamic fatigue.*
58. ASTM-D 623–78 (1978). *Rubber property—heat generation and flexing fatigue in compression.*
59. ASTM-D 671–71 (1971). *Flexural fatigue of plastics by constant amplitude-of-force.*
60. Rabinowitz, S. & Beardmore, P. (1974). *J. Mater. Sci.*, **9**, 81.
61. Beardmore, P. & Rabinowitz, S. (1975). In: *Treatise on materials science and technology Vol. 6*, Ed. by R. J. Arsenault, Academic Press, New York, p. 267.
62. Riddell, M. N. (1974). *Plast. Eng.*, **30**(4), 71.
63. Ferry, J. D. (1961). *Viscoelastic properties of polymers*, Wiley, New York, pp. 14 and 609.
64. Tauchert, T. R. & Afzal, S. M. (1967). *J. Appl. Phys.*, **38**, 4568.
65. Foden, E., Morrow, D. R. & Sauer, J. A. (1972). *J. Appl. Polym. Sci.*, **16**, 519.
66. Sauer, J. A., Foden, E. & Morrow, D. R. (1977). *Polym. Eng. Sci.*, **17**, 246.
67. Riddell, M. N., Koo, G. P. & O'Toole, J. L. (1966). *Polym. Eng. Sci.*, **6**, 363.
68. Koo, G. P., Riddell, M. N. & O'Toole, J. L. (1967). *Polym. Eng. Sci.*, **7**, 182.
69. Crawford, R. J. & Benham, P. P. (1974). *J. Mater. Sci.*, **9**, 18.

70. Crawford, R. J. & Benham, P. P. (1975). *Polymer*, **16**, 908.
71. Constable, I., Williams, J. G. & Barns, D. J. (1970). *J. Mech. Eng. Sci.*, **12**, 20.
72. Oldyrev, P. P. & Parfeev, V. M. (1974). *Polym. Mechs.*, **10**, 148.
73. Oldyrev, P. P. & Parfeev, V. M. (1975). *Polym. Mechs.*, **11**, 682.
74. Plumbridge, W. J. (1972). *J. Mater. Sci.*, **7**, 939.
75. Tomkins, B. (1966). In: *Physical basis of yield and fracture*, Inst. Physics, London, p. 187.
76. Kireenko, O. F., Leksovskii, A. M. & Regel, V. R. (1968). *Meckh. Polim.*, **4**(3), 483.
77. Leksovskii, A. M. & Regel, V. R. (1968). *Meckh. Polim*, **4**(4), 501.
78. Regel, V. R. & Leksovskii, A. M. (1969). *Meckh. Polim*, **5**(1), 58.
79. Leksovskii, A. M. & Regel, V. R. (1970). *Meckh. Polim.*, **6**(2), 226.
80. Williams, M. L. & De Vries, K. L. (1970). *Proc. 5th Int. Cong. Rheol.*, **3**, 139.
81. Erdogan, F. (1968). In: *Fracture, an advanced treatise Vol. 2*, Ed. by H. Liebowitz, Academic Press, New York, p. 498.
82. Paris, P. C., Gomez, M. P. & Anderson, W. E. (1961). *Trends in Eng.*, **13**, 9.
83. Paris, P. C. & Erdogan, F. (1963). *J. Basic Eng.*, **85**, 528.
84. Hertzberg, R. W., Manson, J. A. & Skibo, M. D. (1975). *Polym. Eng. Sci.*, **15**, 252.
85. Gent, A. N., Lindley, P. B. & Thomas, A. G. (1964). *J. Appl. Polym. Sci.*, **8**, 455.
86. Lake, G. J. & Lindley, P. B. (1965). *J. Appl. Polym. Sci.*, **9**, 1233.
87. Andrews, E. H. & Walker, B. J. (1971). *Proc. R. Soc.*, **A325**, 57.
88. Teh, J. W., White, J. R. & Andrews, E. H. (1979). *Polymer*, **20**, 755.
89. White, J. R. & Teh, J. W. (1979). *Polymer*, **20**, 764.
90. Elinyck, J. P., Bauwens, J. C. & Homes, G. (1971). *Int. J. Fract. Mechs.*, **7**, 277.
91. Skibo, M. D., Hertzberg, R. W. & Manson, J. A. (1976). *J. Mater. Sci.*, **11**, 479.
92. Mills, N. J. & Walker, N. (1976). *Polymer*, **17**, 335.
93. Hertzberg, R. W. & Manson, J. A. (1973). *J. Mater. Sci.*, **8**, 1554.
94. Hertzberg, R. W., Skibo, M. D. & Manson, J. A. (1978). *J. Mater. Sci.*, **13**, 1038.
95. Skibo, M. D., Hertzberg, R. W., Manson, J. A. & Kim, S. L. (1977). *J. Mater. Sci.* **12**, 531.
96. Williams, J. G. (1977). *J. Mater. Sci.*, **12**, 2525.
97. Mai, Y. & Williams, J. G. (1979). *J. Mater. Sci.*, **14**, 1933.
98. Döll, W., Schinker, M. G. & Konczol, L. (1982). *5th Intern. Conf. on Yield, Deformation and Fracture*, Cambridge, Plastics Rubber Inst., London, 1982, p. 201.
99. Döll, W. (1982). Private communication.
100. Kim, S. L., Skibo, M. D., Manson, J. A. & Hertzberg, R. W. (1977). *Polym. Eng. Sci.*, **17**, 194.
101. Warty, S., Sauer, J. A. & Charlesby, A. (1979). *Eur. Polym. J.*, **15**, 445.
102. Pitman, G. & Ward, I. M. (1980). *J. Mater. Sci.*, **15**, 635.

103. Martin, J. R. & Johnson, J. F. (1974). *J. Appl. Polym. Sci.*, **18**, 3227.
104. El-Hakeem, H. A. & Culver, L. E. (1978). *J. Appl. Polym. Sci.*, **22**, 2691.
105. McEvily, A. J., Boettner, R. C. & Johnston, T. (1964). In: *Fatigue, an interdisciplinary approach*, Ed. by J. J. Burke, N. L. Reed & V. Weiss, Syracuse Univ. Press, New York.
106. Feltner, C. E. (1967). *J. Appl. Phys.*, **38**, 3576.
107. Laird, C. & Smith, C. G. (1962). *Phil. Mag.*, **7**, 847.
108. Hertzberg, R. W., Skibo, M. D., Manson, J. A. & Donald, J. K. (1979). *J. Mater. Sci.*, **14**, 1754.
109. Manson, J. A., Hertzberg, R. W., Kim, S. L. & Skibo, M. D. (1975). *Polymer*, **16**, 850.
110. Hertzberg, R. W., Manson, J. A. & Skibo, M. D. (1978). *Polymer*, **19**, 358.
111. Radon, J. C. & Culver, L. E. (1975). *Polym. Eng. Sci.*, **15**, 500.
112. Martin, G. C. & Gerberich, W. W. (1976). *J. Mater. Sci.*, **11**, 231.
113. Wann, R. J., Martin, G. C. & Gerberich, W. W. (1976). *Polym. Eng. Sci.*, **16**, 645.
114. Mostovoy, S. & Ripling, E. J. (1975). In: *Adhesion science and technology, Vol. 9B*, Ed. by L. H. Lee, Plenum Press, New York, p. 513.
115. Andrews, E. H. (1968). *Fracture in polymers*, Oliver and Boyd, London, p. 74.
116. Turner, S. (1973). *Mechanical testing of plastics*, Iliffe, London, p. 134.
117. ASTM-D 2990–71 (1971). *Tensile creep and creep rupture of plastics.*
118. Crissman, J. M. & Zapas, L. J. (1979). In: *Durability of macromolecular materials*, Ed. by R. K. Eby, Amer. Chem. Soc., Washington, D. C., p. 289.
119. Cooney, J. L. (1964). *J. Appl. Polym. Sci.*, **8**, 1889.
120. Niklas, H. & Kausch, H. H. (1963). *Kunststoffe*, **53**, 839.
121. Niklas, H. & Kausch, H. H. (1963). *Kunststoffe*, **53**, 886.
122. Gaube, E. & Kausch, H. H. (1973). *Kunststoffe*, **63**, 391.
123. Richard, K., Gaube, E. & Diedrich, G. (1959). *Kunstoffe*, **49**, 516.
124. Williams, J. G. (1981). In: *Engineering Design with Polymers*, Plastic Rubber Inst., London, p. 5.1.
125. Crissman, J. M. & Zapas, L. J. (1979). *Polym. Eng. Sci.*, **19**, 99.
126. Andrews, E. H. (1978). *Fracture in polymers*, Oliver and Boyd, London, p. 177.
127. Wolock, I. & Newman, S. B. (1964). In: *Fracture processes in polymeric solids*, Ed. by B. Rosen, Interscience, New York, p. 235.
128. Kausch, H. H. (1978). *Polymer fracture*, Springer-Verlag, Berlin, p. 216.
129. Zhurkov, S. N. & Tomashevsky, E. E. (1966). In: *Physical basis of yield and fracture*, Inst. Physics, London, p. 200.
130. Bauwens, J. C. (1971). *J. Polym. Sci.*, **C33**, 123.
131. Zhurkov, S. N. & Korsukov, V. E. (1974). *J. Polym. Sci. Polym. Phys. Ed.*, **12**, 385.
132. Truss, R. W., Duckett, R. A. & Ward, I. M. (1981). *J. Mater. Sci.*, **16**, 1689.
133. Coleman, B. D. & Knox, A. G. (1957). *Textile Res. J.*, **27**, 393.
134. Kawabata, S. & Blatz, P. J. (1966). *Rubb. Chem. Technol.*, **39**, 923.

135. Valanis, K. C. & Yilmazer, U. (1977). *J. Polym. Sci. Polym. Phys. Ed.*, **15**, 1101.
136. Adams, R. & McMillan, P. W. (1977). *J. Mater. Sci.*, **12**, 643.
137. Wiederhorn, S. M. (1977). *Proc. 4th Int. Conf. on Fracture (ICF4)*, **3**, 893.
138. Evans, A. G. (1972). *J. Mater. Sci.*, **7**, 1137.
139. Evans, A. G. (1973). *Int. J. Fract.*, **9**, 267.
140. Davidge, R. W., McLaren, J. R. & Tappin, G. (1973). *J. Mater. Sci.*, **8**, 1699.
141. McLaren, J. R. & Davidge, R. W. (1975). *Proc. Brit. Ceram. Soc.*, **25**, 151.
142. Braiden, P. M., Davidge, R. W. & Airey, R. (1977). *J. Mech. Phys. Solids*, **25**, 257.
143. Greensmith, H. W. (1964). *J. Appl. Polym. Sci.*, **8**, 1113.
144. Beaumont, P. W. R. & Young, R. J. (1975). *J. Mater. Sci.*, **10**, 1334.
145. Gledhill, R. A. & Kinloch, A. J. (1976). *Polymer*, **17**, 727.
146. Kinloch, A. J., Dukes, W. A. & Gledhill, R. A. (1975). In: *Adhesion Science and Technology*, Vol. *9B*. Ed. by L. H. Lee, Plenum Press, New York, p. 597.
147. Young, R. J. & Beaumont, P. W. R. (1977). *J. Mater. Sci.*, **12**, 684.
148. Scott, J. M., Phillips, D. C. & Jones, M. (1978). *J. Mater. Sci.*, **13**, 311.
149. Gledhill, R. A., Kinloch, A. J. & Shaw, S. J. (1979). *J. Mater. Sci.* **14**, 1769.
150. Kinloch, A. J. & Shaw, S. J. (1981). *Developments in adhesives—2*, Ed. by A. J. Kinloch, Applied Science Publishers Ltd., London, p. 83.
151. Kinloch, A. J. & Williams, J. G. (1980). *J. Mater. Sci.*, **15**, 987.
152. Shih, T. T. (1980). *Eng. Fract. Mechs.*, **13**, 257.
153. Bolotin, V. V. (1969). *Statistical methods in structural mechanics*, Holden-Day, San Francisco, p. 49.
154. Davidge, R. W. (1980). *Metals Sci.*, **14**, 459.

Part II

MATERIALS

Chapter 7

Glassy Polymers I—Thermoplastics

7.1 INTRODUCTION

Many of the classical studies upon the fracture behaviour of polymers have been concerned with the fracture of glassy thermoplastics, with perhaps the most important work concerned with poly(methyl methacrylate) (PMMA), polystyrene (PS) and polycarbonate (PC). The reasons for this are manyfold. Thermoplastics are very simple materials from a structural viewpoint, compared with either thermosets which have a complex three-dimensional molecular structure or semicrystalline polymers with a great variety of morphological forms. Glassy thermoplastics are also transparent and have well-defined and easily observed craze structures. Unlike semicrystalline polymers the mechanical properties of glassy thermoplastics are not strongly dependent upon fabrication conditions or variations between different batches and this makes it possible to correlate the results of different groups of workers. Most of the recent advances in the understanding of the fracture of glassy thermoplastics have been through the application of linear elastic fracture mechanics (LEFM, Section 3.2.2) which is applicable since their bulk deformation is approximately linear elastic and plastic deformation is concentrated in a region close to the crack tip.

In this chapter, the factors which control the fracture behaviour are reviewed and the application of LEFM is considered in some detail. The micromechanisms of the fracture process are then discussed and finally the impact properties and fatigue behaviour are reviewed.

229

7.2 BRITTLE FRACTURE

The fracture behaviour of glassy thermoplastics has been reviewed extensively.[1–4] At a sufficiently low temperature all glassy polymers behave in a brittle manner but as the temperature is raised towards the T_g they become ductile, as shown in Fig. 7.1 for PMMA. The temperature at which this transition in behaviour occurs depends upon the testing rate—the temperature being depressed as the rate of testing is increased. It can also depend upon the sharpness of any notch (see Fig. 6.3) and the specimen thickness both of which affect the balance between plane-stress and plane-strain deformation. Brittle behaviour is encountered with sharp notches and thick specimens where plane-strain conditions prevail.

The ductile/brittle transition temperature also depends upon the chemical structure of the polymer and may or may not correlate with a dynamic mechanical damping peak such as the glass transition or secondary relaxations.[5,6] In addition Vincent[7] has followed the mechanical behaviour of a wide variety of unnotched thermoplastics

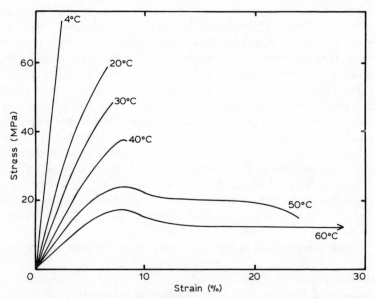

Fig. 7.1. Variation of the stress/strain behaviour of PMMA with test-temperature (after Andrews[3]).

through the ductile/brittle transition and was able to correlate the critical fracture stress at the transition with the polymer structure (Section 7.2.2).

In this section the brittle fracture of glassy thermoplastics is considered. In particular the effects of specimen geometry, testing conditions and polymer structure are discussed in detail.

7.2.1 Effect of Testing Variables

The fracture strength of a brittle thermoplastic depends upon a wide variety of factors such as specimen geometry, test temperature and applied pressure. These effects have to be examined before the effect of structural differences can be considered.

7.2.1.1 Flaws, Notches and Specimen Thickness

In the early 1960s Berry applied the energy balance approach (Section 3.2) to the fracture of glassy polymers such as PMMA[8] and polystyrene[9] by determining the dependence of fracture strength, σ_f, of such materials upon the size of flaws, a, that had been deliberately introduced into specimens (Fig. 7.2). By carefully controlling their length and quality Berry[2] was able to produce 'natural' cracks and found that σ_f rose as a decreased following a relation of the form (eqn. (1.25))

$$\sigma_f = \sqrt{EG_{Ic}/\pi a}$$

where E is the Young's modulus and G_{Ic} is the fracture energy (cf., eqn. (3.27)). However, the increase in strength with decreasing crack length does not go on indefinitely since when the flaw size is reduced below a critical level—about 1 mm for PS and 0·07 mm for PMMA at room temperature—σ_f becomes independent of flaw size. Thus the polymers behave as if they contain natural flaws of these critical sizes, termed 'inherent, or intrinsic, flaws'. These flaws are not present in the material before deformation but appear to be formed during loading.[10] It is thought that the flaws are related to crazes which nucleate under stress and break down to form cracks. The larger flaw size for PS is consistent with this material having much larger crazes than PMMA.[1] Approximate values of G_{Ic} can also be obtained using this analysis and the values determined using eqn. (1.25) are ~600 J m⁻² for PMMA[8] and ~3500 J m⁻² for PS.[9] This would seem to be somewhat of an anomaly since PMMA generally has a higher fracture strength than PS. However, the larger inherent flaw size of PS means that even though the material has a higher fracture energy than PMMA, the fracture

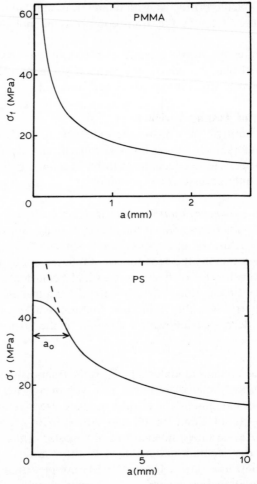

Fig. 7.2. *Dependence of fracture stress, σ_f, upon crack length, a, for PMMA and PS. The inherent flaw size, a_0, is indicated for PS (after Berry[2]).*

strength of unnotched specimens is lower. Also Berry's[9] measurements are for unstable propagation as he used single-edge notched (SEN) specimens and the initial cracks were not particularly sharp. When G_{Ic} is measured for controlled cleavage using sharper cracks, considerably lower values of G_{Ic} are obtained, especially for PS.

    The work of Berry was concerned with 'natural' cracks in brittle polymers but for a given crack length it is found that the fracture strength increases as the radius of the crack tip or notch increases. Vincent[4] has shown that for brittle polymers such as PMMA this effect can be interpreted in terms of the stress concentration at the root of the notch. It is found that for brittle polymers there is a linear relation between the strength and the reciprocal of the stress concentration factor, η, which is given by eqn. (6.2) (Section 6.2.3)

$$\eta = 1 + 2(a/\rho_c)^{\frac{1}{2}}$$

where a is the notch depth and ρ_c the radius at the root of the notch. The effect of the sharpness of notches upon fracture behaviour will be discussed further when the impact properties are considered (Section 7.5.1).

The presence of surface notches rather than edge notches, and increasing the specimen thickness can have a dramatic effect upon the fracture behaviour of ductile polymers such as PC since they can induce a transition from plane-stress to plane-strain deformation. Surface notches on PC specimens cause the material to behave in a brittle manner whereas specimens with edge notches of the same depth are ductile.[11] There is considerably more constraint with surface notches, less plasticity and hence more plane-strain deformation. A transition from ductile to brittle behaviour can be induced in PC by increasing the width of edge-notched specimens[12] and so specimens with surface notches behave as if they are wide edge-notched specimens.[11] Brown[12] has recently explained the effect of specimen thickness upon the ductile/brittle transition in ductile polymers in terms of a competition between plane-stress and plane-strain deformation and the thickness effect is discussed in more detail in Section 7.3.5.

7.2.1.2 Temperature and Rate

The effect of testing-temperature and rate upon the fracture behaviour of glassy polymers is rather complex. Most studies have followed the effect of temperature only, but in general the same changes can be induced by either reducing temperature or increasing rate. Berry[2] found that the fracture strength of PMMA increases as the test temperature is reduced as shown in Fig. 7.3(a). It is found that G_{Ic} also increases (Fig. 7.3(b)) but the inherent flaw size shows a minimum at about 0°C (Fig. 7.3(c)). Beardmore & Johnson[13] also found an increase in σ_f for PMMA as the temperature was reduced although they found that below about −100°C it remained virtually constant. They also

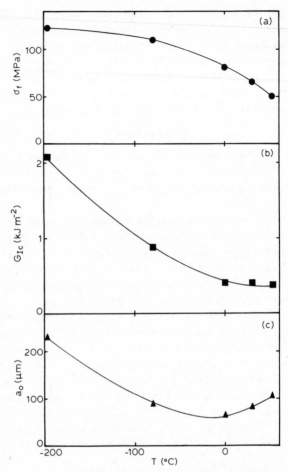

Fig. 7.3. Temperature dependence of fracture parameters for PMMA. (a) Fracture stress, σ_f; (b) Fracture energy, G_{Ic}; and (c) Inherent flaw size, a_0 (data taken from Berry[2]).

found that at low temperatures PMMA appeared to undergo a different type of crazing than at room temperature, forming much longer crazes which caused surface steps on the specimens. In a subsequent series of investigations Brown and co-workers[14-18] have shown that many glassy polymers undergo environmental crazing and cracking at low temperatures in the presence of gaseous coolants such as nitrogen or argon. It is found that the strengths at low temperatures can be reduced in these environments by up to 25 % of the values obtained in inert environments such as helium or a vacuum as shown in Fig. 7.4(a) for PC. Similar behaviour is found for PS[18] where the strength in argon or nitrogen increases as the temperature is reduced down to ~120 K but decreases with a further reduction in temperature (Fig. 7.4(b)).

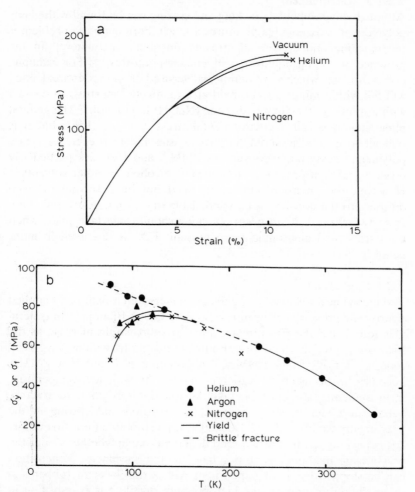

Fig. 7.4. (a) Stress/strain curves for PC measured at ~80 K in different environments (after Brown[15]); (b) Variation of yield stress and fracture stress for PS with temperature in different environments (after Wu & Brown[18]).

However, the 'intrinsic' tensile strength measured in helium increases monotonically as the temperature is reduced. Hence caution must be exercised in measuring the fracture behaviour of glassy polymers at low temperature because of potential environmental crazing that can be encountered in the coolant atmospheres.

7.2.1.3 Environment
Although environmental cracking and crazing can be found with glassy polymers at cryogenic temperatures a much more common problem is the cracking and crazing of stressed polymers encountered in the presence of certain liquids at ambient temperatures.[1,19] For example, polycarbonate, which is sometimes advertised as being 'unbreakable', will fail within minutes when held at a relatively low stress in contact with a solution of sodium hydroxide (NaOH) in ethanol.[19] The general phenomenon is called environmental stress cracking (ESC) but it is difficult to generalise about the mechanisms involved even for glassy polymers. Glassy polymers such as PMMA and PVC are particularly prone to ESC in organic liquids such as alcohols or other solvents.[20] However, the environmental agent need not be a solvent or even diffuse into the polymer at an appreciable rate in the unstressed state. In fact, for true ESC to occur, cracking should only take place when both stress and environment are present. ESC is discussed in more detail in Sections 7.3.8 and 7.4.2.

7.2.1.4 Pressure
The mechanical behaviour of glassy polymers under externally applied hydrostatic pressure has been reviewed by Pae & Bhateja.[21] In general it is found that the fracture stress and fracture strain increase as the hydrostatic pressure increases and brittle/ductile transitions have been reported for PS[22] and PMMA,[23] although it is found that PMMA becomes brittle again at higher pressures. As with low temperature measurements care must be taken in the interpretation of fracture behaviour under pressure because of environmental crazing in the pressure-transmitting fluids. Duckett[24] has also pointed out that different behaviour can be encountered depending upon whether or not the pressurising medium penetrates flaws in the specimens. Penetration can be stopped by coating specimens with a thin layer of rubber and this is found to suppress the high-pressure ductile/brittle transition in PMMA. The mechanical behaviour under pressure is essentially a competititon between yield and fracture with the critical stress for each

having a different pressure dependence. The penetration of fluid into a flaw in a glassy polymer can cause local tensile stresses to be established at the tip of the flaw in a sample subjected to tension or shear under the action of a superposed hydrostatic pressure. In addition the critical craze stress may be reduced by environmental action. Hence uncoated glassy polymers will be liable to show brittle behaviour at high pressure even though brittle fracture may be suppressed with moderate superposed hydrostatic pressure.

7.2.2 Effect of Polymer Structure

The fracture behaviour of a glassy polymer depends upon the chemical structure of the polymer, the average molar mass and molar-mass distribution, the degree and type of orientation, and the thermal treatment to which the polymer has been subjected. These different factors are considered separately.

7.2.2.1 Chemical Structure

The chemical factors which govern the mechanical behaviour of glassy polymers are somewhat complex and are not yet fully understood. It is not possible to say with any certainty if a particular polymer will be brittle or ductile just from a knowledge of its chemical structure. However, some general trends have emerged. For example, Vincent[7] measured the temperature of the ductile/brittle transition for a wide variety of unnotched thermoplastic samples and was able to correlate the critical stress at the transition with the polymer structure. In particular he was able to show that this stress is proportional to the number of polymer backbone bonds per unit area. Thus by comparing the mechanical properties at an equivalent temperature for different polymers it is clear that the fracture strength depends upon the density of the covalent polymer backbone bonds, the strongest polymers having linear molecules and the weakest ones having large side-groups which reduce the density of main-chain bonds.

7.2.2.2 Molar Mass

The effect of molar mass and molar-mass distribution upon the mechanical behaviour of polymers has been reviewed by Martin et al.[25] The effect of molar mass upon the tensile strength of PMMA, PS and PC is shown in Fig. 7.5(a), (b) and (c), respectively. Measurements on many glassy polymers[25-8] have shown that low molar mass polymers have very low tensile strengths but that the strength increases as the

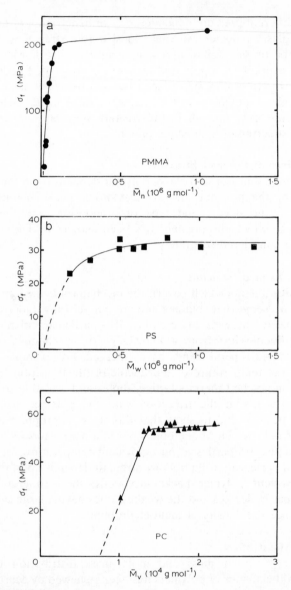

Fig. 7.5. *Dependence of fracture stress, σ_f, upon molar mass for different polymers. (a) Variation of σ_f at $-196°C$ with $\bar{M}_n$ for PMMA (after Vincent[26]); (b) Variation of σ_f with $\bar{M}_w$ for PS (after Martin et al.[25]); and (c) Variation of σ_f with $\bar{M}_v$ for PC (after Golden et al.[28]).*

molar mass is increased. Eventually the polymer reaches a constant level of strength at a critical molar mass above which further increases in molar mass have very little effect.

Many years ago, Flory[29] suggested that some of the physical properties of polymers could be related to the number-average molar mass, $\bar{M}_n$, by an empirical equation of the form

$$P = A_p - B_p/\bar{M}_n \qquad (7.1)$$

where P is the property and A_p and B_p are constants. Although it is clear that the fracture strength data in Fig. 7.5 follow this type of relationship to a first approximation[26] the question of whether to correlate mechanical behaviour with $\bar{M}_n$ or $\bar{M}_w$, or any other type of average, has not been settled.[25] Measurements by Vincent[26] of the fracture strength of PMMA at $-196°C$ as a function of $\bar{M}_n$ follow eqn. (7.1) quite closely especially when $\bar{M}_n < 10^5$ g mol^{-1}.

Gent & Thomas[30] found that they could correlate the 'zero strength' molar mass, M_0 (i.e. the value of molar mass for the curves in Fig. 7.5 when they are extrapolated to $\sigma_f = 0$) with the molar mass at which entanglements start to be obtained in polymer melt, $\bar{M}_e$, as shown in Table 7.1. Thus they suggested that an entanglement network was necessary before the polymer had a significant level of strength. This approach has recently been extended by Turner[31] who showed that by assuming the entangled chains in a polymer glass form a network which is similar to that of a cross-linked rubber, but for which the

TABLE 7.1

COMPARISON OF THE 'ZERO STRENGTH' MOLAR MASS, $\bar{M}_0$, MEASURED IN FLEXURE WITH THE CRITICAL MOLAR MASS AT WHICH ENTANGLEMENTS ARE OBTAINED, $\bar{M}_e$, MEASURED USING MELT VISCOSITY

Polymer	$\bar{M}_0(g\,mol^{-1})$	$\bar{M}_e(g\,mol^{-1})$	Reference
PMMA	22 000	11 000	30
	21 000	27 500	31
PS	50 000	30 000–35 000	30
	72 000	—	31
PE	11 000	4 000	30
	12 000	—	31

cross-links are physical rather than chemical, then a relationship between fracture strength and molar mass of the form

$$\sigma_f = \sigma_{f\infty} - B_s/M \qquad (7.2)$$

is predicted. The parameters $\sigma_{f\infty}$ and B_s are the strength of a polymer of infinite molar mass and a material constant, respectively. There is now an increasing body of evidence that entanglements play a vital role in controlling the fracture behaviour of glassy thermoplastics through their effect upon crazing and shear yielding and this is discussed in detail in Section 7.4.5.

7.2.2.3 Orientation
The fracture strengths of glassy thermoplastics are strongly affected by orientation. The fracture strength increases for cleavage perpendicular to the orientation direction and decreases for cleavage parallel to this direction.[1,2,4,32] This is clearly due to the alignment of the covalently bonded molecules parallel to the orientation direction and is of considerable practical importance because of the orientation that is invariably encountered in moulded samples.[4] The effect of the degree of orientation (given by the birefringence) upon the fracture strengths of PMMA and PS is shown in Fig. 7.6. In both cases there is clearly a strong increase in σ_f with orientation for specimens stressed parallel to the orientation direction and a drop in strength for specimens stressed in the perpendicular direction. Although it has been suggested[33] that one effect of orientation is to change the geometry of inherent flaws it is clear that the overriding effect of orientation is to modify the fracture energy (Section 7.3.7).

7.2.2.4 Annealing
The mechanical behaviour of crystalline materials can often be modified by prolonged heating at elevated temperatures (annealing). The effect of the heating is to induce structural changes in the crystalline structures but even though glassy polymers have amorphous structures they sometimes undergo changes in mechanical behaviour through annealing at temperatures close to the T_g. One polymer which is particularly susceptible is PC which can undergo a transition from ductile to brittle behaviour upon annealing.[12,34,35] Annealing causes an increase in both the density[34] and yield stress[34,35] of PC and the embrittlement has been explained[12,35] in terms of competition between yielding and crazing with a high yield-stress favouring a brittle crazing mechanism (see Section 5.7.1).

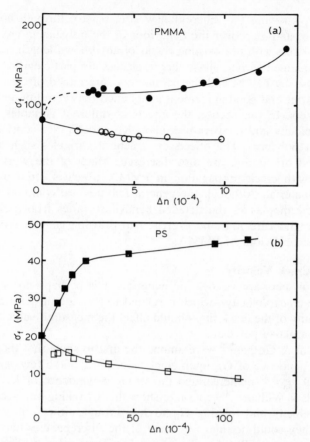

Fig. 7.6. Variation of fracture stress with orientation for different polymers. The degree of orientation is given by the birefringence, Δn. (a) PMMA: ●, specimens deformed longitudinally; ○, specimens fractured in the transverse direction; (b) PS: ■, specimens deformed longitudinally; □, specimens fractured in the transverse direction (after Curtis[32]).

7.3 CRACK PROPAGATION

Although it is often the fracture strength or impact strength of a polymer that is of practical importance much of the effort in the investigations of the fracture behaviour of brittle polymers has been concerned with determination of critical values of K_{Ic} and G_{Ic} for crack propagation. Of course, with a knowledge of these parameters it is possible, knowing the inherent flaw size, a_0, to, through eqn. 1.25, predict σ_f and moreover the behaviour of the polymer in any general state of stress with pre-existing cracks of any known length.

As explained earlier, glassy thermoplastics are particularly amenable to analysis by LEFM and the parameters determined often have very little scatter and good agreement is obtained between different groups of workers. In this section the effects of different variables, such as crack velocity and temperature, upon K_{Ic} and G_{Ic} are considered for different polymers. The effects of structural variables such as molar mass and orientation are also discussed. Much of the work is concerned with crack propagation in PMMA which is often used as a model material. Although the general features are common to many glassy thermoplastics the detailed behaviour varies from polymer to polymer and care must be exercised in drawing general conclusions from the behaviour of PMMA.

7.3.1 Crack Velocity

Since polymers are viscoelastic materials it is perhaps not surprising that the crack velocity—which is related to the rate of deformation in the vicinity of the crack tip—should affect the measured value of K_{Ic} or G_{Ic} for a glassy polymer.

Vincent & Gotham[36] were among the first to show that there was a clear dependence of G_{Ic} upon crack velocity, $\dot{a}$, and a few years later, Marshall et al.[37] demonstrated the strong dependence of K_{Ic} upon $\dot{a}$. Marshall & Williams[38] went on to show that by taking into account the crack velocity and relating G_{Ic} to K_{Ic} through either eqn. (3.55) or (3.56) they could account for many of the discrepancies between the measurements on PMMA of many earlier investigators.[2,8,36,39–42] They presented their data in the form of a $K_{Ic}/\dot{a}$ curve and this type of plot is shown in Fig. 7.7(a). The close agreement between the different groups of workers[37,43–6] who used a variety of testing geometries demonstrates the strength of LEFM for the study of crack propagation in PMMA.

The unique dependence of K_{Ic} upon $\dot{a}$ for PMMA has been interpreted[46–50] in terms of a critical crack-opening displacement, δ_{tc}, criterion (Sections 3.3.2 and 5.6.2). It is found that over a wide range of crack velocities and temperatures the craze can be modelled as a Dugdale line plastic-zone with the value of δ_{tc} being effectively constant and given by eqn. (5.17)[48]

$$\delta_{tc} = \frac{K_{Ic}^{2}}{\sigma_{cs}E}$$

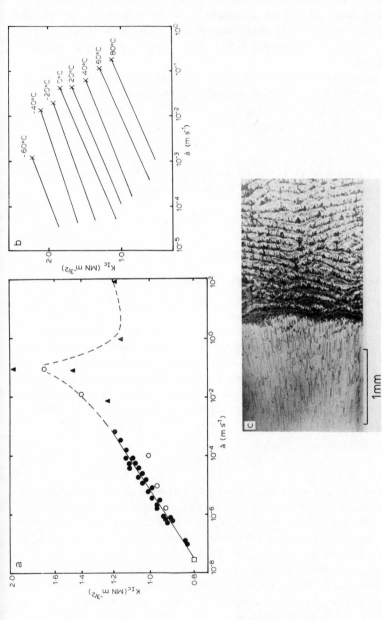

Fig. 7.7. Crack propagation in PMMA. (a) Variation of K_{1c} with crack velocity, $\dot{a}$; ●, Beaumont & Young;[43] ▲, Johnson & Radon,[44] ○, Marshall et al.;[46] □, Weidmann & Döll,[45] (b) Dependence of K_{1c} upon $\dot{a}$ at different temperatures. The cross represents a transition to adiabatic crack growth (after Marshall et al.[46]); (c) Change in fracture surface appearance for PMMA ($\bar{M}_w = 163\,000$ g mol⁻¹) at $\dot{a} \sim 200$ m s⁻¹. The crack propagation direction is from left to right (after Döll & Weidmann[155]).

where σ_{cs} is the craze surface stress and E is the modulus. The criterion was developed originally[47] from measurements of the parameters on the right-hand side of eqn. (5.17) but direct observations of the crack tip using optical interferometry have since confirmed the model.[51,52]

An important question that arises concerning the crack propagation behaviour in PMMA is what controls the relationship between K_{Ic} and $\dot{a}$? The linearity of the log–log plots in Fig. 7.7 clearly implies a relationship of the form (eqn. 5.14))

$$K_{Ic} \propto \dot{a}^n$$

where n is a constant. It was shown in Section 5.5.2 that assuming time dependencies for σ_{cs} and E of the forms (eqn. (5.11))

$$\sigma_{cs} = e_y E_0 t^{-n}$$

and (eqn. (5.18))

$$E = E_0 t^{-n}$$

then K_{Ic} is related to $\dot{a}$ by (eqn. (5.19))

$$K_{Ic} = (\delta_{tc} e_y)^{\frac{1}{2}} \left(\frac{8e_y}{\pi \delta_{tc}} \right)^n E_0 \dot{a}^n$$

where e_y is the yield strain (effectively constant). Hence it follows that the dependence of K_{Ic} upon $\dot{a}$ arises from the time dependence of the modulus.[48–50] This phenomenon has been termed 'relaxation controlled' crack growth[50] as it is clear that the controlling factor is n which is determined by the viscoelastic properties of the polymer. The parameter n may be related to the loss factor, $\tan \delta_r$, by eqn. (5.13)[48]

$$\tan \delta_r = \tan \frac{\pi n}{2}$$

and close agreement has been claimed[48] between measured values of n and those predicted by eqn. (5.13). For example, crack propagation results give a value of ~ 0.07 for PMMA and this is of the same order as the value of n determined from measurements of $\tan \delta_r$[53] upon PMMA at ambient temperature (Table 7.2).

Since cracks generally propagate in a well-controlled stable manner in PMMA many of the studies of crack propagation have been confined to this material. However, there have been reports of similar investigations upon other polymers such as PS[54,55] and PC.[56] It is by no

TABLE 7.2

COMPARISON OF CRACK PROPAGATION PARAMETERS FOR VARIOUS
GLASSY THERMOPLASTICS WITH RELAXATION DATA OBTAINED FROM
REFERENCE 53

Parameter	Polymer		
	PMMA[46]	PS[55]	PC[56] (below $-40°C$)
n	0·07	0·10	0·044
$\tan \delta_r{}^a$	0·06	0·01	0·02
$(2 \tan^{-1} \delta_r)/\pi = n$	0·038	0·0064	0·013
$\Delta H^*(kJ \ mol^{-1})$ (crack propagation)	86	87–220	42
$\Delta H^*(kJ \ mol^{-1})$ (β_r-transition)	74	125	21
$\dot{a}_c(mm \ s^{-1})$	50	3	10

^{a} Reference 53.

means as easy to obtain controlled crack propagation in PS[54] because
of the tendency of the material to undergo multiple crazing at the
crack tip but with careful precracking similar $K_{Ic}/\dot{a}$ curves can be
obtained.[54] Stable propagation of brittle cracks can only easily be
obtained in PC below $-40°C$[56] in the vicinity of the β_r transition which
occurs at about $-100°C$ in PC.[53] Values of n of 0·10 for PS[55] and
0·044 for PC below $-40°C$[56] have been reported and these are clearly
similar to values of n obtained for PMMA (Table 7.2). However, they
do not agree particularly well with values of n calculated from $\tan \delta_r$
measurements[53] using eqn. (5.13).

7.3.2 Temperature

There have been a number of studies upon the effect of testing-
temperature upon G_{Ic} and K_{Ic} for glassy thermoplastics[2,40,46,48,55-7] and
in general it is found that measured values of both parameters decrease
as the temperature is increased so long as the failure is brittle. At first
sight this observation may appear to be in conflict with impact studies
(e.g. Fig. 6.3) where it is generally found that the impact strength
increases as the temperature is increased. However, impact measurements are made at very high rates and the increase in impact strength
obtained by raising the test temperature is due to the polymer going
through a brittle/ductile transition.

The most definitive work on the effect of temperature upon crack propagation in brittle polymers has been done using PMMA and there have been comprehensive measurements of both K_{Ic}[46] and G_{Ic}[57] as a function of both temperature and crack velocity. A series of log–log $K_{Ic}/\dot{a}$ plots are given in Fig. 7.7(b) for temperatures ranging from $-60°C$ to $+80°C$. It can be seen that the data form a series of approximately parallel lines and it is found that the critical crack-opening displacement, δ_{tc}, criterion can be applied over the whole range of temperatures. A value of δ_{tc} of $\sim 1\cdot 6$ μm has been determined for PMMA.[46] The effect of testing-temperature upon the $K_{Ic}/\dot{a}$ plots has been explained in terms of an activated-rate process which could be described by an Arrhenius relationship using the concept of time–temperature equivalence.[46,48] Equation (5.19) is then modified to become

$$K_{Ic} = (\delta_{tc} e_y)^{\frac{1}{2}} \left(\frac{8e_y}{\pi \delta_{tc}} \right)^n E_0 e^{n(\Delta H^*/\mathbf{R})(1/T - 1/T_0)} \dot{a}^n \qquad (7.3)$$

where, ΔH^* is the activation enthalpy for the viscoelastic process, $\mathbf{R}$ is the molar gas constant, T is the test temperature, and T_0 is a reference temperature. Since $\tan \delta_r$ changes with temperature then it would be expected from eqn. (5.13) that the values of n should also change with T and it can be seen from Fig. 7.7(b) that the slope of the $K_{Ic}/\dot{a}$ curves, n, goes through a maximum at about $0°C$ as the temperature is varied, which is consistent with the PMMA going through its β_r relaxation. In fact, below $-80°C$ no stable crack propagation can be obtained in PMMA which has been interpreted[46] as being due to n dropping so low that stable propagation cannot be sustained. However, it is known that environmental crazing can occur in the presence of coolants at low temperature[13-18] and this may complicate matters.

The variation of K_{Ic} as a function of $\dot{a}$ has also been measured for both PS[55] and PC[56] at low temperatures. In the case of PS a critical crack-opening displacement, δ_{tc}, criterion is found to apply for the variation of K_{Ic} with $\dot{a}$ at a given temperature but, unlike PMMA, δ_{tc} increases from $33\cdot 5$ to 50 μm as the temperature is reduced from 90 to $25°C$. On the other hand, a constant value of $\delta_{tc} \sim 37$ μm has been reported for PC between -120 and $-40°C$ (Table 7.2). The error involved in determining these values of δ_{tc} derived from measurements of K_{Ic}, E and σ_y (eqn. (3.45)) is probably too large to decide whether or not it varies with temperature. However, direct measurements of δ_{tc} at the crack tip for both PMMA[51] and PC[58] have shown that δ_{tc} may be truly constant for both these materials over a wide range of temperatures.

7.3.3 Relaxations and Crack Propagation

An important point emerging from the discussions in Sections 7.3.1 and 7.3.2 concerns the relationship between molecular-relaxation processes and crack propagation. It has already been shown that for some polymers the exponent n in eqn. (5.14) can be correlated with $\tan \delta_r$. The other aspect that arises is whether or not relaxation peaks (e.g. the β_r transition) can be correlated to changes in crack propagation behaviour. Measurements of G_{Ic} as a function of $\dot{a}$ for PMMA show peaks in G_{Ic} at a particular crack velocity below $0°C$[57] and this has been interpreted in terms of the β_r transition. Also high values of $\tan \delta_r$ have been proposed as being necessary to give high values of n for stable crack propagation to take place in PMMA[46] and PC.[56] Further support for the control of crack propagation by relaxations has been obtained by interpreting the temperature dependence of $K_{Ic}/\dot{a}$ plots in terms of an activated-rate process (eqn. (7.5)). Arrhenius plots have yielded activation enthalpies, ΔH^*, of 86 kJ mol^{-1} for PMMA,[57] $87–220 \text{ kJ mol}^{-1}$ for PS[55] and 42 kJ mol^{-1} for PC[56] (Table 7.2), all of which have been correlated with the activation enthalpies for the β_r relaxations in these materials. However, the similarity of the activation enthalpies does not prove the dependence upon a relaxation process. At first sight it would seem that such a relationship would be very tenuous since the relaxations normally apply to low strain deformation whereas deformation at the crack tip during fracture clearly involves very high strains. However, it may be possible to have energy absorption in specimens through low-strain elastic deformations in the bulk material. This is clearly an area in which further definitive work is needed. For example, a critical experiment would be one in which $K_{Ic}/\dot{a}$ plots were obtained for a series of similar polymers with different values of $\tan \delta_r$ for the β_r transition or with different transition temperatures. Hopefully the effect of relaxations upon crack propagation could then be tested without ambiguity.

7.3.4 Adiabatic/Isothermal Transitions

Although stable crack propagation in PMMA can be found over a wide range of crack velocities and temperatures, there is a widely reported[44,46–8,59] transition in the behaviour of running cracks at high crack velocities (e.g. above $\sim 50 \text{ mm s}^{-1}$ at ambient temperature).

Below this velocity cracks propagate in a stable manner whereas if an attempt is made to propagate a crack above this velocity the crack jumps unstably to a much higher velocity of 10–$100\,\mathrm{m\,s^{-1}}$. This effect can be seen as the abrupt change in the $K_{\mathrm{Ic}}/\dot{a}$ curve in Fig. 7.7(a). The instability is also accompanied by a change in the fracture surface appearance as can be seen in Fig. 7.7(c). Measurements of crack propagation at different temperatures have shown that the critical crack velocity for the transition, $\dot{a}_{\mathrm{c}}$, decreases as the test temperature is decreased.[46,48] A similar transition has been reported at $\dot{a}_{\mathrm{c}} \sim 3\,\mathrm{mm\,s^{-1}}$ in PS[55] at ambient temperature and at $\dot{a}_{\mathrm{c}} \sim 10\,\mathrm{mm\,s^{-1}}$ in PC[56] at $-100°\mathrm{C}$ (Table 7.2).

Two quite different mechanisms have been proposed to explain this phenomenon in PMMA. Johnson & Radon[44] suggested that the transition in PMMA was due to a peak in the $K_{\mathrm{Ic}}/\dot{a}$ curve caused by the β_{r} relaxation. However, Marshall et al.[46] showed clearly that the variation of $\dot{a}_{\mathrm{c}}$ with temperature for the transition was different from the variation needed if the transition were controlled by β_{r} relaxation. Instead they showed quite convincingly that the change in crack propagation behaviour is due to an adiabatic/isothermal transition. Below $\dot{a}_{\mathrm{c}}$ the crack grows under steady-state conditions with heat being dissipated whereas above $\dot{a}_{\mathrm{c}}$ there is adiabatic heating at the crack tip and material at the crack tip becomes softened thermally. This causes a drop in G_{Ic} or K_{Ic} and as the specimen has excess energy the crack rapidly accelerates. The mechanism is supported by the large increases in temperature that have been estimated from infra-red measurements for rapidly propagating cracks in PMMA.[60] The relatively low thermal conductivities of polymers mean that adiabatic conditions can occur at relatively low crack velocities and Marshall et al.[46] have shown that the instability crack velocity is given by

$$\dot{a}_{\mathrm{c}} = \frac{(\Delta T)^2 \rho_{\mathrm{d}} c_{\mathrm{p}} \bar{k}}{(e_{\mathrm{y}} K_{\mathrm{Ic}}{}^*)^2} \tag{7.4}$$

where

$$\Delta T = \bar{T} - T_0 = (2\mathbf{R}/\Delta H^*)\bar{T}^2 \tag{7.5}$$

$\bar{T}$ is the temperature at the crack tip required to cause instability, T_0 is the test temperature, ρ_{d} is the density of the polymer, c_{p} is the specific heat capacity, $\bar{k}$ is the thermal conductivity and $K_{\mathrm{Ic}}{}^*$ is the value of K_{Ic} at the instability. For PMMA ΔT is found to be of the order of 10–$30\,\mathrm{K}$ and so eqn. (7.5) can be approximated to give

$$\Delta T \simeq (2\mathbf{R}/\Delta H^*)T_0{}^2 \tag{7.6}$$

combining eqns (7.4) and (7.6) gives

$$\dot{a}_c K_{Ic}^{*2} = \rho_d c_p \bar{k} \left(\frac{2\mathbf{R}}{e_y \, \Delta H^*} \right)^2 T_0^4 \qquad (7.7)$$

and Williams[48] has shown that a plot of $\dot{a}_c K_{Ic}^{*2}$ versus T_0^4 (the only experimental variables) is linear with an intercept at the origin and a slope similar to that predicted using reasonable values for the various thermal constants. The theory has also been used successfully to explain the similar adiabatic/isothermal transitions found in PS[55] and PC at low temperatures.[56]

It is found[62] that plane-strain cracks can be propagated stably at ambient temperatures in PC at low velocities but a transition in the behaviour is found if attempts are made to propagate cracks at velocities higher than 10^{-2} mm s^{-1}, when propagation becomes unstable. However, this behaviour which is reminiscent of the adiabatic/isothermal transition cannot be explained in terms of such a transition because the transition velocity is too low and it is thought[62] to arise from differences in the kinetics of shear failure and craze breakdown.

7.3.5 Specimen Thickness

The fracture behaviour of brittle thermoplastics such as PMMA and PS is relatively insensitive to the specimen thickness for normal specimens a few millimetres or so thick. However, more ductile polymers such as PC or poly(ether sulphone) (PES) tested around ambient temperature have fracture properties which are very much more dependent upon specimen thickness.[12] For example, the fracture energy of PC specimens at −20°C increases from 1 to 3 kJ m^{-2} on reducing the thickness from 10 to 2·5 mm.[58] The effect of specimen thickness has been discussed in detail in Section 3.5 where it was shown that the specimen thickness, b, above which plane-strain conditions dominate the behaviour is generally considered to be given by (eqn. (3.58))

$$b > 47 r'_{yc}$$

where r'_{yc} is the radius of the plane-strain plastic zone at fracture. It is the more ductile polymers which have large values of r'_{yc} and so thickness effects are found to be important in PC,[56,58,62–6] poly(butylene terephthalate)[61] and PES.[67] The behaviour of these materials has been explained successfully by assuming that plane-strain conditions are effective over a surface skin of depth r''_{yc}, the plane-stress plastic-zone radius, and that plane-strain conditions prevail over the central region of the specimen. Each region is assigned different values of fracture parameters which are added linearly in proportion to the sizes of the regions. However, two different approaches are used. Parvin & Williams[56,65] add K_{Ic} values and Ward and co-workers[58,66,67] effectively add G_{Ic} values and the two methods are not equivalent (Section 3.5). It is found (Table 7.3) that the plane-strain values of K_{Ic} and G_{Ic} are approximately independent of temperature whereas the plane-stress values tend to increase as the temperature is reduced. It would seem that there is more justification to add G_{Ic} values, which have dimensions of energy per unit area, when the surface is separated into areas of different fracture mode. Also Ward and co-workers[58,66,67] used the measured sizes of shear lips to determine the width of the plane-stress regions whereas the values of r''_{yc} generated in the analysis of Parvin & Williams[56] are calculated using eqn. (3.60) and are an order of magnitude larger than the sizes of the shear lips actually measured in PC.

Brown[12] has recently proposed a model to explain the effect of specimen thickness upon ductile polymers which undergo mixed-mode crack propagation with shear lips. He particularly considered the case of PC which undergoes a transition from 'brittle with shear lips' propagation to ductile failure on increasing the temperature or reducing specimen thickness, b. It is found that at a given temperature propagation will be brittle (with shear lips) when $b > b_{min}$ where

$$b_{min} = 2G'_{Ic}/\phi \qquad (7.8)$$

TABLE 7.3

VALUES OF PLANE-STRAIN, K'_{Ic}, PLANE-STRESS, K''_{Ic}, PLANE-STRAIN, G'_{Ic}, AND PLANE-STRESS, G''_{Ic} FOR POLYCARBONATE AT DIFFERENT TEMPERATURES (AFTER REFERENCES 56 AND 58)

Temperature ($°C$)	Stress intensity factor ($MN\,m^{-3/2}$)		Fracture energy ($kJ\,m^{-2}$)	
	K'_{Ic}	K''_{Ic}	G'_{Ic}	G''_{Ic}
−70	$2·1^a$	$6·5^a$	0·83	67
−60	2·1	6·2	0·81	55
−40	2·0	5·5	0·72	18
−20	$2·0^a$	5·0	0·67	15
0	1·8	5·0	0·59	23
+20	2·2	$5·0^a$	0·37	24

[a] Interpolated values

and ϕ is the fracture energy per volume of shear lip. The material undergoes a brittle/ductile transition when b is reduced to equal the critical thickness, b_{min}, and ductile crack propagation takes place.

7.3.6 Molar Mass

There have been several studies of the dependence of the fracture energy, G_{Ic}, upon molar mass for glassy polymers such as PMMA,[68-70] PS[71] and PC.[66] The general dependence of G_{Ic} upon molar mass is shown in Fig. 7.8 in the form of a schematic log–log plot. The shape of the curve is sigmoidal. When M is low the polymer has a very low fracture energy, approximately G_0. As the molar mass is increased there is a sudden rapid rise in G_{Ic} until it levels off at a constant value as $M \to \infty$. In the high molar mass region the data can be fitted to an empirical equation of the form of eqn. (7.1) such as[68]

$$G_{Ic} = A_G - B_G / M \qquad (7.9)$$

where A_G and B_G are constants. In the region where the slope is rapidly changing the curves can be *extrapolated* to a critical value of

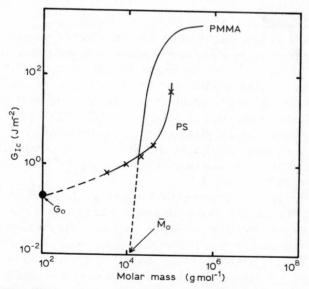

Fig. 7.8. Dependence of G_{Ic} upon molar mass for PMMA[69] and PS[71] (after Kusy & Turner[69]).

molar mass $\bar{M}_0$ as $G_{\mathrm{Ic}} \to 0$. This is, of course, similar to the extrapolation when $\sigma_{\mathrm{f}} \to 0$ (Section 7.2.2) and similar values of $\bar{M}_0$ are obtained using the two methods (Table 7.1), which are also close to $\bar{M}_{\mathrm{e}}$ for the different polymers. The rapid rise in G_{Ic} above $\bar{M}_0$ is therefore thought[69] to be due to the onset of entanglements and this is discussed in detail in Section 7.4.5.

Robertson[71] found for PS, in the region where the molar mass is less than $\bar{M}_0$, and G_{Ic} is very low, that

$$G_{\mathrm{Ic}} \propto M^{\frac{1}{2}} \tag{7.10}$$

Kramer[72] has recently shown from theoretical considerations of the geometry of the craze and the molecular processes involved that this is precisely the relationship expected in the region of low molar mass (see Section 5.7.1). However, when $M > \bar{M}_0$, G_{Ic} increases rapidly being proportional to M^2 or even M^3 but eventually it becomes independent of M (Fig. 7.8). Kramer's theory does not explain this behaviour and there is clearly a need for a theory which can explain the overall sigmoidal shape of the G_{Ic}/M curve. Kusy & Turner[69] have suggested that a theory which properly incorporates the role of entanglements may be successful to this end.

7.3.7 Orientation

One of the earliest investigations into the effect of orientation upon crack propagation in glassy thermoplastics was performed by Broutman & McGarry.[73] They looked at biaxially oriented PMMA and uniaxially stretched PMMA and PS. In the case of the biaxially oriented material cracks could be propagated in different directions perpendicular to the plane of the sheet with $G_{\mathrm{Ic}} \sim 1300 \,\mathrm{J}\,\mathrm{m}^{-2}$ whereas cracks growing in the plane of the sheet propagated with $G_{\mathrm{Ic}} \sim 33 \,\mathrm{J}\,\mathrm{m}^{-2}$, showing clearly the relative ease of cleaving between molecules rather than across the molecules. G_{Ic} for isotropic PMMA was found to be $\sim 250 \,\mathrm{J}\,\mathrm{m}^{-2}$.[73]

In the uniaxially stretched PMMA and PS, G_{Ic} for crack propagation parallel to the orientation direction was found to drop as the degree of orientation was increased, falling by over an order of magnitude for polymer stretched by over 100 %.[73] In similar studies by Curtis[32] upon PMMA and PS, and Miller et al.[74] upon PVC it was found that G_{Ic} for crack propagation parallel to the orientation direction could be directly correlated to the birefringence of the oriented polymer as shown in Fig. 7.9 for the three different polymers. Again the value of G_{Ic} drops

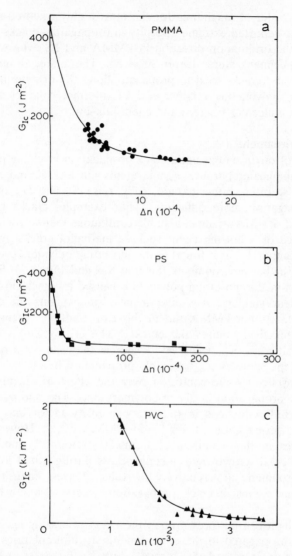

Fig. 7.9. Variation of G_{Ic} with orientation (given by birefringence, Δn) for crack propagation parallel to direction of orientation. (a) PMMA; (b) PS (after Curtis[32]); and (c) PVC (after Miller et al.[74]).

by over an order of magnitude for the most highly oriented samples. Curtis[32] also reported extreme difficulty in propagating cracks perpendicular to the orientation direction in PMMA and PS even when the cleavage specimens were deeply grooved. The material tended to delaminate and cracks tried to propagate along the orientation direction, again showing the relative ease of intermolecular cleavage as opposed to molecular fracture and chain pull-out.

7.3.8   Environment

The effect of environment upon crack propagation in glassy polymers is rather complicated because organic agents which crack and craze the polymers also often, rather paradoxically, raise K_{Ic} and G_{Ic} and make crack propagation more difficult.[75-9] For example, cracks generally propagate in PMMA in air in a stable continuous manner, whereas in the presence of a crazing agent such as methanol cracks grow in a stick/slip manner[77,79] as is found in thermosetting polymers even in the absence of active environments (Section 8.3 and Fig. 8.3). Stick/slip propagation in thermosetting polymers is caused by crack tip blunting through shear yielding. A similar mechanism explains the effect of crazing agents upon PMMA but in this case multiple crazing at the crack tip effectively blunts the crack.[79] The critical stress intensity factor for initiation, K_{Ici}, is increased whereas the value for arrest, K_{Ica}, is virtually the same as K_{Ic} for stable propagation in air.[77]

There has been some confusion over the effect of crazing agents upon crack propagation in glassy polymers since Mai and co-workers have reported reductions in the stress intensity factor and fracture energy for propagation in PS[55] and PMMA.[75,76,78] However, the problem lies in the definition of terms. It is found[78] that a small amount of crack growth and crazing occurs during initial loading in active environments at a relatively low value of stress intensity factor, K_{Ii}, whereas extensive crack propagation occurs at a much higher value, K_{Ici}.

Further light can be thrown upon the effect of crazing agents when cracks are propagated in the environments at different rates. As the testing rate is increased K_{Ici} drops[77] but K_{Ii} increases, until at a sufficiently high rate they both become equal to K_{Ic} for propagation in air.[78] When cracks propagate at a high velocity they grow too rapidly for the environment to flow along the crack and craze to the tip. When the velocity is reduced the environment can reach the crack tip and induce multiple crazing which blunts the crack and causes arrest. The value of the stress intensity factor must therefore be raised to K_{Ici} before the crack can burst through the crazed region and propagate in an unstable manner. On the other hand, the small amount of craze or crack growth at K_{Ii} will depend upon the length of time the specimen is stressed in the environment and so as K_{Ii} increases the rate of testing is increased.

Williams[48] has suggested that the effect of active environments will be to modify the craze surface stress, σ_{cs}, in eqn. (5.17). He proposed that the crazing agents which are chemically inert and diffuse only very slowly into the bulk polymer might rapidly penetrate and plasticise the polymer in a craze because of its highly porous nature. Hence the value of σ_{cs} in eqn. (5.17) will be reduced to $\alpha_c\sigma_{\text{cs}}(\alpha_c < 1)$. If the critical crack opening displacement, δ_{tc}, and modulus, E, remain unchanged then the value of K_{Ic} in eqn. (5.19) will be reduced to give

$$K_{\text{Ic}} = (\delta_{\text{tc}}e_y)^{\frac{1}{2}}\alpha_c^{\frac{1}{2}}\left(\frac{8e_y\alpha_c}{\pi\delta_{\text{tc}}}\right)^n \dot{a}^n \qquad (7.11)$$

and so Williams predicts that the K_{Ic} versus $\dot{a}$ curve for a polymer in a crazing environment which is instantaneously available at the crack tip would be, to a first approximation, parallel to the curve in air but at a lower level of K_{Ic}. Unfortunately this is not found in practice in glassy polymers as the crazing agent normally raises K_{Ic} for propagation. Nevertheless, it would seem that the model is correct in concept because of the low values of K_{Ii} measured but it ignores the change in craze geometry and multiple crazing which has the effect of raising K_{Ic}.

7.4 MICROMECHANISMS

The initiation and propagation of cracks in glassy thermoplastics is essentially a competition between crazing and shear yielding. In brittle polymers, such as PMMA or PS, crazing is the dominant mode whereas in more ductile materials such as PC or PES plane-stress shear yielding plays a more important role and, indeed, is responsible for the ductile fracture. Both of these processes have been discussed in detail in Chapters 4 and 5 and so in this section we will be concerned principally with the way in which these micromechanisms affect the fracture process.

7.4.1 Craze Initiation and Growth

Crazing is a process whereby a thin region of a polymer undergoes localised plane-strain yielding and forms a feature rather like a crack but which is spanned by oriented fibrils (Fig. 5.2). The most widely accepted craze criterion is the one proposed by Bowden & Oxborough[80] who suggested that crazing occurs when the strain in any direction reaches a critical value (Section 5.4.1). The critical strain, e_c, is given by (eqn. (5.7))

$$e_c = Y_1 + \frac{X_1}{I_1}$$

where I_1 is the first stress invariant of the stress tensor, and Y_1 and X_1 are time- and temperature-dependent constants. Although this phenomenological approach has been successful in explaining the effect of different stress states upon crazing in glassy polymers[80] it is not concerned with the micromechanisms involved. Argon and co-workers[81-3] have looked in detail at this aspect of crazing and have accounted for crazing in terms of microcavitation and couched their analysis in terms of a 'meniscus instability'[81] (see Fig. 5.9).

Many of the studies upon craze initiation and growth have been concerned with the effect of environments, principally because of the practical importance of this phenomenon and the relatively large and easily observed crazes that are produced. Williams & Marshall[50] have reported measurements of craze kinetics in PMMA and PC under dry conditions (Fig. 5.10) and they have shown that the craze length, R, is related to time by an equation of the form (eqn. (5.12))

$$R = \frac{\pi}{8}\left(\frac{K_I^2}{(e_y E_0)^2}\right)t^{2n}$$

where n is $d\ln E/d\ln t$ and so is similar to the same exponent relating K_{Ic} to $\dot{a}$ (eqn. 5.19). Hence it is clear that the kinetics of craze growth are similar to those of crack propagation (Section 7.3.1). We will return to this point later.

7.4.2 Environmental Crazing

There have been a number of studies of craze initiation[84-6] and craze growth[1,48,50,87-94] in glassy thermoplastics in different environments, principally aliphatic alcohols. Bernier & Kambour[84] found a correlation between the solubility parameter, δ_s, of a liquid and its effectiveness in initiating crazing and cracking or dissolving the polymer with the most active liquids being those for which δ_s for the liquid and for the polymer are matched. However, more detailed measurements[85,86] have shown that the phenomenon cannot be accounted for in terms of solubility parameters alone and other effects such as hydrogen bonding must also be taken into account.[86]

The role of solvent absorption in the crazing of glassy polymers has been elegantly demonstrated by Andrews *et al.*[87-9] The energy required to cause crazing for PMMA in alcohols, G_{Ico}, is found to fall as the temperature is increased until a constant value is achieved (Fig. 7.10(a)). The temperature at which this occurs, T_c^*, is found to correspond to the T_g of the same polymer swollen to the equilibrium concentration of the crazing agent.[88] The form of the curve in Fig. 7.10(a) was predicted by Andrews & Bevan[87] who derived an equation for G_{Ico} in terms of the work to form craze cavities such that

$$G_{Ico} = 4 \cdot 82 (\delta_c \gamma_{SL}/d_v) v_{fv}^{\frac{2}{3}} + 0 \cdot 66 \tau_y \, \delta_c k_3 v_{fv} \qquad (7.12)$$

where δ_c is the craze thickness, γ_{SL} the interfacial surface energy, d_v the mean distance betwen void centres, v_{fv} the void fraction, k_3 a constant, and τ_y the shear yield stress of the material. The only term in eqn. (7.12) that is strongly temperature dependent is τ_y. As the T_g of the polymer is approached $\tau_y \to 0$ and so G_{Ico} is predicted to become constant above T_c^*. The analysis of Andrews *et al.*[87-9] suggests that at the crack tip the polymer is swollen to its equilibrium level and the effect of the applied stress is to accelerate sorption of solvent into the craze.

Brown & Kramer[90] have measured the surface energy term γ_{SL} directly for PS in methanol and confirmed the predictions of Andrews *et al.*[87-9] They showed that for the PS/methanol system the major effect of the environment upon crazing is to reduce the flow stress by plasticisation. The surface-energy reduction is only of secondary importance. The extent of the plasticisation effect of alcohols upon PES is shown in Fig. 7.10(b). It can be seen that there is a steady decrease in the critical strain for crazing, e_c, as the T_g of the plasticised polymer approaches room temperature (the test temperature). However, e_c does not fall to zero as work has to be done to satisfy the surface-energy term in eqn. (7.12).

The growth rate of crazes is found to be more rapid in the presence of active environments than in air. Marshall *et al.*[91] measured the growth rates of crazes in edge-notched PMMA specimens loaded in methanol using a LEFM approach and showed that craze growth was

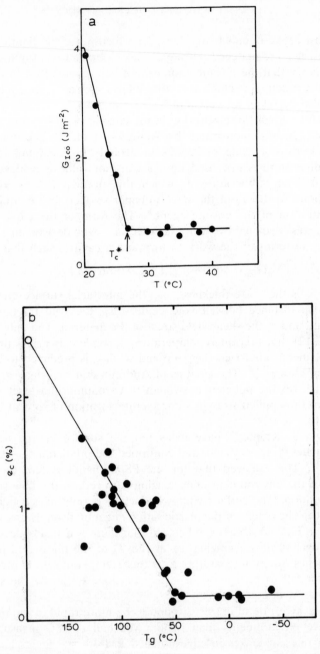

Fig. 7.10. (a) Variation of the energy required to cause crazing, G_{Ico}, with temperature for PMMA in ethanol (after Andrews & Bevan[87]); (b) Variation of critical strain for crazing, e_c, with the glass transition temperature, T_g, of PES plasticised with different alcohols (after Kambour[1]).

controlled by the value of the stress-intensity factor, K_I. Below a critical value, K_{Im} (Regime A), no growth was observed, for $K_{Im} <$ $K_I < K_{In}$ (Regime B) the craze length was found to be proportional to $t^{\frac{1}{2}}$ for a given value of K_I and for $K_I > K_{In}$ (Regime C) crazes grew rapidly at first and then slowed down to a constant rate until the specimen fractured. Obviously K_{Im} corresponds to the critical value of K_I for crazing (cf., K_{Ii}). It is thought[91] that craze growth in Regime C is controlled by fluid flow from the sides of the specimen as K_{In} increases with increasing sheet thickness. Perhaps the most interesting aspect of the behaviour is Regime B where it has been suggested that craze growth is controlled by fluid flow along the crazes.[50,91] The

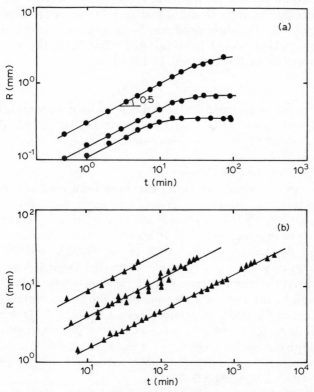

Fig. 7.11. Variation of craze length with time for different polymers in alcohols at 20°C. (a) PMMA in methanol (after Williams & Marshall[50]); (b) PC in ethanol (after Miltz et al.[94]).

variation of craze length, R, with time of loading, t, is given in the form
of log–log plots for PMMA in methanol[50] and PC in ethanol[94] in Fig.
7.11. For both materials the initial slopes of the curves are ~ 0.5
showing that

$$R \propto t^{\frac{1}{2}} \qquad (7.13)$$

The rate of propagation also increases with the level of applied stress
or K_I. Williams[48] has shown that if craze growth is controlled by rate
of fluid flow along the craze then

$$R = \sqrt{2C_c\bar{p}}\, K_I t^{\frac{1}{2}} \qquad (7.14)$$

where C_c is constant for a particular polymer and environment, and $\bar{p}$
is the pressure driving the fluid. Equation (7.14) clearly explains the
proportionality between R and $t^{\frac{1}{2}}$ and also illustrates the dependence
of R upon K_I. This behaviour has been termed[50] 'flow-controlled'
craze growth and should be contrasted with 'relaxation-controlled'
craze growth exemplified by eqn. (5.12) where

$$R \propto t^{2n} \qquad (7.15)$$

The exponent n is controlled by the relaxation behaviour of the
material and, since $2n < 1/2$, relaxation-controlled growth depends
upon a considerably lower power of time.

7.4.3 The Structure of Crazes

The main experimental techniques that have been used to investigate
the structure of crazes in glassy polymers are optical interferometry,[1,51,52,58,66,95,96] small-angle X-ray scattering[97-9] and transmission electron microscopy.[1,100-12] It has been shown by optical interferometry that crazes at the crack tip in PMMA and PC under
plane-strain conditions can be modelled by the Dugdale line plastic-
zone and similar values of critical crack-opening displacement, δ_{tc}, are
found both by direct optical measurement and by substituting measured values of the different parameters into eqn. (5.17). Direct measurements of δ_{tc} for PMMA[51] over a wide range of temperatures have
confirmed that it is effectively constant for this material. It is, however,
found to increase with increasing molar mass for both PMMA[96] and
PC[66] as detailed in Section 5.7.1.

Small-angle X-ray scattering[97-9] can yield detailed information upon
crazes in glassy polymers such as the fibril volume fraction, v_f, fibril
spacing and fibril diameter. This is particularly useful as it can be

obtained for both bulk polymer and environmental crazes with the environment present.[97] However, most of the detailed analysis of the structure of crazes has been obtained using electron microscopy upon crazes in microtomed sections[1,100] or thin films.[101-12] The microstructure of crazes as elucidated by electron microscopy has been described in detail in Section 5.2 and only the main points will be summarised here. There is always the worry that study of thin films will not be representative of crazing in the bulk polymer but it is now thought for polymers such as PS that as long as the film is greater than 150 nm thick the crazes are not significantly different to the bulk.[97] The crazes are essentially cracks bridged by fibrils (Fig. 5.2) and the density of material within a craze in PS is typically about 25% of that of the bulk but the exact value will vary with stress level and other factors.[105] At the craze tip there are microcavities and they grow due principally to surface drawing for air-grown crazes, and fibril creep for environmentally induces crazes.[19]

Active environments are found to have a profound effect upon the structure of crazes in glassy polymers. In environments which cause a high degree of plasticisation such as n-heptane with PS[19] the craze surface stress is very much less than for air crazes. Such crazes are considerably weaker than those in air or other environments which cause less plasticisation (e.g. methanol). It is thought[19] that environments which cause plasticisation and swelling will enhance the kinetics of the chain disentanglement process necessary for crazes to nucleate and grow.

7.4.4 Shear Yielding

Although a great deal of effort has been expended upon understanding the process of crazing in glassy polymers it is becoming increasingly more apparent that shear yielding is also an important micromechanism in the fracture of many polymers (Sections 4.4 and 4.5). There is now conclusive evidence that crazes and cracks can be initiated at the point of intersection of shear bands[113-16] as illustrated in Fig. 4.8 and ahead of shear-yielded zones in specimens containing blunt notches.[117-19] It was also found that shear yielding may take place during crack propagation for both brittle and ductile fracture in glassy thermoplastics (Section 4.5). In the case of brittle fracture, crazing tends to be the predominant mechanism although it is sometimes in competition with localised plane-strain shear yielding. For example, cross-linking causes crazing to be suppressed (Section 8.4.3) and localised shear yielding to become dominant. Also shear bands may blunt crazes[1] or pre-existing shear bands may cause premature craze breakdown when crazes cross them.[120]

In the case of ductile fracture, large plane stress shear-yielded zones are seen ahead of the crack tip.[119,121-4] The dimensions of plastic zones are found to be in good agreement with the Dugdale type zone[119,121] and Donald & Kramer[122-4] adapted their technique of studying crazes

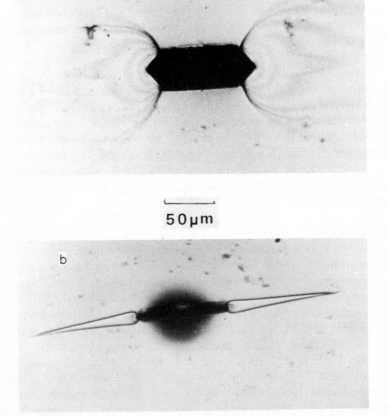

Fig. 7.12. Shear deformation zones in PC. (a) Unannealed polymer; (b) Polymer annealed for 1 h at 132°C (after Donald & Kramer[122]).

to the analysis of such zones by electron microscopy as shown in Fig. 7.12 for PC. The plastic zones in the unannealed polymer tend to be rather diffuse whereas on annealing a more well-defined flame-shaped zone is formed.[122] However, a note of caution must be sounded concerning these observations as care must be exercised in relating the behaviour of PC in the form of very thin films (~1 μm thick) in plane stress to the behaviour of bulk polymer where plane-strain conditions may pertain.

Finally, shear yielding is highly relevant for the formation of 'diamond' cavities[125,126] during the ductile post-yield fracture of glassy polymers particularly at elevated temperatures (Fig. 4.13). These cavities form after bulk yielding as a precursor to ultimate failure of the specimens.

7.4.5 Crazing versus Shear Yielding: Entanglements

The tensile deformation of many glassy polymers can be considered to be a competititon between crazing and shear yielding. If crazing dominates the behaviour the polymer is brittle whereas if bulk shear yielding occurs preferentially the polymer is generally ductile. Hence the fracture behaviour of glassy polymers is controlled by a competition betwen crazing and bulk shear yielding.[127,128] Wellinghoff & Baer[127] have pointed out that there are differences in the chemical structure of polymers which show preference for either crazing or shear yielding. Vinyl polymers such as PS and PMMA (which they termed Type I) are generally brittle and undergo crazing whereas polymers which have flexible main-chain linkages such as PC or PET (Type II) are relatively ductile and undergo extensive shear yielding at ambient temperature.[129] However, both PC and PET show crazing at cryogenic temperatures (perhaps because of environmental attack) and also close to T_g.[129] There have been many explanations for the differences in behaviour of type I and type II glassy polymers. There is now strong evidence that the behaviour is controlled by entanglements but some of the earlier explanations are reviewed first of all.

7.4.5.1 β_r Relaxation

One suggestion for the difference in behaviour of these polymers has again been the β_r relaxation. It is thought that if the relaxation is uncoupled from side-group motion the polymer will undergo bulk shear yielding[127] whereas in type I polymers the β_r relaxation is associated with side-group motion. However, the clasification is not without important exceptions since rigid PVC is a vinyl polymer with such a β_r relaxation but is ductile. Also Wysgoski & Yeh[130] have shown that when the β_r relaxation in PC is suppressed by the addition of low molar mass diluents the polymer has increased ductility. In addition, annealing a polymer has little effect upon the β_r relaxation[127] but makes the polymer more brittle, hence there would seem to be no clear correlation between relaxation behaviour and the competition between crazing and shear yielding.

7.4.5.2 Activation Volume

Various theories[131-6] have been developed to explain the yield behaviour of glassy polymers and although they differ in detail they all produce molecular parameters such as a Burgers vector[131] or activation volume[135,136] which can be related to the dimensions of the molecules (Section 4.2.5). The ductile polymers (type II) tend to have large activation volumes or Burgers vectors whereas type I polymers, such as PS and PMMA, have considerably lower values. Although this helps to differentiate between the types of polymer it does not explain the behaviour.

7.4.5.3 Nodules

Several years ago there was a great deal of interest in the nodular structures that can be seen on the surface or in thin films of glassy polymers[137-9] and attempts were made to relate the mechanical behaviour to this structure.[139] However, small-angle X-ray scattering[140] and careful electron microscope studies[141] have shown that this structure is almost certainly an artefact and not representative of the true structure of glassy polymers.

7.4.5.4 Entanglements

Perhaps one of the most exciting developments in recent years has been the recognition of the importance of entanglements in the polymer network in controlling the deformation behaviour. This has been discussed in Sections 7.2.2 and 7.3.5 with respect to the dependence of σ_f and G_{Ic} upon molar mass. It is found that both σ_f and G_{Ic} fall to very low levels as $M \rightarrow \bar{M}_0$ and this corresponds to a value of molar mass when entanglements start to be formed in a polymer melt, $\bar{M}_e$ (Table 7.1). It is now thought that molecular entanglements in the glassy state may also control the geometry of both crazes and shear yield deformation zones and the type of deformation encountered in a particular polymer.[111,128] The morphology of crazes in PS changes markedly at $\bar{M}_0$. When $\bar{M}_w \gg \bar{M}_0$ crazes are found to have a dense fibrillar structure whereas for $\bar{M}_w < \bar{M}_0$ crazes have only a few fibrils and break down relatively easily.[103,104] Hence it appears that entanglements are essential for stable craze formation.

There is also now strong evidence that when $\bar{M}_w \gg \bar{M}_0$ the tendency for a polymer to undergo either shear yielding or crazing is controlled by the contour length of the polymer chain between entanglements, l_e. This parameter then governs the maximum extension ratio, λ_{max}, for the network i.e. the maximum allowable extension of the network without chain slippage or scission—through eqn. (4.17)

$$\lambda_{max} = \frac{l_e}{\langle \bar{R}^2_{rms} \rangle_e^{\frac{1}{2}}}$$

where $\langle \bar{R}^2_{rms} \rangle_e^{\frac{1}{2}}$ is the root mean square end-to-end distance of a chain of the entanglements molar mass, $\bar{M}_e$. Direct measurements of the extension ratio in both crazes and shear deformation zones by transmission electron microscopy and microdensitometry[111,124,128] have shown that the measured extension ratios of shear deformation zones, λ_{sz}, or craze fibrils, λ_{cf}, increase as λ_{max} and l_e increase. In the case of deformation zones it is found that $\lambda_{sz} \sim 0.6\lambda_{max}$ whereas for crazes λ_{cf} is approximately proportional to λ_{max} except at high values of λ_{max} when $\lambda_{cf} > \lambda_{max}$. The relationship between λ_{cf}, λ_{sz} and λ_{max} is shown in Fig. 7.13 for a large variety of polymers.[111,124] Although the relationship between the measured and calculated extension ratios is apparent, perhaps the most interesting aspect of the behaviour is that polymers with $\lambda_{max} < 3$ (or $l_e \sim 200$ Å) tend to deform by shear yielding, and polymers with $\lambda_{max} > 3$ tend to undergo crazing. Hence a criterion is established to determine whether a polymer will undergo deformation by shear yielding or crazing and therefore whether a polymer is ductile or brittle; the entire behaviour being governed by structural molecular parameters (see Section 5.7.2).

Another aspect of the behaviour of ductile glassy thermoplastics that needs to be explained is the tendency for polymers to undergo brittle crazing rather than extensive shear yielding after prolonged periods of deformation or following annealing. The time dependence is thought[124] to be due to the kinetics of chain scission or disentanglement that may be necessary for crazing and is supported by the observation that $\lambda_{cf} > \lambda_{max}$ for many types of craze. Annealing can cause a ductile/brittle transition in glassy polymers but it is more difficult

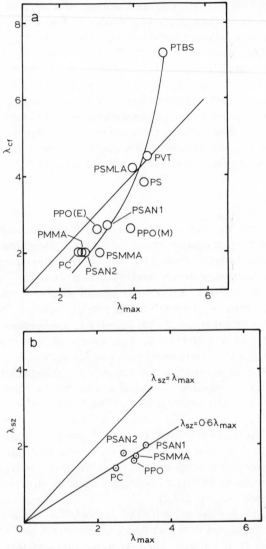

Fig. 7.13. (a) Variation of craze fibril extension ratio, λ_{cf}, with the maximum extension ratio of the polymer network, λ_{max}, for several different polymers: PTBS—poly(tert-butylstyrene); PVT—poly(paravinyl toluene); PSMLA—poly(styrene–maleic anhydride); PSMMA—poly(styrene–methyl methacrylate) copolymer; PSAN1 and PSAN2—poly(styrene–acrylonitrile) copolymers (after Donald & Kramer[111]); (b) Variation of the extension ratio in the shear deformation zone λ_{sz} with λ_{max} for several polymers (after Donald & Kramer[124]).

to account for in terms of entanglements. For the same polymer undergoing both crazing and shear yielding l_e should be constant since it is a property of the molecule whereas λ_{cf} and λ_{sz} are different.[124] In PC, which is not found to craze in the form of thin films at room temperature, the deformation zones become more well defined with annealing.[122] The increased localisation of deformation through either sharper deformation zones or crazing has been proposed as being the reason for annealed glassy polymers being embrittled. However, any changes in molecular processes involved perhaps through variations of l_e or $\langle \bar{R}_{rms}^2 \rangle_e^{\frac{1}{2}}$ on annealing have not been elucidated. A rather different explanation for the effect of annealing upon glassy polymers is that the increase in yield stress[35,142] causes a transition from shear yielding to crazing and hence the polymer becomes more brittle; the craze surface stress remains virtually unchanged with annealing.[35]

Another effect that can be partly explained in terms of entanglements is the suppression of crazing by cross-linking (Section 8.4.3). Clearly the value of l_e is reduced by cross-linking and in epoxy resins, for example, very tight networks can be produced. The observed transition from crazing to shear yielding on increasing the state-of-cure for epoxy resins[143] would clearly therefore be expected but in epoxy resins the shear yielding is localised at the crack tip. However, cross-linking also embrittles polymers and so it appears that *tough* polymers are only obtained when the entanglements are physical rather than chemical and so extensive shear yielding occurs rather than localised shear deformation.

7.4.6 Crack Propagation

Since either crazes or shear yield deformation zones are found at the tips of cracks in glassy polymers it is clear that crack propagation must occur by the breakdown of these crazes and shear deformation zones.

The mechanisms of craze breakdown in glassy polymers have been discussed in Section 5.6.1 and it is clear that the details of the process are not yet fully understood. The two main methods of studying the phenomenon have been direct observation of the moving crack/craze by optical interferometry,[1,66,67,95,144,151] and the examination of surfaces after fracture has taken place.[1,102,145–55] In the simplest case, such as a slowly moving crack/craze entity in PMMA, crack growth takes place by breakdown of the craze along its centre-line[95] which leaves a relatively smooth fracture surface. For more rapidly moving cracks in PMMA the fracture surfaces have regularly spaced 'rib' markings perpendicular to the direction of crack propagation[152-4] and the transition between the two types of surface can be very abrupt.[155] The origin of the rib features is somewhat uncertain although it would appear to be related to a type of stick/slip propagation due to either crack bifurcation or the effect of stress waves.[152] Fracture surfaces of PS have many more features than those of PMMA and so have been studied in more detail.[145-51] Again, for a slowly propagating

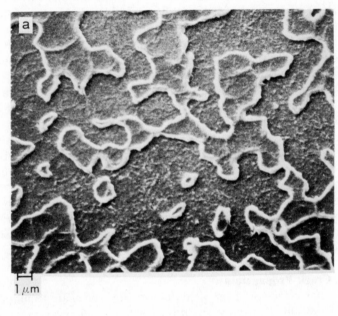

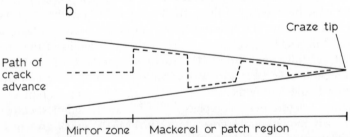

Fig. 7.14. 'Mackerel' or 'patch' patterns on the fracture surface of PS. (a) Scanning electron micrograph; (b) Schematic diagram showing the mechanism of formation of the patterns (after Lauterwasser & Kramer[105]).

crack/craze entity, breakdown occurs along the midrib of the craze[105,150,151] giving a relatively smooth fracture surface. Fracture parabolas[150,151] are often seen on the surfaces when relatively slow crack growth has taken place and these are thought to be due to ductile rupture of the midrib layer nucleated in the craze ahead of the crack front. The parabolic shape is due to interaction between a growing circular crack and the moving planar crack front. For rapidly moving cracks in PS irregular 'mackerel' or 'patch' patterns are seen on fracture surfaces[102,105,149,150] as shown in Fig. 7.14(a), corresponding to separation occurring at the craze/solid interface (Fig. 7.14(b)). However, the fracture surface appearance may also be affected by multiple crazing at high velocities complicating the mechanisms of crack extension.

There have been few detailed studies of the propagation of cracks through shear yield deformation zones in glassy polymers. Donald & Kramer[123] found that as the strain was increased in thin films of PC a characteristic 'half-diamond'-shaped crack developed along the centre of the deformation zone. There is clearly a similarity between this type of crack and the diamond cavities (Fig. 4.13) found by Haward and co-workers in bulk specimens of oriented glassy polymers during post-yield ductile fracture.[125,126,156] It is thought[123] that the cracks in the shear deformation zones are produced by a similar simple shear of the polymer chains parallel to the tensile axis.[156] In bulk specimens of polymers such as PC where the thickness is often less than twice the width of the shear lips cracks propagate through the plastic zone essentially by a ductile tearing process,[62–4] probably without crazing at the crack tip. This gives extensive shear yielding under plane-stress conditions and hence a ductile fracture is observed. The mechanism is likely to be similar to the breakdown of deformation zones in thin films of PC[123] described above.

7.4.7 Crack Healing

An interesting aspect of the fracture behaviour is the observation that if the two fractured halves of a specimen of a brittle polymer such as PMMA are held together and annealed above T_g the crack will completely heal and eventually the specimen will have a similar strength to the virgin specimen.[157] Clearly this healing or welding is a complementary process to fracture and the study of it may help to elucidate the mechanisms of fracture. The critical stress intensity factor to reinitiate a crack increases with contact time, t, and it is found[157] that for annealing above T_g

$$K_{Ic} \propto t^{\frac{1}{4}} \qquad (t < t_{cr}) \qquad (7.16)$$

or

$$G_{Ic} \propto t^{\frac{1}{2}} \qquad (t < t_{cr}) \qquad (7.17)$$

After a critical length of time, t_{cr}, which decreases as the temperature at which the healing takes place is increased, the original strength of the specimen is regained.

Kausch and co-workers[157,158] have considered the mechanisms involved in the healing process and have shown that it cannot be due simply to physical interfacial contacts being reformed as this occurs relatively quickly. They have also shown that the principal mechanism is probably interdiffusion of polymer chains across the boundary and the re-formation of entanglements. This clearly establishes common ground with recent investigations into the mechanisms of crazing and crack propagation, concerned with the effect of entanglements and discussed in Section (7.4.5).

7.5 IMPACT AND FATIGUE

7.5.1 Impact

Impact testing in polymers has been dealt with in detail in Section 6.2 and also in several useful reviews[4,159] with much of the discussion concerned with glassy polymers. In this section we will not be concerned so much with the technique of impact testing but will be dealing with the processes and mechanisms involved in the case of glassy polymers. Most of the investigations into impact behaviour have been concerned with pendulum impact tests.[4,160-3] There have been reports of using other methods such as the shock tube[164,165] and there is now an increasing use, especially in industrial laboratories, of instrumented impact-testing machines.[159,166]

Perhaps the most overriding reason for doing impact testing upon glassy polymers is to study *ductile/brittle transitions* which are accompanied by an abrupt drop in impact strength. This problem obviously has important implications for the use of glassy thermoplastics in engineering applications. A transition from ductile to brittle failure can be induced by modifications to the testing conditions such as

1. Reducing the testing temperature;[4,7,26,163]
2. Changing the testing rate;[26,167,168]

3. Notching with sharp cracks;[4,35,167,171,172]
4. Having surface rather than edge cracks;[11] and
5. Increasing specimen thickness.[12,170]

The first two variables modify the physical properties of the polymers through the normal time- and temperature-dependence. The other three geometrical factors have the effect of producing plane-strain conditions at the crack tip and causing more plastic constraint (Section 3.5). If the testing conditions are kept constant a ductile/brittle transition may be induced by making modifications to the material such as by

6. Annealing;[34,35,169,170]
7. Reducing the molar mass;[25,26,35,169]
8. Reducing plasticiser content;[26,130] and
9. Cross-linking.[26]

Many reasons have been put forward to explain the phenomenon of ductile/brittle transitions in glassy polymers and it is clear that there is no one overriding mechanism responsible for this behaviour. Pitman *et al.*[35] have accounted for the phenomenon in polymers such as PC in terms of a competition between shear yielding and crazing with shear yielding promoting ductile behaviour and crazing causing brittle fracture. This can clearly explain the effect of annealing and reducing the test temperature which both raise the yield stress and cause brittle fracture.[34] Lowering of the molar mass of the polymer causes a reduction in the craze stress, making crazing easier and so causing brittle behaviour[35] although Pitman *et al.* had only indirect evidence for crazing in their specimens. On the other hand, Mills[170] has shown convincingly that crazes form ahead of shear deformation zones during impact testing in PC. The effect of adding plasticiser is quite clear. It reduces the yield stress of the polymer and so promotes ductile behaviour.[130]

Changing the specimen geometry such as the notch tip radius, ρ_c, has a profound effect upon the impact behaviour of glassy polymers[4,35,167] as shown in Fig. 6.2. The effect of changing ρ_c upon the impact strength can be rationalised in terms of stress concentration at the root of the notch[4,171,172] and the effect of specimen geometry is discussed in detail in Section 6.2.3.

It has recently been recognised that significant heating can take place at the tips of cracks during tests at high rates.[167,168] This has the effect of increasing the *initiation* fracture energies or toughness values as the testing rate increases due, it is thought,[167,168] to the suppression of crazing through thermal effects and shear yielding becoming the dominant mode of deformation. At first sight this may seem to be in contradiction to the explanation of the adiabatic/isothermal transition (Section 7.3) where it is thought[48] that heating causes a drop in fracture energy and toughness with increasing crack velocity. However, the two situations are not the same. The adiabatic/isothermal transition takes place for a *rapidly moving* crack with no change in geometry whereas the thermal blunting argument is only applicable to a *stationary* crack which becomes blunted by adiabatic heating.

Over the years there have been many attempts to explain the impact behaviour of glassy polymers in terms of dynamic mechanical properties.[5,130,173,174] For some polymers there is a clear correlation between peaks in plots of the variation of impact strength with temperature and $\tan \delta_r$ with temperature as shown in Fig. 7.15. Unfortunately, this correlation is not universal and Vincent[5] in a survey of a large number of polymers showed that it worked for only about two-thirds of the

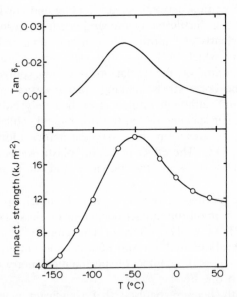

Fig. 7.15. *Variation of impact strength and* $\tan \delta_r$ *with temperature for the polysulphone of bisphenol A (after Vincent[5]).*

polymers he investigated. Heijboer[6] encountered similar problems and suggested that peaks in impact strength and tan δ_r may only correlate when the damping maximum is due to main-chain rather than side-group motion. Even this suggestion does not always work and there is the general philosophical problem of relating low-strain deformations used for dynamic mechanical testing to high-strain deformations encountered during impact. This problem is discussed further in Section 9.4.3 in relation to the impact behaviour of semicrystalline polymers.

7.5.2 Dynamic Fatigue

The general phenomenon of dynamic fatigue in polymers has been discussed in detail in Section 6.3 where it was shown that two particular mechanisms can be identified—namely, thermal fatigue and mechanical fatigue. There are also several excellent reviews of fatigue in polymers[1,3,175-7] and so in this section we will be concerned mainly with the effects of testing and material variables upon the fatigue resistance of glassy polymers.

Two basic approaches are adopted to investigate fatigue in glassy polymers. One is to produce 'S–N' curves, i.e. curves of number of cycles to failure, N_f, versus applied stress amplitude, σ_a, for unnotched specimens (e.g. References 177–80). The fatigue lifetime, N_f, increases as σ_a is reduced and for some polymers a fatigue limit is achieved (Fig. 6.5). Thermal effects are particularly prevalent in unnotched specimens as a relatively large volume of material is deformed and the largest temperature rises are found in polymers which have mechanical relaxations (e.g. β_r transitions) at the test temperature.[177]

A second approach to the analysis of fatigue in glassy polymers has been to use a LEFM analysis with precracked specimens.[48,176,181-92] It has been found that the crack growth rate da/dN can be related to the stress intensity factor range ΔK_I through an empirical relationship of the form (eqn. (6.19))

$$\frac{da}{dN} = A_f \, \Delta K_I{}^m$$

where A_f and m are constants which have values that depend upon the material, temperature, frequency, stress ratio and environment. It is found that for polymers m is only constant for materials which obey the assumptions of LEFM which is generally the case for glassy thermoplastics and the variation of da/dN with ΔK_I is shown for several glassy polymers in Fig. 6.7.

As with the impact behaviour the fatigue resistance of glassy polymers depends upon both testing variables, such as strain-rate or stress state, and material variables, such as polymer structure or molar mass. These two aspects are discussed separately in connection with both fatigue lifetimes for unnotched specimens and fatigue crack propagation rates in precracked test-pieces.

7.5.2.1 Testing Variables

The effect of testing variables upon the dynamic-fatigue behaviour of glassy polymers has been discussed in Section 6.3 and so only the main points will be covered here. Fatigue lifetimes tend to be reduced by increasing the stress amplitude, increasing the temperature and by the presence of surface scratches or notches.[177] The effect of test frequency is rather more complex as high frequencies can induce failure through thermal fatigue caused by hysteretic heating effects.[177] For example, PS which has very low viscoelastic losses at room temperature can be cycled at 30 Hz with only very small rises in temperature whereas PMMA under similar conditions which has a β_r relaxation close to room temperature fails by thermal rupture (Section 6.3.3).

Fatigue crack propagation rates are also affected strongly by testing variables[176] but it is rather difficult to generalise about how they affect the behaviour of glassy polymers. Crack propagation rates, da/dN, are found to decrease with increasing frequency for PMMA, PS and PVC but in polymers such as PC or PES da/dN is relatively frequency insensitive.[176] The effect of changing temperature also varies from polymer to polymer. For example, for a given ΔK_I level da/dN is found to increase with increasing temperature for PMMA and PS[176] but in the case of PC da/dN shows a maximum at about $-60°C$ and decreases at higher and lower temperatures,[190] probably because PC has its β_r relaxation at around $-60°C$. The ΔK_I level obviously affects da/dN through eqn. (6.19) but the exponent m varies from polymer to polymer as reflected by the different slopes of the lines in Fig. 6.7 and this can have repercussions over the ranking of the different polymers in terms of fatigue resistance. For example, at low levels of ΔK_I da/dN is lower for PMMA than PS and when $\Delta K_I > 0·55$ MN m$^{-\frac{3}{2}}$ the crack propagation rate is higher for PMMA.

7.5.2.2 Material Variables

In general, glassy polymers are considerably less resistant to fatigue than crystalline polymers because crystalline polymers are able to absorb energy through crystalline deformation mechanisms leading to shear yielding. The most fatigue-resistant glassy polymers are the ones which more readily undergo shear yielding such as PC and PES. Brittle polymers such as PS and PMMA tend to be more susceptible to fatigue failure.

Increasing the molar mass of brittle polymers such as PS has a dramatic effect upon their fatigue resistance even at high levels of molar mass. For example, the fatigue lifetime of PS can be increased by over two decades by increasing the molar mass from $1 \cdot 6 \times 10^5$ to 2×10^6 g mol^{-1}.[180] On the other hand, the tensile fracture properties of the polymer are not significantly affected in this molar mass range (Fig. 7.5(b)) and the improvement in fatigue resistance has been attributed to an increase in craze strength.[177] The molar mass distribution is also found to have an important effect on fatigue properties.[183] For example, fatigue crack propagation rates are reduced by the presence of small amounts of high-molar-mass polymer, again probably because the crazes are stabilised by more molecular entanglements.[177] In contrast, cross-linking, which inhibits crazing generally, reduces fatigue resistance.[176]

Modifications to polymers, such as the addition of rubber particles or plasticiser, which may improve the impact properties dramatically do not necessarily improve the fatigue resistance. It is found that rubber particles may produce a small improvement in fatigue behaviour[177] whereas plasticiser addition may either improve or worsen the fatigue behaviour depending upon the polymer/plasticiser system studied.[176,177]

7.5.2.3 Micromechanisms

As with the normal fracture process, the initiation and propagation of fatigue cracks is intimately concerned with crazing and shear yielding. The micromechanisms involved in fatigue fracture in polymers have been described in detail in Section 6.3.4 and so only those aspects relevant to glassy polymers will be amplified here. For unnotched specimens fatigue cracks are thought to initiate at surface flaws where, as in normal fracture, crazes form which then break down into cracks.[179] Most of the evidence for the mechanisms of fatigue crack propagation has been obtained from examination of the surface morphologies where striations are invariably found as shown in Fig. 7.16.[179,182] By employing precracked specimens Skibo *et al.*[182] were able to compare the number of fatigue cycles that specimens had been

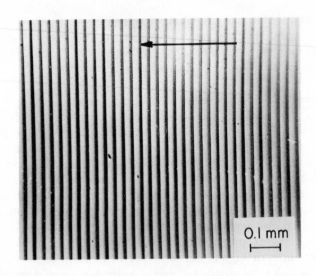

Fig. 7.16. Discontinuous fatigue crack propagation bands on the fracture surface of PS (after Skibo et al.[182]).

subjected to with the number of surface striations. In the low ΔK_I region there is a large discrepancy with up to 10^3 cycles for each striation whereas in the high ΔK_I region there is a one-to-one correspondence. Clearly, therefore, in the low ΔK_I region the cracks must grow *discontinuously* and the spacing between successive bands has been correlated with the length R_c of a Dugdale plastic zone[182] (Sections 3.3.2 and 6.3.4). It is thought[182,188] that during the cycles for which there is no crack growth a craze is developing at the crack tip. Since cracks grow under fatigue loading at considerably lower stresses than during monotonic loading it has been suggested[188] that the stress cycling must cause damage in the craze region. Applying a critical crack-opening displacement criterion, δ_{tc}, for PMMA gives a value of δ_{tc} for fatigue growth of about $0.5 \ \mu\text{m}$[188] which is only one-third of the value for monotonic loading, an observation consistent with the damage model. For fatigue crack growth in the high ΔK_I region, where each striation corresponds to one loading cycle, the values of $K_{I\text{max}}$ are obviously higher and it has been suggested[182] that in PS cracks propagate through bundles of crazes at the crack tip.

Finally, recent studies[193] of discontinuous fatigue crack growth in PC have shown that the craze breakdown model may be over-simplistic and that shear yielding may also be involved in this material. Observation of fatigue cracks growing discontinuously in PC has shown that fine shear deformation bands emanate from the crack surfaces. Moreover, the spacing of the shear bands is found to be the same as the spacing of the striations on the fracture surface. The obvious conclusion of this observation is that discontinuous fatigue crack growth in PC is associated with, and perhaps controlled by, localised shear yielding in the polymer. However, the effect may not be universal since similar observations upon other polymers such as PS, PVC and PPO did not reveal any shear bands at the crack tip.[193]

7.5.3 Static Fatigue

The phenomenon of static fatigue in glassy polymers has been discussed in detail in Section 6.4. In many ways it is difficult to differentiate between static fatigue and slow monotonic loading and since glassy polymers can often be analysed using LEFM it has been possible to predict the static-fatigue behaviour of glassy thermoplastics from crack propagation data for monotonic loading.[48,194,195]

It is necessary to separate the static fatigue of glassy polymers into two distinct processes, initiation and propagation. It follows that the total time-to-failure, t_f, is given by eqn. (6.24) such that

$$t_f = t_i + t_p$$

where t_i and t_p are the times required to initiate and propagate cracks, respectively. However, the extent to which each of these processes controls the behaviour is often difficult to determine. One way in which the situation can be simplified is to measure t_f for precracked specimens ($t_i = 0$) as shown in Fig. 7.17 for PMMA.[195] The value of t_f can be calculated as the relationship between K_{Ic} and $\dot{a}$, and for PMMA is (eqn. (6.25))

$$K_{Ic} = A_v \dot{a}^n$$

It can be shown (Section 6.4.3) that t_f is given by (eqn. (6.30))

$$t_f \approx \frac{2nA_v^{\frac{1}{n}}K_{Ic}^{(2n-1)/n}}{Q^2\sigma_c^2(1-2n)}$$

where K_{Ic} is the initial applied value of the stress intensity factor, Q is a geometrical factor, σ_c is the applied stress, and A_v and n are constants from eqn. (6.25). The line in Fig. 7.17 is eqn. (6.30) plotted using

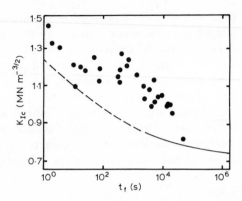

Fig. 7.17. *Variation of the time-to-failure, t_f, with K_{Ic} for PMMA. The line is calculated using eqn. (6.31) (after Young & Beaumont[195]).*

values of the various constants determined from monotonic crack-propagation experiments. It can be seen that all the experimental points lie to the right of the theoretical line showing that the theory gives a conservative prediction of t_f. Young & Beaumont[195] suggested that the discrepancy may be due to the precracked specimens not having sharp cracks and pointed out that applying a critical crack-opening displacement, δ_{tc}, criterion to static fatigue in PMMA leads to the conclusion that the behaviour is controlled solely by the rate dependence of the modulus of the polymer (i.e. the viscoelastic properties).

The LEFM approach can also be used to predict the failure of unnotched specimens if it is assumed that the inherent flaws are initiated instantly (i.e. $t_i \to 0$). Again a conservative prediction of t_f will be obtained.[195] A completely different approach has been used by Zhurkov and co-workers (Section 2.3) who employed the kinetic theory of fracture to model static fatigue as an activated-rate process.[196] Under an applied stress of σ_c the time-to-failure is given by eqn. (2.11) such that

$$t_f = t_0 \exp{(\Delta G^* - v^* \sigma_c)}/\mathbf{R}T$$

and this approach has been used to explain experimental static-fatigue data on glassy polymers such as PMMA[196,197] (Fig. 2.4). Papazian[198,199] followed a similar kinetic approach and looked at the effect of environment upon static fatigue. He showed that, by carrying out similar tests in air and a vacuum, $v^* \to 0$ in a vacuum and so the stress dependence in eqn. (2.11) may be due to an environmental effect. He also questioned the assumptions of the kinetic approach and suggested that the reasons why it works may be fortuitous. Clearly, it is rather difficult to rationalise the kinetic theory with LEFM and many of the parameters derived from kinetic theory have questionable significance (Table 6.4).

One aspect of the static-fatigue behaviour of glassy polymers that is of particular practical importance is the failure of PVC water-pipes through internal pressurisation over long periods of time.[200,201] The time-to-failure decreases as the pressure is increased and the failure mechanisms depend upon the pressure level. At high pressure the pipes fracture in a brittle manner over relatively short time periods. At moderate pressures the failure is ductile over medium periods of time. Finally, at low stress levels, the pipes fail by the growth of crazes over long periods of time. Clearly the behaviour of these PVC pipes is complex with several mechanisms operating. Obviously the simplistic approach exemplified by eqn. (6.30) cannot be applied as it stands. There is competition between crazing and shear yield and the mechanism that is dominant is controlled by the effective loading rate and stress level.

7.6 CONCLUDING REMARKS

Over the years there has been an enormous interest in the fracture of glassy thermoplastics but even so there are many questions remaining unanswered and several problems still unresolved. For example, the role of viscoelastic relaxations is still not fully understood. There is a clear correlation between relaxation phenomena and thermal fatigue but the way in which they affect impact properties or crack-propagation behaviour is not yet fully understood. On the other hand, it is well established that crazing is the dominant micromechanism controlling the fracture of brittle polymers such as PMMA or PS. It is also known that for more ductile polymers such as PC, crazing is in competition with shear yielding and this controls ductile/brittle transitions in such polymers.

Over recent years there have been attempts to correlate the fracture behaviour of glassy polymers with molecular structure. One aspect that has become particularly apparent is the way in which entanglements control deformation and fracture. Donald & Kramer[111,124] have shown that the entanglement structure determines whether a particular polymer will undergo crazing or shear yielding and hence whether it is brittle or ductile. Entanglements have also been shown to control the dependence of the fracture energy and fracture strength upon the molar mass of the polymer. In addition the re-entanglement of polymer chains is thought to be involved in crack healing.

In conclusions, therefore, it is clear that we are now beginning to understand the relationship between polymer structure and the fracture behaviour but we are a long way from being able to predict from the knowledge of the physical and chemical structure of a glassy thermoplastic how it will behave at a given temperature under a particular set of testing conditions, such as impact or fatigue. We would like to suggest that this might be the long-term aim of future investigations.

REFERENCES

1. Kambour, R. P. (1973). *J. Polym. Sci., Macro. Rev.*, **7**, 1.
2. Berry, J. P. (1972). In: *Fracture VII*, Ed. by H. Liebowitz, Academic Press, New York.
3. Andrews, E. H. (1968). *Fracture in polymers*, Oliver and Boyd, London.
4. Vincent, P. I. (1971). *Impact tests and service performance of thermoplastics*, Plastics and Rubber Inst., London.
5. Vincent, P. I. (1974). *Polymer*, **15**, 111.
6. Heijboer, J. (1968). *J. Polym. Sci.*, **C16**, 3755.
7. Vincent, P. I. (1972). *Polymer*, **13**, 558.
8. Berry, J. P. (1961). *J. Polym. Sci.*, **50**, 107.
9. Berry, J. P. (1961). *J. Polym. Sci.*, **50**, 313.
10. Earl, B. L., Loneragan, R. J. & Crook, M. (1973). *J. Mater. Sci.*, **8**, 370.
11. Parvin, M. & Williams, J. G. (1975). *Int. J. Fract.*, **11**, 963.
12. Brown, H. R. (1982). *J. Mater. Sci.*, **17**, 469.
13. Beardmore, P. & Johnson, T. L. (1971). *Phil. Mag.*, **23**, 1119.
14. Parrish, M. F. & Brown, N. (1972). *Nature*, **237**, 122.
15. Brown, N. (1973). *J. Polym. Sci., Polym. Phys. Ed.*, **11**, 2099.
16. Imai, Y. & Brown, N. (1976). *J. Mater. Sci.*, **11**, 417.
17. Imai, Y. & Brown, N. (1976). *J. Mater. Sci.*, **11**, 425.
18. Wu, J. C. B. & Brown, N. (1982). *J. Mater. Sci.*, **17**, 1311.
19. Kramer, E. J. (1979). In: *Developments in polymer fracture–1*, Ed. by E. H. Andrews, Applied Science Publishers Ltd, London, p. 55.
20. Vincent, P. I. & Raha, S. (1972). *Polymer*, **13**, 283.
21. Pae, K. D. & Bhateja, S. K. (1975). *J. Macromol. Sci.-Revs. Macromol. Chem.*, **C13**, 1.

22. Biglione, G., Baer, E. & Radcliffe, S. V. (1969). In: *Proceedings of 2nd international conference on fracture, Brighton,* Chapman and Hall, London, p. 503.
23. Rabinowitz, S., Ward, I. M. & Parry, J. S. C. (1970). *J. Mater. Sci.,* **5,** 29.
24. Duckett, R. A. (1980). *J. Mater. Sci.,* **15,** 2471.
25. Martin, J. R., Johnson, J. F. & Cooper, A. R. (1972). *J. Macromol. Sci-Revs. Macromol. Chem.,* **C8,** 57.
26. Vincent, P. I. (1960). *Polymer,* **1,** 425.
27. McCormick, H. W., Brower, F. M. & Kin, L. (1959). *J. Polym. Sci.,* **39,** 87.
28. Golden, J. H., Hammant, B. L. & Hazell, E. A. (1964). *J. Polym. Sci.,* **A2,** 4787.
29. Flory, P. J. (1945). *J. Amer. Chem. Soc.,* **67,** 2048.
30. Gent, A. N. & Thomas, A. G. (1972). *J. Polym. Sci.,* **A-2 10,** 571.
31. Turner, D. J. (1982). *Polymer.* **23,** 626.
32. Curtis, J. W. (1970). *J. Phys. D., Appl. Phys.,* **3,** 1413.
33. Sternstein, S. S. & Rosenthal, J. (1976). In: *Toughness and brittleness of plastics,* ACS series **154,** American Chemical Society, Washington D.C. p. 35.
34. Legrand, D. G. (1969). *J. Appl. Polym. Sci.,* **13,** 2129.
35. Pitman, G. L., Ward, I. M. & Duckett, R. A. (1978). *J. Mater. Sci.,* **13,** 2092.
36. Vincent, P. I. & Gotham, K. V. (1966). *Nature,* **210,** 1254.
37. Marshall, G. P., Culver, L. E. & Williams, J. G. (1969). *Plast. and Polym.,* Feb., 75.
38. Marshall, G. P. & Williams, J. G. (1973). *J. Mater. Sci.,* **8,** 138.
39. Benbow, J. J. & Roesler, F. C. (1956). *Proc. Phys. Soc.,* **70B,** 201.
40. Broutman, L. J. & McGarry, F. J. (1965). *J. Appl. Phys.,* **9,** 589.
41. Williams, J. G., Radon, J. C. & Turner, C. E. (1968). *Polym. Eng. Sci.,* **8,** 130.
42. Van den Boogaart, A. (1966). In: *Physical basis of yield and fracture,* Institute of Physics, London, p. 167.
43. Beaumont, P. W. R. & Young, R. J. (1975). *J. Mater. Sci.,* **10,** 1334.
44. Johnson, F. A. & Radon, J. C. (1973). *J. Polym. Sci., Polym. Chem. Ed.,* **11,** 1995.
45. Weidmann, G. W. & Döll, W. (1976). *Coll. Polym. Sci.,* **254,** 205.
46. Marshall, G. P., Coutts, L. H. & Williams, J. G. (1974). *J. Mater. Sci.,* **9,** 1409.
47. Williams, J. G. (1972). *Int. J. Fract. Mech.,* **8,** 393.
48. Williams, J. G. (1978). *Adv. Polym. Sci.,* **27,** 67.
49. Young, R. J. & Beaumont, P. W. R. (1976). *Polymer,* **17,** 717.
50. Williams, J. G. & Marshall, G. P. (1975). *Proc. Roy. Soc.,* **A342,** 55.
51. Morgan, G. P. & Ward, I. M. (1977). *Polymer,* **18,** 87.
52. Weidmann, G. W. & Döll, W. (1978). *Int. J. Fract.,* **14,** R189.
53. McCrum, N. G., Reed, B. E. & Williams, G. (1967). *Anelastic and dielectric effects in polymeric solids,* John Wiley, London.
54. Marshall, G. P., Culver, L. E. & Williams, J. G. (1973). *Int. J. Fract.,* **9,** 295; and Young, R. J. & Beaumont, P. W. R. unpublished results.

55. Mai, Y. W. & Atkins, A. G. (1976). *J. Mater. Sci.*, **11**, 677.
56. Parvin, M. & Williams, J. G. (1975). *J. Mater. Sci.*, **10**, 1883.
57. Atkins, A. G., Lee, C. S. & Caddell, R. M. (1975). *J. Mater. Sci.*, **10**, 1381.
58. Fraser, R. A. & Ward, I. M. (1978). *Polymer*, **19**, 220.
59. Döll, W. & Weidmann, G. W. (1976). *J. Mater. Sci.*, **11**, 2348.
60. Fuller, K. N. G., Fox, P. G. & Field, J. E. (1974). *Proc. Roy. Soc.*, **A341**, 537.
61. Hobbs, S. Y. & Bopp, R. C. (1980). *Polymer*, **21**, 559.
62. Kambour, R. P., Holik, A. S. & Miller, S. (1978). *J. Polym. Sci., Polym. Phys. Ed.*, **16**, 91.
63. Kambour, R. P. & Miller, S. (1976). *J. Mater. Sci.*, **11**, 1220.
64. Kambour, R. P. & Miller, S. (1976). *J. Mater. Sci.*, **11**, 823.
65. Parvin, M. & Williams, J. G. (1975). *Int. J. Fract.*, **11**, 963.
66. Pitman, G. L. & Ward, I. M. (1979). *Polymer*, **20**, 895.
67. Hine, P. J., Duckett, R. A. & Ward, I. M. (1981). *Polymer*, **22**, 1745.
68. Berry, J. P. (1964). *J. Polym. Sci.*, **A2**, 4069.
69. Kusy, R. P. & Turner, D. T. (1976). *Polymer*, **17**, 161.
70. Kusy, R. P. & Katz, M. J. (1976). *J. Mater. Sci.*, **11**, 1475.
71. Robertson, R. E. (1976). In: *Toughness and brittleness of plastics*, Advances in Chemistry **154**, American Chemical Society, Washington D.C., p. 89.
72. Kramer, E. J. (1979). *J. Mater. Sci.*, **14**, 1381.
73. Broutman, L. J. & McGarry, F. J. (1965). *J. Appl. Polym. Sci.*, **9**, 609.
74. Miller, L. E., Puttick, K. E. & Rider, J. G. (1971). *J. Polym. Sci.*, **C33**, 13.
75. Mai, Y. W. (1974). *Int. J. Fract.*, **10**, 288.
76. Mai, Y. W. (1975). *J. Mater. Sci.*, **10**, 943.
77. Hakeem, M. I. & Phillips, M. G. (1978). *J. Mater. Sci.*, **13**, 2284.
78. Mai, Y. W. (1979). *J. Mater. Sci.*, **14**, 2264.
79. Hakeem, M. I. & Phillips, M. G. (1979). *J. Mater. Sci.*, **14**, 2901.
80. Bowden, P. B. & Oxborough, R. J. (1973). *Phil. Mag.*, **28**, 547.
81. Argon, A. S. (1975). *Pure and Appl. Chem.*, **43**, 247.
82. Argon, A. S. & Salama, M. M. (1977). *Phil. Mag.*, **35**, 1217.
83. Argon, A. S. & Hannoosh, J. G. (1977). *Phil. Mag.*, **36**, 1195.
84. Bernier, G. A. & Kambour, R. P. (1968). *Macromolecules*, **1**, 393.
85. Kambour, R. P., Gruner, C. L. & Romagosa, E. E. (1973). *J. Polym. Sci., Polym. Phys. Ed.*, **11**, 1879.
86. Vincent, P. I. & Raha, S. (1972). *Polymer*, **13**, 283.
87. Andrews, E. H. & Bevan, L. (1972). *Polymer*, **13**, 337.
88. Andrews, E. H., Levy, G. M. & Willis, J. (1973). *J. Mater. Sci.*, **8**, 1000.
89. Andrews, E. H. & Levy, G. M. (1974). *Polymer*, **15**, 599.
90. Brown, H. R. & Kramer, E. J. (1981). *Polymer*, **22**, 687.
91. Marshall, G. P., Culver, L. E. & Williams, J. G. (1970). *Proc. Roy. Soc.*, **A319**, 165.
92. Weidmann, G. W. & Williams, J. G. (1975). *Polymer*, **16**, 921.
93. Graham, I. D., Williams, J. G. & Zichy, E. L. (1976). *Polymer*, **17**, 439.

94. Miltz, J., Dibenedetto, A. T. & Petrie, S. (1978). *J. Mater. Sci.*, **13**, 1427.
95. Brown, H. R. & Ward, I. M. (1973). *Polymer*, **14**, 469.
96. Weidmann, G. W. & Döll, W. (1978). *Proc. of mechanisms of deformation and fracture*, Univ. of Lulea, Sweden, p. 323.
97. Brown, H. R. & Kramer, E. J. (1981). *J. Macromol. Sci.-Phys.*, **B19**, 487.
98. Legrand, D. G., Kambour, R. P. & Haaf, W. R. (1972). *J. Polym. Sci.*, **A-2 10**, 1565.
99. Parades, E. & Fischer, E. W. (1979). *Makromol. Chem.*, **180**, 2707.
100. Beahan, P., Bevis, M. & Hull, D. (1971). *Phil. Mag.*, **24**, 1267.
101. Beahan, P., Bevis, M. & Hull, D. (1972). *J. Mater. Sci.*, **8**, 162.
102. Beahan, P., Bevis, M. & Hull, D. (1975). *Proc. Roy. Soc.*, **A343**, 525.
103. Lainchbury, D. L. G. & Bevis, M. (1976). *J. Mater. Sci.*, **11**, 2222.
104. Wellinghoff, S. T. & Baer, E. (1975). *J. Macromol. Sci.*, **B11**, 367.
105. Lauterwasser, B. D. & Kramer, E. J. (1979). *Phil. Mag.*, **A39**, 469.
106. King, P. S. & Kramer, E. J. (1981). *J. Mater. Sci.*, **16**, 1843.
107. Farrar, N. R. & Kramer, E. J. (1981). *Polymer*, **22**, 691.
108. Donald, A. M. & Kramer, E. J. (1981). *Phil. Mag.*, **A43**, 857.
109. Donald, A. M., Chan, T. & Kramer, E. J. (1981). *J. Mater. Sci.*, **16**, 669.
110. Chan, T., Donald, A. M. & Kramer, E. J. (1981). *J. Mater. Sci.*, **16**, 676.
111. Donald, A. M. & Kramer, E. J. (1982). *J. Polym. Sci., Polym. Phys. Ed.*, **20**, 899.
112. Donald, A. M. & Kramer, E. J. (1982). *Polymer*, **23**, 457.
113. Wu, J. B. C. & Li, J. C. M. (1976). *J. Mater. Sci.*, **11**, 43.
114. Chau, C. C. & Li, J. C. M. (1979). *J. Mater. Sci.*, **14**, 2172.
115. Wellinghoff, S. & Baer, E. (1978). *J. Appl. Polym. Sci.*, **22**, 2025.
116. Camwell, L. & Hull, D. (1973). *Phil. Mag.*, **27**, 1135.
117. Narisawa, I., Ishikawa, M. & Ogawa, H. (1980). *Phil. Mag.*, **41**, 331.
118. Ishikawa, M., Ogawa, H. & Narisawa, I. (1981). *J. Macromol. Sci.-Phys.*, **B19**, 421.
119. Mills, N. J. (1974). *Eng. Fract. Mech.*, **6**, 537.
120. Donald, A. M., Kramer, E. J. & Kambour, R. P. (1982). *J. Mater. Sci.*, **17**, 1739.
121. Brinson, H. F. (1970). *Expt. Mech.*, **27**, 72.
122. Donald, A. M. & Kramer, E. J. (1981). *J. Mater. Sci.*, **16**, 2967.
123. Donald, A. M. & Kramer, E. J. (1981). *J. Mater. Sci.*, **16**, 2977.
124. Donald, A. M. & Kramer, E. J. (1982). *Polymer*, **23**, 1183.
125. Cornes, P. L. & Haward, R. N. (1974). *Polymer*. **15**, 149.
126. Cornes, P. L., Smith, K. & Haward, R. N. (1977). *J. Polym. Sci., Polym. Phys. Ed.*, **15**, 955.
127. Wellinghoff, S. T. & Baer, E. (1978). *J. Appl. Polym. Sci.*, **22**, 2025.
128. Donald, A. M. & Kramer, E. J. (1982). *J. Mater. Sci.*, **17**, 1871.
129. Kastelic, J. R. & Baer, E. (1973). *J. Macromol. Sci., Phys.*, **B7**, 679.
130. Wysgoski, M. G. & Yeh, G. S. (1974). *J. Macromol. Sci.-Phys.*, **B10**, 441.
131. Bowden, P. B. & Raha, S. (1974). *Phil. Mag.*, **29**, 149.
132. Argon, A. S. (1973). *Phil. Mag.*, **28**, 839.
133. Argon, A. S. & Bessonov, M. I. (1977). *Polym. Eng. Sci.*, **17**, 174.
134. Yamini, S. & Young, R. J. (1980). *J. Mater. Sci.*, **15**, 1814.

135. Bauwens-Crowet, C., Bauwens, J. C. & Homes, G. (1972). *J. Polym. Sci.,* **A-2 7,** 735.
136. Bauwens-Crowet, C., Bauwens, J. C. & Homes, G. (1976). *J. Mater. Sci.,* **7,** 176.
137. Yeh, G. S. Y. (1972). *CRC Crit. Rev. Macromol. Sci.,* **1,** 173.
138. Neki, K. & Geil, P. H. (1973). *J. Macromol. Sci.-Phys.,* **B8,** 295.
139. Yeh, G. S. Y. (1973). *J. Macromol. Sci.-Phys.,* **B7,** 729.
140. Uhlmann, D. R. (1979). *Farad. Disc.,* **68,** 87.
141. Thomas, E. L. *Structure of crystalline polymers,* Ed. by I. H. Hall, Applied Science Publishers Ltd., London, to be published.
142. Parvin, M. (1981). *J. Mater. Sci.,* **16,** 1796.
143. Van den Boogaart, A. (1966). In: *Physical basis of yield and fracture,* Inst. Phys., London, p. 167.
144. Murray, J. & Hull, D. (1970). *J. Polym. Sci., Polym. Lett.,* **8,** 159.
145. Bird, R. J., Mann, J., Pogany, G. & Rooney, G. (1966). *Polymer,* **7,** 307.
146. Bird, R. J., Rooney, G. & Mann, J. (1971). *Polymer,* **12,** 742.
147. Murray, J. & Hull, D. (1970). *J. Polym. Sci.,* **A-2, 8,** 583.
148. Murray, J. & Hull, D. (1970). *J. Polym. Sci.,* **A-2, 8,** 1521.
149. Hull, D. (1970). *J. Mater. Sci.,* **5,** 357.
150. Doyle, M. J., Maranci, A., Orowan, E. & Stork, S. T. (1972). *Proc. Roy. Soc.,* **A329,** 137.
151. Doyle, M. J., (1982). *J. Mater. Sci.,* **17,** 760.
152. Kusy, R. P., Lee, H. B. & Turner, D. T. (1976). *J. Mater. Sci.,* **11,** 118.
153. Kusy, R. P. (1976). *J. Mater. Sci.,* **11,** 1381.
154. Kusy, R. P. & Turner, D. T. (1977). *Polymer,* **18,** 391.
155. Döll, W. (1975). *J. Mater. Sci.,* **10,** 935.
156. Walker, N., Haward, R. N. & Hay, J. N. (1979). *J. Mater. Sci.,* **14,** 1085.
157. Jud, K., Kausch, H. H. & Williams, J. G. (1981). *J. Mater. Sci.,* **16,** 204.
158. Kausch, H. H. (1981). *Coll. Polym. Sci.,* **259,** 917.
159. Reed, P. E. (1979). In: *Developments in polymer fracture—1,* Ed. by E. H. Andrews, Applied Science Publishers Ltd., London, 1979, p. 121.
160. Brown, H. R. (1973). *J. Mater. Sci.,* **8,** 941.
161. Marshall, G. P., Williams, J. G. & Turner, C. E. (1973). *J. Mater. Sci.,* **8,** 949.
162. Platí, E. & Williams, J. G. (1975). *Polymer,* **16,** 915.
163. Plati, E. & Williams, J. G. (1975). *Polym. Eng. Sci.,* **15,** 470.
164. Reed, P. E., Nurse, P. J. & Andrews, E. H. (1974). *J. Mater. Sci.,* **9,** 1977.
165. Squires, H. V. & Reed, P. E. (1975). *J. Mater. Sci.,* **10,** 1465.
166. Gonzalez, H., Jr. & Stowell, W. J. (1976). *J. Appl. Polym. Sci.,* **20,** 1389.
167. Williams, J. G. & Hodgkinson, J. M. (1981). *Proc. Roy. Soc.,* **A375,** 231.
168. Clutton, E. Q. & Williams, J. G. (1981). *J. Mater. Sci.,* **16,** 2583.
169. Ryan, J. T. (1978). *Polym. Eng. Sci.,* **18,** 264.
170. Mills, N. J., (1976). *J. Mater. Sci.,* **11,** 363.
171. Fraser, R. A. & Ward, I. M. (1974). *J. Mater. Sci.,* **9,** 1624.
172. Fraser, R. A. & Ward, I. M. (1977). *J. Mater. Sci.,* **12,** 459.
173. Wada, Y. & Kasahara, T. (1967). *J. Appl. Polym. Sci.,* **11,** 1661.
174. Turley, S. G. (1968). *Appl. Polym. Sym.,* **7,** 237.

175. Plumbridge, W. J. (1972). *J. Mater. Sci.*, **7**, 939.
176. Hertzberg, R. W. & Manson, J. A. (1980). *Fatigue of engineering plastics*, Academic Press, New York.
177. Sauer, J. A. & Richardson, G. C. (1980). *Int. J. Fract.*, **16**, 499.
178. Constable, I., Williams, J. G. & Burns, D. J. (1970). *J. Mech. Eng. Sci.*, **12**, 20.
179. Sauer, J. A., McMaster, A. D. & Morrow, D. R. (1976). *J. Macromol Sci.-Phys.*, **B12**, 535.
180. Sauer, J. A., Foden, E. & Morrow, D. R. (1977). *Polym. Eng. Sci.*, **17**, 246.
181. Hertzberg, R. W., Nordberg, H. & Manson, J. A. (1970). *J. Mater. Sci.*, **5**, 521.
182. Skibo, M. D., Hertzberg, R. W. & Manson, J. A. (1976). *J. Mater. Sci.*, **11**, 479.
183. Kim, S. L., Janiszewski, J., Skibo, M. D., Manson, J. A. & Hertzberg, R. W. (1979). *Polym. Eng. Sci.*, **19**, 147.
184. Constable, I., Culver, L. E. & Williams, J. G. (1970). *Int. J. Fract. Mech.*, **6**, 279.
185. Arad, S., Radon, J. C. & Culver, L. E. (1971). *J. Mech. Eng. Sci.*, **13**, 2.
186. Arad, S., Radon, J. C. & Culver, L. E. (1972). *J. Mech. Eng. Sci.*, **14**, 328.
187. Radon, J. C. (1973). *J. Appl. Polym. Sci.*, **17**, 3515.
188. Williams, J. G. (1977). *J. Mater. Sci.*, **12**, 2525.
189. Martin, G. C. & Gerberich, W. W. (1976). *J. Mater. Sci.*, **11**, 231.
190. Pitman, G. & Ward, I. M. (1980). *J. Mater. Sci.*, **15**, 635.
191. Rimnac, C. M., Manson, J. A., Hertzberg, R. W., Webler, S. M. & Skibo, M. D. (1981). *J. Macromol. Sci.-Phys.*, **B19**, 351.
192. Manson, J. A., Hertzberg, R. W., Kim, S. L. & Wu, W. C. (1976). In: *Toughness and brittleness of plastics, Advances in Chemistry*, **154**, American Chemical Society, Washington, D.C., p. 146.
193. Takemori, M. T. & Kambour, R. P. (1981). *J. Mater. Sci.*, **16**, 1108.
194. Beaumont, P. W. R. & Young, R. J. (1975). *J. Mater. Sci.*, **10**, 1334.
195. Young, R. J. & Beaumont, P. W. R. (1976). *Polymer*, **17**, 717.
196. Zhurkov, S. N. (1965). *Int. J. Fract. Mech.*, **1**, 210.
197. Regel, V. R. (1956). *Sov. Phys. Tech. Phys.*, **1**, 353.
198. Papazian, H. A. (1973). *J. Appl. Polym. Sci.*, **17**, 3809.
199. Papazian, H. A. (1974). *J. Appl. Polym. Sci.*, **18**, 2311.
200. Kausch, H. H. (1971). *J. Polym. Sci.*, **C32**, 1.
201. Kausch, H. H. (1978). *Polymer fracture*, Springer-Verlag, Berlin, Heidelberg, New York, p. 2.

Chapter 8

Glassy Polymers II—Thermosets

8.1 INTRODUCTION

The second class of glassy polymers that will be considered are
thermosets. These are highly cross-linked polymers that are invariably
used below their glass transition temperatures, in contrast to rubbers
which tend to be lightly cross-linked and used above their T_g's. Thermosets have a reputation of being very brittle, intractable materials
and many modern developments have been concerned with methods of
maximising and improving their toughness. One method of doing this
is by the addition of second-phase particles, such as brittle fillers or
rubber particles, and this is covered in Chapter 11. An important use
of thermosetting polymers and especially epoxy resins is as high-
strength adhesives.[1] However, in this chapter only investigations into
the failure of adhesive joints which are relevant to cohesive fracture
will be considered. Another important use of thermosets is as matrix
materials for fibre-reinforced composites but the fracture of fibre
composites will not be considered here as it has been reviewed
extensively elsewhere.[2]

The term 'thermosets' covers a wide range of cross-linked polymers,
the most important of which are epoxy resins, unsaturated polyesters,
phenol-formaldehyde and amino resins. Although the properties of
these different materials vary in detail they have many characteristics
in common. Most of the detailed investigations into the fracture of
thermosets have centred upon the fracture of epoxy resins, generally
the strongest type of thermosets, and there has been rather less
emphasis upon the other materials. Most of the recent advances in the

understanding of the fracture behaviour of brittle polymers have been through the application of fracture mechanics and much of this chapter is concerned with the study of thermosets using fracture mechanics.

Being generally insoluble in all solvents, thermosetting polymers are extremely difficult to characterise in terms of their chemical structure. This structure can be varied by employing different types and amounts of curing agent or hardener which tend to control the degree of cross-linking. Chemical structure will only be described where it is shown to have a direct effect upon the fracture behaviour and the reader is directed to general textbooks[3] for details of the chemistry of thermosets.

The physical microstructure of glassy polymers such as thermosets is rather difficult to study and is a matter of some controversy. There have been suggestions of a nodular microstructure[4] but it is not clear whether this represents the true structure or if it is just an artefact of the techniques used to prepare the specimens for examination. Small-angle X-ray scattering[5] and light-scattering experiments[6] have indicated that there may be structural inhomogeneities on the 10–20 nm level in epoxy resins although the number and nature of these is uncertain. The possible effect of the physical microstructure on the fracture properties of thermosets will be considered in some detail.

8.2 BRITTLE FRACTURE

8.2.1 Stress/Strain Behaviour

Thermosetting polymers are some of the most brittle types of polymer and this is reflected in their simple stress/strain behaviour. A series of stress/strain curves for an epoxy resin obtained at different temperatures are shown in Fig. 8.1. The glass transition temperature quoted for the particular resin was 150°C. It can be seen that at low temperatures (<30°C) the material is completely brittle with a linear relationship between stress and strain, and the fracture stress drops as the temperature is increased. Within about 100 K of the T_g the curves become non-linear but the material is still brittle. Above 100°C the polymer starts to show a limited degree of 'ductility' but unlike some thermoplastics approaching T_g there is no cold-drawing or associated necking. Above T_g epoxy resins undergo tearing in a similar way to highly cross-linked rubbers.[8]

Although thermosetting polymers are generally thought to be rather

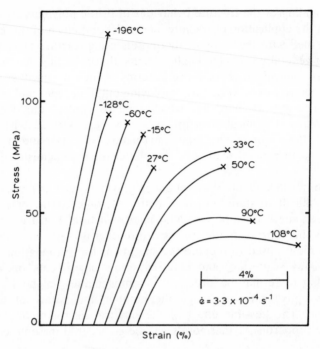

Fig. 8.1. Stress/strain curves for an epoxy resin deformed in tension at different temperatures (after Pink & Campbell[7]).

brittle this type of behaviour can be suppressed by using different stressing systems. Figure 8.2 shows a series of stress/strain curves for an epoxy resin deformed under different states of stress. In simple uniaxial tension they are brittle, failing at very low strains. They will yield and undergo considerable plastic deformation in uniaxial compression or in pure shear, obeying a pressure-dependent yield criterion (Section 4.2.4) in a similar way to other glassy polymers. The amount of post-yield plastic strain in compression varies from about 10 % to over 50 % depending upon the state of cure of the resin. Indeed, Yamini & Young[9] have shown that the yield behaviour of an epoxy resin is very similar to that of an uncross-linked polymer glass such as polystyrene and that epoxy resins generally obey the yield theories of Argon[10] and Bowden and co-workers.[11,12] It is found, however, that the amount of plastic deformation after yield in thermosets is rather less than in thermoplastics. It appears, therefore, that it is the inability

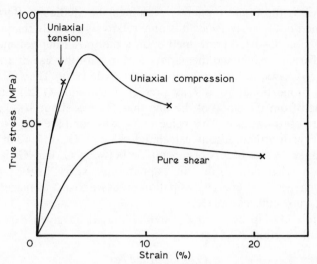

Fig. 8.2. Variation of true stress with strain for an epoxy resin (DGEBA cured with 5 phr of piperidine) deformed at 20°C under different states of stress (Kinloch & Shaw unpublished results).

of cross-linked thermosets to undergo crazing (Section 8.4.3) and the lower amount of post-yield deformation which causes them to be more brittle than linear thermoplastics during tensile deformation.

8.2.2 Fracture Strength, Fracture Energy and Flaws

It was shown in Chapter 2 that the theoretical strength to cause cleavage fracture in a brittle solid is of the order of $E/10$, i.e. one-tenth of the Young's modulus. Since glassy polymers such as thermosets have moduli typically of the order of 3 GPa their theoretical strengths are predicted to be 300 MPa. The fracture stresses of thermosets are typically in the range of 10–100 GPa; the reduction in strength being due to the presence of flaws.[13]

Early studies of the fracture of brittle thermoplastics undertaken by Berry[14] and described in Chapter 7 showed that the relationship between the fracture stress, σ_f, and the size of the flaws, a, artificially induced or 'natural', could be fitted to a modified Griffith equation (eqn. (1.25)) of the form

$$\sigma_f = \left(\frac{EG_c}{\pi a}\right)^{\frac{1}{2}}$$

where G_c is the fracture energy. Although the studies of Berry were performed in the early 1960s it is only relatively recently that a similar investigation has been performed upon a thermosetting polymer. Nelson & Turner[15] examined the variation of σ_f with the size of artificially introduced flaws, a, for a phenol-formaldehyde resin. They found that σ_f was proportional to $a^{-\frac{1}{2}}$ as predicted by eqn. (1.25) and they calculated from the slope of the line that G_c was about $100 \, \text{J m}^{-2}$ for the thermosetting resin. This value of G_c was compared by Nelson & Turner[15] with a theoretically calculated value of G_0 of $1 \cdot 4 \, \text{J m}^{-2}$. This discrepancy of two orders of magnitude between G_c and G_0 is a clear indication that even in the apparently very brittle phenol-formaldehyde resin, energy dissipation processes, such as plastic deformation, must still take place.

The relationship between G_c and G_0 has been given explicitly in eqn. (3.8) (Section 3.2.1) as

$$G_c = G_0 \Phi(\dot{a}, T, e)$$

and when viscoelastic and plastic energy losses are made negligible, for example by growing cracks slowly, then $\Phi(\dot{a}, T, e) \rightarrow 1$ and the measured value of fracture energy becomes equal to G_0. This approach has been followed by King & Andrews[8] who, by determining the fracture energies of a series of epoxy resins at different rates above their T_gs (typically $\sim 70°C$), found that G_0 was in the range of $3-4 \, \text{J m}^{-2}$. The behaviour was interpreted using a modified version of the theory of Lake & Thomas[16] which assumes that, for a polymer network, in order to break one particular bond, all the bonds in the length of the chain between cross-links must be stressed to almost the breaking strain (Sections 2.2.2 and 10.3.3). Andrews & King[8] went on to show that the measured values of G_0 agreed closely with the theoretically calculated ones. They also commented that the values of G_0 for epoxies were an order of magnitude lower that those for rubbers which, they suggested, was due to the smaller number of epoxy resin bonds capable of storing energy when the main chain is stressed.

8.2.3 Cross-link Density

The degree of cross-linking for a thermoset can be estimated by measuring the modulus of the polymer in the rubbery state above the T_g[8,17-19] and the parameter which is normally quoted is $\bar{M}_c$, the average molar mass between cross-links. It is found that the fracture stress, Young's modulus and fracture strain for several epoxy resins are virtually unaffected by variations in $\bar{M}_c^{17-19}$ even though T_g falls markedly as $\bar{M}_c$ increases. On the other hand, there have been reports of maxima in both the Charpy[17] and notched Izod[19] impact strengths for different epoxy resins at values of $\bar{M}_c$ around 500–1000 g mol^{-1} although the reason for this is not known.

A link between thermoplastics and thermosets has been established by Berry[14] and Broutman & McGarry[20] by investigating the effect of different degrees of cross-linking upon the fracture energy of PMMA. Although the degree of cross-linking was not precisely defined they were able to show that as the cross-link density increased G_{Ic} dropped and it was found that the most highly cross-linked PMMA had a value of G_{Ic} of over an order of magnitude less than the uncross-linked polymer. This is an excellent demonstration of the general observation that thermosets generally have lower fracture energies than thermoplastics.[21]

8.3 CRACK PROPAGATION

8.3.1 Fracture Mechanics Testing

One of the most convenient ways of studying the propagation of cracks in thermosetting polymers is through the application of linear elastic fracture mechanics (LEFM, Section 3.2.2). Since thermosets are generally relatively brittle and display approximately linear elastic deformation behaviour with very little plastic deformation they readily meet the requirements for LEFM to be applied. In the past a variety of specimen geometries have been used to follow the fracture of thermosets. Some of the most reproducible and interesting results have been obtained using test-pieces in which the stress intensity factor K_{Ic} is independent of crack length (linear compliance variation specimens, Section 3.6.2) such as the tapered double cantilever beam (TDCB) or double torsion (DT) specimens. In these specimens there is generally good control of crack propagation. In test-pieces such as the single-edge crack or three-point bend the crack accelerates as soon as it starts to propagate and grows in an unstable manner—they are also prone to scatter in data because of the variation in sharpness of the original crack. Normally data are only recorded from the TDCB or DT specimens when a natural crack has formed and is propagating.

The earliest investigations into crack propagation in thermosets were performed by Broutman & McGarry[20] and Mostovoy & Ripling.[22]

Both of these studies showed that one of the most characteristic features is that in thermosets cracks often propagate in an unstable, stick/slip manner[21,23] in contrast to glassy thermoplastics where propagation is normally stable and continuous[20] although continuous propagation can also sometimes be obtained in thermosets. The two types of behaviour are represented in the load/displacement (or time) curves shown in Fig. 8.3—in both plots the cross-head speed is constant. For continuous propagation the crack grows at a fixed load (or fixed value of K_{Ic}) whereas when stick/slip propagation takes place the curves have a characteristic sawtooth shape with propagation taking place at a peak

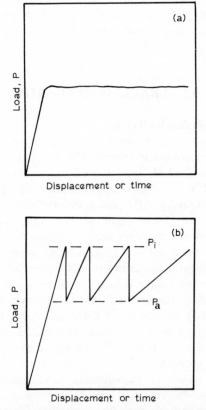

Fig. 8.3. Schematic load/displacement or load/time curves for crack propagation in thermosetting polymers. (a) Stable, continuous propagation; (b) Unstable, stick/slip propagation (after Young[21]).

load, P_i, and arrest occurring at the minimum load, P_a. These loads correspond to the critical stress intensity factors for initiation and arrest, K_{Ici} and K_{Ica} respectively. The differences between the initiation and arrest values of P and K_{Ic} characterise the magnitude of the jumps. Possible reasons for unstable crack propagation in thermosetting polymers are discussed later (Section 8.3.5).

8.3.2 Material Variables

It is now well established[21,23] that there are a variety of structural material variables that affect the stability of crack propagation and the stress levels at which it occurs in thermosetting polymers. The variables include the type of polymer and curing agent used, the amount of curing agent, and the temperature and time of the curing treatment. In the numerous studies of crack propagation in thermosets there have been few systematic investigations into the effect of each of these factors which makes generalisation rather difficult. By far the most widely studied thermosets have been epoxy resins and the effect of the type and quantity (in parts per hundred, phr) of curing agent used upon the fracture energies, G_{Ic}, of a series of epoxy resins is shown in Table 8.1. The values of G_{Ic} quoted are initiation values when the mode of propagation is stick/slip and all measurements have been made at room temperature. The details of the cure schedule, testing geometry and rate can be found by consulting the original references.[20,22,24–30] It is difficult to make generalisations from the data in Table 8.1 since they have been obtained from such a wide variety of resins and curing agents, using different test geometries and rates. It can be seen that the measured values of G_{Ic} are typically of the order of 100–300 J m^{-2} but they can be somewhat larger. These are considerably higher than the values of G_{Ic} obtained for other thermosetting polymers which are normally less than 100 J m^{-2}.[21,31] This shows that epoxy resins are some of the toughest thermosets available and hence are used in the most critical applications such as structural adhesives or matrices for high-performance composites.

Because they are intractable, insoluble polymers the structure of thermosets is normally difficult to analyse and so no detailed correlations have been made between their structure and crack propagation behaviour. However, there have been several systematic studies concerned with the effect of structural changes—brought about by changing the curing agent content and cure schedule—upon crack propagation in certain epoxy resins. Yamini & Young[32] have recently followed

TABLE 8.1

G_{Ic} VALUES MEASURED AT ROOM TEMPERATURE FOR CRACK PROPAGATION IN DGEBA EPOXY RESINS CURED WITH VARIOUS HARDENERS[a] (AFTER REFERENCE 23)

Resin	Hardener (phr)	G_{Ic} $(J\,m^{-2})$	Reference
Epikote 828	10 DETA	172	20
	95 MNA + 0·5 BDMA	154	24
	27 DDM	340	25
	14·6 MPD	110	25
	4 DMP	180	25
	27 DDM	312	26
CT 200	13 PA	220	27
DER 332	5 PIP	121	28
	Various TEPA	52–227	22
	Various HHPA	158–262	29
MY 750	8·3 EDA	329	30
	12·2 TDA	489	30
	16·1 HDA	575	30
	11·5 DETA	130	30
	11·0 TETA	141	30
	15·0 TEPA	136	30

[a] Hardeners

DETA = diethylene triamine   PA = phthalic anhydride
TETA = triethylene tetramine   EDA = ethylene diamine
TEPA = tetraethylene pentamine   TDA = tetramethylene diamine
MNA = methyl nadic anhydride   HDA = hexamethylene diamine
BDMA = benzyl dimethylamine   PIP = piperidine
DDM = diphenyl diaminomethane   HHPA = hexahydrophthalic anhydride
MPD = m-phenylene diamine   DMP = tris(dimethylaminomethyl)phenol

the effect of changing the curing agent content, and post-cure temperature and period upon crack progagation in a DGEBA (bis phenol-A-diglycidyl ether) epoxy resin cured with triethylene tetramine (TETA). They found that the critical stress intensity factor for initiation, K_{Ici}, tended to increase with an increased degree of cure characterised by the use of more curing agent, a higher cure temperature and a longer cure period. This behaviour can be seen in Fig. 8.4 for an increasing curing agent content. The increase in K_{Ici} is accompanied by a higher degree of instability since it is found that the value of K_{Ica} remains virtually constant. Mijovic & Koutsky[33] carried out a similar investigation upon a similar resin cured with diethylene triamine (DETA) and

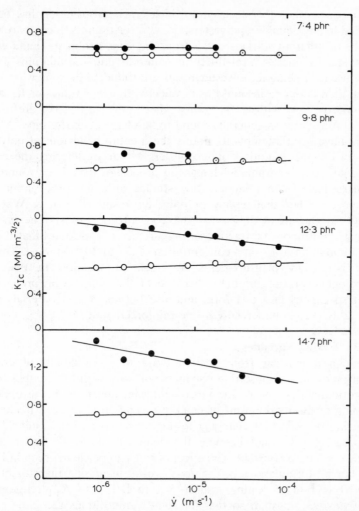

Fig. 8.4. Variation of K_{Ic} with cross-head speed, $\dot{y}$, for a DGEBA epoxy resin cured with different stated phr of TETA and tested at 20°C. ●, K_{Ici}; ○, K_{Ica}; ☉, K_{Ic} continuous. (After Young[21]).

found that G_{Ici} peaked at a particular value of curing agent content. The apparent discrepancy between this observation and the work of Yamini & Young[32] may be due to the fact that the relationship between K_I and G_I ($K_I^2 \simeq EG_I$) involves the Young's modulus, E, which can also vary with the state of cure.[18,34]

The only other thermosets for which crack propagation has been studied in any detail are polyesters.[20,24,31,35-7] Attempts to compare the results of different workers suffer from the same problems found with epoxy resins since several different materials and formulations have been used. In general, polyester resins are found to be somewhat less tough than epoxy resins and this is reflected in lower values of K_{Ic} and G_{Ic} reported. As with epoxy resins, when stable test-pieces are used, crack propagation is generally found to be of the stick/slip type.[24,31,37] There have been attempts to modify the fracture behaviour of polyesters by the incorporation of flexibilisers[36,37] or by altering the cure schedule[37] but no dramatic changes in properties have been found.

There have been relatively few studies of crack propagation in thermosets other than epoxy or polyester resins. Brown & Ward[38] looked at the effect of varying the concentration of styrene cross-linking agent upon the fracture of polyurethanes and found that there was a minimum in K_{Ic} at a concentration of about 30 % styrene. There have been few measurements of crack propagation in phenol-formaldehyde resins, probably because of the difficulty in preparing sheet specimens in a cast form and also because these materials are invariably used commercially in the reinforced state.

8.3.3 Testing Variables

Although it is clear from Section 8.3.2 that the details of crack propagation in thermosetting polymers will vary with the composition of the material, some of the most significant advances in the understanding of the mechanisms of crack propagation have been made by following the effect of changing testing variables such as rate[39,40] or temperature[32,40,41] and keeping the composition of the resins and curing conditions constant. The effect of rate can be clearly seen in Fig. 8.4. For all formulations of the epoxy resin, increasing the crosshead speed (i.e. rate of testing) causes K_{Ici} to fall, with K_{Ica} remaining approximately constant so that for some compositions the jump size decreases and eventually there is a transition to continuous propagation at high cross-head speeds. The stabilisation of crack propagation at high speeds has been shown to be a common phenomenon for a wide variety of thermosetting polymers.[21,23,32,34,39-41]

It is possible to shed more light upon the crack-propagation process by following the effect of changing the testing temperature. Figure 8.5 shows the variation of K_{Ici} and K_{Ica} for three different formulations of an epoxy resin cured under identical conditions but tested at different

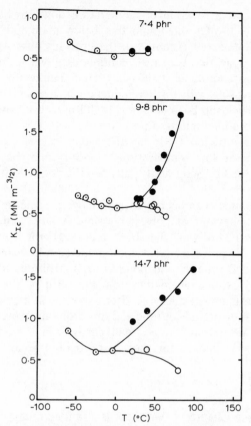

Fig. 8.5. *Variation of* K_{Ic} *with temperature for the same epoxy resins as in Fig. 8.4. The symbols have the same meaning and a cross-head speed of* $0.5 \, mm \, min^{-1}$ *was used in each case (after Young[23]).*

temperatures. It is clear that in each case propagation is continuous at low temperatures but becomes unstable at higher temperatures and it is found that this behaviour is typical of other epoxy resin formulations.[30,32,41,42] It is also consistent with the effect of testing-rate since epoxy resins are viscoelastic solids and so it would be expected that reducing the rate of testing would be similar to increasing the testing-temperature—both factors promoting stick/slip propagation.

Some recent observations by Scott *et al.*[42] have shown that the picture may be more complex than was previously thought. They measured G_{Ic} as a function of temperature down to liquid-nitrogen temperature ($-196°C$) and found that below about $0°C$ propagation became continuous, consistent with the previous observations. It was found that propagation remained continuous down to about $-100°C$ but became discontinuous (stick/slip) again below this temperature with K_{Ici} increasing with further reduction in temperature. The low-temperature stick/slip behaviour was found in a series of amine-cured epoxy resins but its origin is at present unknown. It is well known that gases such as nitrogen (N_2) can affect the crazing and fracture of thermoplastics at low temperatures[43] and it may be that the N_2 environment used by Scott et al.[42] affected the epoxy resins in a similar way.

The environment has been shown to have a significant effect upon the fracture behaviour of polyester resins. A large reduction in K_{Ic} from 0·84 to 0·24 MN m$^{-\frac{3}{2}}$ has been reported[44] for a highly unsaturated isophthalic polyester resin upon immersion in water at $80°C$ for up to 90 days. This large reduction has been attributed to the leaching of non-bound extractable matter from the resin by the hot water.[44] The reduction is most noticeable after exposure at elevated temperatures and for long periods of time and this probably explains why other investigators have found only small changes in fracture behaviour when resins are exposed for short periods of time at low temperatures.[24,37]

8.3.4 Crack Velocity

It was shown in Chapter 7 that there is a unique relationship between the values of fracture energy, G_{Ic}, or critical stress intensity factor, K_{Ic}, and crack velocity for many brittle thermoplastics with PMMA being one of the best examples of this phenomenon.[45,46] A similar relationship is found with thermosetting polymers when stable continuous propagation takes place. Brown & Ward[38] have shown that for a cross-linked polyurethane polymer there is a steady increase in K_{Ic} with crack velocity between 10^{-8} and 10^{-4} m s^{-1} and Gledhill et al.[41] have found that when stable propagation takes place in amine-cured epoxy resins there is a slight increase in K_{Ic} with increasing crack velocity. Williams[47] has suggested that the dependence of K_{Ic} upon crack velocity in a viscoelastic material should follow a relationship of the form (eqn. (5.14))

$$K_{Ic} \propto \dot{a}^n$$

where n is given by (eqn. (5.13))

$$\tan \delta_r = \tan \frac{\pi n}{2}$$

Hence n determined from stable crack propagation can be related to the loss factor, $\tan \delta_r$, and quite good agreement has been found for some glassy thermoplastics (Table 7.2). A value of n of the order of 0·02 was found for crack propagation in the stable epoxy resin studied by Gledhill et al.[41] which is consistent with values of $\tan \delta_r$ of ~0·02 measured for the same resin at room temperature.[48] It seems, therefore, that stable crack propagation in both brittle thermoplastics and thermosetting polymers may be controlled by the viscoelastic properties of the polymer.

When crack propagation is unstable the crack velocity is rather difficult to evaluate. This can be appreciated from the load/displacement curve for a linear compliance variation specimen shown in Fig. 8.3. As the specimen is loaded the crack remains stationary until P_i is reached when it starts to move and accelerates to an undefined velocity. Eventually the crack decelerates until it becomes stationary again at P_a, just beyond the minimum in the load/displacement curve.[49] Since the crack velocity varies during the jump it can only be evaluated with the use of sophisticated measuring equipment. Gledhill & Kinloch[50] have measured the crack velocity during jumps for unstable crack propagation in an epoxy resin using a conductive grid painted on the side of the specimen giving a relatively coarse resolution. They found that the velocity was always in excess of 20 m s^{-1} during jumps and that the velocity increased with the size of the jump (i.e. with increasing G_{Ici}). Kalthoff et al.[51] measured crack velocities during unstable propagation in an epoxy resin using a more sensitive high-speed photographic technique. They were able to show that for most of the jumps the crack velocity was constant at a value which also depended upon K_{Ic}. It was found that the crack velocity decreased from its plateau value to lower values before the crack finally arrested.

It has been suggested by Phillips & Scott[52] that it may be possible to determine the velocity of a crack during a jump from the instantaneous slope of the load/displacement curve at any point and so removing the necessity for direct measurement. Hakeem & Phillips[49] have recently extended the analysis to show that crack arrest does not occur exactly at the minimum in the load/displacement curve but takes place at the point when the curve is rising again and just becoming a straight line. However, great care must be exercised using this technique to ensure that the response time of the testing-machine electronics and load cells is sufficiently high to allow reliable measurements to be made.

8.3.5 Causes of Unstable Propagation

An important question which arises concerning crack propagation in thermosetting polymers is, 'what causes the unstable behaviour?' It has been suggested[53] that the high-temperature stick/slip propagation in epoxy resins may also be due to an environmental effect such as the absorption of water vapour from the atmosphere. Indeed, Ripling *et al.*[54] have shown that exposure of epoxy resins to water can promote unstable behaviour. However, the phenomenon cannot be entirely an environmental effect since stick/slip behaviour is found even when cracks propagate under vacuum.[40] An alternative explanation was proposed by Mai & Leete[55] who suggested that the transition to unstable propagation might be caused by an adiabatic/isothermal transition similar to the one found in PMMA.[45] This is very unlikely since the transition in epoxy resins can occur at very low velocities where isothermal conditions pertain and the behaviour becomes unstable on *reducing* the velocity. In contrast, the transition to adiabatic crack growth in PMMA takes place on increasing the velocity.[45] The most convincing explanation of the transition to unstable behaviour stems from the observation of Gledhill *et al.*[41] who pointed out that epoxy resins with low yield stresses tend to undergo stick/slip propagation whereas the propagation is continuous in high-yield-stress resins. They suggested that the low yield stress might promote crack tip blunting and hence unstable propagation. This explanation is also consistent with the effect of testing-rate and environment. The yield stress drops as the strain-rate is reduced[41] and so unstable propagation will occur at low velocities. It will also tend to take place if the yield stress is reduced by plasticisation with water. Crack tip blunting is discussed in more detail later.

Two ingenious methods have been proposed by Mai & Atkins[56] to promote stable crack propagation behaviour in test-pieces of samples such as epoxy resins in which propagation would be mainly unstable. The two methods are: (1) putting adhesive tape across the crack path in beam-like specimens, and (2) making a sandwich of a stable material, such as PMMA, with the epoxy resin. Using such techniques Mai & Atkins[56] were able to measure the relationship between G_{Ic} and $\dot{a}$ for an unstable epoxy resin and showed that $dG_{Ic}/d\dot{a} < 0$ during unstable propagation. They suggested that the relationship between G_{Ic} or K_{Ic} and $\dot{a}$ during crack propagation is

$$\text{Stick/slip propagation} \begin{cases} dK_{Ic}/d\dot{a} < 0 \\ dG_{Ic}/d\dot{a} < 0 \end{cases}$$

$$\text{Continuous propagation} \begin{cases} dK_{Ic}/d\dot{a} > 0 \\ dG_{Ic}/d\dot{a} > 0 \end{cases}$$

It is a matter of some debate[21,56] as to whether the different relationships are a cause or a consequence of the type of crack propagation behaviour. In addition, direct measurements of the crack velocity[50,51] have shown that both $dK_{Ic}/d\dot{a}$ and $dG_{Ic}/d\dot{a}$ are positive during crack jumps. There is obviously a discrepancy in the observations. It is likely that it may not be possible to compare directly the relationship between K_{Ic} or G_{Ic} and $\dot{a}$ for the two types of crack propagation since the crack velocity varies during jumps but is constant for continuous propagation.

8.4 FAILURE MECHANISMS

8.4.1 Crack Propagation

The fracture surfaces of thermosetting polymers are relatively featureless when compared with the surfaces of other brittle polymers such as polystyrene.[57] The detailed appearance of the fracture surface of a thermosetting polymer depends upon both the structure of the polymer and the fracture conditions such as specimen geometry. The surfaces from unstable test-pieces such as single-edge notched (SEN) or three-point bend types can show a variety of features because the crack velocity changes considerably as the crack grows whereas if stable test-pieces such as DT or TDCB are employed the surfaces tend to have a more regular appearance.

There have been a considerable number of investigations into the fracture of thermosetting polymers using unstable test-pieces[15,31,36,44] and they have been reviewed by Pritchard & Rhoades.[31] The features seen by optical microscopy are an initiation region (particularly when the specimens are not precracked) and a region of slow growth which is followed by an area of rapid growth covering the remainder of the surface. The direction of crack growth can usually be determined from river markings in the slow-growth region which radiate from the point at which the crack initiated. In most thermosets the region of rapid growth is relatively smooth and featureless.[31]

With the use of stable test-pieces it is possible to closely relate features observed on the fracture surfaces to the mode of crack propagation. Three distinct propagation modes have been observed for epoxy resins depending upon the state of cure of the polymer and the testing conditions.[23,32,34,39,40,42,58] When failure takes place by continuous propagation the fracture surfaces are relatively smooth and propagation is by a 'stable brittle' mode. If propagation occurs by a stick/slip process the mode can be termed 'unstable brittle'. Finally, in epoxy resins tested at high temperatures, propagation takes place through a tearing process which can be termed 'stable ductile' crack propagation. These three modes are now discussed separately.

8.4.1.1 Stable Brittle Propagation

This type of propagation tends to take place at low temperatures and in fully cured polymers.[32] The surfaces are relatively featureless and since cracks grow at low levels of K_{Ic} (typically $0.5\,\text{MN}\,\text{m}^{-\frac{3}{2}}$) stable brittle propagation can be thought of as a classic example of brittle fracture.

8.4.1.2 Unstable Brittle Propagation

When propagation takes place by a stick/slip mode then crack arrest lines are seen on the fracture surface—each line corresponding to a jump/arrest event.[26,34,39,42] The regions of crack arrest are found to vary from fine lines to broad bands depending upon the composition of the material and the testing conditions[23,32,40]—an example of a broad arrest line is shown in Fig. 8.6. The extensive areas of fracture surface between the arrest lines are relatively smooth and featureless, similar to the surfaces found during brittle fracture.

8.4.1.3 Stable Ductile Propagation

This type of crack propagation has only been recognised recently[58–60] and tends to be found at high temperatures in under-cured resins[58] and in thin sheets[59] and takes place at high values of K_{Ic} and fracture energy. The fracture surfaces have a ridged and furrowed structure running parallel to the propagation direction. There is a gradual transition to this type of behaviour from the unstable brittle mode on raising the test temperature. The arrest lines tend to broaden and

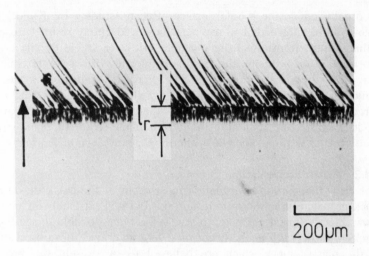

Fig. 8.6. Optical micrograph of a crack arrest line in a DGEBA epoxy resin
cured with 14·7 phr TETA. The arrow indicates the direction of crack propagation (after Yamini & Young[61]).

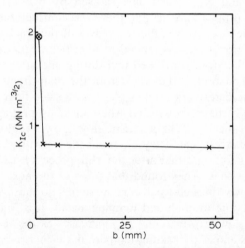

Fig. 8.7. Variation of K_{Ic} with specimen thickness, b, for a compact tension
specimen of a DGEBA resin cured with 5 phr of piperidine and tested at
$\dot{y} = 1 \, mm \, min^{-1}$ (after Kinloch & Shaw[59]). ×, brittle unstable crack growth;
⊗, ductile stable crack growth.

eventually cover the whole surface. Recent studies by Kinloch & Shaw[59] have shown that in a piperidine-cured epoxy resin there is a rather abrupt transition from unstable brittle to stable ductile crack propagation on reducing the specimen thickness for a CT test-piece. This behaviour is shown in Fig. 8.7 where the transition is accompanied by a large jump in the value of K_{Ic} when the specimen thickness is reduced from 2 to 1 mm. It appears that the change in propagation mode may be due to a transition from plane-strain to plane-stress conditions as is found for glassy thermoplastics (Section 7.3.5).

8.4.2 Plastic Deformation

It is clear that plastic deformation must occur at the crack tip during crack propagation in thermosetting resins but it is extremely difficult to show directly that it has taken place. It has been possible to see blunt cracks with tip radii of the order of several microns[60] but observation of the plastic zones which are believed to be present has proved extremely difficult. Yamini & Young[32] have looked closely at the nature of the arrest line zone that is present on both sides of the fracture surface after stick/slip propagation in an epoxy resin. They showed that there was a general correlation between the width of the zone and the magnitude of the jumps as given by the difference between K_{Ici} and K_{Ica}. They also showed by measurement of the surface profile using a Talysurf that there was considerable deviation of the crack at the arrest zones, the two halves of the crack surface in the vicinity of the arrest regions tended to interlock at the level of about $10 \ \mu m$. They therefore concluded that during and after arrest there is considerable deviation of the crack from the main fracture plane and that any plastic deformation takes place on a scale finer than $10 \ \mu m$.

Phillips et al.[30] have shown that when stick/slip propagation occurs in epoxy resins there is a characteristic slow-growth region in the zone after the crack arrest line. They observed the growth of a crack in an epoxy sample and found that after the 'slip' process it became stationary at the arrest line. They found that prior to the next 'slip' step the crack grew slowly through small regions similar to those shown in Fig. 8.6 before bursting through and jumping ahead. It is found[61] that the length of the slow-growth region, l_r, increases as the temperature of curing is raised and as the testing-temperature is increased. Hence, it is not surprising that a correlation between l_r and K_{Ici} is found for different formulations of epoxy resins tested under a variety of experimental conditions. In fact, it is found[61] that l_r is approximately the same as the length of a Dugdale plastic zone, R_c, calculated using eqn. (3.47) (Section 3.3.2)

$$R_c = \frac{\pi}{8}\left(\frac{K_{Ic}}{\sigma_y}\right)^2$$

where σ_y is the yield stress of the material. Figure 8.8 is a plot of $(K_{Ici}/\sigma_y)^2$ against l_r for different formulations of epoxy resins tested at different temperatures.[34,41] The straight line has a slope of $8/\pi$ and represents the relationship between R_c and $(K_{Ici}/\sigma_y)^2$ if a Dugdale plastic zone is present at the crack tip. The proximity of the experimentally determined points to the theoretical line strongly suggests that l_r is closely related to R_c.

A clear picture of what happens during stick/slip propagation can be described. It appears that during loading after crack arrest a plastic zone forms at the tip of a crack. Propagation then takes place by slow growth through the plastic zone followed by rapid growth through virgin material. The slow-growth region therefore defines the plastic zone at the crack tip.

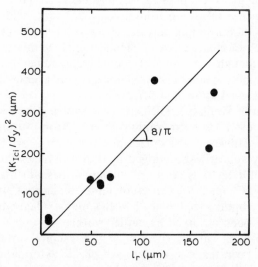

Fig. 8.8. Plot of $(K_{Ici}/\sigma_y)^2$ against l_r for a TETA-cured DGEBA epoxy resin. The line is drawn with a slope of $8/\pi$ according to eqn. (3.47) assuming that $l_r \simeq R_c$ (after Young[23]).

8.4.3 Crazing

It is well known that glassy polymers will readily undergo deformation by crazing and the process of crazing has been described in detail in Chapter 5. Although crazing is found widely in thermoplastics there is little conclusive evidence for it occurring to any great extent in thermosetting polymers. Brown & Ward[38] showed that craze zones were almost certainly formed in a vinyl–urethane polymer cross-linked by different amounts of styrene. They were able to measure a craze stress and showed that it decreased monotonically with increasing styrene content.

There is some evidence for crazing in epoxy resins. Lilley & Holloway[62] have reported seeing crazes in the vicinity of crack tips in some epoxy resins although the features they showed could also have been microcracks. Van den Boogaart[63] has observed crazes at the tips of moving cracks in under-cured epoxy resins and reported that the crazes appeared to be identical to those found in PMMA, although no micrographs of the epoxy resin crazes were shown. In fully cured resins the crazes were not found.[63] This observation is consistent with the work of Donald & Kramer[64] who showed that in thermoplastics there is a transition from crazing to shear yielding as the length of the polymer chain between physical entanglements, l_e, decreases below ~20 nm. Hence a transition from crazing to shear yielding might be expected in a thermosetting polymer as the cross-link density increases and the length of chain between chemical entanglements (cross-links) decreases, although the work of Donald & Kramer does not fully explain why highly localised shear yielding occurs at crack tips in epoxy resins, as discussed in Section 5.7.2.

More recently Morgan & O'Neal[65] have shown craze-like entities in transmission electron micrographs obtained from strained films of epoxy resins. However, the crazes are relatively short ($\sim 1\mu$m) and although they appear to be bridged by drawn polymer they are by no means as well-defined as crazes in thermoplastics which can be many microns long (Chapter 5). Crazes of these dimensions would not be observable by optical techniques and this may explain why they have not generally been observed by earlier workers.

The presence of surface colours on the fracture surface of glassy polymers has been taken as evidence of plastic deformation occurring during the fracture process[15,20,31] and in thermoplastics this has been interpreted as an indication that crazing has taken place.[66] The coloration is thought to be due to layers of material on the fracture surfaces having a different refractive index from the bulk. The surface colours are particularly noticeable on the fracture surfaces of PMMA but the amount of coloration is considerably reduced when the material is cross-linked.[20] Nelson & Turner[15] have reported surface coloration on the fracture surfaces of phenol-formaldehyde resins although when the testing temperature was raised the coloration became less noticeable until at 175°C it was completely absent.

8.4.4 Polymer Microstructure

More details of the failure mechanisms in thermosetting polymers can be revealed using scanning electron microscopy and Morgan et al.[65,67–9] have looked at the effect of different structural variables upon the fracture topography of epoxy resins using this technique. They showed that several different types of feature could be observed and suggested that some are due to crazing.[65] They have also shown that irregularities in the fracture surfaces can be caused by the presence of DGEBA epoxy monomer crystals.[67] More structural details are revealed by taking replicas of fracture surfaces and examining them at high magnification in the transmission electron microscope. Fracture surface replicas show a granular appearance at the 10–100 nm level[65,70] and this has been interpreted as being due to the epoxy resins having an underlying nodular microstructure. An electron microscope replica of the fracture surface of an epoxy resin in the vicinity of a crack arrest line is shown in Fig. 8.9. The underlying nodular structure on the 100 nm scale can be seen clearly in the replica. Unfortunately, no consistent relationship has been established between composition or cure and the nodule size or density.[70] The granular appearance can be enhanced by etching the fracture surfaces[65] and Morgan & O'Neal have also reported the existence of a domain structure on a similar level within films viewed by transmission electron microscopy. However, care must be taken in the interpretation of these electron micrographs of amorphous solids since much of the 'structure' observed has been shown by Thomas[71] to probably be an artefact of an out-of-focus image. Gledhill & Kinloch[50] and Koutsky and co-workers[70,72] have suggested that the mechanical properties of epoxy resins may be controlled by the nodular structure. This is an attractive proposition as there is a well-established dependence of the properties of many materials upon microstructure. However, even the existence of the nodular morphology is a matter of some controversy and Uhlmann[5] has suggested that this type of microstructure in glassy

Fig. 8.9. Electron micrograph of a replica of the fracture surface of an epoxy resin (DGEBA resin cured with 9·8 phr of TETA and fractured at 22°C). The arrow indicates the crack growth direction (after Young[23]).

polymers is an artefact. Supporters of the existence of the nodular structure have problems explaining the lack of strong small-angle X-ray scattering[4] that should occur if nodules are present but even Uhlmann[5] suggests that the X-ray-scattering evidence is ambiguous for epoxy resins. It would seem reasonable that thermosetting polymers which are normally made by the addition of a curing agent to a pre-polymer could have a non-uniform two-phase structure. Gledhill & Kinloch[50] found that there was a variation in nodule size with the type of curing agent used. The work of Mijovic & Koutsky[72] suggests tha the nodule size of a given resin/curing-agent system also depends upon the state of cure. Since the properties of the resin vary with curing conditions it is tempting to relate the mechanical properties to the nodular microstructure. It has been tentatively suggested[50] that unstable brittle crack propagation is encountered with a large nodule size of 41 nm whereas stable brittle propagation is found for smaller nodule sizes (24–28 nm).[50] Mijovic & Koutsky[72] also found variations of properties with microstructure although in neither of these studies has it been possible to explain why a particular microstructure and nodule size lead to the properties obtained.

8.5 FAILURE CRITERIA

In recent years there have been important developments in the determination of failure criteria for brittle polymers. For example, it has been shown that slow stable crack growth takes place in PMMA in accordance with a constant crack-opening displacement, δ_{tc}, criterion.[46,73,74] It has been further shown that in this material propagation takes place through a region of crazed polymer at the tip of the crack which can be modelled accurately by a Dugdale line plastic-zone.[46,74] Crack propagation in thermosetting polymers is more complex and one of the main problems with thermosets has been to produce a criterion which accounts for the transition betwen continuous and stick/slip propagation to explain why the two different types of propagation occur. Rather different theories have been used to account for the two modes of crack growth although it will be shown that the basic criterion controlling failure is the same in both cases.

8.5.1 Constant Crack-Opening Displacement

The low-temperature continuous propagation that takes place in epoxy resins is somewhat similar to continuous propagation in PMMA and there is evidence that a constant crack-opening displacement is also applicable to this type of failure in some epoxy resins.[41] The value of δ_t has been shown in Chapter 3 to be given by eqns (3.45) and (3.46)

$$\delta_t = \frac{K_I^2}{E\sigma_y} \qquad \text{Plane stress}$$

$$\delta_t = \frac{K_I^2}{E\sigma_y}(1 - \nu^2) \qquad \text{Plane strain}$$

where σ_y is the yield stress of the material and E is the Young's modulus. The criterion for continuous propagation is that crack growth occurs when δ_t reaches a critical value, δ_{tc}. It is found[41] that when δ_{tc} is calculated from measurements of K_{Ic}, σ_y and E, its value is often approximately constant during continuous propagation in epoxy resins and this can be seen in Fig. 8.10. However, the value of δ_{tc} rises rapidly as soon as stick/slip propagation ensues, indicating that severe crack tip blunting is associated with unstable crack growth. The effect of a constant δ_{tc} criterion upon the value of K_{Ic} for continuous propagation in epoxy resins at low temperatures can be clearly seen in

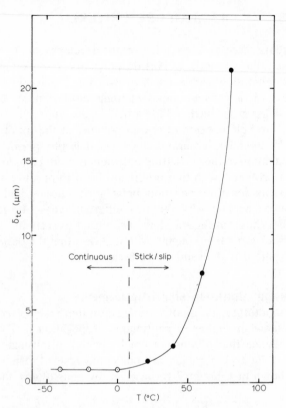

Fig. 8.10. Variation of critical crack-opening displacement, δ_{tc}, with test temperature for a DGEBA epoxy resin cured with 9·8 phr TETA (after Gledhill et al.[41]).

Fig. 8.5. Because both σ_y and E decrease as the temperature increases the value of K_{Ic} (continuous) also decreases with increasing temperature.

Although in PMMA the constant δ_{tc} criterion is associated with the growth of cracks through a single craze it was explained in Section 8.4.3 that evidence for crazing in thermosetting polymers, such as epoxy resins, is not strong. It remains to be proven whether or not crazing does occur when there is continuous propagation in an epoxy resin, as implied by the observations of Van den Boogaart,[63] but the likelihood is that this type of crack growth can occur without crazing.

8.5.2   Critical Stress/Distance Criterion

There have been recent important developments in the understanding of stick/slip propagation in thermosetting polymers and it is now thought that this type of behaviour can be explained in terms of blunting at the crack tip and a quantitative theory has been developed[60,61] to explain both stick/slip and continuous propagation. It has been known for several years[41] that if the resin has a high yield-stress then crack propagation is continuous whereas if the material has a low yield-stress, due to changes in composition or testing variables, propagation tends to be stick/slip in nature. This can be explained in simple terms as a high yield-stress favouring sharp cracks and a low yield-stress favouring blunt cracks. Since epoxy resins are brittle, measurements of yield stress can normally only be made in compression. This behaviour can be quantified as shown in Fig. 8.11 where K_{Ici} is plotted against σ_y for a whole range of TETA-cured epoxy resins tested at different rates and temperatures. The values of K_{Ici} and σ_y have been taken from several publications.[34,41,61] It can be seen that all the data follow the same general trend. Kinloch & Williams[60] have

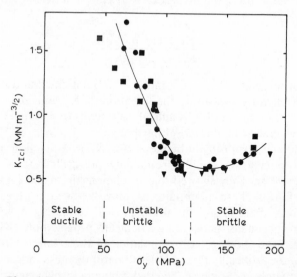

Fig. 8.11. Plot of K_{Ici} versus the yield stress, σ_y, for different formulations of a DGEBA epoxy resin tested at a variety of rates and temperatures. The regions of different types of crack growth are indicated: ▼, 7·4 phr TETA; ●, 9·8 phr TETA; ▲, 12·3 phr TETA; ■, 14·7 phr TETA (after Young[23]).

obtained a similar correlation between K_{Ici} and σ_y for a series of resins hardened with different curing agents. This correlation has allowed stick/slip propagation to be explained quantitatively.[60,61]

It was shown in Chapter 4 that for a crack under an applied stress of σ_0 the stress, σ_{11}, normal to the axis of the crack at a small distance, r, ahead of the crack is given by (eqn. (4.18))

$$\sigma_{11} = \sigma_0 \left(\frac{a}{2r}\right)^{\frac{1}{2}} \frac{(1 + \rho/r)}{(1 + \rho/2r)^{\frac{3}{2}}}$$

where ρ is the radius of the crack tip and a is the crack length. If it is postulated that the failure criterion is that fracture occurs when a critical stress, σ_{tc}, is reached at a distance $r = c$ then eqn. (4.18) can be written as (eqn. (4.19))

$$\sigma_{tc} = \sigma_c \left(\frac{a}{2c}\right)^{\frac{1}{2}} \frac{(1 + \rho_c/c)}{(1 + \rho_c/2c)^{\frac{3}{2}}}.$$

The term $\sigma_{tc}\sqrt{2\pi c}$ can be considered to be the critical stress intensity factor for initiation of a 'sharp' crack, K_{Ics}, and $\sigma_c\sqrt{\pi a}$ as the stress intensity factor for a blunt crack, K_{Ic}. Hence it follows that (eqn. (4.23))

$$\frac{K_{Ic}}{K_{Ics}} = \frac{(1 + \rho_c/2c)^{\frac{3}{2}}}{(1 + \rho_c/c)}$$

This equation relates K_{Ic} to the radius of a blunt crack and the theory can be checked by measuring the variation of K_{Ic} with ρ_c.

Direct measurement of ρ_c is difficult as it tends to be small ($\sim 10 \ \mu$m) for natural cracks in thermosetting polymers. Kinloch & Williams[60] have overcome this problem by measuring K_{Ic} as a function of ρ_c for a series of epoxy resin samples containing pre-drilled holes of large, known diameter. They showed that a relationship of the form of eqn. (4.23) held for these materials, as may be seen in Fig. 8.12(a). Nevertheless, there is still the problem of determining ρ_c for natural cracks in specimens undergoing stick/slip propagation. Kinloch & Williams[60] have shown that extrapolation of the relationship between K_{Ic} and ρ_c for artificially drilled holes to natural cracks indicates that ρ_c is approximately the same as the crack-opening displacement, δ_{tc}. This is in agreement with a theoretical analysis by McMeeking[75] and experimental observations. Moreover, it has been shown in Section 8.4.2 that there is strong evidence for a Dugdale plastic zone at the crack tip

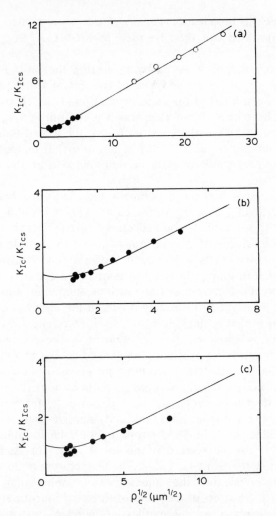

Fig. 8.12. *Variation of* K_{Ic}/K_{Ics} *with* $\rho_c^{\frac{1}{2}}$ *for different epoxy resins. The curves are eqn. (4.23) fitted to the data using the values of* σ_{tc} *and* c *given below. (a) DGEBA resin cured with 5 phr piperidine. The open circles are for drilled holes and the closed circles are for naturally blunted cracks.* $\sigma_{tc} = 350\,MPa$; $c = 0·7\,\mu m$ *(after Kinloch et al.[76]); (b) DGEBA resin cured with 9·8 phr TETA;* $\sigma_{tc} = 360\,MPa$; $c = 0·6\,\mu m$; *(c) DGEBA resin cured with 14·7 phr TETA;* $\sigma_{tc} = 270\,MPa$; $c = 1·6\,\mu m$ *(data taken from Young[23]).*

during stick/slip propagation and so ρ_c can be estimated from δ_{tc} in eqn. (3.46) which can then be used to predict K_{Ic}/K_{Ics} using eqn. (4.23).

The theory has been tested by measuring the ratio K_{Ic}/K_{Ics} as a function of $\sqrt{\rho_c}$ as shown in Fig. 8.12 (cf., Fig. 4.15). The theoretical lines have been fitted to the experimental points by choosing suitable values of the critical distance, c, which is the only fitting parameter. K_{Ics} has been taken as the value of K_{Ics} at the lowest temperature of measurement and K_{Ic} as the value of K_{Ici} at higher temperatures. The values of critical stress, σ_{tc}, can be determined from the relationship $K_{Ics} = \sigma_{tc}\sqrt{2\pi c}$.

The agreement between experiment and theory has been found to be equally good for epoxy resins cured with many different curing agents,[60,61,76] for rubber-modified epoxy resins[60,76] and even, under certain circumstances, for structural adhesive joints.[77] Indeed, in the case of adhesive joints it has been shown[42,77] from using a LEFM approach that in joints consisting of unmodified epoxy resins bonding relatively rigid substrate materials, such as aluminium alloy and steel, then crack propagation invariably occurs in the epoxy adhesive and is very similar to that in the bulk epoxy resin. Differences may, however, be observed when a hostile environment is present, which causes interfacial failure,[1,77-9] or when a toughened rubber-modified epoxy is employed as the adhesive, since the joint geometry in this case has a major influence on the crack propagation behaviour (Section 11.5).

Values of critical stress, σ_{tc}, and distance, c, for various epoxy materials, obtained from both bulk and adhesive joint specimens are given in Table 8.2. The yield stress, σ_y, of each formulation is also given and it can be seen that the ratio σ_{tc}/σ_y for each system is approximately the same, i.e. $\sim3-4$. The temperature of 25°C is only an arbitrary reference but the constant ratio implies that the failure criterion is that a stress of the order of three- or four-times σ_y must be reached in the plastic zone, regardless of the resin composition or yield stress. These critical stress, σ_{tc}, values may possibly be interpreted as a constrained yield stress, which is in agreement with the analysis of McMeeking,[75] Rice & Rosengren[80] and Rice & Johnson[81] especially if a degree of post-yield strain-hardening occurs as has been reported[41] for epoxy materials. Also, these values from an essentially elastic analysis are in good agreement with the maximum stress, σ_{11}, ahead of a crack preceded by a plastic zone recently deduced by Narisawa et al.[82] who used a slip-line field solution for perfectly plastic bodies.

TABLE 8.2

VALUES OF CRITICAL STRESS, σ_{tc}, AND CRITICAL DISTANCE, c

Formulation	Configuration	σ_{tc} (MPa)	c (μm)	σ_y (25°C) (MPa)	σ_{tc}/σ_y	Reference
9·8 phr TETA[a]	Bulk and joint	370	0·5	112	3·2	61, 77
12·3 phr TETA[a]	Bulk	300	1·1	91	3·3	61
14·7 phr TETA[a]	Bulk	270	1·6	86	3·1	61
9·4 phr tertiary amine	Bulk and joint	360	0·4	83	4·3	60, 77
10·0 phr TEPA[a]	Bulk and joint	495	0·1	117	4·2	60, 77
5·0 phr Piperidine	Bulk and joint	350	0·7	80	4·4	60, 76, 77
Rubber-modified epoxy	Bulk	200	10·0	70	2·9	60, 76

[a] TEPA = tetraethylene pentamine
TETA = triethylene tetramine

They calculated values of σ_{11} (max) of the order of several hundred megapascals for three different epoxy formulations. However, although a physical interpretation of the critical stress, σ_{tc}, is possible, the significance of the critical distance, which varies in size from about 0·1 to 10 μm, is not yet clear.

To summarise, the fracture data and mode of crack growth over a wide range of rates and temperatures may all be rationalised by the concept of a critical stress acting over a critical distance and this provides a unique failure criterion for thermosetting polymers.

8.6 IMPACT AND FATIGUE

The failure of polymers through impact and static- and dynamic-fatigue loading has been discussed in general in Chapter 6. In this section the specific ways in which these types of failure take place in thermosetting polymers will be considered in detail.

8.6.1 Impact

There has not been a large number of investigations reported into the impact behaviour of thermosetting polymers probably because they are generally brittle and so have low impact strengths. Kalthoff et al.[83] have investigated the influence of dynamic effects during the instrumented impact-testing of an epoxy resin. They found that the dynamic stress intensity factor increased as the notches were made blunter although no change was observed on the load/time traces. The effect of resin composition upon the impact behaviour has been determined for some amine-cured epoxy resins.[17,19] The Charpy impact strengths (Fig. 6.1a) are found to be quite sensitive to the resin composition. A peak in impact strength has been reported[17] at a molar mass between cross-links, $\bar{M}_c$, of about 400–500 g mol^{-1} which corresponds to an excess of amine curing agent over the stoichiometric composition.

There has been considerable interest in finding methods of improving the impact strengths of thermosets through the incorporation of fillers or fibres to give a multiphase material. Methods of modifying the properties of polymers through the development of multiphase microstructures are discussed in Chapter 11.

8.6.2 Dynamic Fatigue

It is often quite difficult to propagate stable fatigue cracks in thermosetting polymers. For example, although Hertzberg et al.[84] were able to follow the fatigue behaviour of many different thermoplastics they reported difficulty in obtaining the propagation of fatigue cracks in epoxy resins. On the other hand, Sutton[85] has shown that it is possible to measure fatigue crack propagation in an epoxy resin and obtained a relationship between the fatigue crack growth rate, da/dN, and the range of stress intensity factors, ΔK_I, consistent with the Paris equation (eqn. (6.19), Section 6.3.4)

$$\frac{da}{dN} = A_f \Delta K_I{}^m$$

This type of relationship has been found for many metals and polymers (Chapter 6) with m lying typically between 2 and 7 for such materials. However, Sutton[85] reported that m was of the order of 10 for his epoxy resin which is extremely high and probably explains why Hertzberg et al.[84] had problems in obtaining fatigue crack growth in their resins. More recently, Kim et al.[17] obtained success in propagating dynamic-fatigue cracks in epoxy resins provided that their specimens were carefully notched. They also found that m was relatively high (>10). They reported that m was also independent of resin composition and found that there was a fatigue striation for each increment of loading, and associated crack growth increments, in contrast to the behaviour of polymers which are capable of crazing (Section 6.3.4).

It appears that high values of m are a general feature of fatigue crack growth in thermosetting polymers. Harris & Ward[86] obtained values of m between 4 and 10 for cross-linked vinyl–urethane polymers and Owen & Rose[87] found m to be of the order of 5 for polyester resins. High values of m are desirable as it means that the fatigue growth rate will drop rapidly as ΔK_I is reduced but, in general, crack propagation is easier than in thermoplastics since the absolute values of ΔK_I are quite low (Fig. 6.7). However, the relatively good performance of the epoxy resins in S–N (σ_a–N_f) curves (Fig. 6.5) implies that the initiation of fatigue cracks is relatively difficult.

8.6.3 Static Fatigue

The failure of polymers through static-fatigue loading has been reviewed in detail in Section 6.4 and it has been shown that the total time-to-failure may be given by (eqn. (6.24))

$$t_f = t_i + t_p$$

where t_i is the time required to initiate a crack, and t_p is the time for the crack to propagate. It is thought that in glassy polymers, such as PMMA, t_f is controlled by t_p with $t_i \to 0$. In contrast there is now accumulated evidence that in thermosetting polymers, such as many epoxy resins, the time-to-failure is controlled principally by t_i.

The most successful investigations into the static fatigue of epoxy resins have involved a fracture mechanics approach.[30,77,88,89] It is known that under certain conditions thermosetting polymers are prone to failure at constant load by static fatigue but the results of different groups of workers appear to be in conflict. Some people have observed static fatigue in epoxy resins[88] and others have not.[30] It seems that this conflict may be resolved by examination of the careful work of Gledhill et al.[88,89] who have shown that, at least at room temperature, certain formulations of epoxy resins appear to show static fatigue while others do not. They looked at the failure of TDCB aluminium adhesive joints (Fig. 8.13(a)) bonded with a thin layer of epoxy (0·5 mm thick). This particular test-piece is useful because similar ones made from the pure resin are prone to creep in the arms over long periods of loading which complicates the stress distribution.

Gledhill & Kinloch[88] found that if the epoxy was cured with a tertiary amine the fracture energy, G_{Ic}, required to cause failure dropped dramatically as the loading time was increased, as shown in Fig. 8.13(b). The G_{Ic} measured after 10^8 s (~3 years) was only 25 % of

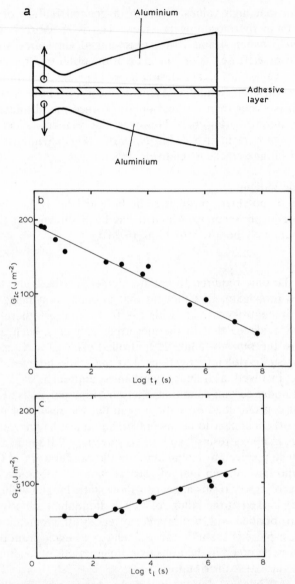

Fig. 8.13. Time-dependent failure in epoxy resins. (a) TDCB aluminium adhesive joint test-piece; (b) Variation of t_f with G_{Ic} for a DGEBA resin cured with a tertiary amine (after Gledhill & Kinloch[50]); (c) Increase in G_{Ici} with loading time, t_l, for a DGEBA resin cured with TEPA (after Gledhill et al.[89]).

that needed to propagate a crack during short-term loading (over a few seconds). Using exactly the same testing geometry and testing procedure Gledhill *et al.*[89] found that when the same epoxy resin cured with tetraethylenepentamine (TEPA) was used in the adhesive joint, static fatigue was not observed. Moreover, they found that, when such specimens had been held under a load corresponding to 86 % of the failure load required to cause crack growth during rapid loading, there was an increase in failure load measured on subsequent rapid loading of the specimens. This effect is shown in Fig. 8.13(c) where G_{Ici} measured on re-testing the specimen following static loading is plotted against the static loading period. This means that the epoxy resin is actually becoming tougher on static loading and this effect has been termed a 'self-toughening mechanism'.[77,89]

The question that must be answered is, 'why does the same resin hardened with different curing agents show such a difference in behaviour?' The answer almost certainly lies in the behaviour of the two systems during testing at a constant loading-rate. The tertiary-amine-cured resin shows stick/slip propagation at room temperature whereas there is continuous propagation in the TEPA-cured resin.[88] This means that cracks are relatively blunt even during short-term loading in the tertiary-amine cured material and this is reflected in the significantly higher values of G_{Ic} that this material can sustain over short periods of time. On the other hand, since the TEPA-cured resin undergoes continuous propagation at room temperature the cracks are relatively sharp, leading to low values of G_{Ic} during short-term loading. However, as the loading period increases, blunting starts to take place and so the value of G_{Ic} increases. Indeed, it is found that the blunting only occurs for the initial crack since after the initial 'jump', propagation takes place in a continuous way as for an unprestressed specimen. Increasing the period of loading is equivalent to either reducing the testing rate or increasing the temperature, both of which have the effect of causing stick/slip propagation and hence promoting blunting. The drop in G_{Ic} observed for the tertiary-amine-cured resin has been explained in terms of propagation taking place when a critical plastic-zone size or crack-opening displacement is achieved. The yield stress and modulus of the resin will drop as the loading time increases and so the critical conditions can be reached at a lower value of G_{Ic}.

It is worth considering at this stage whether or not the two types of behaviour can be reconciled. Examination of Figs 8.13(b) and 8.13(c) shows that the lowest value of G_{Ic} found for both systems is about the same ($\sim 50\,\mathrm{J\,m^{-2}}$) and it may be that the two plots are representing similar types of behaviour. Clearly, measurements over longer periods of time are required to see if eventually a limiting value of G_{Ic} is reached for the tertiary-amine-cured resin and if static fatigue will occur in the TEPA-cured material after a sufficiently long loading period.

8.7 CONCLUDING REMARKS

Over recent years there has been a great deal of interest in the fracture of thermosetting polymers, and, in particular, epoxy resins. One reason for this is that LEFM can be readily applied to thermosetting polymers since they are generally relatively brittle. However, they differ in an important respect from glassy thermoplastics in that fracture can occur without any associated crazing. The micromechanisms of fracture are dominated by localised shear yielding at the crack tip and a relationship has been established between the fracture properties and yield behaviour through a process of crack tip blunting. Another reason for the interest is that it is possible to modify the molecular structure of thermosetting polymers by altering the curing conditions but as yet no clear correlations have been established between the polymer structure and the fracture properties.

Because of the increasing use of thermosetting polymers as matrix materials in high-performance composites and as high-strength adhesives there is still a need for more knowledge of their fracture behaviour. There have been few detailed studies of the localised deformation at the crack tip using electron microscopy. More information is needed upon the effect of cross-link density and environment upon fracture. Finally, because most of the studies have concentrated upon epoxy resins, it would be useful to have more detailed information on other types of thermosetting polymer since the behaviour of epoxy resins may not necessarily be typical.

REFERENCES

1. Kinloch, A. J. (1982). *J. Mater. Sci.*, **17**, 617.
2. Hull, D. (1981). *Introduction to composite materials*, Oxford University Press; Richardson, M. O. W. (Ed.), (1977). *Polymer engineering composites*, Applied Science Publishers Ltd., London.

3. May, C. & Tanaka, Y. (Eds.) (1974). *Epoxy resins and their technology*, Marcel Dekker, New York.
4. Dušek, K., Pleštil, J., Lednicky, F. & Luňák, S. (1978). *Polymer*, **19**, 393.
5. Uhlmann, D. R. (1979). *Farad. Disc.*, **68**, 87;Matyi, R. J., Uhlmann, D. R. & Koutsky, J. A. (1980). *J. Polym. Sci., Polym. Phys. Ed.*, **18**, 1053.
6. Stevens, G. C., Champion, J. V., Liddell, P. & Dandridge, A. (1980). *Chem. Phys. Lett.*, **71**, 104.
7. Pink, E. & Campbell, J. D. (1974). *Mater. Sci. Eng.*, **15**, 187.
8. King, N. E. & Andrews, E. H. (1978). *J. Mater. Sci.*, **13**, 1291.
9. Yamini, S. & Young, R. J. (1980). *J. Mater. Sci.*, **15**, 1814.
10. Argon, A. S. (1973). *Phil. Mag.*, **28**, 839.
11. Bowden, P. B. & Raha, S. (1974). *Phil. Mag.*, **29**, 149.
12. Thierry, A., Oxborough, R. J. & Bowden, P. B. (1974). *Phil. Mag.*, **30**, 527.
13. Griffith, A. A. (1920). *Phil. Trans. Roy. Soc.*, **A221**, 163.
14. Berry, J. P. (1972). *Fracture VII*, Ed. by H. Liebowitz, Academic Press, New York.
15. Nelson, B. F. & Turner, D. T. (1973). *J. Polym. Sci., Polym. Phys. Ed.*, **11**, 1949.
16. Lake, G. J. & Thomas, A. G. (1967). *Proc. Roy. Soc.*, **A300**, 108.
17. Kim, S. L., Skibo, M. D., Manson, J. A., Hertzberg, R. W. & Janiszewski, J. (1978). *Polym. Eng. Sci.*, **18**, 1093.
18. Misra, S., Manson, J. A. & Sperling, L. H. (1979). *ACS Symposium Series*, **114**, 137.
19. Bell, J. P. (1970). *J. Appl. Polym. Sci.*, **14**, 1901.
20. Broutman, L. J. & McGarry, F. J. (1965). *J. Appl. Polym. Sci.*, **9**, 609.
21. Young, R. J. (1979). In: *Developments in polymer fracture—1*, Ed. by E. H. Andrews, Applied Science Publishers Ltd., London, p. 183.
22. Mostovoy, S. & Ripling, E. J. (1966). *J. Appl. Polym. Sci.*, **10**, 1351.
23. Young, R. J. (1980). In: *Developments in reinforced polymers—1*, Ed. by G. Pritchard, Applied Science Publishers Ltd., London, p. 257.
24. Diggwa, A. D. S. (1974). *Polymer*, **15**, 101.
25. Meeks, A. C. (1974). *Polymer*, **15**, 675.
26. Selby, K. & Miller, L. E. (1975). *J. Mater. Sci.*, **10**, 12.
27. Griffiths, R. & Holloway, D. G. (1970). *J. Mater. Sci.*, **5**, 302.
28. Bascom, W. D., Cottington, R. L., Jones, R. L. & Peyser, P. (1975). *J. Appl. Polym. Sci.*, **19**, 2545.
29. Mostovoy, S. & Ripling, E. J. (1971). *J. Appl. Polym. Sci.*, **15**, 641.
30. Phillips, D. C., Scott, J. M. & Jones, M.(1979). *J. Mater. Sci.*, **13**, 1609.
31. Pritchard, G. & Rhoades, G. V. (1976). *Mater. Sci. Eng.*, **26**, 1.
32. Yamini, S. & Young, R. J. (1979), *J. Mater. Sci.*, **14**, 1609.
33. Mijovic, J. & Koutsky, J. A. (1979). *Polymer*, **20**, 1095.
34. Yamini, S. (1979). *Crack Propagation in Epoxy Resins*, PhD Thesis, University of London, London.
35. Pritchard, G., Rose, R. G. & Taneja, N. (1976). *J. Mater. Sci.*, **11**, 718.
36. Owen, M. J. & Rose, R. G. (1975). *J. Mater. Sci.*, **10**, 1711.
37. Christiansen, A. & Shortall, J. B. (1976). *J. Mater. Sci.*, **11**, 1113.
38. Brown, H. R. & Ward, I. M. (1973). *J. Mater. Sci.*, **8**, 1365.

39. Young, R. J., & Beaumont, P. W. R. (1976). *J. Mater. Sci.*, **11**, 779.
40. Yamini, S. & Young, R. J. (1977). *Polymer*, **18**, 1075.
41. Gledhill, R. A., Kinloch, A. J., Yamini, S. & Young, R. J. (1978). *Polymer*, **19**, 574.
42. Scott, J. M., Wells, G. M. & Phillips, D. C. (1980). *J. Mater. Sci.*, **15**, 1436.
43. Imai, Y. & Brown, N. (1976). *J. Mater. Sci.*, **11**, 417.
44. Pritchard, G., Rose, R. G. & Taneja, N. (1976). *J. Mater. Sci.*, **11**, 718.
45. Marshall, G. P., Coutts, L. H. & Williams, J. G. (1974). *J. Mater. Sci.*, **9**, 1409.
46. Beaumont, P. W. R. & Young, R. J. (1975). *J. Mater. Sci.*, **10**, 1334.
47. Williams, J. G. (1978). *Adv. Polym. Sci.*, **27**, 67.
48. Kinloch, A. J. Unpublished results.
49. Hakeem, M. I. & Phillips, M. G. (1978). *Int. J. Fract.*, **14**, R 287.
50. Gledhill, R. A. & Kinloch, A. J. (1979). *Polym. Eng. Sci.*, **19**, 82.
51. Kalthoff, J. F., Winkler, S. & Beinert, J. (1976). *Int. J. Fract.*, **12**, 161.
52. Phillips, D. C. & Scott, J. M. 1974). *J. Mater. Sci.*, **9**, 1202.
53. Hakeem, M. I. & Phillips, M. G. (1978). *J. Mater. Sci.*, **13**, 2284.
54. Ripling, E. J., Mostovoy, S. & Bersch, C. (1971). *J. Adhes.*, **3**, 145.
55. Mai, Y. W. & Leete, N. B. (1979). *J. Mater. Sci.*, **14**, 2264.
56. Mai, Y. W. & Atkins, A. G. (1975). *J. Mater. Sci.*, **10**, 2003.
57. Hull, D. (1970). *J. Mater. Sci.*, **5**, 357.
58. Cherry, B. W. & Thomson, K. W. (1981). *J. Mater. Sci.*, **16**, 1925.
59. Kinloch, A. J. & Shaw, S. J. Unpublished results.
60. Kinloch, A. J. & Williams, J. G. (1980). *J. Mater. Sci.*, **15**, 987.
61. Yamini, S. & Young, R. J. (1980). *J. Mater. Sci.*, **15**, 1823.
62. Lilley, J. & Holloway, D. G. (1973). *Phil. Mag.*, **28**, 215.
63. van den Boogaart, A. (1966) In: *Physical basis of yield in glassy polymers*, Ed. by R. N. Haward, Institute of Physics, London.
64. Donald, A. M. & Kramer, E. J. (1982). *J. Mater. Sci.*, **17**, 1871.
65. Morgan, R. J. & O'Neal, J. E. (1977). *J. Mater. Sci.*, **12**, 1966.
66. Kambour, R. P. (1973). *J. Polym. Sci. Macromol Rev.*, **7**, 1.
67. Morgan, R. J. & O'Neal, J. E. (1978). *J. Macromol. Sci.—Phys.*, **B15**, 139.
68. Morgan, R. J., O'Neal, J. E. & Miller, D. B. (1979). *J. Mater. Sci.*, **14**, 109.
69. Morgan, R. J., Mones, E. T. & Steele, W. J. (1982). *Polymer*, **23**, 295.
70. Racich, J. L. & Koutsky, J. A. (1976). *J. Appl. Sci.*, **20**, 2111.
71. Thomas, E. L. *Structure of Crystalline Polymers*, Ed. by I. H. Hall, Applied Science Publishers Ltd., London, to be published.
72. Mijovic, J. & Koutsky, J. A. (1979). *Polymer*, **20**, 1095.
73. Young, R. J. & Beaumont, P. W. R. (1976). *Polymer*, **17**, 717.
74. Williams, J. G. & Marshall, G. P. (1974). *Polymer*, **15**, 251.
75. McMeeking, R. M. (1977). *J. Mech. Phys. Solids*, **25**, 357.
76. Kinloch, A. J., Shaw, S. J. & Hunston, D. L. (1982). *Intern. conf. yield, deformation and fracture*, Cambridge, Plastics Rubber Inst., London, p. 19.
77. Kinloch, A. J. & Shaw, S. J. (1981). In: *Developments in adhesives—2*, Ed. by A. J. Kinloch, Applied Science Publishers Ltd., London, p. 82.

78. McMillan, J. C. (1981). In: *Developments in adhesives—2*, Ed. by A. J. Kinloch, Applied Science Publishers Ltd., London, p. 243.
79. Comyn, J. (1981). In: *Developments in adhesives—2*, Ed. by A. J. Kinloch, Applied Science Publishers Ltd., London, p. 279.
80. Rice, J. R. & Rosengren, G. F. (1968). *J. Mech. Phys. Solids*, **16**, 1.
81. Rice, J. R. & Johnson, M. A. (1970). *Inelastic behavior of solids*, Ed. by M. F. Kanninen, W. Alder, A. Rosenfield & R. Jaffe, McGraw Hill, New York, p. 641.
82. Narisawa, I., Murayama, T. & Ogawa, H. (1982). *Polymer*, **23**, 291.
83. Kalthoff, J. F., Winkler, S. & Beinert, J. (1977). *Int. J. Fract.*, **13**, 371.
84. Hertzberg, R. W., Nordberg, H. & Manson, J. A. (1970). *J. Mater. Sci.*, **5**, 521.
85. Sutton, S. A. (1974). *Eng. Fract. Mech.*, **6**, 587.
86. Harris, J. S. & Ward, I. M. (1973). *J. Mater. Sci.*, **8**, 1655.
87. Owen, M. J. & Rose, R. G. (1973). *J. Phys. D., Appl. Phys.*, **6**, 42.
88. Gledhill, R. A. & Kinloch, A. J. (1976). *Polymer*, **17**, 727.
89. Gledhill, R. A., Kinloch, A. J. & Shaw, S. J. (1979). *J. Mater. Sci.*, **14**, 1769.

Chapter 9

Crystalline Polymers

9.1 INTRODUCTION

The fracture behaviour of crystalline polymers is somewhat different from that of amorphous polymer glasses or rubbers because of significant structural differences between crystalline and amorphous polymers. The structure of crystalline polymers is discussed briefly in Section 1.3.3 and has been reviewed in standard textbooks.[1,2] Crystalline polymers are found in a variety of morphological forms ranging from single crystals to semicrystalline polymers in which the non-crystalline component can be either rubbery or glassy. In addition, semicrystalline polymers can be obtained either in an isotropic form or as oriented fibres which have contrasting mechanical properties. The structural and morphological variations have a strong effect upon the fracture behaviour of crystalline polymers and this is a phenomenon not normally encountered with amorphous polymers.

Unlike amorphous polymers the application of fracture mechanics to the fracture of crystalline polymers is not very straightforward even for isotropic materials. This is principally because crystalline polymers are not normally brittle and their deformation can be non-linear but is also because there is often large-scale yielding in the vicinity of the crack tip. Hence it is generally impossible to apply linear elastic fracture mechanics unless the polymer is at low temperature or has been embrittled through environmental action.

9.1.1 General Mechanical Behaviour
Typical stress/strain curves for a series of crystalline polymers of different morphological forms are given in Fig. 9.1. Isotropic semicrys-

talline polymers deformed at temperatures above the T_g of the amorphous phase are usually ductile, and yield and flow forming a neck with the specimen often drawing up to 30 times its original length. Below the T_g the amorphous phase is much less compliant and the semicrystalline sample has a higher yield stress but flow is unable to take place and so failure occurs at a lower strain. In conventional crystalline polymer fibres there is a high degree of molecular orientation along the fibre axis and the fibres have a higher modulus than isotropic samples. Consequently the initial slope of the stress/strain curve is relatively high and fracture occurs at low strains with little plastic deformation. Polymer single crystal fibres show even higher values of modulus and strength sometimes fracturing at stresses in excess of 2 GPa. Hence, it can be seen that crystalline polymers display a wide range of mechanical properties ranging from relatively flexible but tough polymers to very stiff, strong fibres. Because of this wide

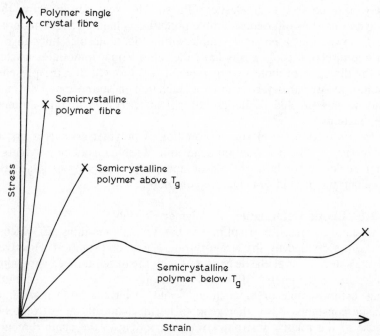

Fig. 9.1. Schematic stress/strain curves for crystalline polymers in different morphological forms drawn approximately to scale.

variation in mechanical properties the fracture behaviour of the different morphologies is discussed separately. Since there is an intimate relationship between the deformation and fracture of polymers, the way in which polymers respond to elastic and plastic deformation is reviewed.

9.2 DEFORMATION

The relationship betwen deformation and fracture behaviour is especially apparent for crystalline polymers which can exhibit such a wide range of deformation characteristics (Fig. 9.1). The relative ease of plastic deformation means that semicrystalline polymers are generally tough above the T_g of the amorphous phase. The high degree of molecular alignment in polymer fibres and polymer crystals means that they are elastically stiff and have high fracture strengths. Indeed, Frank[3] has pointed out that materials will only have high strength if they also possess high elastic stiffness. He went on to show that polymer crystals offer considerable potential as high-strength materials and showed that a polymer sample with all its molecules fully aligned in one direction could easily have the same Young's modulus as steel in the direction of molecular alignment. It is thought that the presence of morphological defects causes a reduction in stiffness and strength and so has precluded the use of polymer crystals in high-strength applications.

In this section the elastic deformation of polymer crystals is first of all discussed. The deformation behaviour of semicrystalline polymers is then reviewed for both the elastic and plastic regions and finally the mechanisms of cold-drawing are considered.

9.2.1 Elastic Deformation of Polymer Crystals
The simplest measure of stiffness is the Young's modulus, E, which is the stress divided by the strain during elastic deformation. However, crystals have several elastic constants with the exact number depending upon crystal symmetry.[4] Polymer crystals tend to be of low symmetry (e.g. orthorhombic or monoclinic)[1,2] and so have a large number of elastic constants. Also, they tend to be mechanically anisotropic because of the relatively strong covalent bonding in the chain direction and weak secondary bonding between the chains. A full set of elastic constants for a crystal are normally measured by deforming large single

crystal samples but such crystals are not generally available for polymers. Because of this most attention has been paid to determining the most easily measured or calculated elastic constants. The elastic constant that is normally determined is the one for tensile or compressive deformation parallel to the chain direction since this is also of the most practical interest. A full set of elastic constants has never been measured for a polymer crystal and only in one case[5] has a set even been calculated.

9.2.1.1 Calculation of Crystal Moduli

Holliday & White[6] have reviewed the attempts at calculating the moduli of many different polymer crystals. Some of the calculated values are given in Table 9.1. An early valence force field calculation of Treloar[7] used the force constants for bond opening and stretching determined from spectroscopic measurements. More recent improvements have included the use of a Urey–Bradley force field[6] and taking into account interatomic repulsions and bond twisting[5,8] as well as bond bending and stretching. The calculated value of the chain direction modulus for polyethylene has tended to increase as more interactions are included. It should be pointed out that these force-field calculations rely upon spectroscopically measured data and so completely theoretical modulus values are not obtained. Quantum mechanical methods[9,10] have now been developed which have allowed the whole stress/strain curve for a polyethylene crystal to be determined up to the point of fracture. The initial slope of the curve yields a 'theoretical' modulus which can be determined without the knowledge of experimentally measured force constants. This method has yielded a value of chain-direction modulus of 407 GPa[10] which has given relief to experimentalists who have recently been measuring values of modulus approaching 300 GPa which are well in excess of earlier calculated values (Table 9.1).

It can be seen from Table 9.1 that the chain-direction modulus is higher for polyethylene than for other polymer crystals. The polyethylene molecules are in a planar zigzag and there are no sidegroups on the polymer chain. The presence of side-groups reduces the modulus for two reasons. Firstly, they tend to lower the density of chain packing, and secondly they can often force the molecule to adopt a helical conformation. A helical chain such as the polypropylene molecule will readily deform by bond bending and uncoiling the helix and Wool & Boyd[11] have shown that the latter mechanism will be the

TABLE 9.1

CALCULATED AND MEASURED VALUES OF CHAIN-DIRECTION MODULI FOR POLYMER CRYSTALS (AFTER REFERENCES 6, 10, 13)

Polymer	Calculated			Measured	
	$E(GPa)$	Method	Reference	$E(GPa)$	Method	Reference
Polyethylene	182	Valence force field	7	240	X-ray	14
	340	Urey–Bradley force field	8	358	Raman	17
	256	Urey–Bradley force field	5	329	Neutron $(CD_2)_n$	6
	297	Quantum mechanical	9	255	X-ray (low T)	15
	405	Quantum mechanical	10			
Polypropylene	49	Urey–Bradley force field	6	42	X-ray	6
	40	Morse function	11			
Polyoxymethylene	150	Urey–Bradley force field	6	54	X-ray	6
Polytetrafluoroethylene	160	Urey–Bradley force field	6			
Polydiacetylenes						
(pTS)	50	Valence force field	12	43	Brillouin	19
(pDCH)	44	Valence force field	21	46	Brillouin	22
				45	Mechanical	21

main process occurring when propylene is strained in the chain direction. They also predicted that straightening of the helix would cause the slope of the stress/strain curve to increase as the strain increases, leading to an increase in modulus with strain. Polyoxymethylene and polytetrafluoroethylene also have relatively low moduli due to the molecules adopting helical conformations. On the other hand, the low values for polydiacetylene single crystals[12] are due to a reduction in the density of chain packing caused by bulky side-groups on the planar zigzag molecule.

9.2.1.2 Experimentally Measured Crystal Moduli

The crystal moduli can be measured in semicrystalline polymers if a technique is employed which can be used to measure only crystal strains when a stress is applied to the whole specimen (Table 9.1). The main method that has been used is X-ray diffraction[14] whereby the position of the X-ray maxima is followed as the specimen is stressed. Since the amorphous component does not give rise to any discrete X-ray reflections only changes in the crystal are followed but there can be problems in determining the stress on the crystalline elements from the overall applied stress.[15,16] Other indirect methods of crystal modulus determination have included Raman scattering,[17] inelastic neutron scattering[18] and Brillouin scattering.[19]

The simplest and most direct method of determining the crystal modulus is to deform a single crystal sample and follow the variation of strain with the applied stress. However, in the past this has been impossible because of morphological problems. Solution-grown lamellar single crystals[1,2] are too small to handle and semicrystalline polymers possess an amorphous component. The crystal modulus can be partly realised in highly oriented fibres of polyethylene. The room-temperature moduli of such fibres are of the order of 70–150 GPa (i.e. 25–50 % of the crystal modulus) but when the temperature was reduced to 77 K, below the T_g of the non-crystalline component, a modulus of the order of 290 GPa was reported for a fibre grown from stirred solution.[20] This is obviously very close to the crystal modulus of polyethylene in the chain direction (Table 9.1).

An important breakthrough in the direct measurement of polymer crystal moduli has been through the preparation of macroscopic polymer single crystals by the solid-state polymerisation of monomer crystals.[1,13,21] The crystals are often fibrous with macroscopic dimensions (several centimetres long) and so can be gripped and deformed

using conventional fibre testing techniques. The chain-direction modulus is found to increase with the percentage conversion from
monomer to polymer for single crystal textured fibres of polyoxymethylene[23] and for polydiacetylene single crystals tested mechanically[1,21] or measured using Brillouin scattering.[19,22] Fully polymerised
polydiacetylene single crystal fibres are found to have mechanically
measured values of modulus[21,24,25] which approach the theoretical
values[12,21,25] determined from spectroscopically measured force constants which is not surprising because of their high degree of perfection.

9.2.2 Elastic Deformation of Semicrystalline Polymers

The Young's moduli of semicrystalline polymers vary greatly and depend upon the type of polymer, degree of crystallinity and crystallite
orientation. For example, it has been known for many years that the
formation of crystals in natural rubber[26] stored for prolonged periods
of time causes a dramatic increase in the modulus of the rubber. In
unoriented semicrystalline polymers the specimen modulus is dominated by the relatively low transverse and shear moduli.[5] For example,
if the measured modulus values for spherulitic polyethylene are extrapolated to 100 % crystallinity a modulus of ~ 5 GPa is found for the
fully crystalline material.[27] The modulus of a polycrystalline isotropic
sample can be predicted, if a full set of elastic constants is known,
using the Voigt or Reuss averaging procedures[28] with their respective
assumption of uniform strain and uniform stress. The modulus of
100 % crystalline polyethylene is predicted to be 4·9 GPa using the
Reuss model and 15·6 GPa for the Voigt model using the elastic
constants of Odajima and Maeda,[5] implying that the uniform stress
conditions are more appropriate for spherulitic polyethylene. The
two-phase composite nature of semicrystalline polymers was recognised by Halpin & Kardos[29] who showed that it is possible to calculate
the stiffness of partly crystalline samples using theories developed for
fibre-reinforced composites. The idea was extended by Andrews[30] who
showed that this approach could be used to model the mechanical
behaviour of semicrystalline polymers with spherulitic, row-nucleated
or fibrillar morphologies.

The high chain-direction modulus of polymer crystals can be realised
to a certain extent in oriented polymer fibres such as the new generation of ultra-high-modulus polymer fibres.[15,16,20,31-4] Although they are
still semicrystalline there is often a high degree of chain extension and

TABLE 9.2

MECHANICAL PROPERTIES OF DIFFERENT HIGH-STRENGTH FIBRES

Material	Specific gravity	Tensile modulus (GPa)	Specific modulus (GPa)	Tensile strength (GPa)	Specific strength (GPa)	Reference
Highly drawn poly-ethylene	0·966	68	71	>0·3	>0·3	126
High-modulus ex-truded polyethy-lene	0·97	67	69	0·48	0·49	127
Polydiacetylene single-crystal fibres	1·31	61	50	1·7	1·3	21
'Kevlar' 49 fibres	1·45	128	88	2·6	1·8	142
Glass fibres	2·5	69–138	28–55	0·4–1·7	0·15–0·7	127
Carbon steel	7·9	210	27	0·5	0·07	127
Carbon fibres	2·0	200–420	100–210	2–3	1·0–1·5	127

chain orientation and short-term room-temperature moduli up to 50 % of the chain-direction crystal moduli can be obtained. These can be increased by reducing the testing temperature so that the non-crystalline component becomes glassy.[20] The modulus values for highly oriented polymer fibres are given in Table 9.2 along with modulus values for other high-modulus materials. For many purposes it is the specific stiffness that is important (i.e. Young's modulus divided by specific gravity) especially when light, stiff, high-strength materials are required. It can be seen from Table 9.2 that since polymers have low specific gravities their specific stiffnesses compare extremely well with non-polymeric materials.

9.2.3 Plastic Deformation and Drawing

It is the ability of semicrystalline polymers to undergo plastic deformation that leads to the toughness for which they are renowned. In these polymers the non-crystalline component is normally rubbery and this allows the crystals to deform plastically and change shape without cleavage since polymer crystals do not generally possess the five independent slip systems necessary for general deformation.[4,35] Indeed, if the amorphous phase is absent, as is the case with chain-extended polyethylene crystallised under pressure, the material is brittle.[35,36] Polymer crystals, like crystals of other materials, are capable of undergoing plastic deformation in three general ways: by slip,[35,37,38] by twinning[39–42] and through martensitic transformations.[39] The deformation mechanisms occur in such a way that the polymer molecules remain unbroken during the deformation.[13,35]

Semicrystalline polymers are often so ductile that they can be deformed to very high draw ratios before the specimens eventually fail. During the early stages of deformation the original spherulitic structure becomes elongated through slip and other deformation mechanisms.[43] The chain axes of the crystals which are originally oriented randomly become aligned parallel to the drawing direction. Eventually the original lamellar and spherulitic structures break up and a new fibrous structure is formed with the molecules aligned approximately parallel to the extension direction.[35,44,45]

There is now considerable interest in using mechanical extension[15,31] to produce polymers with a high degree of molecular alignment and having high values of stiffness and strength. It is found that, in general, the Young's modulus of the polymer is controlled principally by the draw ratio[15] which is in turn controlled, at a given temperature, by the molar mass of the polymer.[46] Optimisation of the thermal treatment of the undrawn polymer, the selection of the correct molar mass and the choice of the best drawing conditions has now allowed polyethylene samples to be produced with draw ratios in excess of 30 and moduli of up to 70 GPa.[15,47]

9.3 FRACTURE OF POLYMER CRYSTALS

Polymer single crystals can be obtained in two basic forms, either as solution-grown chain-folded lamellae[1,2,48] or as solid-state polymerised extended-chain crystals.[1,49,50] In general, there are two ways in which polymer crystals may fracture. If they are stressed parallel to the chain direction molecular fracture will occur, at very high stresses, with cracks running across the molecules and breaking the primary covalent bonds. Alternatively if the crystals are stressed in directions not parallel to the chain direction, intermolecular cleavage occurs with cracks running parallel to the molecules, breaking the secondary bonds between molecules at relatively low stresses. These two situations will be considered separately.

9.3.1 Molecular Fracture: Macroscopic Single Crystals

It was shown in Chapter 2 that molecular fracture can be followed using electron spin resonance (ESR) and is found to occur when highly oriented polymer fibres are deformed to failure. However, it is not normally possible to know if the molecular fracture occurs in the crystalline or amorphous regions and it is only relatively recently that molecular fracture has been demonstrated clearly in polymer crystals. Figure 9.2 shows a fractured polydiacetylene single crystal fibre[21] and it can be seen that the fracture plane has severed the molecules which are parallel to the fibre axis. A stress/strain curve for a similar fibre is given in Fig. 9.3 and fracture stresses of up to 2 GPa have been obtained corresponding to a strain of ~4 %.

Macroscopic single crystals of conventional polymers such as polyethylene are not available and so a stress/strain curve for a polyethylene single crystal has not been measured. However, complete stress/strain curves have been calculated for polyethylene by Boudreaux[9] and Crist *et al.*[10] using quantum mechanical methods—these calculated stress/strain curves are given in Fig. 9.4. Although the behaviour cannot be confirmed by experiment the calculated curves give an excellent demonstration of the expected deformation and

Fig. 9.2. Electron micrograph of a fractured polydiacetylene single crystal fibre (after Galiotis[21]).

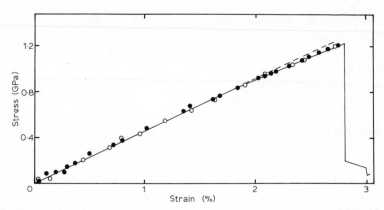

Fig. 9.3. *Typical stress/strain curve for a polydiacetylene single crystal fibre. The closed circles are for loading and the open circles correspond to unloading (after Galiotis[21]).*

fracture behaviour of a *perfect* polymer crystal. The modulus of the polymer can be determined from the initial slopes of the curves but the most interesting aspect of the behaviour is the position of the maximum which gives the stress and strain at failure. Crist *et al.*[10] have predicted that for a polyethylene crystal the fracture strain will be 43 % at an enormously high stress of 66 GPa. However, they pointed out that this corresponds to the conditions to fragment a perfect crystal at absolute zero. The fracture stress will be clearly reduced at higher temperatures and when the effect of crystal defects is taken into account. Nevertheless, this gives an indication of the potentially very high strengths that polymer crystals may display.

Although the behaviour of polyethylene crystals cannot be tested experimentally, complete stress/strain curves have been obtained for polydiacetylene crystals as was seen in Fig. 9.3. The fracture strain of ~2·5 % is well below that predicted for polyethylene and it is thought that this is due to the presence of defects in the polydiacetylene crystals. This can be demonstrated by following the dependence of crystal strength upon the fibre diameter[21] as shown in Fig. 9.5(a). There is a marked reduction in the fibre strength as the crystal diameter increases which is thought to be due to the presence of defects such as surface steps.[21,51,52] It can be shown that for such steps the dependence of fracture strength, σ_f, upon fibre diameter, d_f, will be given by an

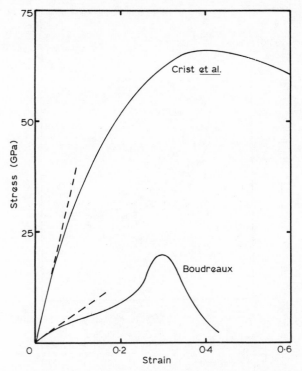

Fig. 9.4. *Theoretically calculated stress/strain curves for a polyethylene crystal deformed in tension parallel to the chain direction (after Boudreaux[9] and Crist et al.[10]).*

equation of the form[52]

$$\frac{1}{\sigma_f} = k_4 + \frac{k_5 \, d_f^{\frac{1}{2}}}{\sigma_{theo}} \tag{9.1}$$

where σ_{theo} is the strength of a step-free crystal or 'theoretical strength' and k_4 and k_5 are constants which depend upon the geometry of the step and the type of polymer. The value of σ_{theo} can be obtained from the slope of the plot of $1/\sigma_f$ versus $d_f^{\frac{1}{2}}$ shown in Fig. 9.5(b) and is found to be ~2·5 GPa. This corresponds to a fracture strain of ~5 % and is clearly well below the value of 66 GPa expected for a polyethylene crystal (Fig. 9.4). However, no account has been taken of internal defects such as dislocations[53] or chain ends and so the true 'theoretical strength' would be expected to be considerably higher.

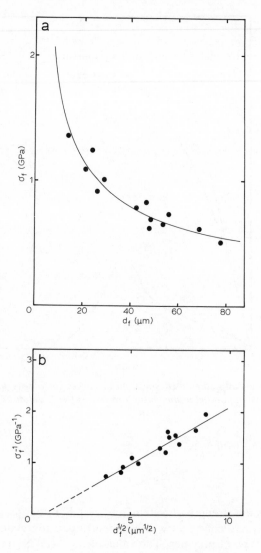

Fig. 9.5. (a) Dependence of fracture stress, σ_f, upon fibre diameter, d_f, for polydiacetylene single crystal fibres; and (b) Variation of $1/\sigma_f$ with $d_f^{\frac{1}{2}}$ for polydiacetylene single crystal fibres (after Galiotis[21]).

There are several monomers which undergo solid-state polymerisation but do not form polymer single crystals. There is still a high degree of molecular orientation but the register perpendicular to the chain direction is lost and the monomer single crystals transform to give microfibrillar polymer crystals. Trioxane needles polymerise to give polycrystalline polyoxymethylene fibres[23,54] and disulphur dinitride (S_2N_2) can be polymerised to give fibrillar $(SN)_x$ crystals.[55] These polymers contain many more defects than macroscopic single crystals such as the polydiacetylenes and this is reflected in lower levels of fracture strength. For example, both the polyoxymethylene fibres[23,54] and $(SN)_x$[55] crystals are found to have fracture strengths of the order of $0 \cdot 2$ GPa corresponding to failure strains of 1–2 %. Failure in these types of solid-state polymerised fibrillar crystal is thought to occur through a fibril pull-out mechanism[23,54,55] rather than molecular cleavage.

In Table 9.2 the mechanical properties of various high-strength fibres are compared. The specific properties are also listed and it can be seen that polymer single crystal fibres compare well with other materials. It is expected[52] that considerable improvements will be made when polydiacetylene single crystal fibres are prepared with smaller side-groups leading to a higher density of chain packing. Improvements can also be obtained for semicrystalline polymers such as polyethylene by improving the degree of molecular alignment and crystal perfection and so enabling the theoretical modulus (>300 GPa, Table 9.1) and hence higher strengths to be realised.

9.3.2 Intermolecular Cleavage

In contrast to the relatively high levels of strength exhibited when they are deformed parallel to the chain direction, polymer crystals readily cleave at low stresses when deformed in tension perpendicular to the chain direction. Solution-crystallised lamellar single crystals of polyethylene are too small to be gripped in a testing machine but they can be deformed on an extensible substrate.[56,57] The polymer molecules are oriented perpendicular to the lamellar surface and so the crystals can only be stressed perpendicular to the chain direction. Crystals deformed in this way have cleavage cracks and the nature of these cracks has been used to advantage to show fold planes, and to give strong support to the theory of adjacent re-entry in single crystals of PE[48,58] and PP.[59] Irradiation can produce intermolecular cross-links and it is found to have a profound effect upon the cleavage of lamellar single crystals of PE.[60,61] At low doses fibrils are pulled across the cleavage cracks but above 35–40 Mrad, fibril formation is inhibited[60] and material is drawn across the crack in the form of a thin continuous film.[61]

Microscopic lamellar single crystals of polydiacetylene crystals can be prepared by solid-state polymerisation in which the molecules are aligned in the planes of the lamellae.[62] They can also be deformed on extensible substrates[63] and are found to undergo intermolecular cleavage at low strains when stressed in tension perpendicular to the chain axes. However, they can also be deformed parallel to the chain direction and in this case fracture is much more difficult.

9.4   FRACTURE OF ISOTROPIC SEMICRYSTALLINE POLYMERS

When deformed at room temperature semicrystalline polymers tend to be relatively tough and undergo considerable plastic deformation before rupture. For example, HDPE will not undergo cleavage fracture unless it is notched or loaded under impact conditions[64] and if the molar mass is high ($\bar{M}_w > 10^6$ g mol^{-1}) cleavage fracture does not occur at all.[65] Also polypropylene subjected to repeated and reversed bending will form a stable hinge which is a property that can be utilised in PP artefacts. However, semicrystalline polymers can be induced to behave in a brittle manner by reducing the temperature or using certain hostile environments. Fracture surfaces of HDPE deformed at liquid-nitrogen temperature appear relatively smooth when examined at low magnification but detailed studies[65] have shown that plastic deformation occurs on a local level even when the fracture appears to be completely brittle.

9.4.1   Effect of Morphology and Structure
The highest level of morphology in semicrystalline polymers is the spherulitic microstructure and this has been found to have an influence upon the mechanical behaviour of PE,[30,66] PP[67–9] and nylon 6.[70] The fracture of HDPE in an active environment is virtually completely brittle[66] and it is found that failure is interlamellar within the spherulites but that the exact mode of crack propagation depends upon the relative position of the crack front and spherulite centre.[66]

Since PP generally has a better-defined and more easily varied

spherulitic microstructure than PE there have been rather more extensive studies of the effect of spherulite structure upon the fracture of
PP.[67-9] By using PP with different molar mass and tacticity and using a
variety of heat treatments Friedrich[68] has been able to produce
morphologies ranging from fine spherulites ($\sim$20 μm diameter) to
coarse spherulites ($\sim$500 μm diameter). He found that cracks propagated most easily at the interfaces between coarse spherulites (Fig.
9.6(a)). The resistance to this type of failure increased as the molar
mass of the PP was increased.[71] It is thought that this is due to more
plastic-deformation occurring at the spherulite boundaries as can be
seen from Fig. 9.6(b). The higher-molar-mass material will have more
intercrystalline and interspherulitic links.[72]

Way et al.[69] have shown that spherulite size has a pronounced effect
upon the deformation characteristics of PP. This is demonstrated
clearly in Fig. 9.7 where stress/strain curves are given for PP in which
the spherulite size is varied by using different heat treatments. The
material with the highest spherulite size ($\sim$250 μm diameter) is brittle
but it becomes more ductile as the spherulite size is reduced. Material
with a spherulite diameter of 90 μm is so ductile that it can be drawn
to strains in excess of 700 %. The brittleness of the slow-cooled
material with the largest spherulites has been interpreted[69] as being
due to the segregation of impurities and the formation of voids at the
spherulite boundaries.

The fracture behaviour of nylons is strongly dependent upon the
water content and so Bessell et al.[70] used dry specimens when they
investigated the effect of structure and morphology on the mechanical
properties of nylon 6. They found that the behaviour depended most
strongly upon the degree of crystallinity with the spherulite size only
having a secondary effect. Specimens with a degree of crystallinity in
excess of 40 % were brittle whereas at low levels of crystallinity
(<30 %) the material was ductile.

Certain semicrystalline polymers crystallised under pressure have
'extended-chain' crystals[2,36,73-5] in which the lamellae are very thick
($\sim$1 μm). A similar morphology is found in PTFE[76] crystallised slowly
at ambient pressure. Chain-extended HDPE is normally brittle at
room temperature[36] but oriented material can be induced to undergo
plastic deformation at 80°C.[73] Chain-extended nylon 6 is brittle and
cleavage occurs either between the hydrogen-bonded sheets within the
crystals or between the lamellae at the surfaces containing chain ends
or impurities. In either case the polymer molecules are not broken.

Fig. 9.6. Interspherulitic fracture surfaces of polypropylene with coarse spherulites with: (a) low, and (b) high molar masses (after Hornbogen & Friedrich[71]).

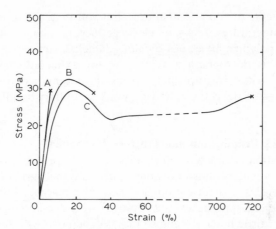

Fig. 9.7. *Stress/strain curves for three polypropylene samples with different average spherulite radii. A, average radius* 126 μm; *B, average radius* 87 μm; *and C, average radius* 46 μm *(after Way et al.[69]).*

Fig. 9.8. *Fracture surface of chain-extended PTFE fractured at low temperature* (−196°C) *(after Young[1]).*

PTFE is ductile at room temperature but will undergo brittle fracture at low temperatures.[76] Again cleavage occurs either along planes containing polymer molecules or along lamellar surfaces as shown in Fig. 9.8. This micrograph is typical of any extended-chain polymer undergoing brittle fracture and reflects the strength of the covalent bonds compared with the relatively weak secondary bonding between molecules.

9.4.2 Crack Propagation and Fracture Mechanics

The application of fracture mechanics to crack propagation in semi-crystalline polymers must be done with care because of the large amounts of plastic deformation that can take place at the crack tip. Rather different approaches must be used with ductile polyolefins and other more brittle polymers and so they will be dealt with separately.

9.4.2.1 Ductile Polyolefins

Because of their ductility at room temperature polyolefins such as PE and PP do not in any way satisfy the requirements for linear elastic fracture mechanics to be applied. Hence the techniques used to study the propagation of cracks in these materials have been the ones developed to cope with more ductile materials such as modifications of the trouser leg tear test,[77-9] a generalised fracture theory[80] or the 'J-integral' analysis.[81]

Some of the earliest attempts to measure G for thin sheets were made by Anderton & Treloar[77] for LDPE and Sims[78] for PP using the trouser leg tear test originally developed for the study of tearing in rubbers (Section 3.6.1, Fig. 3.12). Anderton & Treloar determined G_c for three different grades of LDPE and one grade of HDPE. They found that G_c for stable tearing in LDPE was of the order of $150 \, \text{kJ m}^{-2}$ with no significant difference between the grades and was about $80 \, \text{kJ m}^{-2}$ for the HDPE. They noted that cracks started to propagate at significantly lower values of G_c and they related the increase in G_c to the increase in crack tip diameter as specimens were loaded. It was also found that G_c dropped dramatically when oriented polymers were used with a reduction by a factor of 100 in G_c for the most highly oriented samples. Sims[78] carried out a similar investigation upon tearing in PP and obtained similar results. He also followed the variation of G_c with temperature and found that for isotropic specimens G_c increased slowly from 30 to $40 \, \text{kJ m}^{-2}$ between -60 and $-10°C$ and then increased rapidly above $0°C$ to about $200 \, \text{kJ m}^{-2}$ at room temperature as shown in Fig. 9.9. This transition in behaviour is probably due to the glass transition in PP which occurs at about -10 to $-20°C$. The trouser leg tear test would appear to be a relatively simple method of evaluating the tearing behaviour of ductile polyolefins. However, it is difficult to distinguish between crack initiation or propagation and the mode of crack growth may be uncertain.[79] Also in the thin sheets that are used it has been shown[79] that the modulus of the material may affect the results.

Andrews & Fukahori[80] measured the fracture energies of 2-mm thick single-edge notched (SEN) specimens of LDPE and found values of G_c of the order of 30–60 kJ m^{-2} depending upon the crack velocity. Using the generalised theory of Andrews (Section 3.2.4) they were able to determine G_0, the energy required for bond breakage, as 400 ± 200 J m^{-2} which they compared with the theoretical value of

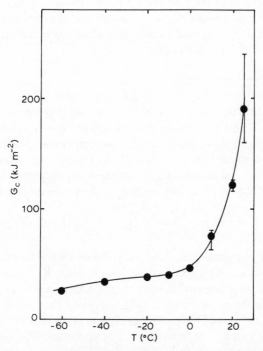

Fig. 9.9. Variation of fracture energy, G_c, with test temperature for isotropic polypropylene (after Sims[78]).

$62 \pm 12 \, \text{J m}^{-2}$ calculated using eqn. (2.8). This discrepancy may be due to the lack of reliable parameters for the calculation of G_0 or highly localised loss processes occurring close to the crack tip increasing the measured value of G_0. Hodgkinson & Williams[81] have also measured G_c for SEN samples of LDPE sheet (3 mm) using the J-integral analysis (Section 3.2.3). They found that there was some dependence of G_c upon crack length and quote an initiation (plane strain) value of about $4 \, \text{kJ m}^{-2}$ and a propagation (plane stress) value of $20 \, \text{kJ m}^{-2}$.

The publication of the paper by Hodgkinson & Williams[81] has prompted a lively discussion between them and Andrews.[82,83] The two groups agree upon the value of G_c for propagation but Hodgkinson & Williams[81,83] questioned the validity of measured values of G_0 in the light of the possibility of highly localised plastic deformation occurring near the crack. A claim that the J-integral analysis is simpler to perform than the generalised theory[81] was also refuted by Andrews[82] who suggested that there are problems with the J-integral analysis and pointed out that only the generalised theory allows G_0 to be measured. Clearly both approaches are of interest for the fracture of ductile polymers and it is envisaged that there will be important developments in this area in the years to come.

9.4.2.2 Brittle Semicrystalline Polymers

Linear elastic fracture mechanics has been used to explain the low-temperature fracture behaviour of semicrystalline polymers, such as PP and nylon 6[84] and a nitrocellulose/nitroglycerine-based propellant,[85] which are sufficiently brittle below room temperature, with any plastic deformation localised at the crack tip. For these materials it is found that the fracture toughness, K_{Ic}, is strongly dependent upon specimen thickness and this has been successfully interpreted using eqn. (3.59):

$$K_{Ic} = \left(\frac{b - 2r''_{yc}}{b}\right)K'_{Ic} + \left(\frac{2r''_{yc}}{b}\right)K''_{Ic}$$

The material is assumed to have two values of fracture toughness, a plane-stress value, K''_{Ic}, and a plane-strain value, K'_{Ic}, and it is further assumed that the plane-stress conditions pertain over a surface skin of depth $\sim r''_{yc}$ with plane-strain conditions over the remainder of the specimen. It is found[84,85] for the three polymers that the plane-strain value, K'_{Ic}, is virtually independent of temperature whereas K''_{Ic} tends to increase as the temperature is reduced. There is a similar increase in the yield stress, σ_y, with decreasing temperature and Kinloch &

Gledhill[85] have found a linear dependence of K''_{Ic} upon σ_y for the propellant. They interpreted this as being due to the material having a constant value of r''_{yc} of 1·3 mm which is independent of temperature but the value of r''_{yc} is found to vary with temperature for PP and nylon 66. Mai & Williams[84] have suggested that a constant crack-opening displacement criterion, δ_{tc}, operates in these materials in the region of the secondary transitions. Attempts have been made to correlate features in the plot of K''_{Ic} against temperature with β- and γ-transitions in PP and nylon 66 although the correlations claimed appear somewhat tenuous. Kinloch & Gledhill[85] suggested that since both G_{Ic} and tan δ_r are concerned with energy losses in a material, it might be more appropriate to correlate G''_{Ic} with tan δ_r as shown in Fig. 9.10 for the propellant, where both parameters peak at approximately −40°C. It would seem likely that a better correlation might have been

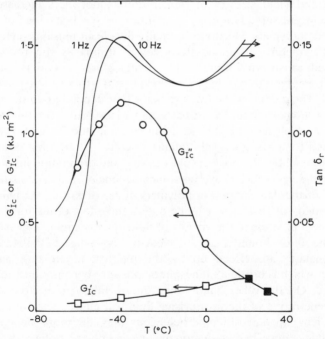

Fig. 9.10. Variation of G'_{Ic} and G''_{Ic} and tan δ_r with temperature for a nitrocellulose/nitroglycerine-based polymeric propellant (after Kinloch & Gledhill[85]).

obtained by Mai & Williams[84] if they had used G''_{Ic} rather than K''_{Ic} for their PP and nylon 66 results.

9.4.3 Effect of Testing Conditions

The response of semicrystalline polymers to mechanical deformation is strongly dependent upon the conditions under which they are tested. Because of this the mechanical behaviour of these materials when tested under pressure, rapidly (under impact conditions), slowly (creep rupture) or under cyclic conditions (fatigue), will be reviewed together. Most of these factors have been discussed from a general viewpoint in Chapter 6 and so only the features relevant to semicrystalline polymers and not covered already will be discussed at this stage.

9.4.3.1 Pressure

The effect of superimposed hydrostatic pressure upon the mechanical properties of polymers has been reviewed by Pae & Bhateja.[86] The moduli and yield stresses of semicrystalline polymers increase with increasing pressure. However, in contrast to the behaviour of glassy polymers, polymers which are normally ductile in tension, such as PE and PP, fracture at progressively lower strains as the pressure is increased as shown in Fig. 9.11. Brittle glassy polymers, such as polystyrene, tend to become more ductile as the hydrostatic pressure is applied. The details of the fracture behaviour depend upon the type of polymer. For example, PP[86] clearly undergoes brittle fracture at high pressure which may be due to an increase in the T_g with pressure, whereas PE shows essentially infinite ductility[87,88] necking down to a fine point without the normal cold-drawing and orientation hardening.

Over the years there have been inconsistencies and discrepancies in reports of the deformation of polymers under pressure, but Duckett[89] has pointed out that these may be due to the effect of the local tensile component of stress in the vicinity of flaws. For example, internal flaws at spherulite boundaries in heavily crystallised poly(ethylene terephthalate) are closed up by the hydrostatic pressure and the polymer which is brittle at atmospheric pressure becomes ductile under pressure. On the other hand, when failure takes place from surface flaws penetration of the pressurising fluid will affect the state of stress at the flaw tip and different behaviour may therefore be obtained depending upon whether or not the specimens are isolated from the pressurising fluid such as by surrounding with a rubber sheath.

A recent study by Truss et al.[90] was concerned with the yield and

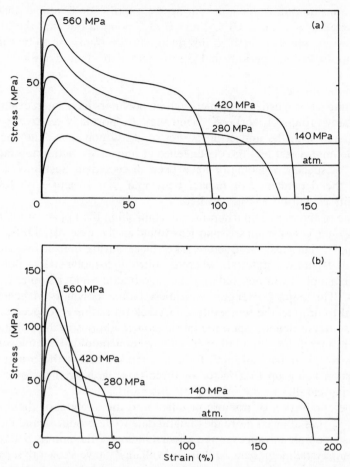

Fig. 9.11. Stress/strain curves for crystalline polymers deformed in tension under the stated superimposed hydrostatic pressures. (a) Medium-density polyethylene; and (b) Polypropylene (after Pae & Bhateja[86]).

fracture of HDPE under hydrostatic pressure. They found that under a superimposed hydrostatic pressure ductile/brittle transitions could be induced by either increasing or decreasing the strain-rate and they interpreted the behaviour as being due to a competition between yield and fracture processes which have different strain-rate dependencies. The fracture stress falls below the yield stress at both high and low strain-rates. The low strain-rate ductile/brittle transition is similar to the transition in behaviour during long-term static-fatigue loading discussed in Section 9.4.3.4. Truss *et al.*[90] pointed out that the use of hydrostatic pressure enabled this ductile/brittle transition to be shifted to shorter loading periods making its study considerably easier.

9.4.3.2 Impact

The impact properties of semicrystalline polymers have been examined by many groups of workers[91–8] and they are normally relatively good compared with the impact properties of glassy polymers. The analysis of the impact test and the dependence of impact strength upon factors such as specimen geometry have been discussed in Section 6.2 and only the dependence of impact behaviour and structure on testing conditions will be considered here.

One of the most important factors controlling the impact strength of a polymer is molar mass[91] and it is found in the case of HDPE,[65] for example, that cleavage fracture takes place during impact loading for low-molar-mass material whereas ultra-high-molar-mass polymer ($>10^6$ g mol^{-1}) will not undergo cleavage fracture under similar conditions. The impact strength of semicrystalline polymers is generally found to drop as the temperature or crack tip radius is reduced and is also found to depend upon the fabrication conditions of the polymer.[91] For instance, the orientation in an injection moulded sample of PP leads to the impact strength for crack growth across the orientation direction being up to a factor of three times greater than for cracks growing parallel to the orientation direction.

The application of fracture mechanics to the analysis of the impact tests[92,93] has allowed more meaningful data to be produced and has led to considerable advances in the understanding of the impact behaviour of semicrystalline polymers. Plati & Williams[92] have shown that essentially the same values of impact fracture energy, G_{Ic}, could be generated from a fracture mechanics analysis of both Charpy and Izod samples of various types of polymer and some of their results are reproduced in Table 9.3.

It can be seen that for the different PE's the value of G_{Ic} increases as the density (i.e. degree of crystallinity[1]) decreases. Temperature is also found to have a strong effect upon the impact fracture energy, G_{Ic}, which decreases as the temperature of testing is reduced.[94]

It is possible to change the effective loading rate during impact testing by varying the specimen dimensions; Birch & Williams[95] suggested that the variation in the values of G_{Ic} with rate for MDPE

TABLE 9.3
VALUES OF G_{Ic} FOR SEMICRYSTALLINE POLYMERS[92]

Polymer	$G_{Ic}(kJ\ m^{-2})$	
	Charpy	Izod
Low density polyethylene (LDPE)	34·7	34·4
Medium density polyethylene (MDPE)	8·10	8·40
High density polyethylene (HDPE)	3·40	3·10
Nylon 66	5·30	5·00

and PTFE may be related to loss processes in the materials. The correlation of impact behaviour with loss processes is by no means a new idea and similar suggestions were made several years ago.[91,96] The idea has been tested by Kisbenyi et al.[97] for PTFE which has several well-defined loss peaks. They measured both tan δ_r and G_{Ic} for PTFE over a wide range of temperatures ($-100°$–$+200°C$) and showed that there was a good correlation between peaks in G_{Ic} and tan δ_r as shown in Figs 9.12(a) and (b). They suggested that this would be more likely when mutliple crazing at the crack or notch tip was a major mechanism since the presence of a loss peak would be conducive to craze formation and the consequential energy absorption. A possible correlation between impact data and molecular relaxations—the latter usually being obtained from dynamic mechanical tests such as the torsion pendulum—was suggested several years ago by Heijboer.[96] He concluded that a dynamic mechanical damping or loss peak was not always accompanied by a peak or transition in the impact strength. If the peak originates from main-chain segmental motions the correlation with impact data is likely whereas if it is due to side-group movements then no effect upon impact strength is found.

Recently, Williams & Hodgkinson[98] have followed the effect of loading-rate upon the impact behaviour of MDPE and PTFE (Fig. 9.12(c)). They found that G_{Ic} could be related to the loading period, t_1, through a relationship of the form

$$G_{Ic} \propto t_1^{-\frac{1}{2}} \tag{9.2}$$

They suggested that the most likely explanation for this behaviour is that the notch tip of the stationary crack is blunted by adiabatic

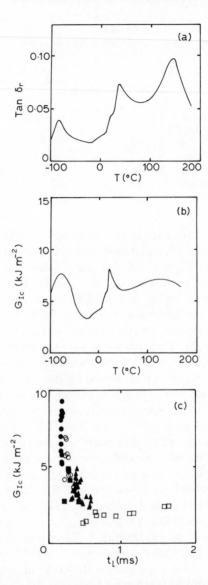

Fig. 9.12. Impact behaviour of PTFE. (a) Variation of tan δ_r with temperature, T; (b) Variation of impact fracture energy, G_{Ic} with T (after Kisbenyi et al.[97]); and (c) Dependence of G_{Ic} upon loading period, t_1, at $-30°C$. The different symbols correspond to different strain rates (after Williams & Hodgkinson[98]).

heating at the tip during the impact test, hence raising the value of G_{Ic} required to propagate the crack. The temperature rise and G_{Ic} will be larger when the loading period is short as shown in Fig. 9.12(c). This blunting analysis is not inconsistent with the idea of viscoelastic-loss processes being involved in impact since the adiabatic heating must be caused by energy dissipating processes such as viscoelastic deformations, crazing or shear yielding.[97]

9.4.3.3 Dynamic Fatigue

The behaviour of semicrystalline polymers under dynamic-fatigue loading has been dealt with from a general viewpoint in Section 6.3. It was shown that they generally possess superior resistance to crack growth under fatigue conditions than do glassy polymers—the highest resistance being found when the molar mass is high and the degree of crystallinity low.[99] The behaviour of semicrystalline polymers is found to follow the Paris equation (eqn. (6.19)) approximately, although since many show inelastic mechanical behaviour a crack growth relationship of the form (eqn. (6.20))

$$\frac{da}{dN} = B_f \Delta G^q$$

is thought[100] to be more appropriate, where B_f and q are a pre-exponential factor and an exponent, respectively. It is found[100,101] for semicrystalline polymers that q is more accurately constant than m when eqn. (6.20) is used (Fig. 9.13(a)) instead of the Paris equation (eqn. (6.19)).

Since the basic mechanics and mechanisms have been covered already, only some very recent studies[101–5] upon the micromechanisms of fatigue crack propagation in semicrystalline polymers will be discussed. White & Teh[102] have examined the micromechanisms of fatigue crack propagation in PE using fractography and showed that different features on the fracture surfaces could be related to different stages of growth revealed from crack propagation measurements. They found that at low propagation rates the fracture surface was rough and fibrous, as shown in Fig. 9.13(b), and this is thought to be due to interspherulitic failure. In contrast, at high fatigue crack propagation rates fine striations can be seen on the fracture surface (Fig. 9.13(c)) but since their spacing is smaller than each increment of crack growth they are thought to be lamellae—either the exposed ends or fractured

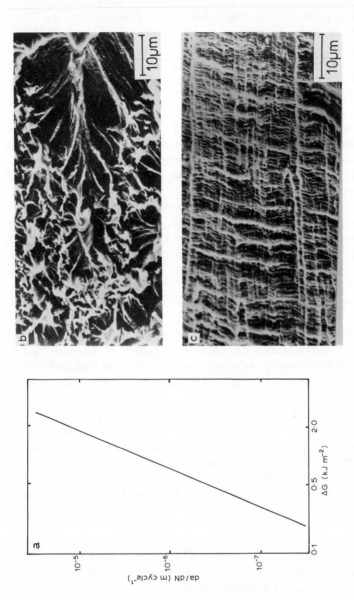

Fig. 9.13. Fatigue-crack propagation in low-density polyethylene. (a) Dependence of fatigue crack propagation rate, da/dN, upon ΔG (after Teh et al.[101]); (b) Fracture surface at a low propagation rate; and (c) Fracture surface at a high propagation rate (after White & Teh[102]).

sections. There must clearly be reorganisation of the lamellar crystal structure under the high tensile stresses at the crack tip.

Bretz *et al.*[104,105] have shown that for several semicrystalline polymers, such as poly(vinylidene fluoride) and nylon 66, fatigue damage starts as crazing in interlamellar regions within both the spherulites and interspherulitic regions. As the stresses and strains increase the crazes lengthen and join up with others to form large crazes which have dimensions greater than the spherulite diameters. Inside the plastic zone the spherulite/craze structure is heavily deformed by tensile and compressive yielding and the original microstructure is completely destroyed. This behaviour is found only when samples are fatigued above the T_g. Plastic deformation is severely limited below T_g and the original microstructure is still reflected in the fracture-surface morphologies. The effect of plastic deformation is further reflected in the fatigue behaviour of different polyamides plasticised with water.[103,104] In general, the crack-growth rates decrease with an increasing water content due to enhanced crack tip blunting. However, at high water contents the fatigue properties deteriorate due, it has been suggested,[103,104] to a lowering of the modulus of the polymer. In conclusion, therefore, it would seem that the main reason why semicrystalline polymers have a high resistance to fatigue crack propagation is their ability to undergo plastic deformation at the crack tip.

9.4.3.4 Static Fatigue

The behaviour of semicrystalline polymers under static-fatigue loading has been discussed in detail in Section 6.4. The behaviour of HDPE is typified in Fig. 6.10(a). After short loading periods the material fails in a ductile manner whereas failure following prolonged loading is, perhaps rather surprisingly, brittle.[65,106] This ductile/brittle transition is accompanied by a 'knee' in the log–log plots of fracture strength versus time-to-failure in Fig. 6.10(a) and the drop in strength has serious consequences in design considerations.[65] For example, the long-term brittleness is particularly worrying in the case of HDPE pipes which can be subjected to static stresses over long periods of time. There is clearly a competition in HDPE between ductile shear yielding and brittle crack growth which have different time or rate dependencies. For short loading periods the yield stress is less than the fracture stress and the polymer is ductile whereas for longer periods of loading the fracture stress is less than the yield stress and so the material is brittle.

The variation in the tensile behaviour of PE with strain-rate or loading period has been neatly summarised by Zapas & Crissman[107] in terms of failure envelopes on stress/strain/time diagrams. They pointed out that, depending upon molar mass, there is only a relatively narrow range of strain-rate or applied stress for which the material can be deformed to high draw-ratios. Polyethylene tends to be brittle in both impact and long-term loading and can only be deformed to high strains using intermediate strain-rates (e.g. loading periods of $\sim 10^4$ s). Increasing the molar mass tends to increase the range of strain-rate or loading period over which the polymer is ductile,[107] probably because of the larger number of tie molecules in the high-molar-mass polymer.

9.4.4 Environmental Fracture and Crazing

The premature failure of semicrystalline polymers in certain aggressive environments is a long-standing problem and there have been several excellent reviews of the subject.[108-110] A particularly spectacular example of the phenomenon is the brittle failure of polyethylene which occurs at relatively low stresses in certain polar liquids such as alcohols, detergents or different types of oil. This is in stark contrast to the normally ductile behaviour of the material. In the past there has been some confusion[108] over terminology especially concerning the difference between solvent cracking and environmental stress cracking (ESC). Solvent cracking in PE occurs in liquids which are solvents, such as xylene. It is most pronounced at high temperatures when the material may become solvated and swollen. However, failure in this case is ductile whereas ESC is characterised by brittle fracture.

An example of the failure of PE through ESC is shown in Fig. 9.14(a) where the time-to-failure for a series of samples of PE held at a fixed stress in a detergent ('Teepol') is plotted against melt flow index (MFI, inversely related to average molar mass). The polymer with the highest MFI (lowest molar mass) fails after the shortest period of time, demonstrating clearly that the ESC behaviour is dependent upon the molar mass of the polymer with low molar mass material having the worst ESC resistance.[110,111] Other factors controlling the ESC resistance include thermal history, orientation and degree of crystallinity.[108] Because ESC is controlled by so many factors, much effort in the past has been expended upon optimising the properties of the polymers to increase the ESC resistance and obtaining reliable engineering design data. It is only relatively recently that attempts have been made to elucidate the mechanics and mechanisms of the process.

Since polyethylene is brittle when it undergoes ESC, linear elastic

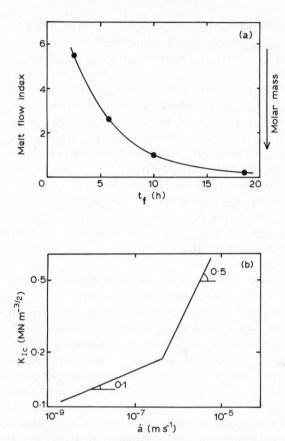

Fig. 9.14. (a) *Dependence of the time-to-failure, t_f, upon the melt flow index for high-density polyethylenes subjected to a stress of a quarter of their room-temperature yield stress in a detergent environment at 60°C (after Hinton & Keller[111]); and* (b) *Variation of crack velocity, $\dot{a}$, with K_{Ic} for high-density polyethylene in a detergent environment at 60°C (after Williams & Marshall[113]).*

fracture mechanics can be applied in this case without the normal restrictions for this material. Williams and co-workers[112,113] have found a unique dependence of crack velocity upon K_{Ic} for crack propagation in PE in environments such as methanol, ethanol and a detergent. This is illustrated in Fig. 9.14(b) for HDPE in hot (60°C) detergent and Williams & Marshall[113] have interpreted the change in slope in the plot between 10^{-7} and 10^{-6} m s^{-1} as being due to a change in the fracture mechanism. They suggested that in the slow growth region the crack growth rate is controlled by viscoelastic 'relaxation processes' in the material. However, at higher velocities it is thought that the different slope corresponds to crack propagation in this region being controlled by transport of the environment to the crack tip. They were able to correlate the velocity at which the transition between the two types of behaviour occurred with the viscosity of the fluid, with the transition taking place at the lowest crack velocities for fluids with the highest viscosity. Shanahan & Schultz[114] have shown that the time-to-failure, t_f, of specimens of LDPE stressed in silicone fluids is similarly affected by the viscosity of the environment. For low levels of applied stress the viscosity has little effect but at higher stresses the t_f increases with increasing viscosity for a given applied stress. This behaviour at higher stress may be analogous to the region of high K_{Ic} found by Williams & Marshall[113] where propagation is controlled by flow of environment to the crack tip.

Over the years there has been a considerable debate concerning the mechanisms of ESC in polymers—one of the main points of contention has been concerned with how much ESC is due to plasticisation of the material or is caused by a reduction in surface energy.[109] Attempts have been made to elucidate the mechanisms of failure in PE by fractographic analyses.[115,116] Hannon[115] suggested that the brittle failure in PE was due to the nucleation and growth of voids which was then followed by viscoelastic deformation of the surrounding material. Bandyopadhyay & Brown[116] have show that failure during ESC in PE is due to environmental attack in the interlamellar regions and following this investigation Brown[117] proposed a theory to explain the phenomenon in PE. It is suggested that ESC is due to stress-induced swelling and plasticisation of the amorphous regions in the stressed polymer and that failure occurs in these regions at relatively low stresses. The theory is couched in terms of Treloar's[118] combination of the Flory–Huggins theory of polymer solutions and the Gaussian theory of rubber elasticity. Brown[117] predicted that the effectiveness of an ESC agent should depend upon its solubility parameter, δ_s, and its molar volume, v, with the most effective agents for PE being liquids with a similar value of δ_s and larger molar volumes. Moreover, the interlamellar nature of ESC in PE is clearly consistent with the observation that samples with the highest values of molar mass are most resistant.[110] The number of interlamellar tie molecules is known to increase with increasing molar mass[72] and the effect will be to reinforce the interlamellar regions.

Although the discussion so far has been principally concerned with ESC in polyethylene, the premature failure of polyamides, such as nylon 6 in aqueous or alcoholic solutions of metal salts, is well documented.[109,119-21] It has been suggested[109] that the ESC is due to the formation of a complex between the metal salt and the polyamide which disrupts the interchain hydrogen bonding and plasticises the amorphous regions. Recent studies[121] have demonstrated that zinc chloride ($ZnCl_2$) solutions produce swelling in fine powders of polyamides whereas thick sheets appear unswollen. Kramer[109] has suggested that the presence of an environment which is a good plasticiser but diffuses slowly will produce a weak craze in the polymer. This has been supported by observations of crazes in thin films of nylon 6.10 undergoing stress cracking in $ZnCl_2$ solution.[109] Craze-like entities have also been found in PE films and single crystals deformed in aggressive environments[122,123] and there is also evidence from infra-red spectroscopy that ESC agents such as methanol can be absorbed in the PE film and so may aid the fibrillation process within the craze.

In conclusion, therefore, it must be stressed that the question of whether ESC agents for semicrystalline polymers reduce the surface energy or cause plasticisation is not yet fully resolved. It may be that both or either process can occur depending upon the polymer and environment and there is clearly a need for further definitive studies in this area.

9.5 FRACTURE OF ORIENTED SEMICRYSTALLINE POLYMERS

The alignment of the covalently bonded polymer molecules in a particular direction in a polymer specimen leads to the material having considerable strength when deformed in that direction. This property has been utilised for many years in synthetic textile fibres where orientation is normally achieved either by solvent- or solution-spinning followed by further drawing. The structure and mechanical behaviour of textile fibres have been extensively reviewed elsewhere.[124,125] In this section we will be concerned mainly with recent developments in the preparation of highly oriented fibres of conventional polymers[15,31-3,126-30] and high-strength fibres obtained using rigid-chain polymer molecules[131-5] both of which are used principally in engineering applications.

9.5.1 Tensile Strength

The tensile strength of an oriented polymer depends upon the chemical structure of its molecules, their molar mass and the degree of orientation. The strength of nylon 6 fibres is found to increase as the temperature of initial drawing is increased[64] reflecting an increase in molecular orientation. The effect of molar mass is rather more complex.[125] When the molar mass is low, chain slippage occurs relatively easily and the strength is low. There is an increase in strength as the molar mass increases because of a lower density of chain ends and more entanglements which stop slippage. Eventually the strength reaches a peak and decreases for higher molar masses because defects introduced during the processing of a high-molar-mass polymer outweigh the reduction in chain-end defects.

There has been considerable interest over recent years in producing fibres with high strengths and stiffnesses through high degrees of chain orientation produced by tensile drawing,[15,34,126,129,130,136] extrusion[15,31,128] or flow-controlled crystallisation.[32,34] The strengths ob-

TABLE 9.4

MAXIMUM STIFFNESSES AND STRENGTHS OF ORIENTED POLYMER FIBRES PRODUCED BY A VARIETY OF TECHNIQUES

Polymer	Technique	Modulus (GPa)	Strength (GPa)	Reference
Polyethylene	Tensile-drawing	68	0·35	126
	Extrusion	70	0·4	128
	Flow crystallisation	100	4	32
	Hot-drawing with solvent	120	3·7	136
Polypropylene	Tensile-drawing	22	0·93	129
Acetal polymer	Tensile-drawing	35	1·7	130
PBA	Spun from HF	63·9	1·5	33
	(+ heat treatment)	150	2·3	33
PPD–T	Spun from HF	26·6	1·2	33
	(+ heat treatment)	140	1·8	33
Aromatic	Melt spun	40·2	0·47	133
copolyester	(+ heat treatment)	46·7	1·5	133
PBT	Spun from acids	50–110	0·6–1·1	134
	(+ heat treatment)	260–300	2·5–3·0	135
Substituted polydiacetylene	Solid-state polymerised	62	1·7	21
Nylon 66	Industrial grade	3·8	0·77	133

tained are listed in Table 9.4. Most of the studies have concentrated upon polyethylene which has the highest crystal modulus (Section 9.2.1) and so potentially the best mechanical properties. The highest strengths for this polymer have been attained using either the flow-controlled crystallisation method or hot-drawing fibres containing solvent with both methods developed by Pennings and co-workers.[32,136] However, the 4 GPa reported[32] is still well below the theoretical strength of 19 GPa[9] or 66 GPa[10] predicted from quantum mechanical calculations. All of these techniques of producing chain orientation result in polymer fibres which have a high degree of chain orientation but they are also microfibrillar and contain many defects which give rise to the shortfall in strength.

Another route to producing high modulus/strength polymer fibres is by solvent spinning of rigid-rod type molecules. Perhaps the most well-known examples are aromatic polyamides such as Kevlar[33] but there is now a wide variety of related rigid-rod-type polymers available.[33,131-5] There are several different grades of Kevlar and it is thought that they are based on the polymers poly(p-benzamide) (PBA)

$$\left[NH-\bigcirc-CO \right]_n$$

and poly(p-phenyleneterephthalamide) (PPD–T)

$$\left[NH-\bigcirc-NH-CO-\bigcirc-CO \right]_n$$

High-molar-mass polyamides can be spun from various aggressive solvents such as sulphuric or hydrofluoric acids to give high strength/modulus fibres (Table 9.4). The properties can be improved by heat treatment under tension[33] which presumably improves the orientation and removes defects. Such fibres are often compared with conventional polyamide fibres such as nylon 66 used, for example, in tyre cord. It can be seen from Table 9.4 that their moduli are over an order of magnitude higher and their tensile strengths considerably better than nylon 66. Aromatic copolyesters can be spun from the melt into fibres which have high strengths and moduli.[133] Melt-spinning is much more convenient than the solution-spinning from aggressive acids necessary to produce the aromatic polyamides.

There have been developments recently in the preparation of polymer fibres of poly(p-phenylenebenzobisthiazole) (PBT) which can be spun from a mixture of methane-sulphonic and chlorosulphonic acids.[134] These polymers are very exciting since their properties can not only be improved by heat treatment[135] to better Kevlar but they also have good high temperature resistance.

All of these rigid-rod molecules have liquid-crystal structures in the melt or solution which aid orientation. They also have no side-groups giving rise to good chain packing. The molecules are inherently rigid and deform by bond stretching rather than bond bending because of the presence of the phenylene rings. These factors lead to high values of both modulus and strength. However, the perfection that is present in a single crystal is lacking in these oriented polymer fibres which means that they do not have properties which are significantly better than those of polydiacetylene single crystal fibres[21] where the molecules are less rigid and have large side-groups.

9.5.2 Fatigue

Polymer fibres suffer from premature failure in dynamic-fatigue loading and under prolonged static loading (creep rupture). The dynamic-fatigue properties have been studied widely[137–40] since they have important practical significance, particularly when the polymer fibres are used as tyre cord.[138] The investigations have been concerned principally with the effect of the range of cyclic stressing upon the fatigue lifetime, N_f (number of cycles to failure). For conventional textile fibres, such as polyamides, polyesters and polyacrylonitrile, there is a significant fatigue effect with fatigue lifetimes of 10^4–10^5 cycles when fibres are stressed to ~60 % of their fracture strength for monotonic loading.[139] The fracture morphology in fatigue is also found to be different from that found during simple tensile loading with a tendency for splitting at a slight angle to the fibre axis. In contrast, Kevlar fibres[140] are relatively resistant to fatigue with fatigue strengths which are only slightly less than their tensile strengths, with both types of failure occurring by axial splitting.

The failure of polymer fibres during static loading has been studied widely, particularly by Zhurkov and co-workers (e.g. Reference 141) and has been interpreted in terms of the kinetic theory of fracture (Section 2.3). It has been widely reported that there is a linear dependence of the logarithm of the failure-time upon the applied tensile stress (e.g. Fig. 2.4). It has further been suggested[33] that there

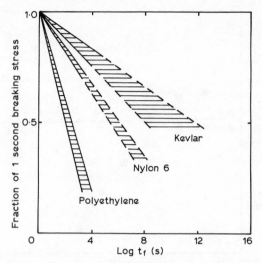

Fig. 9.15. Decrease in fracture stress of different polymer fibres as a function of failure time, t_f (after Schaefgen et al.[33]).

may be a correlation between the creep rupture behaviour of highly oriented polymers and their melting temperatures. The tensile strengths of Kevlar, nylon 66 and polyethylene fibres are shown as a function of failure-time in Fig. 9.15. It can be seen that Kevlar with a high value of T_m shows the best creep rupture behaviour whereas polyethylene with a relatively low T_m shows the worst. In fact, although highly oriented polyethylene has excellent short-term properties its high-temperature properties and long-term endurance are poor and efforts have been made to improve this by, for example, increasing the molar mass of the polymer.[15]

9.5.3 Failure Mechanisms

Many of the studies of molecular failure mechanisms in polymers have used oriented semicrystalline polymers as model materials, principally because they produce relatively strong electron spin resonance (ESR) signals when deformed (Chapter 2). The failure mechanisms have been investigated experimentally using a wide range of techniques such as infra-red spectroscopy,[143-5] ESR[146-8] and small-angle X-ray scattering,[149] and the results have been considered from a theoretical viewpoint by Peterlin.[150-3] The micromechanisms have been reviewed in detail in Section 2.5 and so only a brief summary will be given here.

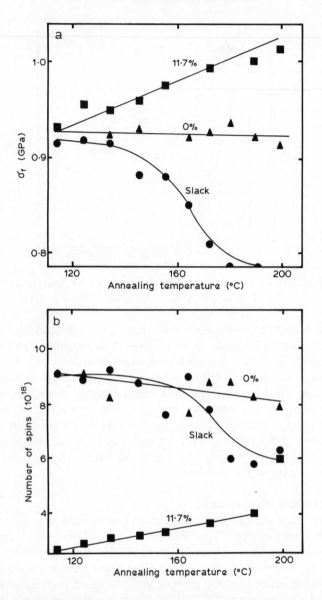

Fig. 9.16. *Effect of annealing upon the fracture behaviour of nylon 6 fibres.* (a) *Dependence of fracture stress* σ_f *upon annealing temperature for the different stated degrees of pre-strain; and* (b) *Number of spins measured using ESR for the fibres broken in* (a) *(after Kausch & DeVries[148]).*

The fracture mechanisms in oriented polymer fibres such as highly oriented polyethylene or nylon 6 are intimately associated with the structure of the fibres which are thought[152] to consist of clusters of microfibrils 5–20 μm long and 10–20 nm wide—the microfibrils being made up of single crystal blocks separated by amorphous layers. The amorphous layers contain chain loops, chain ends and tie molecules and it is thought[152,153] that these tie molecules are a vital component in the structure controlling the fracture behaviour.

When the fibres are deformed up to the fracture stress there is clearly a distribution in the stresses upon the different molecules in the structure which is seen as asymmetry in infra-red absorption bands in deformed specimens.[145] Most of the molecules are deformed to a stress close to the applied stress but there is a small but significant number of overstressed bonds[145] which are almost certainly tie molecules. ESR signals can be detected at strains well below the failure strain (Fig. 2.8) corresponding to free radicals formed by the rupture of the overstressed tie molecules.[148] The number of radicals produced increases up to the fracture strain when there is widespread molecular fracture. Following this chain scission, microvoids are found to form[149] and eventual macroscopic failure takes place by the coalescence of these microvoids.[151]

Annealing can modify the structure of polymer fibres and results in a change in their fracture strength and failure mechanisms.[148] Different effects are found depending upon whether the fibres are annealed slack, at zero strain (to prevent shrinkage) or under a large fixed strain as shown in Fig. 9.16. The fibres annealed under stress are found to have a higher room-temperature strength with fewer radicals produced at fracture than the slack annealed or zero strain fibres. The high-strain annealing is thought[148] to lead to a relaxation in the local molecular strains in tie molecules and produce a larger number of extended chain segments. Hence the number of broken overstressed bonds is reduced and the strength of the fibres is increased (Fig. 9.16).

9.6 CONCLUDING REMARKS

The most overriding factor which controls the fracture behaviour of crystalline polymers is the effect of polymer morphology. The wide variety of morphological forms lead to properties which range from tough flexible isotropic polymers to oriented polymer fibres with very high values of stiffness and strength. The failure mechanisms also depend upon morphology. Polymer crystals stretched parallel to the chain direction can only fail by molecular fracture whereas semicrystalline polymers fail by a combination of molecular fracture and chain slippage. One aspect of the behaviour that has become increasingly more apparent over the years is the role of intercrystalline tie molecules in semicrystalline polymers. These molecules are anchored in crystals and transfer the stresses between adjacent crystals. There is now conclusive evidence from ESR and other studies that tie molecules carry a high level of stress and are broken during deformation and fracture. The behaviour of tie molecules may be compared with entanglements in amorphous thermoplastics—both are responsible for the strength of the polymers and without them both types of polymer are extremely weak.

On a higher level of morphology there is still not yet any clear idea how factors such as crystal structure or spherulite size affect the fracture behaviour. A few *ad hoc* studies have shown that, in general, large spherulites cause the polymer to be more brittle but the micromechanisms are not yet fully understood. This may be contrasted with the studies of the behaviour of glassy polymers described in Chapter 7 or metals where a great deal is known about the micromechanisms of deformation and fracture. This is clearly an area where more work needs to be done. Similarly, the application of fracture mechanics to ductile semicrystalline polymers is in its infancy, again in contrast to amorphous polymers and metals. It is only possible to apply LEFM to semicrystalline polymers at low temperatures or in the presence of active environments. New developments in the area of generalised fracture theories or the *J*-integral analysis are now starting to enable the fracture of these ductile polymers to be understood.

Finally, to end on an optimistic point, it is clear that some of the recent developments in preparing highly oriented polymer fibres and polymer single crystal fibres have provided a new generation of light, strong materials. These polymers offer a unique opportunity for use in structural engineering applications, for example, as a reinforcement for a matrix in an all-polymer composite. They are offering considerable weight savings over conventional materials in aerospace applications and should eventually find more general use in wider engineering applications.

REFERENCES

1. Young, R. J. (1981). *Introduction to Polymers*, Chapman and Hall, London.
2. Wunderlich, B. (1973/6). *Macromolecular physics*, Vols 1 and 2, Academic Press, New York.
3. Frank, F. C. (1970). *Proc. Roy. Soc. (London)*, **A319**, 127.
4. Kelly, A. & Groves, G. W. (1970). *Crystallography and crystal defects*, Longman, London.
5. Odajima, A. & Maeda, T. (1966). *J. Polym. Sci.*, **C15**, 55.
6. Holliday, L. & White, J. W. (1971). *Pure and Appl. Chem.*, **26**, 545.
7. Treloar, L. R. G. (1960). *Polymer*, **1**, 290.
8. Shimanouchi, T., Asahina, M. & Enomoto, S. (1962). *J. Polym. Sci.*, **59**, 93.
9. Boudreaux, D. S. (1973). *J. Polym. Sci., Polym. Phys. Ed.*, **11**, 1285.
10. Crist, B., Ratner, M. A., Brower, A. L. & Savin, J. R. (1979). *J. Appl. Phys.*, **50**, 6047.
11. Wool, R. P. & Boyd, R. H. (1980). *J. Appl. Phys.*, **51**, 5116.
12. Batchelder, D. N. & Bloor, D. (1979). *J. Polym. Sci., Polym. Phys. Ed.*, **17**, 569.
13. Young, R. J. (1979). In: *Developments in polymer fracture—1*, Ed. by E. H. Andrews, Applied Science Publishers Ltd., London, p. 223.
14. Sakurada, I., Ito, T. & Nakame, K. (1966). *J. Polym. Sci.*, **C15**, 75.
15. Capaccio, G., Gibson, A. G. & Ward, I. M. (1979). In: *Ultra-high modulus polymers*, Ed. by A. Ciferri & I. M. Ward, Applied Science Publishers Ltd., London, p. 1.
16. Clements, J., Jakeways, R. & Ward, I. M. (1978). *Polymer*, **19**, 639.
17. Shauffele, R. F. & Shimanouchi, T. (1967). *J. Chem. Phys.*, **47**, 3605.
18. LaGarde, V., Prask, H. & Trevino, S. (1969). *Disc. Farad. Soc.*, **48**, 15.
19. Leyrer, R. J., Wettling, W. & Wegner, G. (1978). *Ber. Bunseges. Phys. Chem.*, **82**, 697.
20. Barham, P. J. & Keller, A. (1979). *J. Polym. Sci., Polym. Lett. Ed.*, **17**, 591.
21. Galiotis, C. (1982). *Polydiacetylene single crystal fibres*, PhD Thesis, University of London, London.
22. Enkelmann, V., Leyrer, R. J., Schleier, G. & Wegner, G. (1980). *J. Mater. Sci.*, **15**, 168.
23. Andrews, E. H. & Martin, G. E. (1974). *J. Mater. Sci.*, **9**, 1507.
24. Baughman, R. H., Gleiter, H. & Sendfeld, N. (1975). *J. Polym. Sci., Polym. Phys. Ed.*, **13**, 1871.
25. Galiotis, C. & Young, R. J. *Polymer*, to be published.
26. Treloar, L. R. G. (1958). *The physics of rubber elasticity*, Clarendon Press, Oxford.
27. Wang, T. T. (1973). *J. Appl. Phys.*, **44**, 4052.
28. Kambour, R. P. & Robertson, R. E. (1972). In: *Polymer science*, Ed. by A. D. Jenkins, North-Holland, London.

29. Halpin, J. C. & Kardos, J. L. (1972). *J. Appl. Phys.*, **43**, 2235.
30. Andrews, E. H. (1974). *Pure and Appl. Chem.*, **39**, 179.
31. Zachariades, A. E., Mead, W. T. & Porter, R. S. (1979). In: *Ultra-high modulus polymers*, Ed. by A. Ciferri & I. M. Ward, Applied Science Publishers Ltd., London, p. 77.
32. Pennings, A. J. & Meihuizen, K. E. (1979). In: *Ultra-high modulus polymers*, Ed. by A. Ciferri & I. M. Ward, Applied Science Publishers Ltd., London, p. 117.
33. Schaefgen, J. R., Bair, T. I., Ballou, J. W., Kwolek, S. L., Morgan, P. W., Panar, M. & Zimmerman, J. (1979). In: *Ultra-high modulus polymers*, Ed. by A. Ciferri & I. M. Ward, Applied Science Publishers Ltd., London, p. 173.
34. Keller, A. (1979). In: *Ultra-high modulus polymers*, Ed. by A. Ciferri & I. M. Ward, Applied Science Publishers Ltd., London, p. 321.
35. Bowden, P. B. & Young, R. J. (1974). *J. Mater. Sci.*, **9**, 2034.
36. Bassett, D. C. & Carder, D. R. (1973). *Phil. Mag.*, **28**, 535.
37. Young, R. J., Bowden, P. B., Ritchie, J. M. & Rider, J. G. (1973). *J. Mater. Sci.*, **8**, 23.
38. Young, R. J. (1974). *Phil. Mag.*, **30**, 85.
39. Young, R. J. & Bowden, P. B. (1974). *Phil. Mag.*, **29**, 1061.
40. Frank, F. C., Keller, A. & Connor, A. O. (1958). *Phil. Mag.*, **3**, 64.
41. Young, R. J., Bloor, D., Batchelder, D. N. & Hubble, C. L. (1978). *J. Mater. Sci.*, **13**, 62.
42. Young, R. J., Dulniak, R., Batchelder, D. N. & Bloor, D. (1979). *J. Polym. Sci., Polym. Phys. Ed.*, **17**, 1325.
43. Hay, I. L. & Keller, A. (1965). *Kolloid-Z*, **204**, 43.
44. Peterlin, A. (1971). *J. Mater. Sci.*, **6**, 490.
45. Peterlin, A. (1979). In: *Ultra-high modulus polymers*, Ed. by A. Ciferri & I. M. Ward, Applied Science Publishers Ltd., London, p. 279.
46. Andrews, J. M. & Ward, I. M. (1970). *J. Mater. Sci.*, **5**, 411.
47. Capaccio, G. & Ward, I. M. (1974). *Polymer*, **15**, 233.
48. Keller, A. (1968). *Rep. Prog. Phys.*, **31**, 623.
49. Wegner, G. (1977). *Pure and Appl. Chem.*, **49**, 433.
50. Bloor, D., Koski, L., Stevens, G. C., Preston, F. H. & Ando, D. J. (1975). *J. Mater. Sci.*, **10**, 1678.
51. Marsh, D. M. (1963). In: *Fracture in solids*, Ed. by D. D. Crucker & J. J. Gilman, Interscience, New York, p. 119.
52. Galiotis, C. & Young, R. J. *J. Mater. Sci.*, to be published.
53. Young, R. J. & Petermann, J. (1982). *J. Polym. Sci., Polym. Phys. Ed.*, **20**, 961.
54. Patell, Y. R. & Schultz, J. M. (1973). *J. Macromol. Sci.-Phys.*, **B7**, 445.
55. Davidson, A. T. & Joffe, A. D. (1977). *Phil. Mag.*, **36**, 1083.
56. Kiho, H., Peterlin, A. & Geil, P. H. (1964). *J. Appl. Phys.*, **35**, 1599.
57. Allan, P. & Bevis, M. (1974). *Proc. Roy. Soc.*, (*London*), **A341**, 75.
58. Geil, P. H. (1964). *J. Polym. Sci.*, **A2**, 3857.
59. Cerra, P., Morrow, D. R. & Sauer, J. A. (1969). *J. Macromol. Sci.-Phys.*, **B3**(1), 33.
60. Andrews, E. H. & Voigt-Martin, I. G. (1972). *Proc. Roy. Soc.*, (*London*), **A327**, 251.

61. Petermann, J. & Gleiter, H. (1973). *J. Polym. Sci., Polym. Phys. Ed.*, **11**, 359.
62. Read, R. T. & Young, R. J. (1979). *J. Mater. Sci.*, **14**, 1968.
63. Read, R. T. & Young, R. J. (1980). *Phil. Mag.*, **42**, 629.
64. Kausch, H. H. (1978). *Polymer fracture*, Springer-Verlag, Berlin.
65. Gaube, E. & Kausch, H. H. (1973). *Kunststoffe*, **63**, 391.
66. Bandyopadhyay, S. & Brown, H. R. (1978). *Polymer*, **19**, 589.
67. Menges, G. & Alf, E. (1972). *Kunststoffe*, **62**, 259.
68. Friedrich, K. (1978). *Prog. Coll and Polym. Sci.*, **64**, 103.
69. Way, J. L., Atkinson, J. R. & Nutting, J. (1974). *J. Mater. Sci.*, **9**, 293.
70. Bessell, T. J., Hull, D. & Shortall, J. B. (1975). *J. Mater. Sci.*, **10**, 1127.
71. Hornbogen, E. & Friedrich, K. (1980). *J. Mater. Sci.*, **15**, 2175.
72. Keith, H. D., Padden, F. J. & Vadimsky, R. G. (1971). *J. Appl. Phys.*, **42**, 192.
73. Attenburrow, G. E. & Bassett, D. C. (1977). *J. Mater Sci.*, **12**, 192.
74. Gogolewski, S. (1977). *Polymer*, **18**, 63.
75. Gogolewski, S. & Pennings, A. J. (1977). *Polymer*, **18**, 647.
76. Young, R. J. (1975). *Polymer*, **16**, 450.
77. Anderton, G. E. & Treloar, L. R. G. (1971). *J. Mater. Sci.*, **6**, 562.
78. Sims, G. L. A. (1975). *J. Mater. Sci.*, **10**, 647.
79. Isherwood, D. P. & Williams, J. G. (1978). *Eng. Fract. Mech.*, **10**, 887.
80. Andrews, E. H. & Fukahori, Y. (1977). *J. Mater. Sci.*, **12**, 1307.
81. Hodgkinson, J. M. & Williams, J. G. (1981). *J. Mater. Sci.*, **16**, 50.
82. Andrews, E. H. (1981). *J. Mater. Sci.*, **16**, 1705.
83. Williams, J. G. & Hodgkinson, J. M. (1981). *J. Mater. Sci.*, **16**, 1707.
84. Mai, Y. W. & Williams, J. G. (1977). *J. Mater. Sci.*, **12**, 1376.
85. Kinloch, A. J. & Gledhill, R. A. (1981). *J. Spacecraft and Rockets*, **18**, 333.
86. Pae, K. D. & Bhateja, S. K. (1975). *J. Macromol. Sci., Revs. Macromol. Chem.*, **C13**, 1.
87. Silano, A. A., Bhateja, S. K. & Pae, K. D. (1974). *Int. J. Polym. Mater.*, **3**, 117.
88. Mears, D. R., Pae, K. D. & Sauer, J. A. (1969). *J. Appl. Phys.*, **40**, 4229.
89. Duckett, R. A. (1980). *J. Mater. Sci.*, **15**, 2471.
90. Truss, R. W., Duckett, R. A. & Ward, I. M. (1981). *J. Mater. Sci.*, **16**, 1689.
91. Vincent, P. I. (1971). *Impact tests and service performance of thermoplastics*, The Plastics and Rubber Institute, London.
92. Plati, E. & Williams, J. G. (1975). *Polym. Eng. Sci.*, **15**, 470.
93. Brown, H. R. (1973). *J. Mater. Sci.*, **8**, 941.
94. Plati, E. & Williams, J. G. (1975). *Polymer*, **16**, 915.
95. Birch, M. W. & Williams, J. G. (1978). *Int. J. Fract.*, **14**, 69.
96. Heijboer, J. (1968). *J. Polym. Sci.*, **C16**, 3755.
97. Kisbenyi, M., Birch, M. W., Hodgkinson, J. M. & Williams, J. G. (1979). *Polymer*, **20**, 1289.
98. Williams, J. G. & Hodgkinson, J. M. (1981). *Proc. Roy. Soc.*, **A375**, 231.
99. Hertzberg, R. W. & Manson, J. A. (1980). *Fatigue of engineering plastics*, Academic Press, New York.

100. Andrews, E. H. & Walker, B. J. (1971). *Proc. Roy. Soc.*, **A325**, 57.
101. Teh, J. W., White, J. R. & Andrews, E. H. (1979). *Polymer*, **20**, 755.
102. White, J. R. & Teh, J. W. (1979). *Polymer*, **20**, 764.
103. Bretz, P. E., Hertzberg, R. W. & Manson, J. A. (1981). *J. Mater. Sci.*, **16**, 2061.
104. Bretz, P. E., Hertzberg, R. W. & Manson, J. A. (1981). *J. Mater. Sci.*, **16**, 2070.
105. Bretz, P. E., Hertzberg, R. W. & Manson, J. A. (1981). *Polymer*, **22**, 1272.
106. Williams, J. G. (1981). *The use of fracture mechanics in design with polymers*, Paper presented at Plasticon 81—Engineering Design with Plastics, Plastics and Rubber Institute, London.
107. Zapas, L. J. & Crissman, J. M. (1979). *Durability of macromolecular materials*, Ed. by R. K. Eby, ACS Symposium Series, **95**, ACS Washington, p. 301.
108. Howard, J. B. (1965). In: *Crystalline olefin polymers, part II*, Ed. by R. A. V. Raff & K. W. Doak, Interscience, New York, p. 47.
109. Kramer, E. J. (1979). In: *Developments in polymer fracture—1*, Ed. by E. H. Andrews, Applied Science Publishers Ltd., London, p. 55.
110. Martin, J. R., Johnson, J. F. & Cooper, A. R. (1972). *J. Macromol. Sci.—Revs. Macromol. Chem.*, **C8**, 59.
111. Hinton, T. & Keller, A. (1969). *J. Appl. Polym. Sci.*, **13**, 745.
112. Marshall, G. P., Culver, L. E. & Williams, J. G. (1970). *Plastics and Polymers*, **38**, 95.
113. Williams, J. G. & Marshall, G. P. (1975). *Proc. Roy. Soc.*, **A342**, 55.
114. Shanahan, M. E. R. & Schultz, J. (1976). *J. Polym. Sci., Polym. Phys. Ed.*, **14**, 1567.
115. Hannon, M. J. (1974). *J. Appl. Polym. Sci.*, **13**, 3761.
116. Bandyopadhyay, S. & Brown, H. R. (1977). *J. Mater. Sci.*, **12**, 2131.
117. Brown, H. R. (1978). *Polymer*, **19**, 1186.
118. Treloar, L. R. G. (1975). *The physics of rubber elasticity*, 2nd Edn. Oxford University Press, London.
119. Dunn, P. & Sansom, G. F. (1969). *J. Appl. Polym. Sci.*, **13**, 1641.
120. Dunn, P. & Sansom, G. F. (1969). *J. Appl. Polym. Sci.*, **13**, 1657.
121. Reimschuessel, A. C. & Young, J. K. (1978). *J. Mater. Sci.*, **13**, 243.
122. Singleton, C. J., Roche, E. & Geil, P. H. (1977). *J. Appl. Polym. Sci.*, **21**, 2319.
123. Soni, P. L. & Geil, P. H. (1979). *J. Appl. Polym. Sci.*, **23**, 1167.
124. Morton, W. E. & Hearle, J. W. S. (1975). *Physical properties of textile fibres*, 2nd Edn. Heinemann, London.
125. Prevorsek, D. (1971). *J. Polym. Sci.*, **C32**, 343.
126. Capaccio, G. & Ward, I. M. (1975). *Polym. Eng. Sci.*, **15**, 219.
127. Capiati, N. & Porter, R. S. (1975). *J. Polym. Sci., Polym. Phys. Ed.*, **13**, 1177.
128. Mead, W. T., Desper, C. R. & Porter, R. S. (1979). *J. Polym. Sci., Polym. Phys. Ed.*, **17**, 859.
129. Taylor, W. N. & Clark, E. S. (1977). *A.C.S. Polym. Preprints*, **18**, 332.
130. Clark, E. S. & Scott, L. S. (1974). *Polym. Eng. Sci.*, **14**, 682.

131. Preston, J. (1979). In: *Ultra-high modulus polymers*, Ed. by A. Ciferri & I. M. Ward, Applied Science Publishers Ltd., London p. 155.
132. Ciferri, A. & Valenti, B. (1979). In: *Ultra-high modulus polymers*, Ed. by A. Ciferri & I. M. Ward, Applied Science Publishers Ltd., London, p. 203.
133. Wooten, W. C., McFarlane, F. E., Gray, Jr., T. F. & Jackson, Jr., W. (1979). In: *Ultra-high modulus polymers*, Ed. by A. Ciferri & I. M. Ward, Applied Science Publishers Ltd., London p. 227.
134. Allen, S. R., Filippov, A. G., Farris, R. J. & Thomas, E. L. (1981). *J. Appl. Polym. Sci.*, **26**, 291.
135. Allen, S. R., Filippov, A. G., Farris, R. J. & Thomas, E. L. (1982). Paper presented at conference '*Deformation, yield and fracture of polymers*', Cambridge, Plastics and Rubber Institute, London.
136. Kalb, B. & Pennings, A. J. (1980). *J. Mater. Sci.*, **15**, 2584.
137. Regel, V. R. & Leksovskii, A. M. (1967). *Int. J. Fract.*, **3**, 99.
138. Prevorsek, D. & Lyons, W. J. (1971). *Rubber Chem. Tech.*, **44**, 271.
139. Bunsell, A. R. & Hearle, J. W. S. (1974). *J. Appl. Polym. Sci.*, **18**, 267.
140. Konopasek, L. & Hearle, J. W. S. (1977). *J. Appl. Polym. Sci.*, **21**, 2791.
141. Zhurkov, S. N. (1965). *Int. J. Fract. Mech.*, **1**, 210.
142. Blades, H., U.S. Patent No. 3869430 (assigned to E. I. Du Pont de Nemours and Co.).
143. Roylance, D. K. & DeVries, K. L. (1971). *J. Polym. Sci. Polym. Lett.*, **9**, 443.
144. Wool, R. P. (1975). *J. Polym. Sci., Polym. Phys. Ed.*, **13**, 1795.
145. Vettegren, V. I., Novak, I. I. & Friedland, K. J. (1975). *Int. J. Fract.*, **11**, 789.
146. Zhurkov, S. N. & Tomashevsky, E. E. (1966). *Physical basis of yield and fracture*, Institute of Physics conference proceedings, p. 200.
147. Lloyd, B. A., DeVries, K. L. & Williams, M. L. (1972). *J. Polym. Sci.*, *A-2*, **10**, 1415.
148. Kausch, H. H. & DeVries, K. L. (1975). *Int. J. Fract.*, **11**, 727.
149. Kuksenko, V. S. & Tamuzs, V. P. (1981). *Fracture micromechanics of polymer materials*, Martinus Nijhoff, The Hague.
150. Peterlin, A. (1969). *J. Polym. Sci.*, *A-2*, **7**, 1151.
151. Peterlin, A. (1972). *J. Macromol Sci.-Phys.*, **B6**, 583.
152. Peterlin, A. (1977). *Fracture 1977*, Vol. 1, ICF4, Waterloo, Canada, p. 473.
153. Peterlin, A. (1981). *J. Macromol Sci.-Phys.*, **B19**, 401.

Chapter 10

Rubbers

10.1 INTRODUCTION

Rubbers consist of long flexible chain-like molecules which are interconnected at various points by cross-links to form a loose molecular network. At temperatures above the glass transition temperature each elementary network chain undergoes rapid Brownian motion among a large number of possible conformations by rotation about single valence bonds in the chain backbone. Upon being stressed the chains are forced to assume conformations which are less probable than those in the undeformed material. Thus energy is stored and retractive forces are exerted primarily because of this decrease in conformational entropy, rather than from an increase in internal energy. The above features account for the characteristic property of rubbers which is their ability to undergo large deformations and, when the stress is released, return to their original shape. Treloar's book[1] provides an excellent source for the experimental and theoretical details of rubber elasticity.

The fracture of rubbers has been discussed in considerable depth in three notable reviews.[2–4] As in other materials, cracks frequently initiate at inclusions and other local inhomogeneities. However, in rubbers the mechanisms whereby microvoids and cracks are initiated are not clearly established. On the other hand, a wealth of information exists concerning the mechanics and mechanisms of crack propagation and, since it appears that cracks are initiated relatively easily in rubbers, this is considered by many to be the critical aspect of the fracture process. Thus crack propagation is discussed in detail in this chapter. However, as in other polymers, the fracture behaviour of rubbers is greatly influenced by the magnitude of the various energy dissipating mechanisms which may operate in the highly strained regions around the tip of a growing crack and in the bulk of the material. This chapter therefore begins with a discussion of such mechanisms.

10.2 ENERGY DISSIPATING MECHANISMS

The energy required for crack growth in rubbers, as in other polymeric materials, is usually considerably greater than the intrinsic fracture energy necessary solely for bond rupture and this arises from other energy dissipating processes occurring during fracture. However, unlike amorphous glassy or crystalline polymers, the main dissipating mechanisms in rubbers do not involve plastic deformations, which are essentially irreversible and give rise to shear yielding and crazing. For although some rubbers, especially those cross-linked to a relatively low degree or containing filler particles, may exhibit plastic strain, termed 'permanent set' (see Fig. 3.4), most rubbers show none or little plastic strain and return to their original dimensions upon being unloaded. Nevertheless, a part of the energy input required to deform them is dissipated by a variety of mechanisms and the stress/strain behaviour associated with this mechanical hysteresis is shown for both unfilled and filled cross-linked natural and styrene–butadiene rubbers in Fig. 10.1. The hysteresis, or loss energy, W_d, may be determined by evaluating the area between the extension and retraction curves and a hysteresis ratio, h_r, may be defined by

$$h_r = \frac{W_0 - W_r}{W_0} = \frac{W_d}{W_0} \qquad (10.1)$$

where, W_0 and W_r are the input and retraction strain-energy densities, respectively (see also Fig. 3.4). The hysteresis ratio, h_r, is obviously related to the loss function, Φ, in eqn. (3.8) and this relationship has been suggested[5] to be of the form

$$\Phi = \{1 - f(h_r)\}^{-1} \qquad (10.2)$$

where f is a function. The value of Φ therefore increases as h_r increases but at $h_r \to 0$, i.e. no energy dissipation due to hysteresis, then $\Phi \to 1$ and $G_c \to G_0$.

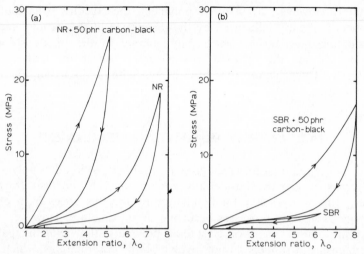

Fig. 10.1. Loading and unloading stress/extension ratio curves taken almost up to the rupture point. (a) Unfilled and filled natural rubber; and (b) Unfilled and filled SBR.

The principal mechanisms which are responsible for mechanical hysteresis in rubbers are:[2,6–8]

1. Internal friction. The internal friction, or internal viscosity, arises from the molecular chains rearranging their conformations and hence segments of them sliding past one another. The internal viscosity is highly dependent upon temperature and its temperature dependence may be described by considering the flow viscosity, η_v. The internal viscosity and flow viscosity, η_v, of rubbers are not equivalent, only the latter, for example, depends upon molar mass, but the flow viscosity may be readily measured and does reflect the mobility of the segments constituting the polymer molecules. The value of η_v for a liquid (uncross-linked) rubber decreases as temperature increases and at $T > T_g$ the value, $\eta_v(T)$, at any temperature may be empirically related to that at the glass transition temperature, $\eta_v(T_g)$, by the Williams–Landel–Ferry (WLF)[9–11] equation for simple viscoelastic materials

$$\log \frac{\eta_v(T)}{\eta_v(T_g)} = \frac{-C_1(T - T_g)}{(C_2 + T - T_g)} \tag{10.3}$$

The WLF equation may also be derived from the semiempirical

TABLE 10.1
WLF PARAMETERS[11]

Polymer	$T_g(K)$	C_1	$C_2(K)$
Poly(1,4-butadiene)	172	11·2	60·5
Natural rubber	200	16·8	53·6
Polyisobutylene	205	16·6	104·4
Polyurethane	238	15·6	32·6
Poly(ethyl methacrylate)	335	17·6	65·5
Polystyrene (atactic)	373	13·7	50·0
Poly(methyl methacrylate)	388	32·2	80·0
'Universal constants'	—	17·4	51·6

Doolittle equation[12,13] which relates the viscosity of a liquid to the free volume, i.e. the volume available for segmental motion. The amount of free volume increases as temperature increases and thus the segmental mobility increases and viscosity decreases. Further, since amorphous polymers have similar thermal expansion coefficients, their viscosities are all in reasonable agreement with eqn. (10.3) up to temperatures of about $T_g + 100°C$. In the WLF equation the constants C_1 and C_2 were originally thought to be universal constants, having values of 17·4 and 51·6 respectively, but they have subsequently been found to vary somewhat from polymer to polymer, as indicated in Table 10.1. In a cross-linked rubber the internal viscosity still impedes the rearrangement of molecular chains and is directly related to segmental mobility. It varies with temperature in the same manner as for uncross-linked rubbers and its temperature dependence is described by the WLF equation.

In the case of filled rubbers, the presence of a particulate filler, such as carbon black, may decrease segmental mobility, and so increase the hysteresis, due to attachment of the polymer chains onto the particle's surface. (It should be noted that such fillers may increase the hysteresis by other mechanisms but these are considered later.)

2. Strain-induced crystallisation. At large extensions orientation of the chains will occur and, with sufficiently regular molecules, micro-crystalline regions may be formed. Strain-induced crystallisation is associated with increased hysteresis and it has been suggested[4] that this arises from the formation and melting of crystalline regions upon extension and retraction of the material; in the retraction cycle the lingering of crystallisation means that a relatively large number of chains do not yet participate in the retraction because they disorientate slower than the stress is being released. Natural rubber provides the classic example of strain-induced crystallisation and associated hysteresis. The significantly greater hysteresis, and resulting higher stress and strain capability, of an unfilled natural rubber compared to an unfilled styrene–butadiene rubber (SBR), which does not strain-crystallise, is evident by comparing Figs 10.1(a) and (b).

3. *Stress softening.* It has been found[3,14–22] that when unfilled and filled cross-linked rubbers are stretched to a given strain and retracted then subsequent extension to the same strain requires a lower stress. However, the subsequent stress/strain relation rejoins the stress/strain curve applicable to the first extension cycle if the strain on the second cycle exceeds the original level. Most of the softening occurs during the first deformation cycle and after a few stressing cycles a steady-state is reached. This phenomenon is also known as the Mullins effect and the aspects described above are illustrated in Fig. 10.2. There has been

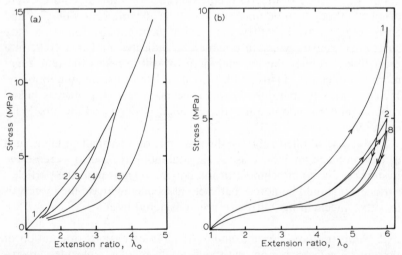

Fig. 10.2. *The phenomena of stress softening in rubbers.* (a) *Stress/extension ratio relationships for a carbon-black filled SBR subjected to successive extensions of increasing amount (after Gent*[26]*); and* (b) *Effect of successive stress/extension cycles on an unfilled natural rubber. Cycles numbered on curve (after Harwood & Payne*[20]*).*

considerable controversy concerning the causes of stress softening—some workers[17,18,23,24] have attributed it to breakage, detachment or slippage of network chains adhering to filler particles. However, since a similar effect has been observed in unfilled rubbers, it has also been ascribed[6–8] to features of the rubber network itself. Such features as the breaking and remaking of cross-links, the residual local orientation of network chains persisting after retraction and the rupture of network chains, have been suggested, and in filled materials these mechanisms may be considerably enhanced by strain amplification caused by the presence of the rigid filler particles.[19,25] Finally, whatever the molecular interpretation, Gent[26] has developed a phenomenological theory to account for stress softening in filled rubbers which is essentially a simple two-phase model; a soft phase resembling the corresponding unfilled rubber and a hard phase in series with the soft phase. The rubber is initially assumed to exist wholly in the hard state and to change progressively into the softened state on stretching.

4. Structural breakdown. In a filled rubber the filler particles, especially if carbon-black particles, generally form long aggregates of particles and adhere strongly to the rubber molecules.[24] Breakdown of these aggregates and of the matrix/filler interfacial bonds gives rise to hysteresis. Gent[27] has recently shown that, if it is assumed that the stress fields associated with the particles do not overlap, i.e. the volume fraction of particles is no more than about 0·1, and that many small debonded areas are present initially on the particle surface, then the hysteresis ratio, h_r, resulting from the debonding mechanism is given by

$$h_r \text{ (debonding)} = \frac{3v_{fp}}{\pi} \tag{10.4}$$

where v_{fp} is the volume fraction of the particulate filler.

5. Deformation of domains. Viscoelastic stress analysis of two-phase systems has shown[25] that the inclusion of particles or domains of a second phase in a viscoelastic medium increases the energy loss even when the domains are perfectly elastic. Further, in some instances the domains themselves may be capable of exhibiting energy dissipating mechanisms. For example, studies of the morphology and other characteristics of rubbers based upon block copolymers[28,29] and interpenetrating networks[30] have shown that many of these materials contain domains of a dispersed, hard-plastic phase. Such rubbers typically exhibit high levels of hysteresis and permanent set and this observation may be largely attributed to the domains undergoing shear yielding upon being stressed.[31,32]

As might be expected from the above comments, it is extremely difficult to predict quantitatively the extent of energy dissipation expected from a given rubber formulation under a particular set of test conditions. However, some general qualitative observations are possible. Firstly, if the chemical structure of the rubber permits close association of the chains then crystallisation may occur which will result in greater hysteresis. Secondly, fillers, such as carbon black, generally increase the hysteresis and hysteresis ratio, as illustrated in Figs 10.1 and 10.3(a), although the percentage increase in hysteresis is less marked if the rubber can undergo crystallisation. Thirdly, from the previous remarks concerning internal viscosity in an unfilled amorphous rubber, then decreasing the temperature would be predicted to steadily increase the hysteresis, since the internal viscosity would steadily increase. However, hysteresis depends upon temperature in a

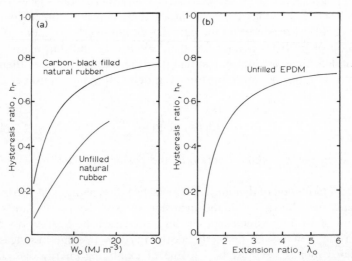

Fig. 10.3. (a) Relationship between hysteresis ratio, h_r, and applied strain-energy density for filled and unfilled natural rubber (after Harwood et al.[8] and Gent[26]); and (b) Relationship between hysteresis ratio, h_r, and extension ratio for an unfilled ethylene–propylene–diene rubber (after Andrews & Fukahori[33]).

more complex manner, as do many properties which appear to be measures of segmental mobility. For example, the value of h_r, from small-strain experiments, passes through a maximum as the temperature is lowered, falling as the glassy state is reached.[2] This is because at high temperatures the deformation is rubber-like and thus directly influenced by the segmental viscosity. At low temperatures, it is glass-like and does not involve segmental viscosity, since the deformation occurs by distortion of the segments *in situ* and the corresponding energy absorption is small. Similar effects are observed if the timescale of the experiment is altered; if the test rate is sufficiently high then the local viscous stresses for segmental flow may exceed those for a glass-like response, and the segments cease to move. Thus increasing the test rate is equivalent to decreasing the temperature. Finally, the hysteresis ratio is often found to be dependent upon the applied strain-energy density, W_0 (which may alternatively be expressed in terms of the applied extension) as may be seen from Figs 10.3(a) and (b).

10.3 INITIATION OF FRACTURE

10.3.1 Introduction

The mechanisms whereby microvoids and cracks are initiated in rubbers are not clearly established. The mechanism discussed in Section 4.4 involving the intersection of shear bands is unlikely to be relevant. This is because such regions of inhomogeneous plastic deformation are usually formed when the material exhibits a well-defined yield point followed by strain softening. Cross-linked rubbers do not generally exhibit this type of mechanical behaviour.

The initiation sites may arise from accidental scratches or nicks in the moulded or cut surfaces but, as Gent[4] has commented, even if such flaws are carefully prevented, for example by moulding against polished glass surfaces, the breaking stress of the material is not drastically increased. Thus it appears that other sources of flaws such as dirt and dust particles must inevitably be present.[34] Apart from such foreign bodies the common assumption that the cross-links are uniformly disposed is not necessarily true and local fluctuations occur within the material.[35] Thus both of these features will give rise to local inhomogeneities in the material which may act as microvoid initiation sites.

An indication of the likely size of intrinsic flaws present in rubbers may be obtained by using eqn (3.22) and taking the value of G to be the intrinsic, or threshold, fracture energy, G_0 (see Table 3.1 and Section 10.3.3). This reveals that the intrinsic flaws are equivalent to edge cracks of lengths, a_0, between about 25–50 μm. It is interesting that between these limits the value of a_0 is almost independent of the particular rubber and the detailed compound formulation, although these factors greatly affect the tensile strength. This aspect will be discussed in detail in Section 10.3.3. However, as Gent[4] has commented, the value of a_0 is the depth of an edge-crack equivalent in stress-concentrating power to natural flaws which may be smaller and sharper, or larger and blunter, than these calculated edge-cracks.

10.3.2 Initiation Under Triaxial Stresses

An area where the mechanisms and mechanics of microvoid growth, leading to crack initiation and propagation, have been studied in detail is the failure of rubber under the action of triaxial tensile stresses. Such a stress state is generated under two situations of considerable practical importance: adhesively bonded rubber layers and particulate-filled rubbers.

10.3.2.1 Adhesively Bonded Layers

Firstly, when a thin disc of rubber is bonded between relatively rigid end-plates and subjected to an applied uniaxial tension then, since the rubber cannot contract laterally except by a small amount, triaxial tension develops within the rubber layer. Indeed, if a value of ν of 0·5 is assumed for the layer the stress-state becomes one of hydrostatic tension. Gent & Lindley[36] have conducted such experiments employing various SBR and natural rubbers and they found that small internal cracks were initiated in the rubber at relatively low applied stress and strain levels and the point of internal fracture was clearly marked by an inflexion in the stress/strain curve. The initiated cracks then propagated relatively slowly and fracture of the specimen occurred at a considerably greater applied stress than that for the initiation stage. Lindley[37] has conducted similar experiments using a polyurethane rubber. He also observed that formation of the initial cavities occurred sharply at a certain stress but that a crack then propagated spherically, in a radial fashion, extremely rapidly. This probably reflects the lower fracture energy of the polyurethane rubber and resulted in the breaking stress of the specimen being only slightly greater than the crack initiation stress.

Gent and co-workers[36,38,39] have modelled these observations by a small spherical microvoid within a block of rubber which expands elastically from its original radius, a, to a new radius, λa, under the action of the inflating pressure, p. From the theory of large elastic deformations the relation for the inflating pressure, p, is

$$p = \frac{\mathscr{G}}{2}(5 - 4\lambda^{-1} - \lambda^{-4}) \tag{10.5}$$

where $\mathscr{G}$ is the elastic shear modulus and λ is the ratio of the radius or circumference of the hole in the deformed state to that in the unde-formed state. Equation (10.5) does not involve the value of a and it predicts that at a critical pressure, p_c, of $5\mathscr{G}/2$ any small void will grow to an infinite size. In reality, of course, the original void will form an internal crack when the expansion of its wall reaches the fracture strain of the rubber. Thus, the pressure for crack initiation, p_c, is given by

$$p_c = \frac{5\mathscr{G}}{2} \tag{10.6}$$

but, since

$$E = 2\mathscr{G}(1 + \nu)$$

then, taking $\nu = 0 \cdot 5$ and combining the above equations to eliminate $\mathscr{G}$, yields

$$p_c = \frac{5E}{6} \tag{10.7}$$

Studies of the critical conditions for internal crack initiation in various rubbers under different pressurising conditions have yielded results in good agreement with this prediction.[36,38,39] It should be noted that the above model treats the problem simply as a consequence of an elastic instability of pre-existing cavities too small to be readily detected. It does not involve the fracture energy because it is principally a trans-formation of potential energy from one strained state to another. A consequence is that the critical stress given in eqn. (10.7) depends only upon the rubber's elastic modulus and not on its fracture stress or energy.

In order to improve the accuracy of the above analysis for values of p in the case of very small voids, Gent & Tompkins[40] considered the addition of a surface energy term, thus

$$p_c = \frac{\mathscr{G}}{2}(5 - 4\lambda^{-1} - \lambda^{-4}) + \frac{2\gamma}{a} \tag{10.8}$$

where γ is the surface free-energy of the rubber and a is the current radius of the void. Taking typical values for $\mathcal{G}$ and γ (e.g. $0 \cdot 1$–1 MPa and 25–40 mJ m^{-2}, respectively) reveals that only for voids less than about $0 \cdot 1\,\mu$m in size does the surface free-energy term become a significant additional restraint on expansion.

Alternative theories have been proposed by Lindsey[37] and Williams & Schapery[41] which consider that the propagation phase of cracks generated from the microvoids is important. In the former the entire resistance to void growth was attributed to a surface energy term which was then discussed in terms of the fracture energy. In the latter, both deformation energy and fracture energy terms were considered.

10.3.2.2   Rigid-Particulate Fillers

Secondly, when rubbers containing rigid-particulate fillers are subjected to an applied tensile stress then triaxial stresses are generated immediately above and below the filler particles. These regions may act as favourable sites for the initiation and growth of internal voids and cracks. Two mechanisms of crack initiation may be identified: interfacial debonding and matrix cavitation.

If the adhesion between the filler particle and rubber matrix is relatively low and the particle size relatively large then interfacial debonding may occur and Gent[27] and Nicholson[42] have considered the mechanics of a spherical inclusion detaching from an elastic matrix by such a mechanism. This clearly involves the creation of new surfaces and Gent[27] employed an energy-balance analysis and obtained an expression for the minimum applied stress for debonding, σ_{ic}, as

$$\sigma_{ic} = 2\left[\frac{\pi G_{ic} E}{3 r_p}\right]^{\frac{1}{2}} \qquad (10.9)$$

where G_{ic} is the interfacial fracture energy and r_p is the radius of the filler particle. Nicholson's[42] analysis suggested an almost identical relationship. Note that σ_{ic} increases as G_{ic} increases, as would be expected, but also as r_p decreases.

Considering the matrix cavitation mechanism, then analysis of the stress distribution around a rigid, spherical filler particle in a rubber matrix has indicated[43] that the maximum triaxial stress-state is not actually at the filler/matrix interface but a short distance into the matrix material, above and below the filler particle. Thus, assuming the adhesion at the filler/matrix interface is above a certain minimal level or the radius of the particle is very small (see eqn. (10.11)), these

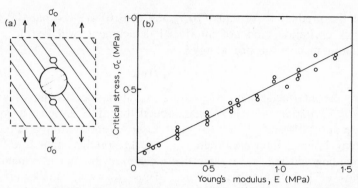

Fig. 10.4. (a) Schematic representation of matrix cavitation near a rigid particle
in a rubber; and (b) Critical applied stress, σ_c, for crack initiation as a function
of Young's modulus, E, of polyurethane rubbers containing rigid inclusions (after
Oberth & Bruenner[43]).

regions will be the most favourable initiation sites for cavitation, as
shown schematically in Fig. 10.4(a). Oberth & Bruenner[43] and
Oberth[44] have studied cavitation in polyurethane rubbers containing
steel spherical inclusions. They observed that the cavities appeared as
small cracks, distinctly located within the rubber matrix above and
below an inclusion, and that an applied uniaxial stress level for crack
initiation could be clearly defined. This stress level, σ_c, was a function
of the modulus of the rubber, as shown in Fig. 10.4(b). The agreement
of these results with the model proposed by Gent & Lindley[36] (eqn.
(10.7)) is striking and Oberth & Bruenner[43] suggested an analogous
relation

$$\sigma_c = \frac{E}{\eta} - p \qquad (10.10)$$

where η is the stress concentration factor (approximately 2 for spherical inclusions) and $-p$ is any externally applied hydrostatic compression (typically $E \gg -p$[atmospheric]). Thus, in this mechanism the
matrix does not detach from the particle directly but instead it undergoes internal rupture near the particle surface, nucleated by a precursor microvoid present within the rubber matrix. This microvoid is
expanded by the triaxial stresses generated and, when its walls attain
the fracture strain of the rubber, a crack is initiated at an applied stress
of σ_c.

If the predictions of eqns (10.9) and (10.10) are compared[26] then matrix cavitation, and not interfacial detachment, will be the crack initiating mechanism providing

$$G_{ic}/r_p > 3E/16\pi \qquad (10.11)$$

since the interfacial debonding stress, σ_{ic}, then exceeds the stress for matrix cavitation, σ_c. Gent[26] has argued that if E is given a typical value of 3 MPa and G_{ic} a value of 10 kJ m^{-2}, representing a relatively weakly bonded interface, then eqn. (10.11) predicts that interfacial debonding will not be an operative mechanism for particles having a radius of less than about 50 μm. Thus, for very small particles, interfacial debonding is unlikely even if the filler/matrix adhesion is low. However, it is noteworthy that the level of intrinsic adhesion does significantly affect the subsequent stage of crack propagation. If the adhesion is low, or only moderate, then the crack will invariably tend to *propagate* around the filler/matrix interface, even though it may have *initiated* in the rubber via the matrix cavitation mechanism. Thus, whilst the crack initiation site and required stress may differ, the end result is the same; detachment of the filler from the matrix. This phenomenon is known as 'dewetting' and it results in poor mechanical performance of the material as it is further loaded past the crack initiation stress. Alternatively, if the adhesion at the filler/matrix interface is good then the initiated crack will not propagate around the interface but through the rubber matrix. Hence, dewetting is not observed and the fracture energy of the rubber layer adjacent to the particle becomes an important consideration. The practical outcome is that whilst good adhesion does not necessarily increase the crack initiation stress it does prevent, or delay, dewetting and so improves the mechanical properties of the filled rubber. Unfortunately for the technologist the critical levels of adhesion are obviously dependent upon the particle size and are difficult to quantify.

10.3.3 Intrinsic Fracture Energies
From dynamic-fatigue experiments conducted on various rubbers Lake & Lindley[45] reported the existence of a threshold or intrinsic fracture energy, G_0, below which no crack growth occurred in the absence of chemical attack. The values of G_0 were of the order of 40–100 J m^{-2} and were characteristic of each rubber. However, unlike the gross strength properties, such as tensile strength, the values of G_0 did not correlate with the viscoelastic behaviour of the materials. More re-

cently Mueller & Knauss[46,47] and Ahagon & Gent[48] have determined values of G_0 for polyurethane and polybutadiene rubbers, respectively, by measuring crack growth at low rates and high temperatures on specimens swollen with a mobile liquid. These test conditions, like the very slow fatigue tests conducted by Lake & Lindley,[45] reduce the viscoelastic energy losses, i.e. ψ in eqn. (3.5), to virtually zero. A value of G_0 of 40 J m^{-2} was obtained for polyurethane and 40–80 J m^{-2} for polybutadiene—these values being independent of rate and temperature. Thus the results from all the above studies are in good agreement.

As discussed in Section 2.2.2, while these values of G_0 are much smaller than the usually measured fracture energies, G_c, which take into account other energy absorbing fracture processes such as viscoelastic deformations, they are considerably higher than the energy required to break primary bonds (about 0·5 J m^{-2}). This discrepancy has been attributed by Lake & Thomas[49] to the chain structure of cross-linked rubbers—the term 'chain' being used to denote the part of a parent long-chain molecule lying between adjacent cross-links. They considered the plane of crack propagation ahead of the tip of a microvoid or flaw which, in a cross-linked rubber, will be crossed by a number of polymer chains whose cross-links lie on opposite sides of the plane. For crack propagation these chains must be broken but, since forces are transmitted primarily via the cross-links, in order to break one particular bond all the bonds in a molecular chain must be stressed to almost the breaking force. Thus the energy required will be much greater than the dissociation energy of a single bond and the expression Lake & Thomas[49] derived for G_0 was (eqn. (2.8))

$$G_0 = \tfrac{1}{2}\bar{L}N_b\bar{n}_b U_b$$

where $\bar{L}$ is the average distance between cross-links in the unstrained state, N_b is the number of chains per unit volume, $\bar{n}_b$ is the average number of primary main-chain bonds between cross-links and U_b is the bond dissociation energy. Hence G_0 may be interpreted in terms of structural parameters, and theoretical values deduced from eqn. (2.8) are of the order of 20–40 J m^{-2}, in good agreement with the experimental values.

An interesting aspect of the Lake & Thomas[49] theory is their prediction of the dependence of G_0 upon the degree of cross-linking. Essentially, the greater the molar mass between cross-links the larger the number of bonds which must be stressed in order to break a molecular chain. However, when the chains are long, the number crossing a random fracture plane will be smaller. As Ahagon & Gent[48] have emphasised, these effects do not cancel out but yield a dependence of the form

$$G_0 = k_6(\bar{M}_c^{-1} + \bar{M}_e^{-1})^{-\frac{1}{2}}(1 - 2\bar{M}_c\bar{M}^{-1}) \qquad (10.12)$$

where $\bar{M}$ is the molar mass of the polymer before cross-linking, $\bar{M}_c$ the molar mass between chemical cross-links, $\bar{M}_e$ the molar mass between physical cross-links, and k_6 a constant which involves the density of the polymer, the mass, length and effective flexibility of a monomer unit, and the dissociation energy of a carbon–carbon bond. Ahagon & Gent[48] determined values of G_0 for polybutadiene rubbers as a function of the molar mass, $\bar{M}_c$, between cross-links. Their experimental values are shown in Fig. 10.5 and are in good agreement with the theoretical predictions deduced from eqn. (10.12).

The values of G_0 referred to above are applicable when no hostile environment is present to assist the failure process. If environmental

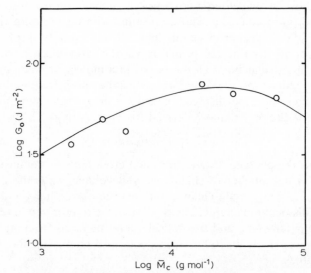

Fig. 10.5. *Dependence of the intrinsic fracture energy, G_0, upon molar mass, $\bar{M}_c$, between cross-links for polybutadiene rubbers. Points experimental; solid curve theoretical from eqn. (10.12) assuming $\bar{M}_e = 10^4$ g mol^{-1}, $\bar{M} = 3 \times 10^5$ g mol^{-1} and $k_3 = 1.05$ J m^{-2} (g mol^{-1})$^{-\frac{1}{2}}$ (after Ahagon & Gent[48]).*

attack aids the scission of the primary main-chain bonds then crack growth will occur at values lower than 40–$100\,\mathrm{J\,m^{-2}}$. For example, DeVries *et al.*[50-2] have used electron spin resonance to demonstrate that if a strained rubber specimen is exposed to ozone then main-chain bond rupture occurs more rapidly and to a greater extent than in an inert environment. This observation is reflected by the value of $G_0(\text{ozone})$ determined by Braden & Gent[53] being of the order of $0\cdot 1\,\mathrm{J\,m^{-2}}$. This is approximately twice the surface free-energy which is the energy required to create a new surface solely by the rupture of *secondary* bonds. From dynamic, rather than static, crack growth experiments Lake & Lindley[54] have suggested that the value of $G_0(\text{ozone})$ may even be appreciably lower than 2γ. However, it is agreed that below $G_0(\text{inert environment})$ the rate of crack growth is essentially independent of the value of the fracture energy and at temperatures well above T_g is directly proportional to the ozone concentration.[55] This independence of the crack growth rate upon the fracture energy in the range $G_0(\text{ozone}) < G < G_0(\text{inert})$ appears to contradict the basis of the activated-rate theories described in Chapter 2 and embodied in eqn. (2.11). It probably arises because the activation energy, ΔG^*, for the ozone scission of primary bonds is very low, less than about $4\,\mathrm{kJ\,mol^{-1}}$. This exceptionally low value indicates a most efficient process where the application of a stress is unlikely to increase appreciably the rate of reaction. Considering *oxidative* processes, then it is of interest to note that Lake & Lindley[45] reported that there was sufficient oxygen in the laboratory atmosphere to lower the measured value of G_0 under these conditions by a factor of up to about 3, compared to *in vacuo* conditions, for unsaturated rubbers containing no antioxidant.

Finally, Gent & Kinloch[56] and Andrews & Kinloch[57-9] have extended the concept of an intrinsic fracture energy to crack growth in adhesive joints consisting of a rubbery adhesive adhering to rigid substrates. For those joints which exhibited a solely interfacial locus of failure and in which only secondary bonds were established across the interface then it was predicted that[58,59]

$$G_0(\text{joint}) = W_A \qquad (10.13)$$

where

$$W_A = \gamma_a + \gamma_s - \gamma_{as} \qquad (10.14)$$

W_A is the thermodynamic work of adhesion, and γ_a, γ_s and γ_{as} are the surface free-energies of the adhesive and substrate, and the interfacial

TABLE 10.2

THE INTRINSIC ADHESIVE FRACTURE ENERGY, G_0(JOINT), AND THERMO-
DYNAMIC WORK OF ADHESION, W_A, FOR A STYRENE–BUTADIENE RUBBER
ADHERING TO VARIOUS SUBSTRATES[58,59]

Substrate	$G_0(joint)$ $(mJ\ m^{-2})$	W_A $(mJ\ m^{-2})$
Fluorinated ethylene–propylene copolymer	22	48
Plasma-treated fluorinated ethylene– propylene copolymer	69	57
Polychlorotrifluorethylene	75	63
Nylon 11	71	71
Poly(ethylene terephthalate)	79	72

free-energy, respectively. The agreement between values of G_0(joint), ascertained from crack growth experiments, and values of W_A deduced from measured surface free-energies (eqn. (10.14)) is shown in Table 10.2 and is very good, thus lending support to the concept of an intrinsic fracture energy to the failure of adhesive joints. Again, in the presence of a hostile environment[60] the value of this parameter may be appreciably lower, or may even, theoretically, become negative indicating spontaneous separation.

10.4 CRACK PROPAGATION

10.4.1 Stresses at Crack Tips

The equations developed in Sections 3.3 and 4.5 for the stress distribution around a crack tip are clearly inapplicable to rubber since, even outside of the immediate crack tip vicinity, such materials violate both the requirements of Hookean behaviour and infinitesimal strain which are embodied in classical elasticity. However, Andrews[61-3] has measured the distributions of stress and strain around cracks in rubbers using a photoelastic technique[61] and a method based upon determining the distortion suffered by a reference grid drawn on the material.[62] There are many similarities between Andrews' results and the classical elasticity predictions. For example, the major principal stress, σ_1, decays rapidly along the crack axis from a maximum at the tip to its uniform value in the bulk of the material while the axial stress, σ_2, rises from zero at the tip to a maximum some distance along the axis (cf., Fig. 3.8(a)). However, whilst near the crack tip the maximum value of σ_1 is found along the $\theta = 0°$ plane, i.e. on the axis of the crack, further away the maximum stresses are located on either side of the axis. Thus, it is possible to draw two symmetrically disposed 'maximum stress loci' which coincide near the crack tip but curve away to either side of the axis as r increases. This stress distribution pattern is shown in Fig. 10.6 and may explain aspects of crack propagation behaviour observed in rubbers, as discussed later, and the extent and shape of the dewetting damage field measured in highly filled rubbery propellants by Martinson et al.[64] using dynamic acoustic imaging techniques.

Thomas[65] has considered the strain distribution around the tip of a crack in a strained rubber sheet and deduced a general theoretical relationship between the strain-energy density, W_{tc}, around the tip of a crack of radius ρ_c and the value of the fracture energy, G_c. An approximate relation is

$$G_c \simeq 2\rho_c W_{tc} \qquad (10.15)$$

where the value of W_{tc} may be equated to the strain-energy density at rupture in uniaxial extension. Thomas[65] confirmed this relationship experimentally and commented that eqn. (10.15) lends strong support to the contention that there is a region surrounding the crack tip where the local energy dissipation, arising from both hysteresis and bond rupture mechanisms, may be considered to be characteristic of the fracture process. Thus the value of G_c determined from any particular

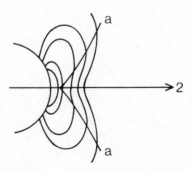

Fig. 10.6. Iso-stress contours (σ_{11}) and maximum stress trajectories (a) near a crack tip in a rubber (after Andrews[61,63]).

test method should be independent of geometrical and loading considerations. In a subsequent study of crack propagation in both uncracked and pre-cracked specimens, Greensmith[66] found that values of an effective tip radius, ρ_c, of a few tenths of a millimetre were generally required to fit the data to eqn. (10.15). These values are comparable in magnitude with the irregularities observed on the fracture surface and, in some instances, direct measurement of the crack tip radius confirmed the calculated values. However, the value of ρ_c is not only a function of the formulation used but also depends upon the temperature and rate of crack growth.

10.4.2 Amorphous Rubbers

The fracture energy, G_c, of an unfilled amorphous SBR has been determined over a wide range of temperatures and rates by Greensmith et al.[67-9] who employed the trouser test specimen (see Table 3.2 and Fig. 3.12). The results are presented in a three-dimensional plot in Fig. 10.7(a). The main feature of these data is the steady increase in the value of G_c with either an increase in rate or a decrease in temperature. This reflects the dominating influence of the hysteresis occurring around the crack tip; each volume element in the path of the

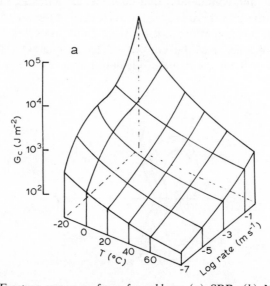

Fig. 10.7. *Fracture energy surfaces for rubbers: (a) SBR; (b) Natural rubber; and (c) Carbon-black filled SBR (after Greensmith et al.[68]).*

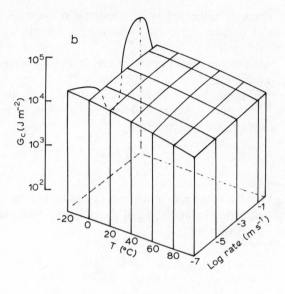

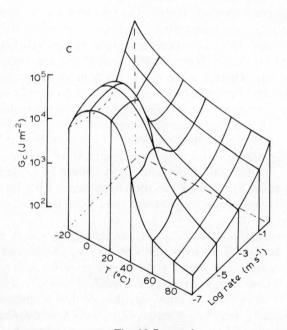

Fig. 10.7. contd.

propagating crack is subjected to a stress/strain cycle as the crack approaches and recedes from its vicinity and energy is dissipated during this strain cycle.

Since the hysteresis in SBR largely results from an internal friction, or viscosity, mechanism then, at temperatures $T > T_g$, the WLF equation may be used to produce a single relation between G_c and rate and temperature.[57,70,71] Such a master curve is constructed by multiplying the rate by a shift factor, a_T, where

$$a_T = \frac{\eta_v(T)}{\eta_v(T_g)} \qquad (10.16)$$

This essentially reduces the rate and temperature to an equivalent rate, with the reference state being the T_g of the polymer. From eqn. (10.3) the value of a_T is given by

$$\log a_T = \frac{-C_1(T - T_g)}{(C_2 + T - T_g)} \qquad (10.17)$$

where T is the temperature of test.

The master curve for SBR is shown in Fig. 10.8 where T_g has been taken as the reference temperature, and the 'universal' values of C_1 and C_2 (see Table 10.1) have been employed in eqn. (10.17). In this figure, $\log(G_c T_g/T)$ has been plotted against the logarithm of the reduced rate, $\dot{a}a_T$, where $\dot{a}$ is the rate of crack propagation. Note that, in accord with usual practice, the ordinate has been multiplied by the ratio T_g/T to account for the increase in retractive force with absolute temperature.[2] (If the glass transition temperature, T_g, is not taken as the reference temperature then the ratio T_r/T is used, where T_r is the reference temperature. Under such circumstance, of course, different values of C_1 and C_2 to those shown in Table 10.1 need to be employed. The use of the WLF equation to construct a master curve of data obtained over a wide range of test rates and temperatures is also shown in Fig. 10.10.)

There are several points of interest concerning the master curve for SBR shown in Fig. 10.8. Firstly, the values of a_T calculated from the WLF equation appear to yield a good master curve for data measured over a wide range of temperatures and rates. However, it has been reported[70,72] that at reduced rates, $\dot{a}a_T$, higher than about 10^{-7} m s^{-1} the experimentally determined values of a_T may be somewhat larger than those calculated from eqn. (10.17) and may provide a better fit to

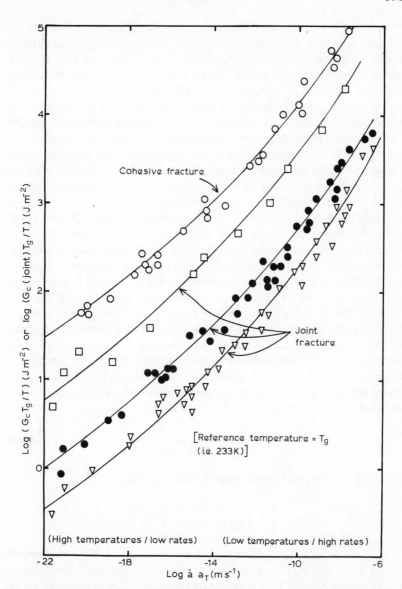

Fig. 10.8. Fracture energy versus reduced rate of crack propagation: ○, G_c *for cohesive fracture of SBR;* □, G_c(*joint*) *for SBR/etched fluorinated ethylene-propylene copolymer joint;* ●, G_c(*joint*) *for SBR/treated fluorinated ethylene-propylene copolymer joint; and* ▽, G_c(*joint*) *for SBR/poly(ethylene terephthalate) joint (after Andrews & Kinloch*[57]).

the data. This discrepancy has been suggested[70] to arise from deviations of the crack when the fracture energy becomes large. Secondly, at lower temperatures and higher rates than those shown in Fig. 10.8 the material becomes glassy and the hysteresis and the fracture energy fall—the value of G_c typically being 10^2–10^3 J m^{-2}.

The importance of internal viscosity is further illustrated by the work of Mullins[72] which demonstrated that the master curves of fracture energy versus equivalent rate for several amorphous rubbers all fell on a single relation when the reference temperature for each was their respective glass transition temperature. Also, the fracture energies could be directly related to a measure of energy dissipation, namely the shear loss moduli, $\mathscr{G}_{loss}$, of the rubbers.

Andrews and co-workers[33,73] and Mueller & Knauss[46,47] have proposed equations to describe the dependence of G_c upon rate and temperature and essentially both approaches are concerned with evaluating the loss function, Φ, in eqn. (3.8). The Andrews' approach necessitates an evaluation of the strain distribution, and hence energy distribution, around the crack tip which, when coupled with a knowledge of the hysteresis ratio and its dependence upon strain, rate and temperature, enables the loss energy associated with the fracture process to be evaluated. This was discussed in Section 3.2.4 since, in principle, it is applicable to any type of material behaviour. Mueller & Knauss[46,47] have also considered the work done by the unloading forces at the crack tip and, assuming linear viscoelastic behaviour, derived the expression

$$\Phi = \frac{1}{E_e f(\Delta l/\dot{a}a_T)} \tag{10.18}$$

where, E_e is the rubbery or equilibrium modulus

$$f(t) = 2\left[\frac{1}{t}\int_0^t D_{cr}(\tau)\,d\tau - \frac{1}{t^2}\int_0^t \tau D_{cr}(\tau)\,d\tau\right]$$

$D_{cr}(t)$ is the creep compliance, t and τ are the time and time-variable respectively, and Δl is a length experimentally determined by fitting data. If this equation is combined with eqn. (3.4), then

$$G_c = G_0\left(\frac{1}{E_e f(\Delta l/\dot{a}a_T)}\right) \tag{10.19}$$

Thus, the rate–temperature dependence of the fracture energy, G_c, arises solely from energy dissipation due to internal friction, which is expressed by other material properties such as the creep compliance. Mueller & Knauss measured the value of G_0 (Section 10.3.3) and the creep compliance and so calculated the value of G_c from eqn. (10.19) for a polyurethane rubber, using a value of 15 nm for Δl. The agreement with the experimentally determined dependence of G_c upon rate and temperature was good.

Finally, it may be seen from Fig. 10.8 that the rate–temperature dependence of the adhesive fracture energy, G_c(joint), for an SBR adhering to various substrate materials may also be rationalised[57-9] by the concepts embodied in eqn. (3.8). Thus

$$G_c(\text{joint}) = G_0(\text{joint})\Phi(\dot{a}, T, e) \qquad (10.20)$$

The interpretation of G_0(joint) for the simple case where the locus of failure is solely interfacial and only secondary bonds are acting across the interface was discussed in Section 10.3.3 but more generally the value of G_0(joint) needs to be expressed as a weighted average of the various failure paths available.[57,60] However, it has more recently been found[60,74] that the value of G_c(joint) may not always be independent of the joint geometry. For example, thin adhesive layers constrained between rigid substrates may restrict the extent of energy dissipation around the crack tip.[74-6] In such cases G_c(joint) may still be expressed by an equation of the form of eqn. (10.20) but the loss function, Φ, would not be identical with that for cohesive fracture but, instead, would be a function of joint geometry.

10.4.3 Strain-Crystallising Rubbers

In strain-crystallising rubbers, such as natural rubber, crystallisation may occur in the high-strain regions surrounding the crack tip and this increases the extent of energy dissipation, as discussed in Section 10.2 and illustrated in Figs 10.1(a) and (b). This is reflected in the larger values of G_c for natural rubber compared to unfilled SBR over the range of temperatures and rates where crystallisation occurs. This may be seen by comparing Figs 10.7(a) and (b). Also, since hysteresis arising from crystallisation is not highly dependent upon rate and temperature, unlike that arising from internal friction, the fracture energy of natural rubber over this range is almost independent of rate and temperature. However, at low temperatures and high rates of propagation[77] crystallisation cannot apparently develop quickly enough and the value of G_c now mainly reflects the energy dissipated from the internal viscosity mechanism, and thus is a function of the polymer's T_g.

The increased hysteresis in natural rubber also results in a far greater degree of stick–slip-type of crack growth being observed, as opposed to continuous, stable tearing. These types of crack growth were discussed in Chapter 9 in connection with thermoset, rigid polymers such as epoxy resins. The same phenomena are therefore observed in rubbers and arise from essentially the same cause, namely hysteresis around the crack tip. However, the detailed mechanism appears to be somewhat different and Andrews[63,78] has proposed an explanation for stick–slip crack growth in rubbers based upon a 'stationary stress distribution' hypothesis. The starting point for his proposal is the stress distribution around a crack in a rubber which is illustrated in Fig. 10.6. Essentially, when a crack propagates its stress distribution usually moves with it so that the locus of maximum stress, along which the crack propagates, coincides with the crack axis. However, severe hysteresis may cause the stress distribution associated with the initial crack to remain stationary when the crack propagates. Thus, for the distribution shown in Fig. 10.6 the growing crack will not follow the axis ($\theta = 0°$) but will propagate along one or both of the loci of maximum stress resulting in deviation or forking of the crack tip. The growing crack will now encounter lower and lower stresses as it propagates and must therefore arrest unless the overall stress on the specimen is increased to compensate. When, at this high stress, the mechanisms maintaining the stationary stress distribution give way, the energy available for crack growth is far greater than that needed for stable growth and a rapid propagation phase follows.

10.4.4 Filled Rubbers

The behaviour of an SBR containing 50 phr of a fine thermal carbon-black filler is shown in Fig. 10.7(c). The increase in hysteresis associated with filled rubbers is clearly reflected in the higher values of G_c (cf., Figs 10.7(a) and (c)) but this strengthening effect is restricted to a specific range of temperatures and rates that depend[69] upon both the concentration and type of filler and rubber. Outside of this range the reinforcement induced by the filler is far less effective and this is an important consideration when designing for the end-application.

As in strain-crystallising rubbers, the crack growth may often be stick–slip in character but in filled rubbers the appearance of the fracture surfaces and the manner in which the crack propagates under such circumstances are particularly distinctive.[69] The fracture surfaces are extremely rough and this results from large deviations of the crack from a straight path; the crack may even turn in a direction parallel to the applied stress, which considerably increases the effective crack tip radius, until a new crack initiates perpendicular to the stress direction. This has been termed 'knotty' tearing and obviously Andrews' stationary stress distribution may also be invoked to explain this more severe type of stick–slip behaviour. The importance of knotty tearing is that it is observed when the reinforcing ability of the filler is at a maximum. Under these conditions theoretical (eqn. (10.15)) and experimental determinations of the crack tip radius reveal that it may be high, of the order of $0 \cdot 5$ mm, and the values of G_c are therefore also relatively high. Indeed, if knotty tearing is suppressed by restraining the crack from deviating and it is forced to follow a linear path, by using closely spaced metal guides,[70] then the values of ρ_c and G_c are much lower. Thus, by reference to eqn. (10.15), the effect of hysteresis upon the value of G_c may be attributed to both its effect on the strain-energy density and the crack tip radius at the onset of crack propagation—both parameters increasing with increasing hysteresis, unless external factors intervene.

10.4.5 Fatigue Failure

Fatigue failure of rubber has much in common with that of other polymers, as discussed in Chapter 6—it occurs primarily under conditions of repeated loading and results from the growth of one or more cracks.

The effect of dynamic, as opposed to static, loading is particularly pronounced in the case of strain-crystallising rubbers such as natural rubber.[79] As may be seen from Fig. 10.7(b) for static or monotonic loading, there is virtually no time-dependent crack growth below a fairly well-defined critical, plateau value of G_c; once this level is exceeded unstable growth occurs and the crack may propagate rapidly for some distance before arresting. However, if dynamic loading conditions are employed crack growth now occurs below this critical value of G_c. The mechanism has been attributed to the crystallisation disappearing on the unloading cycle if the rubber is relaxed to zero strain. This allows the stress distribution around the crack tip to move forward and a further increment of growth to occur on the next cycle. If the rubber is not completely relaxed at its minimum strain, some crystallisation may be retained at the tip and crack growth retarded or prevented.

The relation between da/dN and G_c for a natural rubber is shown, on logarithmic scales, in Fig. 10.9(a). Lake & Lindley[45,80] have proposed that this behaviour may be described by four distinct regions of stressing

1. At $G < G_0$ crack growth occurs only by chemical (ozone) attack (Section 10.3.3) and

$$\frac{da}{dN} = C_f \qquad (10.21)$$

and the value of C_f is proportional to ozone concentration.[45]

2. $G_0 < G_c < G_{cl}$, then

$$\frac{da}{dN} = B_f(G_c - G_0) + C_f \qquad (10.22)$$

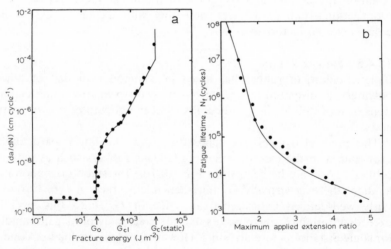

Fig. 10.9. The dynamic fatigue of natural rubber: (a) Crack growth rate, da/dN, as a function of fracture energy obtained in the laboratory atmosphere at a frequency of 1·67 Hz. Specimens were allowed to relax to zero strain on each cycle. Points experimental, solid curve represents eqns (10.21) to (10.23); (b) Fatigue lifetime under the same conditions. Points experimental, solid curve represents the theoretical prediction from eqn. (10.26) (after Lake & Lindley[45,80]).

3. $G_{cl} < G_c < G_c(\text{static})$, then

$$\frac{da}{dN} = D_f G_c^{\,q} \tag{10.23}$$

4. $G_c(\text{static}) < G_c$, then rapid crack growth as shown in Fig. 10.7(b), where, B_f, F_c and C_f are crack-growth constants, q has a value of 2 for natural rubber and 4 for SBR, and G_{cl} is a distinctive value of G_c as defined in Fig. 10.9(a).

The fatigue lifetime of tensile specimens may be estimated by recalling eqn. (3.22) which relates the fracture energy to the crack length, a, and strain-energy density, W_c

$$G_c = 2k_1 a W_c$$

Hence, by using this equation and the dynamic relationships given in eqns (10.21) to (10.23) the number of cycles, N, required for a crack to grow from a length a_1 to a length a_2 in a simple-extension specimen (Fig. 3.2) deformed to a given $2k_1 W_c$ value may be calculated. For example, for the region for a natural rubber when eqn. (10.23) is valid, then substituting for G_c from eqn. (3.22) yields[81]

$$N = \int_{a_1}^{a_2} \frac{da}{D_f(2k_1 a W_c)^2} \tag{10.24}$$

Upon integrating

$$N = \frac{1}{D_f(2k_1 W_c)^2}\left(\frac{1}{a_1} - \frac{1}{a_2}\right) \tag{10.25}$$

In a fatigue experiment the specimen does not always contain an inserted crack but it may be assumed that crack growth commences from naturally occurring flaws of length a_0. At failure the crack length is usually much larger than a_0, so that $1/a_2$ may be neglected. Thus, for relatively large strains where eqn. (10.25) is applicable, the fatigue life, N_f, is given by

$$N_f = \frac{1}{D_f(2k_1 W_c)^2 a_0} \tag{10.26}$$

The experimentally measured fatigue life is plotted against the maximum extension ratio for natural rubber in Fig. 10.9(b). Also shown is the calculated relation from eqn. (10.26) assuming values of

D_f of 5×10^{-11} mm per cycle per $(J\,m^{-2})^2$ and an a_0 of $25\,\mu$m. The agreement is extremely good, thus demonstrating that the fatigue failure of rubber may indeed be modelled as a crack-growth process starting at small, intrinsic flaws.

The inclusion of fillers does not greatly affect the form of the da/dN versus G_c curves shown in Fig. 10.9(a) but does tend to displace the curves towards higher fracture energies. This probably results from the additional hysteresis caused by the presence of the filler particles, as discussed in Section 10.2. However, this improvement in fatigue behaviour may, at least in some filled rubbers, be cancelled out by the larger intrinsic flaw size, a_0, which the addition of fillers may create.[45,82]

10.5 TENSILE FRACTURE

10.5.1 Failure Under Combined Stresses

Most of the discussions on tensile fracture will be concerned with those properties which have been obtained from tests conducted in uniaxial tension. This reflects the fact that few studies have been made of the failure of rubber under combined stresses, largely because of the difficulty in designing and conducting such experiments. However, in engineering applications a rubber component is often subjected to a complex stress-state and, even when the macroscopic applied stress is uniaxial tension, the stress on a microscopic scale may be more complex because of filler particles, flaws or other inhomogeneities in the material.

Smith and co-workers[83,84] have measured the fracture stress, σ_f, and extension ratio at fracture, λ_f, of an unfilled SBR subjected to constrained-biaxial, equibiaxial and uniaxial tension. The constrained-biaxial tensile tests were conducted by stressing a thin-walled cylindrical specimen axially whilst maintaining its outside diameter constant by applying pressure internally. For an incompressible material this test results in $\lambda_1 = \lambda$, $\lambda_2 = 1$, and $\lambda_3 = 1/\lambda$ with no rotation of the strain axes and is, therefore, equivalent to a pure-shear condition.[85] However, rubbers do not fail along shear planes but cracks initiate and grow normal to the principal tensile stress. The equibiaxial tensile tests were conducted by inflating clamped, circular sheets of rubber. Comparing firstly the constrained-biaxial to the uniaxial tensile results, then over a wide range of test temperatures and rates the values of λ_f were the same, within experimental error. However, under the former stress state the value of σ_f was generally about 20 % greater. The behaviour under equibiaxial tension was more complex since, whilst the values of σ_f and λ_f from the constrained-biaxial and uniaxial tensile tests were highly rate- and temperature-dependent, the values from the equibiaxial tensile conditions exhibited far less dependence. At relatively high temperatures/low rates the values of σ_f and λ_f from the equibiaxial tensile tests were *considerably higher* than those from the uniaxial tensile tests whilst at low temperatures/high rates the values were of a similar order.

The mechanical behaviour of rubbers under triaxial tension was discussed in detail in Section 10.3.2. Essentially, while most rubbers are highly deformable in either uniaxial or biaxial tension, the ultimate elongation is reduced in triaxial tension and becomes quite small in hydrostatic (equitriaxial) tension.[86] However, the exact relationships between the fracture stresses in triaxial and uniaxial tension, and the applied stress, σ_c, at which microvoids initiate under hydrostatic tension, are not clearly established. For example, Lindsey[37] has shown that for a polyurethane rubber $\sigma_f(\text{triaxial tension}) \approx \sigma_c(\text{triaxial tension}) > \sigma_f(\text{uniaxial tension})$ whilst Gent & Lindley's[36] work indicates that for natural rubber and SBR $\sigma_f(\text{uniaxial tension}) > \sigma_f(\text{triaxial tension}) > \sigma_c(\text{triaxial tension})$. Such differences might well be expected to occur since the rupture stress in uniaxial tension is highly dependent upon factors such as whether crystallisation occurs under the associated high strains. Also, it will be recalled that the value of σ_c is largely dependent upon the modulus of the rubber, rather than any failure property, since void initiation and growth under hydrostatic tension may be simply modelled as an elastic instability problem.

The above comments indicate that no single failure criterion based upon a simple relationship, such as the Tresca, von Mises or modified forms of these equations (Section 4.2.4), is generally applicable to the fracture of rubbers under combined stresses. However, in some circumstances a simple failure criterion may have limited applicability and provide an empirical, but practically useful, method for predicting the effect of various stress-states on the fracture behaviour. For example, Jones & Kruse[87] have obtained data in uniaxial, biaxial and triaxial tension for a solid rocket propellant based upon a polyurethane rubber filled with ammonium perchlorate. They found that under these conditions failure occurred when, over a wide range of test temperatures and rates

$$(\sigma_1 + \sigma_2 + \sigma_3)_{max} \geqslant \sigma_f(\text{uniaxial tension}) \qquad (10.27)$$

where the σ's refer to the true principal stresses at the moment of failure. Jones & Kruse[87] also showed that in some rubbery propellants the value of σ_f(uniaxial tension) may increase somewhat under a superimposed hydrostatic pressure. As with other materials, this effect undoubtedly arises from the hydrostatic pressure causing closure of microvoids and flaws and so inhibiting fracture.

10.5.2 Effect of Rate and Temperature

The effect of test rate and temperature on the fracture stress, σ_f, and the extension ratio, λ_f, of an amorphous SBR determined in uniaxial tension is shown in Fig. 10.10. As may be seen, the results[88] obtained

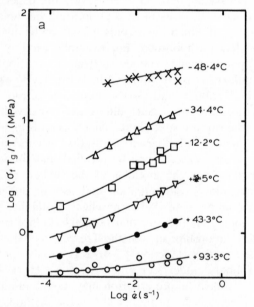

Fig. 10.10. The effect of strain rate, $\dot{e}$, and temperature, T, on the tensile fracture stress, σ_f, and extension ratio, λ_f, for an SBR: (a) Variation of σ_f with rate and temperature; (b) Master curve of σ_f versus reduced rate, $\dot{e}a_T$, obtained using WLF relation (eqn. (10.17)) from data in Fig. 10.10(a); and (c) Master curve of λ_f versus reduced rate, $\dot{e}a_T$, obtained using WLF relation (eqn. (10.17)) (after Smith[88]).

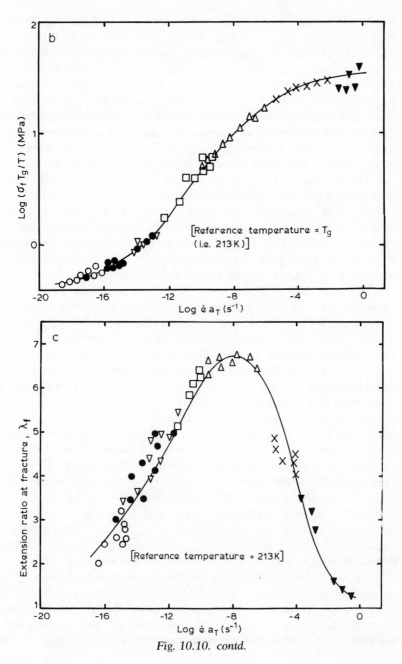

Fig. 10.10. contd.

over a wide range of rates and temperatures have been reduced to yield a single master curve with respect to σ_f (Fig. 10.10(b)) and λ_f (Fig. 10.10(c)) using the WLF relation (eqn. (10.17)) for simple visco-elastic materials. Thus, the variation of σ_f and λ_f with temperature and rate, like that of the fracture energy, G_c, of amorphous rubbers, primarily arises from changes in segmental mobility. These master curves are widely employed to predict the tensile fracture properties at reduced rates equivalent to temperature/rate combinations which are difficult to obtain experimentally—for example, it is often easier to conduct tests at low temperatures and interpret these as being equivalent to high rates—and they are also often used to compare the fracture behaviour of different rubber formulations.

The fracture stress, σ_f, of rubbers which are capable of strain-induced crystallisation is generally considerably greater than that of amorphous rubbers (see, for example, Fig. 10.1) and, in contrast to the above results, is comparatively little affected by the temperature over a large range.[89,90] In the case of natural rubber this range is from about -50 to about $100°C$, although at the high-temperature end of this range the value of σ_f falls abruptly to a value comparable to that of amorphous rubbers.[90,91] This fall is associated[91] with the temperature at which no crystallisation occurs in the bulk of the specimen. Also, at high rates of extension crystallisation would not be expected to have time to develop and under such conditions, for example at strain rates approaching $10^3 \, s^{-1}$, the fracture stress of crystallising rubbers again approaches that of amorphous rubbers.[92]

The presence of reinforcing fillers, such as carbon black, also increases the stress at fracture, although the effect of such fillers is more marked when added to amorphous rubbers (Section 10.5.4). Reinforcing fillers tend to produce a more gradual decline of fracture stress with increasing temperature for both crystallising and amorphous rubbers, compared to the unfilled materials.[89]

Smith[93-5] has proposed another, most useful, method for representing the tensile properties obtained over a range of rates and temperatures, namely the concept of a failure envelope. Provided time-temperature superposition is applicable then rupture data obtained at different temperatures and strain rates, or failure times, will superpose on a plot of $\log(\sigma_f T_g/T)$ versus $\log(\lambda_f - 1)$ (equivalent to $\log e_f$) to yield a single curve termed the 'failure envelope'. A typical failure envelope is shown in Fig. 10.11 and exhibits the characteristic parabolic shape. Rate and temperature are not shown explicitly but

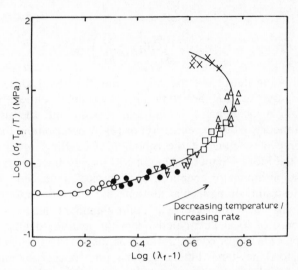

Fig. 10.11. Failure envelope for SBR from data determined at various rates and temperatures, as indicated in Fig. 10.10 (reference temperature taken as T_g) (after Smith[93]).

decreasing the temperature or increasing the rate merely shifts the rupture point in an anticlockwise direction around the envelope. Failure envelopes have become a popular concept since they can readily incorporate the effects of varying the cross-link density (see below) and may provide a useful failure criterion by dividing stress/strain space into an inner, stable and an outer, unstable, region. However, the location of the failure envelope will depend upon the test method employed to generate the rupture data, e.g. the envelope obtained via constant strain-rate tests will be different from that via cyclic tests.[94] Also, rubbers, such as crystallising rubbers, which do not follow the WLF relation over a large range of temperatures and rates, will not yield a simple failure envelope.[95]

10.5.3 Effect of Degree of Cross-Linking
One of the main variables in any cross-linked rubber is the degree of cross-linking. It may be expressed most conveniently in terms of the average molar mass, $\bar{M}_c$, between cross-links or the effective number of network chains, ν_{ef}, per unit volume. The two parameters are

related by[96]

$$\nu_{ef} = \frac{\rho_d N}{\bar{M}_c}\left(1 - 2\frac{\bar{M}_c}{\bar{M}_n}\right) \qquad (10.28)$$

where ρ_d is the density of the rubber and N is Avogadro's number. Values of ν_{ef} or $\bar{M}_c$ are typically ascertained either: (1) from stress/strain measurements in uniaxial tension and the use of the statistical theory of rubber elasticity; or (2) by determining the equilibrium degree of swelling of the rubber in a swelling liquid and then applying the Flory–Rehner, or modified Flory–Rehner, equation.[96,97]

The establishment of chemical, and physical, cross-links obviously imposes restraints on molecular motions and raises the internal viscosity. They may also interfere with chain alignment and crystallisation and, because of local fluctuations from the average degree of cross-linking, provide stress concentrations, as discussed in Section 10.3.1. These factors inevitably influence the tensile properties and, essentially, the modulus increases and the extension ratio at break, λ_f, decreases steadily with an increasing degree of cross-linking. The effect on the fracture stress, σ_f, is, however, more complex and depends on the temperature and type of cross-linking involved.[98–104] For example, several workers[98–101] have reported that the value of σ_f passes through a maximum as the cross-link density is progressively increased in SBR (Fig. 10.13), natural and ethylene–propylene rubbers. Alternatively, in the case of a polyurethane elastomer[102] the value of σ_f was found to increase in direct proportion to $\nu_{ef}^{\frac{1}{2}}$. Obviously, theories advanced to describe the tensile properties and fracture mechanisms of rubber must explain the effect of cross-link density and these are discussed later in Section 10.5.6.

The influence of the type of cross-linking upon the value of σ_f has been examined by Tobolsky & Lyons.[103] The fracture stresses of rubbers cross-linked to equivalent degrees by carbon–carbon, monosulphide, disulphide, polysulphide and salt linkages were found to increase in this order and this is also the order of *decreasing* thermal bond strength of these cross-linkages, as reflected by stress-relaxation measurements. It was suggested that the higher σ_f values associated with rubbers cross-linked by weak linkages arise from an internally relaxed network formed by the thermal lability of the cross-links at the vulcanisation temperature. Alternatively, a different mechanism, better supported by experimental observations, has been proposed by Bateman *et al.*[100] Their mechanism considers that if the cross-links are weaker than the bonds in the main polymer chains they will slip under localised high-stress concentrations. This will reduce the stress concentrations by causing the applied load to be shared over neighbouring chains and thereby permits the deformed network as a whole to bear a higher stress. The term 'slip' implies that the bonds in the cross-links continually rupture and reform and such bond rearrangements which can continually adjust themselves under suitable conditions may be the basis of the special position attaching to polysulphide bonds as cross-links in rubber networks.

At the phenomenological level two methods have been proposed to extend the failure envelope concept to describe the effect of cross-link density. The first involves[101] plotting $\log[(\lambda_f \sigma_f)(T_r/T)]$ against $\log[(\lambda_f - 1)/(\lambda_f - 1)_{max}]$. Thus, the true fracture stress, $\lambda_f \sigma_f$, is used rather than the engineering fracture stress, σ_f, and the extension ratio at fracture, λ_f, is effectively scaled in terms of its maximum value which is, of course, dependent upon the degree of cross-linking. The second method[104] plots $\log[(\sigma_f/\nu_{ef})(T_r/T)]$ versus $\log(\lambda_f - 1)$. Both approaches have experimental support and, as Gent[4] has commented, further work is necessary to decide between these two methods or combine them into a more comprehensive reduction system.

Finally, following the work of Plazek,[105] Fedors[106] and Fedors & Landel[107] have proposed the use of a shift factor, a_x, which accounts for the dependence of the tensile properties upon the degree of cross-linking in amorphous rubbers. The shift factor, a_x, is given by

$$a_x = \left(\frac{k_7}{\nu_{ef}}\right)^{7 \cdot 7} \tag{10.29}$$

where k_7 is a constant. Fedors & Landel found that for SBR the rate–temperature–cross-link density effects could all now be rationalised to yield a single master curve by combining this shift factor with that from the WLF equation. This suggestion leads to plots of $\log[(\sigma_f/\nu_{ef})(T_r/T)]$ versus $\log(\dot{e}a_T a_x)$ and $\log \lambda_f$ versus $\log(\dot{e}a_T a_x)$.

10.5.4 Energy Dissipating Mechanisms and Tensile Fracture

The variation of σ_f and λ_f upon rate and temperature in accord with the WLF equation for simple viscoelastic materials, as shown in Figs 10.10(b) and (c), emphasises the direct influence that energy dissipative mechanisms have upon the fracture behaviour of rubbers. As Gent[4] has remarked, the master curve for σ_f has the form expected of a viscosity-controlled quantity, rising steadily with increasing rate to a maximum value at high rates (or low temperatures), when the segments are unable to move and so the material behaves as a brittle glass. The extension ratio at failure, λ_f, at first increases with increasing rate, reflecting the enhanced strength, and then falls at higher rates (or lower temperatures) as the segments become unable to respond sufficiently quickly.

Payne and co-workers[22,108,109] have examined the quantitative inter-relationship between energy dissipation and tensile failure properties for a number of different rubbers. They found that for amorphous rubbers the applied strain-energy density at fracture, W_f, could be expressed in terms of the energy, W_{df}, dissipated up to almost the fracture point by[109]

$$W_f = 410 W_{df}^{\frac{2}{3}} \qquad (10.30)$$

where W_f and W_{df} are in J m^{-3}. Thus, the tensile failure properties are directly related to the extent of hysteresis and rubbers possessing the highest combination of σ_f and λ_f values are precisely those in which a major portion of the energy is dissipated before rupture.

Hence, to obtain rubbers possessing high values of σ_f and λ_f it is necessary to encourage energy dissipating mechanisms. For example, in single-phase amorphous rubbers the principal such mechanism is solely due to internal friction or viscosity whilst in natural and carbon-black filled rubbers other dissipative mechanisms, such as strain-induced crystallisation and extensive stress-softening respectively, may operate, as discussed in Section 10.2. Thus, the failure properties of all single-phase amorphous rubbers are somewhat similar when compared at corresponding states (e.g. the same rate and temperature interval, $(T - T_g)$) and account is taken of the dependence on cross-link density. Also, and most importantly, over a wide range of temperatures and rates, the fracture stresses for natural rubber and carbon-black filled rubbers are far greater than those for the relatively weak, amorphous rubbers. This need for a multiphase structure in order to produce high strengths and good strain-capability is a recurring theme in materials science and the importance of such structures in rubber technology is considered below.

10.5.5 Multiphase Rubbers

Strain-induced crystallisation in a rubber results in the formation of a second phase of crystalline domains. Compared to a completely amorphous, single-phase rubber, the creation of such domains enables new energy dissipating mechanisms to operate and so increases the material's hysteresis energy. This is reflected in higher values of fracture energy, G_c, and fracture stress, σ_f, over a wide range of temperatures and rates. These aspects have been considered in detail previously and are illustrated in Figs 10.1 and 10.7.

Another class of multiphase rubbers are the thermoplastic rubbers based upon block copolymers. They are exemplified by the styrene–butadiene–styrene (SBS) triblock polymers which are usually prepared by anionic polymerisation techniques, as reviewed by Fetters[110] and Allport & James.[29] When the styrene content is about 25 %, and the molar mass of the polymer is not unduly low, the rubber is exceptionally strong and tough.[28,111,112] These good mechanical properties arise from the microstructure which is comprised of a rubbery polybutadiene matrix in which aggregates, or domains, of polystyrene chains are dispersed. These colloidal, glassy polystyrene domains serve two important functions. Firstly, they effectively anchor the ends of the triblock molecules and so prevent viscous flow of the rubber below the softening temperature of the domains. Secondly, when the material is stressed they undergo plastic deformation and eventual disruption. This is the energy dissipating mechanism which is largely responsible for the good tensile failure properties and, as would be expected, also results in the triblock polymers possessing higher fracture energies, compared to the conventionally cross-linked random SBR materials. It is noteworthy that these attributes are also observed when the triblock SBS materials are used as adhesives.[32] Evidence for this plastic deformation and disruption process comes from the microscopic studies of Beecher et al.[113] They observed that connected spherical domains of polystyrene, of about 1·2 nm in diameter, plastically deformed to give isolated ellipsoidal domains. However, it should be noted that the initial domain shape and size is not necessarily limited to small spheres but may be, for example, cylinders or lamellae of one phase in a second. Keller and co-workers[114–16] have prepared SBS multiphase rubbers possessing cylindrical- or lamellae-shaped domains and have shown that the mechanical properties are highly anisotropic. The type of microstructure obtained is governed by the chemical structure and method of manufacture. Finally, Smith[112,117] and others[28,29] have examined the properties of other thermoplastic block copolymers, such as segmented polyurethanes. These polyurethane rubbers are essentially alternating block copolymers of flexible segments, such as polyether and polyester, and relatively rigid segments such as polyurethane or polyurea (formed by the reaction of a diisocyanate with a diol or diamine). The relatively hard segments are associated by interchain hydrogen-bonds to form discrete, sometimes crystalline, domains which again act as physical cross-links. As with the SBS triblock polymers, the principal energy dissipating mechanism responsible for the good tensile rupture properties is plastic deformation and ductile rupture of the domains.

Interpenetrating polymer networks (IPN's) provide yet another source of multiphase rubbers. They have recently been the subject of a monograph by Sperling[30] who suggested that, in its broadest definition, an IPN is any material containing two polymers each in network form but that a practical restriction requires that the two polymers have been synthesised and/or cross-linked in the immediate presence of each other. However, only when the two polymers are totally mutually soluble does complete interpenetration occur at the molecular level. Generally most IPN's phase-separate to a greater or lesser extent and, in some case, true molecular interpenetration is thought to occur only at the phase boundaries. The multiphase nature of an IPN is shown[118] in Fig. 10.12(a). This multiphase rubber was produced by the mutual coagulation and subsequent cross-linking of polyacrylate and poly-urethane lattices, this being one of several routes for producing IPN materials, and at a composition of 30 % w/w polyacrylate both phases display co-continuity whilst at 70 % w/w polyacrylate the polyurethane phase exists as discrete particles. Hence, over this composition range, molecular interpenetration in this IPN is restricted to the interfaces of the two phases. The fracture stress, σ_f, and extension ratio, λ_f, of these polyacrylate/polyurethane IPN's, as a function of a wide range of compositions, are shown[119] in Fig. 10.12(b). Considering firstly the fracture-stress data, then a minimum is observed at about 20 % w/w polyacrylate and this was attributed to the polyacrylate acting essentially as a plasticiser, implying no phase-separation at least in this concentration range. At about 75 % w/w a maximum is reached, which is actually above the fracture stress of either component and, from Fig. 10.12(a), it may be seen that this corresponds to a microstructure of well-dispersed, polyurethane particles. Secondly, examination of the extension ratio at fracture, λ_f, indicates that at the composition of about 75 % w/w polyacrylate, at which the maximum σ_f value results, the measured λ_f value is substantially above the computed arithmetic mean value. However, at higher polyacrylate levels the value of λ_f decreases rapidly and this may arise from the complete loss of phase continuity with respect to the polyurethane phase.

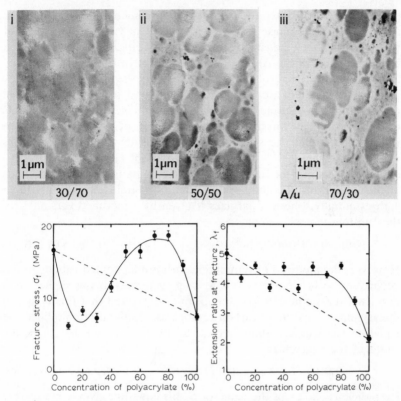

Fig. 10.12. (a) Electron micrographs of interpenetrating polymer networks from mixed and cross-linked polyacrylate and polyurethane lattices. The polyurethane has been stained with osmium tetroxide (i) 30/70; (ii) 50/50; (iii) 70/30 polyacrylate/polyurethane (after Matsuo et al.[118]); and (b) Stress, σ_f, and extension ratio, λ_f, at fracture as a function of composition for the poly-acrylate/polyurethane interpenetrating polymer networks (after Klempner et al.[119]). - - -, Computed arithmetic mean.

Finally, multiphase rubbers, where the second phase is a rigid-particulate filler, need to be considered. These are extremely important materials since in the case of rubbers which are amorphous and contain no second-phase domains energy dissipation will mainly occur via internal friction (Section 10.2) and is therefore only relatively large at temperatures approaching the T_g—this is reflected by their generally poor failure properties. Such rubbers, for example SBR, are therefore nearly always compounded with a rigid, reinforcing filler, usually carbon black, to improve their fracture properties and so make them practically useful materials. Indeed, reinforcement of basically weak amorphous, single-phase rubbers by carbon black is the foundation of the present rubber industry. There are many different types of carbon black available to the compounder and, apart from the obvious variable of concentration of carbon-black filler, the main carbon-black property parameters are surface area, degree of primary aggregation, or 'structure', and surface activity. A detailed discussion of the effects of these variables on the tensile properties of carbon-black filled rubbers is beyond the scope of the present text and the reader is referred elsewhere[24,120-2] for such information. However, a few general comments may be made. Firstly, rigid fillers increase the modulus of the rubber and the equilibrium Young's modulus of a rubber filled with essentially spherical particles is given by a modified version[123] of the Einstein viscosity equation

$$E(\text{filled}) = E(\text{unfilled})(1 + 2 \cdot 5 v_{\text{fp}} + 14 \cdot 1 v_{\text{fp}}^2) \qquad (\dot{e}, e \to 0) \quad (10.31)$$

However, the modulus of reinforcing carbon-black filled rubbers often depart seriously from this relationship, generally being higher than predicted from eqn. (10.31), and Guth[123] suggested that this is due to the asymmetric nature of carbon aggregates. He therefore modified the equation to include a shape factor, S, the ratio of the length to the width of the aggregates

$$E(\text{filled}) = E(\text{unfilled})(1 + 0 \cdot 67 S v_{\text{fp}} + 1 \cdot 62 S^2 v_{\text{fp}}^2) \qquad (10.32)$$

By judicious choice of the value of S this equation gives a reasonable representation but it has been noted[123] that in some instances a shape factor has to be used which bears little resemblance to that determined from electron microscopy studies of the aggregate structure. These observations may be attributed[124] to the structure of the carbon black which results in occlusion of part of the rubber within the interstices of the aggregates. The occluded rubber is shielded from deformation and thus acts as a filler. Secondly, considering the tensile failure properties, then when the carbon-black loading is varied the hysteresis increases continuously with increasing filler concentration, but σ_f and λ_f pass through maxima. This may reflect physical interference between neighbouring particles as the concentration becomes sufficiently high.[121] If the concentration of carbon black is held constant and the specific surface area (as measured by nitrogen absorption) of the black is steadily increased, then the hysteresis, σ_f, and λ_f generally increase.[120,122] However, the effect of the structure and surface affinity of the carbon black upon σ_f and λ_f appears to be secondary to that of surface area, although under some conditions, such as very low or high filler concentrations or high test-temperatures, the value of σ_f has been found[120,122] to increase as the degree of structure or surface affinity increases.

Other rigid fillers besides carbon black are added to rubbers. Some, such as colloidal silica, also act as reinforcing agents[120] and, as a general rule, only the colloidal active fillers, such as fine silica and carbon black, improve the overall fracture properties to any significant extent. However, other fillers are sometimes added to achieve a property characteristic of the rubber compound where failure properties may still be important but are really a secondary consideration. For example, ammonium perchlorate is added to polyurethane elastomers to act as the oxidiser in rocket propellants. To obtain the optimum failure properties from such filler rubbers interest has focussed upon the filler–rubber interface with the prevention of filler debonding, or 'dewetting' (Section 10.3.2), being of primary concern.[27,43,44,82,125-34] The influence of filler–rubber adhesion has recently been studied by Dreyfuss et al.[82] who have conducted some interesting experiments on model filled rubbers consisting of polybutadiene with glass beads incorporated. The glass beads were pretreated with various polysiloxanes, some of which could form covalent bonds with the polybutadiene matrix during free-radical cross-linking of the latter and some of which could not. Addition of glass beads ($v_{fp} = 0 \cdot 16$, $r_p = 75 \ \mu$m) increased the value of G_c from about $0 \cdot 4$ to $0 \cdot 5$ kJ m^{-2} and this effect was independent of the degree of interfacial bonding and was attributed to an increased roughness of the fracture path in the glass-filled rubbers. The value of λ_f always decreased upon the addition of the glass and was also independent of the degree of bonding. However, the fracture stress, σ_f, was increased when the degree of interfacial bonding was high but decreased when it was low. Such complex interrelationships are difficult to understand and predict, especially since no quantitative assessment of the degree of interfacial bonding is readily available.

10.5.6 Theories of Tensile Failure

A number of theories have been advanced to predict the uniaxial tensile failure of rubber and explain the observed dependence of the fracture properties upon such factors as degree of cross-linking and test rate and temperature. Some of the theories attempt to relate the fracture stress, σ_f, to purely molecular parameters whilst others appeal also to continuum approaches, using either fracture mechanics or viscoelasticity concepts.

10.5.6.1 Fracture Mechanics Approach

Greensmith[135] has adopted a standard fracture mechanics approach and assumed that failure occurs by growth of a crack from some imperfection in the material which may be considered, in terms of stress-concentrating power, as being equivalent to a small intrinsic crack. Hence tensile failure is assumed to be solely controlled by the crack propagation behaviour.

If a tensile test conducted at a constant rate of extension, $\dot{y}$, is considered, then the extension ratio is given by

$$\lambda_0 - 1 = \dot{y}t \tag{10.33}$$

The applied strain-energy density, W_0, was assumed to be related by

$$W_0 = k_8(\lambda_0 - 1)^{\ell} \tag{10.34}$$

where k_8 and ℓ are fitting constants. Combining eqns (10.33) and (10.34) then, at fracture

$$W_f \approx k_8(\dot{y}t_f)^{\ell} \tag{10.35}$$

where t_f is the time-to-failure. Greensmith then essentially combined eqns (3.22), (10.23) and (10.35) which, upon integration, yielded

$$t_f = \frac{(\ell q + 1)[1 - (2k_1 a_0 W_f/G_c)^{q-1}]}{D_f(q-1)(2k_1)^q W_f^q a_0^{q-1}} \tag{10.36}$$

where a_0 is the length of any inserted crack or, in the absence of any artificially inserted crack, the intrinsic flaw size (Section 10.3.3) and the value of G_c was taken as that value at which the crack velocity increased rapidly. Greensmith[135] found reasonable agreement between experimental and theoretical determinations of t_f as a function of W_f for SBR, obtained over a wide range of rates of extension. However, problems do arise when using eqn. (10.36), especially with respect to assigning a particular value to G_c at which the crack velocity may be assumed to rise very rapidly, as may be appreciated by reference to Figs 10.7(a) and 10.8.

10.5.6.2 Molecular Approach

Over the last twenty-five years or so several theories[136-40] have attempted to relate the tensile properties of rubbers to molecular parameters.

Taylor & Darin[136] have proposed that the stress in the specimen at rupture will be borne mainly by those chains which are orientated in the direction of extension and nearly at their ultimate elongation. The fracture stress, σ_f, is therefore proportional to the number of effective chains per unit volume, ν_{ef}, which are orientated within some small angle, θ_f, of the direction of extension. Thus, as cross-linking initially increases the value of ν_{ef} increases and so does σ_f. However, the extension ratio at fracture, λ_f, steadily decreases with increasing ν_{ef} and this results in fewer chains being orientated along the axis of strain at the instant of fracture. These features combine to cause a maximum in the relation between σ_f and degree of cross-linking and were embodied mathematically in the relation

$$\sigma_f = \frac{k_9}{\bar{M}}\left[\frac{\bar{M}}{\bar{M}_c} - 1\right][1 - (1 + \theta_f^2 \lambda_f^2)^{-\frac{1}{2}}] \qquad (10.37)$$

where k_9 is a proportionality constant, $\bar{M}$ is the initial molar mass and $\bar{M}_c$ is the molar mass between cross-links. An experimental relation between σ_f and $\bar{M}_c$ for SBR is shown in Fig. 10.13 together with the theoretical predictions from eqn. (10.37). The agreement is good but it should be noted that values of the constants k_9 and θ_f were obtained by fitting to the data and values of λ_f were experimentally measured. Taylor & Darin[136] extended their theory by relating λ_f to the number of links per network chain, and developing a modified equation for crystallising rubbers. This modification assumed that the effect of crystallisation was to increase the number of network chains per unit volume orientated at a given angle to the direction of extension. Temperature- and rate-dependence were only briefly considered but the values of both k_9 and λ_f varied with these parameters.

A. M. Bueche[137] has proposed a theory which relates the stored energy at rupture to the form of the stress/strain curve, the degree of cross-linking and the activation energy for fracture of network chains. He considered the rupture of network chains to be governed by an activated-rate process (Chapter 2) and derived an expression for the rate of bond rupture which included the configurational entropy change on deformation in the free-energy of activation. The theory was in good agreement with experimental results obtained on

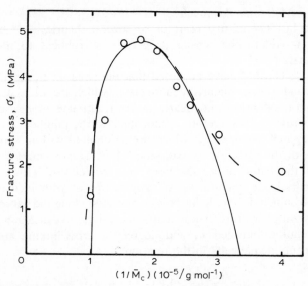

Fig. 10.13. Tensile fracture stress, σ_f, as a function of degree of cross-linking for SBR. Points experimental, dashed curve Taylor & Darin's theory, solid curve F. Bueche's theory (after Taylor & Darin[136] and F. Bueche[139]).

poly(dimethylsiloxane) rubbers but values from the measured stress/strain curve are needed and, by ignoring the actual molecular details of the failure process, it casts little light upon the molecular mechanisms involved.

It is generally considered that F. Bueche[138-41] has proposed the most realistic molecular theory. He also considered the probability of the rupture of one network chain placing sufficient stress upon neighbouring chains to cause a runaway sequence of fracture. However, he also took into account the wide variation in the number of links per chain that would be expected in a typical cross-linked rubber. From rather complex computations it was demonstrated that the effect of this uneven distribution of stress became more serious at high degrees of cross-linking than at low degrees of cross-linking. As a result, the number of highly stressed chains increases as the degree of cross-linking increases and as the number of very highly stressed chains increases then rupture will occur more readily. Thus, the conclusion was that too high a degree of cross-linking could be deleterious since it results in wide variations in stress applied to the network chains. The theoretical predictions from F. Bueche's analysis are shown in Fig. 10.13 and the agreement is satisfactory in the region of the maximum but is poor at high degrees of cross-linking. The theory was extended to take into account the effects of crystallisation and reinforcing fillers by assuming that the presence of crystallites or particles decreased the additional force placed upon neighbours when a chain ruptures.

10.5.6.3 Viscoelastic Approach

Bueche & Halpin[142] and Halpin[143] have combined aspects of the molecular theories with the material's viscoelastic behaviour. In their model tensile creep failure is considered. Obviously, with increasing time the specimen as a whole extends under the applied stress and the viscoelastic response is described quantitatively by the creep curve for the material. Simultaneously, small cracks are assumed to be initiated and begin to grow. The growth of the crack is then viewed as a simple process which involves the molecular chains at the crack tip stretching viscoelastically under the influence of a high stress concentration until they rupture. The failure criterion advanced was based upon the attainment of a critical strain. Thus, the failure mechanism is a non-equilibrium process, developing with time and involving the consecutive rupture of the molecular chains. However, as it is largely controlled by the viscoelastic response of the rubber it may be described in terms of the creep curve. As the cracks grow a point is eventually reached when the specimen as a whole ruptures. Bueche & Halpin derived a theoretical relation for the failure envelope (Section 10.5.2) from a knowledge of the creep behaviour of the rubber together with a phenomenological description of the form of the stress/strain curve. Theoretical and experimental failure envelopes for SBR and ethylene–propylene rubber were in good agreement. Subsequent papers extended the model to include[144] the effects of reinforcing filler particles and to predict[145] the statistical variability of the fracture data by using a Poisson distribution.

As Andrews[146] has commented, this approach aims to calculate from first principles what Greensmith's[135] approach takes as empirically given—the rate of crack propagation as a function of stress, temperature and rate. The relations derived by Mueller & Knauss[46,47] may be viewed as intermediate between these two approaches (see Section 10.4.2, eqn. (10.19)).

10.6 CONCLUDING REMARKS

From the above discussion it is evident that the current understanding of the mechanics and mechanisms of fracture in rubber is highly advanced in some areas but most limited in others. For example, the early recognition of the importance of crack propagation mechanisms led to the mechanics being mathematically described about thirty years ago, and being the subject of almost continuous development since. On the other hand, our knowledge of how intrinsic flaws are initiated, and hence how to limit their size and number, is minimal.

Other important areas which warrant further investigation include the detailed identification of the mechanisms involved in energy dissipation, especially in filled rubbers, and of the relationships between energy dissipation and fracture behaviour. The broad relationship between the two has been a recurring theme in the present chapter; high hysteresis appears to be a necessary, although not the sole, requirement for high strength and crack resistance. Also, it is obviously advantageous if the dissipating mechanisms mainly come into play at high strain levels, so that at low strains the rubber behaves elastically and excessive heat build-up is prevented in low-strain dynamic-fatigue. In such a study of hysteresis it would be of particular interest to investigate the influence of the degree of intrinsic adhesion between filler particles and the rubber matrix, and effect of the stress state, e.g. uniaxial versus triaxial tension.

REFERENCES

1. Treloar, L. R. G. (1958). *The physics of rubber elasticity*, Oxford University Press, London.
2. Gent, A. N. (1972). In: *Fracture, an advanced treatise, Vol. 7*, Ed. by H. Liebowitz, Academic Press, New York.
3. Eirich, F. R. & Smith, T. L. (1972). In: *Fracture, an advanced treatise, Vol. 7*, Ed. by H. Liebowitz, Academic Press, New York, p. 612.
4. Gent, A. N. (1978). In: *Science and technology of rubber*, Ed. by F. R. Eirich, Academic Press, New York, p. 419.
5. Fukahori, Y. & Andrews, E. H. (1978). *J. Mater. Sci.*, **13**, 777.
6. Harwood, J. A. C., Mullins, L. & Payne, A. R. (1965). *J. Appl. Polym. Sci.*, **9**, 3011.
7. Payne, A. R. (1974). *J. Polym. Sci. Sympos.*, **48**, 169.
8. Harwood, J. A. C., Mullins, L. & Payne, A. R. (1967). *J. Inst. Rubber Ind.*, **1**, 17.

9. Williams, M. L., Landel, R. F. & Ferry, J. D. (1955). *J. Amer. Chem. Soc.*, **77**, 3701.
10. Aklonis, J. J., Macknight, W. J. & Shea, M. (1972). *Introduction to polymer viscoelasticity*, Interscience, New York, p. 49.
11. Ferry, J. D. (1970). *Viscoelastic properties of polymers*, John Wiley, New York, p. 314.
12. Doolittle, A. K. (1951). *J. Appl. Phys.*, **22**, 1471.
13. Doolittle, A. K. (1952). *J. Appl. Phys.*, **23**, 236.
14. Mullins, L. (1947). *J. Rubber. Res.*, **16**, 275.
15. Mullins, L. (1950). *J. Phys. Colloid Chem.*, **54**, 239.
16. Blanchard, A. F. & Parkinson, D. (1952). *Ind. Eng. Chem.*, **44**, 799.
17. Bueche, F. (1960). *J. Appl. Polym. Sci.*, **4**, 107.
18. Bueche, F. (1962). *J. Appl. Polym. Sci.*, **6**, 271.
19. Mullins, L. & Tobin, N. R. (1965). *J. Appl. Polym. Sci.*, **9**, 2993.
20. Harwood, J. A. C. & Payne, A. R. (1966). *J. Appl. Polym. Sci.*, **10**, 1203.
21. Harwood, J. A. C. & Payne, A. R. (1966). *J. Appl. Polym. Sci.*, **10**, 315.
22. Payne, A. R. (1974). *J. Polym. Sci. C.*, **48**, 169.
23. Dannenberg, E. M. (1966). *Trans. Inst. Rubber Ind.*, **42**, T26.
24. Dannenberg, E. M. (1975). *Rubb. Chem. Technol.*, **48**, 410.
25. Radok, J. R. M. & Tai, C. L. (1962). *J. Appl. Polym. Sci.*, **6**, 518.
26. Gent, A. N. (1974). *J. Appl. Polym. Sci.*, **18**, 1397.
27. Gent, A. N. (1980). *J. Mater. Sci.*, **15**, 2884.
28. West, J. C. & Cooper, S. L. (1978). In: *Science and technology of rubber*, Ed. by F. R. Eirich, Academic Press, New York, p. 531.
29. Allport, D. C. & Janes, W. H. (1973). *Block copolymers*, Applied Science Publishers Ltd., London.
30. Sperling, L. H. (1981). *Interpenetrating polymer networks and related materials*, Plenum Press, New York.
31. Smith, T. L. (1974). *J. Polym. Sci., Polym. Phys. Ed.*, **12**, 1825.
32. Gent, A. N. & Hamed, G. R. (1978). *Plast. Rubber Mat. Appl.*, **3**, 17.
33. Andrews, E. H. & Fukahori, Y. (1977). *J. Mater. Sci.*, **12**, 1307.
34. Eldred, R. J. (1972). *J. Polym. Sci.*, **B10**, 321.
35. Stein, R. S. (1969). *J. Polym. Sci.*, **B7**, 657.
36. Gent, A. N. & Lindley, P. B. (1959). *Proc. Roy. Soc.*, **A249**, 195.
37. Lindsey, G. H. (1967). *J. Appl. Phys.*, **38**, 4843.
38. Dencouer, R. L. & Gent, A. N. (1968). *J. Polym. Sci. A2*, **6**, 1853.
39. Gent, A. N. & Tompkins, D. A. (1969). *J. Appl. Phys.*, **40**, 2520.
40. Gent, A. N. & Tompkins, D. A. (1969). *J. Polym. Sci. A2*, **7**, 1483.
41. Williams, M. L. & Schapery, R. A. (1965). *Intern. J. Fract. Mechs.*, **1**, 64.
42. Nicholson, D. W. (1979). *J. Adhesion*, **10**, 255.
43. Oberth, A. E. & Bruenner, R. S. (1965). *Trans. Soc. Rheol.*, **9**, 165.
44. Oberth, A. E. (1967). *Rubber Chem. Technol.*, **40**, 1337.
45. Lake, G. J. & Lindley, P. B. (1965). *J. Appl. Polym. Sci.*, **9**, 1233.
46. Mueller, H. K. & Knauss, W. G. (1971). *Trans. Soc. Rheol.*, **15**, 217.
47. Mueller, H. K. & Knauss, W. G. (1971). *Trans. A.S.M.E.*, **38**(E2), 483.
48. Ahagon, A. & Gent, A. N. (1975). *J. Polym. Sci., Polym. Phys. Ed.*, **13**, 1903.
49. Lake, G. J. & Thomas, A. G. (1967). *Proc. Roy. Soc.*, **A300**, 108.

50. DeVries, K. L., Simonson, E. R. & Williams, M. L. (1970). *J. Appl. Polym. Sci.*, **14**, 3049.
51. DeVries, K. L., Simonson, E. R. & Williams, M. L. (1970). *J. Macromol. Sci. Phys.*, **B4**(3), 671.
52. DeVries, K. L., Moore, N. B. & Williams, M. L. (1972). *J. Appl. Polym. Sci.*, **16**, 1377.
53. Braden, M. & Gent, A. N. (1960). *J. Appl. Polym. Sci.*, **3**, 100.
54. Lake, G. J. & Lindley, P. B. (1965). *J. Appl. Polym. Sci.*, **9**, 2031.
55. Gent, A. N. & McGrath, J. E. (1965). *J. Polym. Sci. A*, **3**, 1473.
56. Gent, A. N. & Kinloch, A. J. (1971). *J. Polym. Sci. A2*, **9**, 659.
57. Andrews, E. H. & Kinloch, A. J. (1973). *Proc. R. Soc.*, **A332**, 385.
58. Andrews, E. H. & Kinloch, A. J. (1973). *Proc. R. Soc.*, **A332**, 401.
59. Andrews, E. H. & Kinloch, A. J. (1974). *J. Polym. Sci. Sympos.*, **46**, 1.
60. Kinloch, A. J. & Shaw, S. J. (1981). In: *Developments in adhesives—2*, Ed. by A. J. Kinloch, Applied Science Publishers Ltd., London, p. 83.
61. Andrews, E. H. (1961). *Proc. Phys. Soc.*, **77**, 483.
62. Andrews, E. H. (1963). *J. Mech. Phys. Solids*, **11**, 231.
63. Andrews, E. H. (1968). *Fracture in polymers*, Oliver and Boyd, London, p. 151.
64. Martinson, R. H., Hartog, J. H. & Knollman, G. C. *Expt. Mech.*, to be published.
65. Thomas, A. G. (1955). *J. Polym. Sci.*, **18**, 177.
66. Greensmith, H. W. (1960). *J. Appl. Polym. Sci.*, **3**, 183.
67. Greensmith, H. W. & Thomas, A. G. (1955). *J. Polym. Sci.*, **18**, 189.
68. Greensmith, H. W., Mullins, L. & Thomas, A. G. (1960). *Trans. Soc. Rheol.*, **4**, 179.
69. Greensmith, H. W. (1956). *J. Polym. Sci.*, **21**, 175.
70. Gent, A. N. & Henry, A. W. (1967). *Proc. Int. Rubb. Conf.*, Brighton, England, 193.
71. Bennett, S. J., Anderson, G. P. & Williams, M. L. (1970). *J. Appl. Polym. Sci.*, **14**, 735.
72. Mullins, L. (1959). *Inst. Rubb. Ind. Trans.*, **35**, 213.
73. Andrews, E. H. (1974). *J. Mater. Sci.*, **9**, 887.
74. Gent, A. N. & Hamed, G. R. (1978). *Plastic and Rubber: Mater. Applications*, **3**, 17.
75. Bascom, W. D., Cottington, R. L., Jones, R. L. & Peyser, P. (1975). *J. Appl. Polym. Sci.*, **19**, 2545.
76. Kinloch, A. J. & Shaw, S. J. (1981). *J. Adhesion*, **12**, 59.
77. Kadir, A. & Thomas, A. G. (1972). In: *Elastomers: criteria for engineering design*, Ed. by C. Hepburn & R. J. W. Reynolds, Applied Science Publishers Ltd., London, p. 67.
78. Andrews, E. H. (1961). *J. Appl. Phys.*, **32**, 542.
79. Thomas, A. G. (1958). *J. Polym. Sci.*, **31**, 467.
80. Lake, G. J. & Lindley, P. B. (1966). *Physical basis of yield and fracture*, Physics Inst., London, p. 176.
81. Gent, A. N., Lindley, P. B. & Thomas, A. G. (1964). *J. Appl. Polym. Sci.*, **8**, 455.
82. Dreyfuss, P., Gent, A. N. & Williams, J. R. (1980). *J. Polym. Sci., Polym. Phys. Ed.*, **18**, 2135.

83. Smith, T. L. & Rinde, J. A. (1969). *J. Polym. Sci. A-2*, **7**, 675.
84. Dickie, R. A. & Smith, T. L. (1969). *J. Polym. Sci. A-2*, **7**, 687.
85. Treloar, L. R. G. (1958). *Physics of rubber elasticity*, Oxford University Press, London, p. 88.
86. Knauss, W. G. (1967). *Int. J. Fract. Mechs.*, **3**, 267.
87. Jones, T. M. & Kruse, R. B. (1966). *J. Spacecraft and Rockets*, **3**, 265.
88. Smith, T. L. (1958). *J. Polym. Sci.*, **32**, 99.
89. Greensmith, H. W., Mullins, L. & Thomas, A. G. (1963). In: *The chemistry and physics of rubber-like substances*, Ed. by L. Bateman, Maclaren, London, p. 249.
90. Boonstra, B. S. (1949). *India Rubber World*, **121**, 299.
91. Thomas, A. G. & Whittle, J. M. (1970). *Rubb. Chem. Technol.*, **43**, 222.
92. Villars, D. S. (1950). *J. Appl. Phys.*, **21**, 565.
93. Smith, T. L. (1963). *J. Polym. Sci. A*, **1**, 3597.
94. Smith, T. L. (1964). *J. Appl. Phys.*, **35**, 27.
95. Smith, T. L. (1965). *Polym. Eng. Sci.*, **5**, 270.
96. Flory, P. J. (1953). *Principles of polymer chemistry*, Cornell Univ. Press, New York.
97. Bateman, L., Moore, C. G., Porter, M. & Saville, B. (1963). In: *The chemistry and physics of rubber-like substances*, Ed. by L. Bateman, Maclaren, London, p. 449.
98. Taylor, G. & Darin, S. R. (1955). *J. Polym. Sci.*, **17**, 511.
99. Bueche, F. & Dadek, T. (1963). *Rubb. Chem. Technol.*, **36**, 1.
100. Bateman, L., Cunneen, J. I., Moore, C. G., Mullins, L. & Thomas, A. G. (1963). In: *The chemistry and physics of rubber-like substances*, Ed. by L. Bateman, Maclaren, London, p. 715.
101. Smith, T. L. & Chu, W. H. (1972). *J. Polym. Sci. A-2*, **10**, 133.
102. Smith, T. L. (1969). In: *Rheology, Vol. 5*, Ed. by F. R. Eirich, Academic Press, New York, p. 127.
103. Tobolsky, A. V. & Lyons, P. F. (1968). *J. Polym. Sci. A2*, **6**, 1561.
104. Landel, R. F. & Fedors, R. F. (1963). *J. Polym. Sci. B*, **1**, 539.
105. Plazek, D. J. (1966). *J. Polym. Sci. A-2*, **4**, 745.
106. Fedors, R. F. & Landel, R. F. (1975). *J. Polym. Sci., Polym. Phys. Ed.*, **13**, 419.
107. Fedors, R. F. (1975). *J. Appl. Polym. Sci.*, **19**, 787.
108. Harwood, J. A. C. & Payne, A. R. (1968). *J. Appl. Polym. Sci.*, **12**, 889.
109. Grosch, K. A., Harwood, J. A. C. & Payne, A. R. (1966). *Physical basis of yield and fracture*, Physics Inst., London, p. 144.
110. Fetters, L. J. (1969). *J. Polym. Sci. C*, **26**, 1.
111. Smith, T. L. & Dickie, R. A. (1969). *J. Polym. Sci. C*, **26**, 163.
112. Smith, T. L. (1970). In: *Block copolymers*, Ed. by S. L. Aggarwal, Plenum Press, New York, p. 137.
113. Beecher, J. F., Marker, L., Bradford, R. D. & Aggarwal, S. L. (1969). *J. Polym. Sci. C*, **26**, 117.
114. Folkes, M. J. & Keller, A. (1973). In: *Physics of glassy polymers*, Ed. by R. N. Haward, Applied Science Publishers Ltd., London.
115. Dlugosz, J., Keller, A. & Pedemmte, E. (1970). *Kolloid Zu. z. Polym.*, **242**, 1125.
116. Folkes, M. J. & Keller, A. (1971). *Polymer*, **12**, 222.

117. Smith, T. L. (1974). *J. Polym. Sci., Polym. Phys. Ed.*, **12,** 1825.
118. Matsuo, M., Kwei, T. K., Klempner, D. & Frisch, H. L. (1970). *Polym. Eng. Sci.*, **10,** 327.
119. Klempner, D., Frisch, H. L. & Krisch, K. C. (1970). *J. Polym. Sci. A2,* **8,** 921.
120. Kraus, G. K. (1978). In: *Science and technology of rubber*, Ed. by F. R. Eirich, Academic Press, New York, p. 339.
121. Mullins, L. (1963). In: *The chemistry and physics of rubber-like substances*, Ed. by L. Bateman, Maclaren, London, p. 301.
122. Sambrook, R. W. (1970). *J. I.R.I.*, **4**(5), 210.
123. Guth, E. (1945). *J. Appl. Phys.*, **16,** 20.
124. Medalia, A. I. (1970). *J. Coll. Interf. Sci.*, **32,** 115.
125. Farris, R. J. (1964). *J. Appl. Polym. Sci.*, **8,** 25.
126. Lepie, A. & Adicoff, A. (1972). *J. Appl. Polym. Sci.*, **16,** 1155.
127. Blackley, D. C. & Sheikh, M. W. (1973). *Br. Polym. J.*, **5,** 285.
128. Blackley, D. C. & Sheikh, M. W. (1973). *Br. Polym. J.*, **5,** 297.
129. Granatstein, D. L. & Williams, H. L. (1974). *J. Appl. Polym. Sci.*, **18,** 1.
130. Martin, C. & Williams, A. L. (1974). *J. Appl. Polym. Sci.*, **18,** 21.
131. Knollman, G. C., Martinson, R. H. & Bellin, J. L. (1979). *J. Appl. Phys.*, **50,** 111.
132. Knollman, G. C. & Martinson, R. H. (1979). *J. Appl. Phys.*, **50,** 8034.
133. Knollman, G. C., Martinson, R. H. & Bellin, J. L. (1980). *J. Appl. Phys.*, **51,** 3164.
134. Diamont, Y. & Folman, M. (1979). *Polymer*, **20,** 1025.
135. Greensmith, H. W. (1964). *J. Appl. Polym. Sci.*, **8,** 1113.
136. Taylor, G. R. & Darin, S. R. (1955). *J. Polym. Sci.*, **17,** 511.
137. Bueche, A. M. (1956). *J. Polym. Sci.*, **19,** 275.
138. Bueche, F. (1955). *J. Appl. Phys.*, **26,** 1133.
139. Bueche, F. (1957). *J. Polym. Sci.*, **24,** 189.
140. Bueche, F. (1959). *Rubb. Chem. Technol.*, **32,** 1269.
141. Bueche, F. & Dudek, T. (1963). *Rubb. Chem. Technol.*, **36,** 1.
142. Bueche, F. & Halpin, J. C. (1964). *J. Appl. Phys.*, **35,** 36.
143. Halpin, J. C. (1964). *J. Appl. Phys.*, **35,** 3133.
144. Halpin, J. C. & Bueche, F. (1964). *J. Appl. Phys.*, **35,** 3142.
145. Halpin, J. C. & Polley, H. W. (1967). *J. Composite Mater.*, **1,** 64.
146. Andrews, E. H. (1969). *Fracture in polymers*, Oliver and Boyd, London, p. 158.

Chapter 11

Toughened Multiphase Plastics

11.1 INTRODUCTION

It is evident from the preceding chapters that many plastics, particularly glassy polymers, are susceptible to brittle fracture. This is because although energy absorbing processes such as crazing or shear yielding mechanisms operate in these polymers they do so only in highly localised regions around the crack tip. This arises from strain softening and geometric considerations, as discussed in Chapters 4 and 5. Thus, while these mechanisms involve large plastic strains and considerable local energy absorption by the material, the fact that they are confined to a very small volume compared to the size of the specimen means that the total amount of plastic energy absorbed is low.

To increase the toughness it is therefore necessary to ensure that the volume in which these or other energy dissipating mechanisms occur is sufficiently large whilst at the same time limiting the growth and breakdown of voids and crazes to prevent premature crack initiation.

In the case of shear yielding, the ductile tearing mode of crack extension in single-phase polymers is an example where this requirement is met, as discussed in Section 4.5.1. However, it is not always possible to attain the conditions necessary for this type of crack growth whilst maintaining other desirable properties. For example, plasticisation of a glassy polymer by a low-molar-mass liquid may lower the material's yield stress, and so promote ductile fracture, but the plasticised polymer will have a greatly reduced modulus and glass transition temperature.

An alternative approach is to initiate *localised* energy absorbing

421

mechanisms, such as crazing and shear yielding, but from *many* sites, rather than a few isolated ones, so that a much greater volume of the polymer is involved than solely that encompassed by the immediate crack tip. This multiple-deformation mechanism has been most successfully achieved by the incorporation of a second phase of dispersed rubbery particles into the matrix polymer and several recent good reviews[1-5] have been concerned with the general science and technology of such rubber-toughened polymers. The most well-known examples of this class of materials are high-impact polystyrene (HIPS) and acrylonitrile–butadiene–styrene copolymer (ABS) and both of these rubber-modified polymers possess greatly improved toughness compared to the unmodified polystyrene and styrene–acrylonitrile copolymer, respectively. Other plastics which have been toughened using this technology include PVC, PMMA, polypropylene, polycarbonate, poly(phenylene oxide), nylons and, most recently, thermosetting resins such as epoxies, polyimides and polyesters. The improvement in toughness that may be achieved in such multiphase polymers without significant loss in other important properties is illustrated in Table 11.1 where a rubber-modified epoxy resin is compared to the unmodified material.

However, multiple-deformation mechanisms are not only observed in polymers where the particulate second phase is rubbery in character. Other toughened polymers have been developed where the second phase is a rigid-particulate filler, such as glass beads or silica.[7] These low-cost particulate fillers are usually added to polymers for reasons of

TABLE 11.1

PROPERTIES OF AN UNMODIFIED AND RUBBER-MODIFIED EPOXY MATERIAL[6]

	Unmodified epoxy	Rubber-modified epoxy
Added rubber content	—	5 phr
Rubber particle size (μm)	—	Bimodal: <1 μm and 1–5 μm
Heat distortion temperature (°C)	83	83
Fracture stress (MPa)	66	64
Fracture strain (%)	4·8	9·0
Young's modulus (GPa)	2·8	2·7
Fracture energy (kJ m^{-2})	0·2	5–8
Izod impact strength (J m^{-1} of notch)	0·7	3·5

economy and improvement in moulding characteristics but they may also be effective in increasing the toughness of the more brittle polymers. Hence, they have been used to improve the fracture properties of thermosetting polymers like epoxy and polyester resins. Unfortunately, when rigid-particulate fillers are introduced into relatively tough polymers, such as poly(phenylene oxide) and nylon 6.6, they invariably tend to *decrease* the toughness and the overall mechanical properties of the material. Even in the case of thermosetting polymers, the incorporation of a second rubbery phase is usually the more effective method for improving toughness.

The inclusion of short fibres of glass or carbon, for example, into plastics may also increase their toughness but such fibre-composite materials will not be considered here and the reader is referred elsewhere[7] for details.

In the present chapter the main energy dissipating mechanisms that have been observed to contribute to the enhanced crack resistance of multiphase toughened polymers will first be considered. This will form a basis for a discussion of their failure properties.

11.2 MECHANISMS OF TOUGHENING

11.2.1 Particle Deformation

The earliest theory of the mechanism of toughening in rubber-modified plastics was that of Merz *et al.*[8] proposed in 1956. They observed that in HIPS an increase in volume and a marked increase in whiteness or opacity accompanied elongation of the material and they concluded that these phenomena were associated with the production of a multiplicity of tiny cracks. They suggested that the function of the rubber particles was to bridge the cracks and so prevent the cracks growing to a catastrophic size. The energy absorbed in fracture was attributed to the sum of the energy to fracture the glassy matrix and the work to break the rubber particles. Newman & Strella[9] have calculated, however, that the total amount of deformational energy associated with the rubbery phase cannot account for more than a small fraction of the observed enhanced impact energies and subsequent studies (Section 11.2.3) have conclusively shown that the microcracks are actually crazes.

Nevertheless, more recently Beaumont and co-workers[10,11] have again proposed a toughening mechanism which emphasises the role of deformation and fracture of the rubber particles. From studies on rubber-modified epoxies they suggested a similar model to Merz et al.[8] Essentially, the rubber particles are considered to bridge a crack as it propagates through the material and the increase in toughness of the multiphase polymer may be identified with the amount of elastic energy stored in the rubber particles during stretching which is dissipated irreversibly when the particles rupture. Beaumont and co-workers[10,11] developed a quantitative model where the toughness was given by a simple rule of mixtures

$$G_{Ic} = G_{Ic}(\text{matrix})(1 - v_{fp}) + \Delta G_{Ic}(\text{rubber}) \qquad (11.1)$$

where G_{Ic} is the fracture energy of the matrix, v_{fp} is the volume fraction of rubber particles, and $\Delta G_{Ic}(\text{rubber})$ is the toughening contribution from the rubber particles. The term $\Delta G_{Ic}(\text{rubber})$ was expressed as a function of the extension ratio at failure, λ_f, and fracture energy of the rubber particles, $G_{Ic}(\text{rubber})$, from a consideration of the way in which they ruptured. Hence

$$\Delta G_{Ic}(\text{rubber}) = \left(1 - \frac{6}{\lambda_f^2 + \lambda_f + 4}\right) 4 G_{Ic}(\text{rubber}) v_{fp} \qquad (11.2)$$

Now the term in brackets converges towards 1 when $\lambda_f \geq 4$, thus

$$\Delta G_{Ic}(\text{rubber}) = 4 G_{Ic}(\text{rubber}) v_{fp} \qquad (\lambda_f \geq 4) \qquad (11.3)$$

and substituting for $\Delta G_{Ic}(\text{rubber})$ into eqn. (11.1) yields

$$G_{Ic} = G_{Ic}(\text{matrix})(1 - v_{fp}) + 4 G_{Ic}(\text{rubber}) v_{fp} \qquad (\lambda_f \geq 4) \quad (11.4)$$

The experimental results were in approximate agreement with the predictions of eqns (11.2) and (11.4) but the agreement was not sufficiently good to firmly establish the validity of the model. Also, as mentioned above, this mechanism cannot explain the phenomenon of stress whitening observed in most rubber-toughened plastics, including rubber-modified epoxy resins.[12–15]

Thus, whilst ligaments of rubber spanning a crack must reduce the stress concentration at the crack tip and their fracture involves some energy dissipation, it appears that this mechanism is usually only of secondary importance in increasing the toughness of such multiphase polymers. As will be seen from the discussions to follow, it is principally deformation mechanisms in the *matrix*, enhanced by the presence of the second phase, which improve the toughness.

11.2.2 Shear Yielding

As discussed in previous chapters, extensive shear yielding accompanying the fracture process is a major mechanism in many tough single-phase polymers and this mechanism may be greatly enhanced in many otherwise brittle polymers by the presence of a second particulate phase, especially when it is rubbery in character. The initial evidence for the importance of shear yielding mechanisms in multiphase plastics came from mechanical property and optical microscopy studies[9] on certain ABS materials. These studies revealed that in uniaxial tensile tests necking, drawing and orientation-hardening, indicating shear yield deformations, occurred and that the matrix had undergone localised plastic deformation around *virtually every* rubber particle.

The first step in understanding the role of the rubbery particles is to consider the stress field around a particle. Goodier[16] has derived equations for the stresses around an isolated elastic spherical particle embedded in an isotropic elastic matrix which is subjected to an applied uniaxial tensile stress remote from the particle. His equations reveal that for a rubber particle, which typically possesses a considerably lower shear modulus than the matrix, the maximum stress concentration occurs at the equator of the rubber particle and has a value of about $1 \cdot 9$.[3,17] Furthermore, assuming the particle is well bonded to the matrix, this stress is triaxial tension. This essentially arises because of the volume constraint represented by the bulk modulus of the rubber particle which is comparable with that of the matrix. Broutman & Panizza[18] have developed finite-element stress analyses to obtain the stress concentrations around rubber particles when the rubber volume fraction is sufficiently high that the particles' stress fields interact, i.e. for rubber volume fractions greater than about $0 \cdot 09$. In such cases the maximum stress concentration at the particle's equator may be appreciably higher than for the isolated case.

Newman & Strella[9] have suggested that the principal function of the rubber particles is to produce sufficient triaxial tension in the matrix so as to increase the local free volume and hence enable extensive shear yielding and drawing of the matrix to initiate. They recognised that spherical voids, which have a somewhat higher stress concentration at the equator although the stress is only biaxial in this region, could also initiate shear yielding of the matrix. They postulated, however, that rubber particles could also act as crack stoppers thereby offering an alternative explanation to that given in Section 11.1 as to why voids are generally much less effective than rubber particles in toughening plastics.

However, whilst shear yielding is a major mechanism, the detailed micromechanics suggested by Newman & Strella[9] do not appear to be correct. For example, triaxial tension tends to promote crazing rather than shear yielding, as discussed in Chapters 4 and 5. Also, since even highly orientated shear bands possess a relatively low reflectivity, shear yielding alone cannot readily explain the phenomenon of stress whitening, which invariably accompanies the fracture of toughened polymers. However, it is interesting that Petrich[19] has supported Newman & Strella's detailed mechanism and has suggested that a change in the refractive index of the orientated rubber particles by birefringence is the major cause of stress whitening.

The detailed micromechanisms of the shear yield mechanism in rubber-toughened polymers have been identified by Haaf et al.[20] and Donald & Kramer[21] and their studies offer the most convincing explanation for the observed phenomena. Haaf et al. employed electron microscopy, light scattering and optical microscopy techniques to study the deformation mechanisms in rubber-modified PVC. They concluded that the dispersed rubber phase initiated microshear bands at an angle of 55 to 64° to the direction of the applied stress, depending upon the particle size of the modifier in the blends. Like previous workers who have studied shear bands in glassy polymers (see Section 4.3.3), they were unable to explain the deviation of the shear-band angle from 45°, i.e. the plane along which the maximum shear stress operates. Haaf et al.[20] also found that cavities were initiated in the rubber particles and were aligned along the shear bands. This cavitation of the rubber particles obviously explains the stress whitening. These findings led to the suggestion that multiple shear yielding deformations, accompanied by the initiation of cavities, might not be limited to toughened-PVC and they verified that ABS could show similar cavitation, without crazing being involved.

Donald & Kramer[21] have employed transmission electron microscopy to study the deformations in thin films of two ABS polymers possessing different particle size distributions. They found that in the material having small rubber particles of about $0\cdot1$ μm in diameter, crazing was not initiated but shear deformations, promoted by rubber particle cavitation, were the major toughening mechanism. In the material with large particles, about $1\cdot5$ μm in diameter, these larger particles acted as more favourable sites for craze initiation. The reasons for these different mechanisms being initiated by particles of different size will be considered later.

The observation of cavitation in some rubber-toughened polymers, apart from accounting for the stress whitening, also enables an additional explanation for the enhanced shear yielding of the matrix to be proposed.[21,22] The presence of many closely packed particles which can cavitate enables the local build-up of hydrostatic tension produced by localised (constant volume) shear processes to be relieved. Thus, possibly soon after the development of some initial shear yielding, the constrained conditions are relieved and even relatively thick bulk specimens may behave as if the matrix were everywhere under plane-stress conditions. It will be recalled (Sections 3.5 and 4.2.4) that shear yield deformations occur more readily under a biaxial rather than a triaxial stress state and cavitation of the rubber particles therefore favours local shear yield deformations. However, if the matrix does not readily shear but like polystyrene is far more prone to crazing then this mechanism is not available and cavitation and voiding of the rubber particles can only be damaging.

Apart from ABS and rubber-modified PVC, a similar shear yielding mechanism is probably largely responsible for the enhanced toughness of polycarbonate containing a dispersed phase of polyethylene or methacrylate–butadiene–styrene copolymer[23,24] and rubber-modified epoxies.[11–15,25,26]

Finally, it will be recalled that at the beginning of this section it was mentioned that the presence of rigid-particulate fillers, e.g. glass beads, silica, etc., may also cause enhanced shear yielding of the matrix (see, for example, Fig. 11.5). Such rigid particles induce similar tensile stress concentrations in the matrix compared to rubbery particles, but with the maximum stress concentrations being at the poles of the spherical particle in perfectly bonded particles and at the equator in the case of weak or no adhesion at the particle/matrix interface.[16,27–9] Enhanced shear yielding induced by the presence of the rigid particles has therefore been suggested[30] as a major mechanism to account for the improved toughness that may result from the inclusion of rigid particles. However, although both rubbery and rigid particles may induce shear yield deformation in the matrix, there are significant differences in the mechanical behaviour of these different types of multiphase polymer. Essentially, rigid particles are not nearly as effective as rubbery particles in increasing toughness and this may arise from differences in the post-yield behaviour of the respective multiphase polymers; the extent of post-yield deformation of rigid-particulate filled polymers is often extremely limited compared to rubbery-particulate filled polymers. (This may be readily seen by comparing Figs 11.4 and 11.5.) The limited deformation in the case of the former material will limit the energy absorbed by localised shear yield deformations and lead to more ready crack initiation and growth. The differences in post-yield behaviour probably arise because the rubbery particles may have cavitated and so enabled the constraint to be relieved, as described above, or if cavitation does not occur then they can stretch and so stay well-bonded and still sustain imposed loads. On the other hand, rigid-particulate fillers cannot deform sufficiently and will become debonded and thus obviously cannot transmit any applied loads and cannot relieve the constraint either. Thus debonding by rigid particles cannot enhance post-yield deformation of the matrix.

11.2.3 Crazing

From optical microscopy studies on HIPS, Bucknall & Smith[31] have concluded that the function of the rubber particles is to initiate multiple craze growth in the polystyrene matrix. Subsequent studies[32-41] have examined thin sections of various rubber-toughened polymers in the transmission electron microscope, often first staining any unsaturated rubber phase with osmium tetroxide to aid microtoming and increase contrast,[39-41] and such work has clearly confirmed that crazes frequently initiate from the rubber particles.

A typical micrograph of HIPS illustrating this multiple crazing mechanism is shown in Fig. 11.1. It may also be readily observed from this micrograph that in HIPS, as in many rubber-toughened polymers, suitable polymerisation conditions[3] result in the rubber particles containing occlusions of the glassy polymer. Thus, while only about 5-10 wt % of rubber may typically be added, this occluded structure of the rubber particle can increase the rubber phase volume to 20-30%. This structure also has important consequences for the detailed mechanisms of crazing, as discussed below.

Bucknall and co-workers[3,4,42] have proposed that the rubber particles have two separate but equally important functions. Firstly, under an applied tensile stress, crazes are initiated at points of maximum triaxial stress concentrations, which are usually near the equators of the rubber particles as discussed in the preceding section. The crazes then grow approximately normal to the maximum applied stress, although deviations may occur because of interactions between the

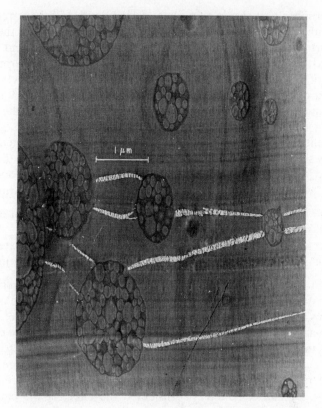

Fig. 11.1. Transmission electron micrograph of a microtomed section of HIPS, stained with osmium tetroxide (after Kambour & Russell[33]).

particles' stress fields. Secondly, the rubber particles are craze terminators, preventing the growth of very large crazes; note that in Fig. 11.1 the crazes run between rubber particles. Poor termination means that large crazes are produced which could act as sites for premature crack initiation and growth. Thus, the result is that a large number of small crazes are generated, in contrast with the small number of large crazes formed in the same polymer in the absence of rubber particles. The multiple crazing that occurs throughout a comparatively large volume of rubber-modified material explains the high energy absorption in fracture tests and the extensive stress whitening which accompanies deformation and failure.

The detailed mechanisms of craze initiation, growth and breakdown around rubber particles in thin films of HIPS and ABS have recently been studied by Donald & Kramer.[21,43,44] In the case of HIPS they[43,44] were particularly concerned with the effects of particle size and structure and relating their mechanistic approach to the experimental observation[36,45,46] that, at a constant rubber phase volume fraction, an optimum particle size of about 2–5 μm may be identified which results in maximum toughness. Donald & Kramer[43] first examined the craze initiation mechanism and found that the ease of initiation is greatly dependent upon particle size and that crazes are rarely nucleated from particles smaller than about 1 μm. Using the Dugdale model (Section 5.3.2) to describe the craze shape and stress distribution, Donald & Kramer[43] proposed that for craze initiation from a rubber particle:

1. The initial elastic stress concentration at the particle must exceed the stress concentration at a static craze tip; and
2. The distance over which this critical stress acts must extend at least three fibril spacings from the particle into the glassy matrix.

Although the stress concentration is independent of particle size the spatial extent of the stress enhancement scales with the particle diameter. Thus, the second condition accounts for the inability of small rubber particles to initiate crazes. This proposal is essentially a critical stress acting over a critical distance and is therefore reminiscent of previous criteria (Section 4.5.2). However, in this instance both parameters may be readily identified with microstructural features. Secondly, Donald & Kramer[44] considered the effect of the particle's internal composition on the tendency for the craze to break down and initiate a crack. They found that only the larger particles contained occlusions of polystyrene whilst the smaller ones tended to be solid rubber. This was important because when crazes formed around the solid rubber particles, either by initiating from them or more likely by intersecting them, then significant lateral contraction accompanied elongation of the particle in the applied stress direction. As this contraction proceeded, debonding at the particle/craze interface resulted and a void was therefore formed. This void grew under increasing load and led to premature craze breakdown and subsequent crack initiation and propagation. In contrast to this behaviour, occluded particles accommodated the displacements due to crazing by local fibrillation of the rubber surrounding each sub-inclusion, without the formation of large voids. Consequently the particles containing glassy inclusions did not act as sites for premature craze breakdown. Donald

& Kramer therefore concluded that the optimum morphology for rubber particles in HIPS would consist of particles: (1) having a size just larger than the critical diameter (to maximise the total particles that initiate crazes); and (2) containing a large number of small polystyrene occlusions each surrounded by a thin layer of rubber (to ensure the size of inherent flaws initiated during crazing is minimised).

It should be noted that other explanations have been advanced to explain the particle size effect. Bucknall[3] has suggested that in order to be effective as craze terminators the rubber particles must be of an adequate size. Alternatively, Argon[47] has examined the stress concentration generated by a particle which will of course be independent of particle size for a homogeneous particle and only slightly dependent upon size for an inhomogeneous particle.[48,49] However, Argon has suggested that additional stress concentrations may arise because the outer shell of the rubber particle is rippled and his model reveals that this effect will be most pronounced for large inhomogeneous particles, which will consequently act as the most efficient craze initiators. Nevertheless, the elegant work of Donald & Kramer appears to currently offer the most convincing explanation.

Whilst crazing has been clearly established as an important toughening mechanism in many rubber-modified polymers, little attention has been directed towards the kinetics and criteria of crack initiation, growth and breakdown in such materials. Oxborough & Bowden[17] have applied their critical strain criterion (Section 5.4.1, eqns (5.7) to (5.9)) to craze initiation from rubber particles in HIPS with reasonable success. However, since they used the Goodier[16] analysis to deduce the stresses around the particles, they had to work with a specimen containing an unrealistically low rubber phase volume fraction to enable the particles to be considered as non-interacting. More recently, Donald & Kramer[43] have proposed the critical-stress/critical-distance criteria discussed above. Craze growth kinetics have been studied in rubber-modified polystyrene by Williams & Marshall[50] who derived a time-dependent Dugdale model (see Section 5.5, eqn. (5.12) and results in Fig. 5.10), and by Argon et al.[51] The latter authors examined polystyrene–polybutadiene block copolymers which had the same polybutadiene content but radically different microstructures from each other, and from that shown by the conventional HIPS (see Fig. 11.1) which is usually produced by grafting styrene onto polybutadiene. One block copolymer had a microstructure that consisted of randomly wavy, and often interconnected, rods of polybutadiene of about 20 nm in diameter surrounded by polystyrene. In this copolymer crazes largely initiated at surface imperfections, rather than from the polybutadiene phase, and grew by the meniscus instability mechanism, which was discussed in Section 5.5 and is shown schematically in Fig. 5.9. In the second copolymer the microstructure consisted of lamellae of polybutadiene, with a thickness of about 20 nm and a large aspect ratio, surrounded by a matrix phase of polystyrene. In this material craze initiation occurred throughout the material and growth resulted by the repeated, stable initiation of microvoids in the polybutadiene phase in a zone ahead of the craze. Argon et al.[51] emphasised that craze growth by this microvoid nucleation mechanism is normally very difficult but is favoured in this particular block copolymer because its microstructure enables a relatively high hydrostatic tensile stress to be developed in the sheet-like and ellipsoidal polybutadiene phase. The practical importance of these different microstructures, yielding different mechanisms and kinetics of crazing, is that they result in the latter block copolymer possessing a far greater fracture strain and toughness.

Finally, it has been suggested[4,27] that multiple crazing may occur when rigid-particulate fillers are used to increase the toughness of brittle polymers. As mentioned in the previous section, under an applied stress such rigid particles do induce tensile stress concentrations in the matrix but may become debonded from the matrix more readily since they are unable to deform to any significant degree. Thus, in the case of a multiple crazing mechanism, the observation that rigid-particulate fillers are not nearly as effective as rubber particles in increasing toughness may be ascribed to the poorer ability of rigid particles to act as effective craze and crack terminators. To act as efficient terminators the second phase has to be adequately bonded and when called upon to perform this function rigid particles may have already become debonded from the matrix.

11.2.4 Simultaneous Shear Yielding and Crazing
It is evident from the above discussions that many toughened polymers may exhibit both shear yielding and crazing and both these mechanisms have been observed, for example, in ABS and rubber-toughened PVC. As a general rule the mechanism which is dominant in the toughened polymer will simply reflect the main mechanism which is operative in the matrix when it is unmodified. Thus, in HIPS crazing is usually the dominant mechanism whilst shear yielding is generally the

major mechanism in rubber-toughened PVC and epoxy resins. However, microstructural features of the toughened polymer, such as particle size, will affect the balance of the mechanisms, as will the rate and temperature of test.

The simultaneous initiation of shear bands and crazes is shown in Fig. 11.2 which is a transmission electron micrograph of a replica of a 50/50 blend of HIPS and poly(2,6-dimethyl-1,4-phenylene oxide) taken from the work of Bucknall et al.[37] The shear bands are formed approximately along planes of maximum resolved shear stress and therefore intersect crazes at an angle of about 45°. These observations led Bucknall and co-workers[3,37,42] to suggest that in addition to increasing the energy absorption, shear bands act as effective craze

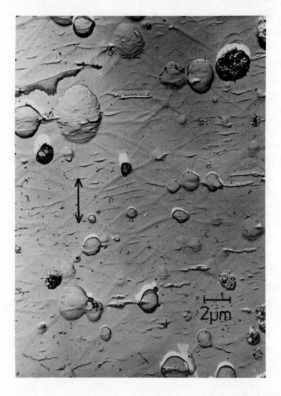

Fig. 11.2. Transmission electron micrograph of a replica of a 50/50 blend of HIPS and poly(2,6-dimethyl-1,4-phenylene oxide). Arrow indicates direction of applied stress (after Bucknall et al.[37]).

terminators for growing crazes. Hence, in those polymers where shear banding occurs in addition to crazing then the necessity for relatively large rubber particles to function as craze terminators is removed and the size of the rubber particle need no longer be increased via sub-inclusions in order to benefit from a given rubber content. Kambour[1] has also advanced this hypothesis and commented that the larger optimum particle size needed in HIPS compared to ABS may partially arise from the absence of shear banding in the former material as a craze-terminating mechanism. However, as is evident from the preceding sections, Donald & Kramer[21,43,44] have rejected these arguments. They question the validity of the assumption that rubber particles or shear bands act as craze terminators and, in any event, do not accept that a large craze is necessarily weaker than a small one, since many crazes grow by surface drawing rather than by fibril creep (Section 5.3.1). They believe that relatively large, occluded particles can effectively initiate and prevent the premature breakdown of crazes whilst smaller rubber particles can only initiate shear bands. Further, as discussed in the previous section, the smaller particles may be composed of solid rubber and when this is the case small particles may even assist craze breakdown, especially if the crazes formed in the matrix are relatively weak. Thus, a complex balance of these factors results in different particle sizes and internal structures being required to obtain maximum toughness from the various rubber-modified polymers.

Finally, it should be noted that various workers[3,4,52-7] have measured volume dilatation during the uniaxial straining of toughened polymers and used the data as a means of identifying the individual contributions from crazing, a dilatational process, and shear yielding, a deviatoric process. However, since in many toughened polymers the formation of voids accompanies both mechanisms[20-3,43,44,58] caution must be exercised in such interpretations. Nevertheless, *providing* the strain remains homogeneous such experiments do enable the volume and area strains as a function of time, at various stress levels, to be deduced. Thus, the kinetics of the dilatational and deviatoric mechanisms may be independently and quantitatively assessed, whatever the intrinsic nature of the dilatational mechanism.

11.2.5 Crack Pinning

In 1971 Lange & Radford[59] reported that the fracture energy of a thermosetting epoxy could be dramatically increased by the inclusion of alumina trihydrate as a rigid-particulate filler but that the degree of toughness enhancement depended upon both the volume fraction and particle size of the filler. They proposed that the process largely responsible for this increased toughness was the crack-pinning mechanism which had been proposed by Lange[60] in 1970.

The increase in fracture energy of a brittle material due to the addition of a brittle second phase was explained by Lange[60] as arising from interactions between the moving crack front and the second-phase dispersion. His evidence for the interactions came from fractographic studies which showed that as a moving crack front interacts with inhomogeneities present in the brittle matrix then tails or steps are formed at the rear of the inclusion due to the meeting of the two arms of the crack front from different fracture planes. The scanning electron micrograph of a fracture surface of glass-filled epoxy,[61,62] shown in Fig. 11.3(a) clearly illustrates this feature. Such evidence led directly to a model which assumes that, as a crack begins to propagate within the material, the crack front bows out between the second-phase dispersion whilst still remaining pinned at all the positions where it has encountered the filler particles. This is shown schematically in Fig. 11.3(b). During this initial stage of crack propagation both a new fracture surface is formed and the length of the crack front is increased due to its change of shape between the pinning positions. The fractional increase in crack-front length per unit crack extension will depend upon the particle spacing. Now energy is not only required to create new fracture surface but, by analogy with the theory of dislocations, energy must also be supplied to the newly formed length of crack front which is assumed to possess a line energy. Lange[60] proposed that when the bowed crack front attains a radius of $d_p/2$, where d_p is the interparticle distance, it breaks away from the pinning positions and creates the characteristic tails or steps. Using this model and crack-growth criterion Lange derived the following expression

$$G_{Ic} = G_{Ic}(\text{matrix}) + 2\frac{T_L}{d_p} \qquad (11.5)$$

where G_{Ic} is the fracture energy of the filled material, $G_{Ic}(\text{matrix})$ is that of the unfilled matrix and T_L is the line energy per unit length of the crack front. This relationship obviously predicts that the fracture energy of the particulate composite will increase as the particle spacing decreases. However, Lange[60] has shown that the spacing between the filler particles must be many times smaller than the initial crack front

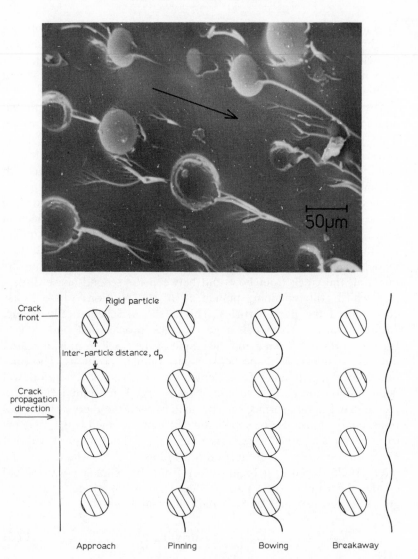

Fig. 11.3. (a) Scanning electron micrograph of a fracture surface of an epoxy resin containing spherical glass particles showing the 'tails' behind the particles. Arrow indicates direction of crack propagation (courtesy of Mr D. Maxwell); and (b) Schematic representation of the crack-pinning mechanism (after Phillips & Harris[7]).

length in order for the crack-pinning mechanism to be effective in increasing the fracture energy.

Several workers[59,63-7] have extended this original hypothesis of Lange. As mentioned earlier, a maximum in G_{Ic} is frequently found with increasing volume fraction of filler and Lange & Radford[59] concluded that the filler particles could become too close for effective crack-front interaction by bowing to occur. Also, the particle size has been found[59,63] to affect the value of the line energy, T_L, which is not in accord with eqn. (11.5). Hence, in a subsequent paper Lange[63] proposed a suitable modification to this equation which described the observation that the larger the pinning particle then the more effective it is in pinning the crack front and allowing it to bow and increase in length before breaking away. Evans[64] has carried out a more detailed calculation of T_L and confirmed that the line energy contribution depends upon both the particle size and shaping. He also reported that line energy is a major contribution only for brittle particles; for ductile filler particles line energy is a minor mechanism. He recommended[64,65] that when brittle particles are employed to induce the crack-pinning mechanism: (1) they should be as fracture resistant as possible, to prevent penetration; and (2) thermal and elastic mismatch should be minimised, to ensure that excessive stress concentrations do not build up in the matrix and so cause premature failure. Finally, Green *et al.*[66,67] have examined, both experimentally and theoretically, the effects of particle shape and particle/matrix adhesion in a model brittle composite of nickel spheres in a glass matrix. They found that low adhesion resulted in the filler particles being relatively ineffective in pinning cracks, i.e. they offer little impedance to the advancing crack and do not cause any significant change in the crack shape.

From this work, and previous discussions, some comments may be made as to the possible reasons why brittle particles do not toughen a ductile matrix. In such a material, high stresses extend well in advance of the crack tip and may cause debonding of the particles well ahead of the tip. These debonded particles cannot act as effective sites for further energy adsorption via the multiple shear yielding or crazing mechanisms and, furthermore, when the crack front does reach the debonded particles they are unable to effectively pin cracks.[61,68]

Many of the detailed aspects of the Lange crack-pinning mechanism will be discussed later when the fracture behaviour of polymers reinforced with brittle particles is considered. However, it should be mentioned that whilst this mechanism is undoubtedly the major mechanism for increasing the toughness of relatively brittle polymers containing rigid-particulate fillers other mechanisms have been suggested to be of importance and may play a role, albeit generally a secondary one, as discussed in previous sections.

11.3   STRESS/STRAIN RELATIONSHIPS

It is difficult to generalise about any changes in a polymer's uniaxial tensile stress/strain curve caused by the inclusion of a second particulate phase with the exception of the tensile or Young's modulus, E. Obviously, the value of E of the multiphase polymer will be lower than the matrix polymer if the second-phase particles are rubbery, but higher if rigid and well-bonded. Various models have been proposed to describe the moduli of multiphase polymers and reviews by Bucknall[3] and Chow[69] should be consulted for details.

Turning to the uniaxial tensile fracture stress, σ_f, and strain, e_f, then no clear pattern emerges. For example, for the epoxy resins shown in Table 11.1 then neither the unmodified nor the rubber-toughened material exhibits a yield point. Hence, both would be classed as brittle materials from their tensile stress/strain characteristics but with the value of σ_f being marginally lower and the value of e_f significantly higher for the toughened material. Nevertheless, the fracture energy, G_{Ic}, has been increased by up to forty-fold and the impact strength by five-fold by the inclusion of a rubbery second phase. In fracture mechanics terms this could be interpreted as due to the rubber phase increasing both the fracture energy, G_{Ic}, and the intrinsic flaw size, a_0. From eqn. (1.25)

$$\sigma_f = \left(\frac{G_{Ic}E}{\pi a_0}\right)^{\frac{1}{2}} \tag{11.6}$$

and this reveals that intrinsic flaw lengths would be approximately 40 μm and 1 mm, respectively, for the unmodified and rubber-toughened epoxies. As discussed in previous chapters, these flaws should not necessarily be thought of as ones that already exist in the unstressed material but rather as cracks that develop, possibly by the coalescence of microvoids, during the fracture test. If the yield behaviours of unmodified and rubber-modified epoxies are investigated, via uniaxial-compression or pure-shear tests, then it has been found[26] that inclusion of the rubbery phase reduces the yield stress by about one-fifth but that the amount of post-yield deformation may increase. These observations are of direct relevance since, as discussed previously, it is generally believed that a multiple shear yielding mechanism is largely responsible for the increases in toughness that may be obtained from rubber-modification of epoxy resins and such changes in the yield characteristics would obviously assist in promoting localised shear yield deformations in the vicinity of the rubber particles.

Considering epoxy resins containing rigid-particulate fillers, then some results are listed in Table 11.2 for an epoxy containing various volume fractions, v_{fp}, and particle sizes of alumina trihydrate; although the intrinsic flaw sizes, a_0, were not calculated in the original source[70] but have now been deduced from eqn. (11.6). Under the filler conditions selected the fracture energies increase with added filler but the fracture stresses all decrease. The average particle sizes were quite small, much less than the matrix intrinsic flaw size of about 40–50 μm and a value of a_0 of this size might well therefore have been expected in the filled polymer. However, the calculated flaw sizes in the multiphase polymers are all of the order of hundreds of micrometres. It was suggested that fracture originated in these materials from trapped bubbles introduced during manufacture but such initiation sites cannot always be found upon fractographic examination. Thus, the formation of the intrinsic flaw during testing is again a likely mechanism. Finally, it is interesting to note that the inclusion of rigid-particulate fillers has been shown,[71] from uniaxial compression tests, to increase the yield stress and greatly *decrease* the plastic strain capability. Following the

TABLE 11.2

EFFECT OF ALUMINA TRIHYDRATE PARTICULATE FILLER ON THE FRACTURE PROPERTIES OF AN EPOXY RESIN[70]

Particle size (μm)	v_{fp}	Tensile modulus E (GPa)	Fracture stress σ_f (MPa)	Fracture strain e_f (%)	Fracture energy G_{Ic} (kJ m^{-2})	Intrinsic flaw size a_0 (μm)
No filler	0	3·80	75·9	2·2	0·22	46
5	0·295	7·20	33·2	0·17	0·25	520
8	0·10	4·14	29·8	0·70	0·36	534
8	0·215	5·52	33·6	0·25	0·41	638
8	0·295	6·55	44·9	0·22	0·35	362
8	0·43	8·96	38·3	0·17	0·23	447
12	0·295	6·55	35·0	0·40	0·39	664

above arguments and the discussions in Section 11.2.2, these changes would be expected to inhibit shear yield processes and so the rigid-particulate-filled epoxies need to rely upon some other toughening mechanism. Indeed, it is generally considered that the crack-pinning mechanism is the major operative mechanism, as discussed in Section 11.4.

Compared to the epoxy materials, the inclusion of rubber particles in polystyrene to produce HIPS results in a vastly different type of tensile stress/strain curve, as shown[3] in Fig. 11.4. The unmodified polystyrene exhibits a stress/strain relation typical of a brittle polymer. The material extends almost linearly to a fracture strain of about 2% with crazing first being observed at a strain of about 1·5%. The initial stress/strain behaviour of the HIPS is also approximately linear, although the modulus is lower due to the presence of the rubber particles. However, at a stress of about 12·5 MPa the specimen begins

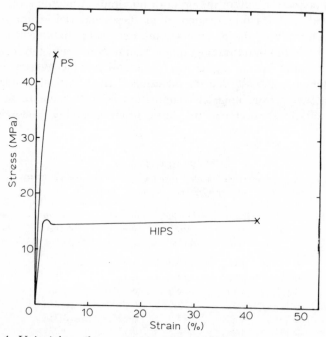

Fig. 11.4. *Uniaxial tensile stress/strain curves for polystyrene and HIPS at room temperature (after Bucknall[3]).*

to stress whiten and thereafter a completely different stress/strain behaviour is observed. There is a yield point at a stress of about 16 MPa followed by strain softening to a lower yield stress of 14 MPa. The stress then rises slowly until the specimen fractures at a stress and strain of 16 MPa and 40 %, respectively. The stress whitening, first observed at a strain of about 1 %, intensifies as the test proceeds but there is no indication of necking. However, in ABS stress whitening and yielding are followed by localised necking. The neck becomes intensely white and the specimen fractures at a lower strain than a comparable HIPS material since the stress is increased in the neck region. The lack of necking in HIPS is readily explained by the main mechanism of toughening in this material arising from multiple crazing, which occurs with an increase in volume. The necking in ABS, on the other hand, reflects the significant contribution from shear yielding mechanisms that occurs in this multiphase polymer.

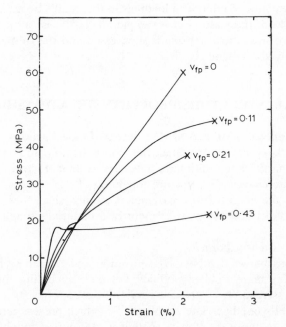

Fig. 11.5. Uniaxial tensile stress/strain curves for styrene–acrylonitrile copolymer containing various volume fractions, v_{fp}, of glass beads at room temperature (after Lavengood et al.[27]).

As Bucknall[4] has commented, rubber particles are not unique in their ability to induce tensile yielding in brittle thermoplastic, glassy polymers. Nicolais and co-workers[27,72,73] have shown that styrene–acrylonitrile copolymers, for example, can be made to yield by adding glass beads, and this is illustrated in Fig. 11.5. However, unlike such polymers toughened by rubber particles, the fracture strain is not significantly increased. It has been suggested[4,27] that this is because while glass particles, like rubber ones, can initiate crazing in the matrix they cannot, however, control growth effectively, as discussed in Section 11.2.3.

The above discussions have been concerned with uniaxial tensile behaviour but other loading conditions are obviously also of interest. The effect of various stress-states on the competing mechanisms of shear yielding and crazing has been discussed in detail in Chapters 4 and 5. Thus, since these two mechanisms are the major toughening processes in many multiphase polymers, the conclusions reached in these chapters would be expected to apply to many toughened polymers. The review of multiaxial loadings in Bucknall's book[3] shows that this is indeed the case. For example, if HIPS is subjected to a compressive stress field, crazing is suppressed and the rubber particles initiate only shear bands.[17,74]

11.4 STRUCTURE/PROPERTY RELATIONSHIPS

11.4.1 Concentration and Size of Second-Phase Particles
Many workers have correlated the concentration and size of the dispersed particles in multiphase polymers to their fracture behaviour. The fracture energy, G_{Ic}, fracture toughness, K_{Ic}, and impact strength have been the main fracture parameters studied since these represent the most direct and useful assessment of a material's toughness.

11.4.1.1 Rubbery Particles
Correlations between rubber concentration and toughness have been reported for many rubber-modified polymers including those based upon polystyrene,[46,75-9] styrene–acrylonitrile copolymer,[80] acrylics,[81] styrene–methylmethacrylate copolymers[82] (which possess refractive indices close to those of rubbers so that a *transparent* toughened multiphase polymer may be produced), epoxy resins[10,11,56,83] and polyester resins.[84] However, in many of these only the initially added rubber

concentration was known. This may, of course, be considerably different from the actual rubber phase volume fraction present after polymerisation, which may be ascertained directly from micrographs, such as that shown in Fig. 11.1, or indirectly from the height of the tan δ_r peak of the rubbery phase measured by relaxation techniques. In many instances the rubbery phase volume will be considerably larger than the rubber volume added to the matrix because of the presence of matrix material in the particles, as may be seen in Fig. 11.1 and as is discussed in References 46, 56 and 76. A further complication in correlating concentration of rubber particles to fracture behaviour is that microstructural features such as rubber volume fraction, particle size, particle-size distribution and internal particle structure are all often interrelated, so it is difficult to progressively change one feature independently of the others.

Several studies have appreciated the above considerations. Wagner & Robeson[76] polymerised a 6% polybutadiene solution in styrene at different rates of agitation recognising that an increasing rubbery phase volume fraction would result upon decreasing the rate of agitation; the lower rates being less likely to cause rupture of the rubber membranes during agitation. The properties of the rubber-modified polystyrenes are listed in Table 11.3 and the impact strength and fracture strain both pass through a maximum at a rubbery phase volume fraction, v_{fp}, of about 0·2. This maximum may be explained from the observation that the average particle size increased with increasing rubber phase volume. As discussed in Section 11.2.3, small particles are poor craze

TABLE 11.3

EFFECT OF RUBBERY PHASE VOLUME FRACTION, v_{fp}, ON THE PROPERTIES OF RUBBER-MODIFIED POLYSTYRENE[a]

True (measured) v_{fp}	T_g (rubber) (°C)	Tensile modulus (GPa)	Pendulum impact[b] (MJ m^{-3})	Fracture strain (%)
0·06	−110	2·8	0·42	3
0·12	−95	2·4	1·9	20
0·22	−87	1·9	11·6	45
0·30	−55	1·0	5·6	34
0·78	—	0·55	1·2	8

[a] Nominal rubber volume fraction: 0·06.
[b] Thin films of material used.

initiators whilst particles that are too large mean that the total number of particles that may initiate crazes is not maximised. Also, although not discussed by Wagner & Robeson, the small particles may have a low level of occlusions and therefore act as sites for premature craze-breakdown and crack initiation. These factors combine to yield a maximum in the toughness versus volume fraction relation.

Bucknall & Yoshii[56] have determined the fracture energy of rubber-modified epoxy resins, all containing $8 \cdot 7$ %w/w of carboxyl-terminated butadiene–acrylonitrile (CTBN) rubber but with various rubbery phase volume fractions, achieved by varying the curing conditions employed. Their results are shown in Fig. 11.6 and there is an approximately linear relationship between G_{Ic} and v_{fp} up to a value of v_{fp} of about $0 \cdot 2$, which was the highest rubber phase volume achieved. It is interesting that this relation is in agreement with the particle-deformation model proposed by Beaumont and co-workers[10,11] and

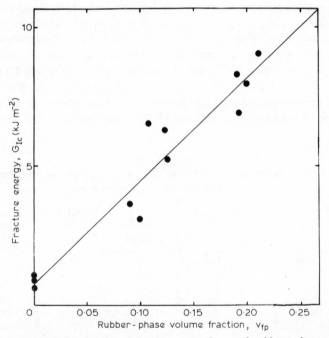

Fig. 11.6. *Relationship between fracture energy, G_{Ic}, and rubbery phase volume fraction, v_{fp}, for CTBN-toughened epoxy resins (after Bucknall & Yoshii[56]).*

stated in eqn. (11.4); although Bucknall & Yoshii, together with other workers, regard this mechanism as only being of secondary importance. If epoxy resins containing a wide range of CTBN rubber concentrations are prepared then Bascom et al.[83] have reported that the fracture energy passes through a maximum at about 20 %w/w. This maximum occurs because at higher concentrations the rubber does not form a separate particulate phase, but instead a single-phase blend is produced.

Bucknall & Yoshii[56] also concluded from their studies that the rubber phase volume fraction had the major influence on the fracture energy of the modified epoxy resin. Other microstructural features, including particle size and particle-size distribution, were of secondary importance. However, the average particle size was only varied between 0·5 and 5 μm and no materials were examined which contained very small particles. This conclusion is in direct contrast to earlier work[12] which suggested that larger particle sizes resulted in the toughest rubber-modified epoxies. However, the rubbery phase volume fraction was not measured, nor controlled, in this earlier work.

It was mentioned above that the rubbery phase volume fraction could be ascertained from the height of the tan δ_r peak of the rubbery phase. Hence, it is not surprising that several authors[75,77,85] have reported a correlation between impact strength and tan δ_r for rubber-modified polymers. Indeed, Sacher[77,85] has proposed that they are linearly related, although this conclusion was only empirically based. The results of Wagner & Robeson[76] and Keskkula et al.[75] demonstrate that such a relation is not generally valid. The presence of the damping peak obviously arises because of the presence of the second phase and hence in this sense is necessary for toughening. Nevertheless, its size does not appear to be related to the extent of toughness enhancement, except within a fairly narrow family of similarly prepared multiphase polymers. Considering the complex relationships between microstructure and toughness a simple direct relation would not really be expected.

11.4.1.2 Rigid Particles

Several studies[59,61,62,71,86-8] have shown that the fracture energy of a rigid-particulate-filled epoxy resin passes through a maximum at a given volume fraction, v_{fp}, but that the position of the maximum depends upon the particle size. This is illustrated in Fig. 11.7(a). In contrast, the stress-intensity factor, K_{Ic}, may increase steadily with

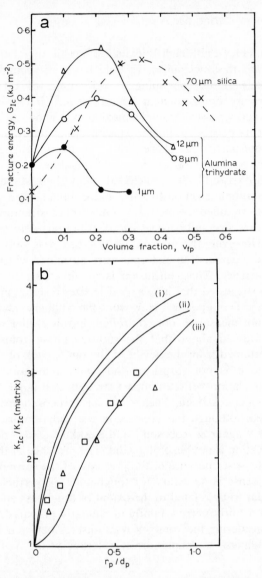

Fig. 11.7. (a) Relationship between fracture energy, G_{Ic}, and volume fraction, v_{fp}, of rigid-particulate fillers in epoxy resins (after References 59 and 88); (b) Relationship between $K_{Ic}/K_{Ic}(\text{matrix})$ and the ratio of the particle size to inter-particle distance, r_p/d_p, for a glass-bead-filled epoxy (after Spanoudakis[61]). The curves are theoretical relations due to Evans[64] and Green et al.[67] and represent: (i) non-interacting semicircular-shaped cracks between particles; (ii) non-interacting semielliptical-shaped cracks betwen particles; and (iii) interacting semielliptical-shaped cracks between particles. $\triangle$, $r_p = 2.5\ \mu m$; $\square$, $r_p = 31\ \mu m$.

increasing volume fraction.[88] This arises because the modulus, E, increases continuously with v_{fp} and, as may be seen from eqns (3.55) and (3.56), the value of K_{Ic} reflects changes in both G_{Ic} and E. A designer has the problem of deciding whether it is better to have a high value of G_{Ic} or K_{Ic}, since it is not possible to optimise both parameters at the same time by varying the volume fraction of particles. The choice will depend upon the application of the material. If it has to sustain high stresses then a high value of K_{Ic} is preferable whereas if it has to absorb energy during fracture, such as in impact applications, the material would require a high value of G_{Ic}.

Turning to theoretical considerations, then the crack-pinning mechanism (Section 11.2.5) is generally considered to be the major cause of increased toughness in these brittle particulate composites and the interparticle distance, d_p, which appears in the Lange model (eqn. (11.5)), may be related to the volume fraction, v_{fp}, and particle radius, r_p, by[59]

$$d_p = \frac{4r_p(1 - v_{fp})}{3v_{fp}} \qquad (11.7)$$

Examination of eqns (11.5) and (11.7) reveals that the value of G_{Ic} would theoretically be predicted to increase continuously with increasing volume fraction at a constant particle size. As mentioned previously, the discrepancy with experimental observations was suggested by Lange & Radford[59] to arise from the particles coming too close together at high volume fractions for effective crack/particle interactions. However, there is also often an inconsistency with respect to the effect of particle size, since if G_{Ic} is plotted against d_p^{-1} for low volume fraction data it has been found[63,71] that a linear relation is indeed obtained but that the slope increases with increasing particle size. This indicates that the line energy, T_L, is a function of particle size which is again inconsistent with Lange's model. As mentioned in Section 11.2.5, Lange[63] suggested that large particles could act as more effective pinning points and modified his original equation by introducing a dimensionless function $F(r_p)$ dependent upon the pinning size, thus

$$G_{Ic} = G_{Ic}(\text{matrix}) + 2F(r_p)\frac{T_L}{d_p} \qquad (11.8)$$

where $0 < F(r_p) < 1$. This modification is not, however, very satisfactory as the physical meaning of $F(r_p)$ is unclear. The problem has been resolved by Evans[64] who performed a detailed analysis of the stresses within a particle-reinforced composite and showed that there is a theoretical justification for the line tension, T_L, to vary with interparticle separation.

The effect of particle size and volume fraction upon the fracture behaviour of epoxy resins containing spherical glass beads has recently been studied in detail[61,62] and analysed in terms of Evans' theory. Some of the results are presented in Fig. 11.7(b) where the ratio of K_{Ic} for the composite to K_{Ic} for the resin matrix is plotted against r_p/d_p. This ratio of the particle size to the interparticle separation is a simple function of v_{fp} (eqn. (11.7)). Evans' theory predicts that all the data should lie on a curve which he calculated would be the same for all particle sizes, hence avoiding the problems of Lange's analysis. The data in Fig. 11.7(b) are for two different particle sizes and the theoretical curves are from the Evans' theory (curve (i)) and modifications to it calculated by Green et al.[67] (curves (ii) and (iii)). The experimental data are a reasonable fit to the theoretical concepts proposed by Evans[64] and the deviations from the theoretical curves have been interpreted[61,62] as being due to a change in toughening mechanism from crack-front pinning to interfacial breakdown at the particle/matrix boundary. It is found that this occurs at a critical value of interparticle separation, d_{pc}, and is not dependent upon the value of either r_p or v_{fp}. This change in mechanism coincides approximately with the maximum in the value of fracture energy, G_{Ic}, for the composite and may also be accompanied by a transition in crack propagation behaviour from stick/slip to continuous growth.

11.4.2 Particle/Matrix Adhesion

11.4.2.1 Rubbery Particles
As discussed earlier, in order for the rubbery particles to be effective as sites for controlled craze or shear-band growth and prevent premature craze breakdown and crack initiation, or even act as simple energy absorbers via deformation and fracture behind the crack front, then the rubbery particle must be adequately bonded to the matrix.

Indeed, some of the early HIPS materials were prepared by melt- or latex-blending together rubber and polystyrene but in these multiphase polymers the rubber particles were only poorly bonded to the surrounding matrix. This resulted in far less tough materials than when the styrene was polymerised in the presence of the rubber which gives well-bonded particles due to chemical grafting. Graft copolymerisation, via a bulk or bulk-suspension process, is currently the standard method for the manufacture of HIPS.[3] Similarly, ABS and related polymers, such as methacrylate–butadiene–styrene copolymers and toughened PMMA, are prepared by techniques which lead to grafting reactions. In these materials such reactions are typically induced by first preparing a rubber latex by emulsion polymerisation and then adding the monomers (e.g. styrene and acrylonitrile) to the reactor vessel and polymerising them in the presence of the rubber latex.[3] Haward & Mann[89] have investigated ABS polymers prepared either by simple blending or by grafting and demonstrated that the former method results in low particle/matrix adhesion and poor impact strength compared to the grafted polymer.

In some materials, such as rubber-toughened PVC, the graft polymerisation techniques cannot be readily adapted so it is necessary to directly blend the rubber into the matrix polymer as a separate process. As Bucknall[3] has commented, under such circumstances the rubber should possess a solubility parameter sufficiently different from the matrix polymer to ensure a fine second-phase dispersion but close enough to promote adequate adhesion of the particle to the matrix.[90] This requirement may limit the choice of rubber at the expense of mechanical properties.

Developments[91-3] in block copolymerisation technology have offered a new range of blended multiphase polymers where good particle/matrix adhesion may be relatively readily obtained without compromising the mechanical properties. Essentially, a suitable block copolymer is added so that it acts as an interphase region between the particle and the matrix. Segments of the block copolymer are located in both particle and matrix and this feature provides good adhesion without the need to sacrifice any of the desired properties of the rubbery phase. Indeed, blends of a rubbery styrene–butadiene block copolymer and polystyrene have been prepared[91] possessing extremely high impact strengths similar to ABS polymers, which are generally superior to normal, grafted HIPS mateials.

11.4.2.2 Rigid Particles

In polymers containing rigid particles it is not always necessary to have good particle/matrix adhesion for the material to possess the optimum mechanical properties since, as discussed below, some mechanical properties are improved whilst others are made worse as the level of adhesion is increased. The degree of adhesion in rigid-particulate composites is generally controlled by employing an appropriate surface pretreatment for the particles, prior to their addition to the matrix. For example, there are many silane-based coupling agents now available which are typically used to promote either primary (chemical) bonding or weaker, secondary (e.g. van der Waals) bonding across the particle/matrix interface.[90,94,95]

Particle/matrix adhesion is found to have a significant effect upon the fracture strengths of both epoxy[61,62,96,97] and polyester[98] resins reinforced with spherical glass particles. With good adhesion it is found that the strength of the composites is approximately the same as that of the unfilled matrices, sometimes rising slightly at high volume fractions. With no surface pretreatments, or release agents, applied to the particles the strength decreases with increasing volume fractions of filler particles. Nicholais & Nicodemo[97] showed that for the lower bound, i.e. no adhesion between the matrix and particle, the strength, σ_f, could be related to the volume fraction by an equation of the form

$$\sigma_f = \sigma_f(\text{matrix})(1 - 1 \cdot 21 v_{fp}^{\frac{2}{3}}) \qquad (11.9)$$

where $\sigma_f(\text{matrix})$ is the fracture strength of the matrix. They suggested that the upper bound in the case of perfect adhesion would be the fracture strength of the matrix, and composites with intermediate levels of adhesion would have strengths between the two bounds. They showed that the data of Sahu & Broutman[96] could be fitted to their theory. A more sophisticated approach has been adopted by Leidner & Woodhams[98] who were able to predict the dependence of the fracture strength of the composite upon the strength of the matrix/filler interfacial bond. This theory has also been shown to work well for particle-filled epoxy resins and has also enabled the actual strength of the bond to be determined.[61,62]

The effect of surface adhesion upon crack propagation in rigid-particle-filled polymers has been studied for both epoxy[61,62,86] and polyester[30,86] resins toughened with glass particles. In contrast to the simple tensile fracture behaviour, it is sometimes found that the highest values of G_{Ic} are obtained when release agents are used and the lowest values are obtained when coupling agents, giving strong interfacial bonds, are employed. The composites with untreated particles have values of G_{Ic} between the two extremes. The high values of G_{Ic} for weak adhesion have not yet been satisfactorily explained. Sahu & Broutman[85] suggested that they are due to increased interfacial debonding above and below the fracture plane whereas Brown[30] has argued that the toughness is due to debonded particles acting as voids and causing more local energy absorbing processes, such as plastic deformation, to take place. Neither explanation is particularly convincing and clearly more work needs to be conducted in this area to quantify the effect of the level of rigid-particle/matrix adhesion on the measured G_{Ic} value and investigate, for example, whether there is an optimum level of adhesion required for the crack-pinning mechanism to operate most effectively.

Thus the effect of particle/matrix adhesion upon fracture behaviour is complex since good adhesion is often found to increase the fracture stress but reduce the toughness. It is therefore necessary to know the applications to which the polymer will be put before the type of particle pretreatment can be chosen. If high strength is required then coupling agents promoting strong interfacial bonding should be used whereas if a tough polymer is needed, release agents, or no treatment, may be required in order that only a moderate level of adhesion is attained.

11.4.3 Matrix Properties
One of the problems when attempting to assess the influence of the properties of the matrix polymer in toughened multiphase materials is the now familiar one of separating the parameter under study from its interdependence on the other microstructural features.

For example, in rubber-modified epoxies, and similar thermosettting resins, the curing agent and cure conditions employed will affect not only the chemical and physical properties of the matrix but also the rubbery phase volume fraction.[56,99,100] Indeed, the results of Bucknall & Yoshii[56] shown in Fig. 11.6 refer to several different epoxy-resin systems all containing the same added rubber content. They suggest that the value of the fracture energy is largely determined by the rubbery phase volume resulting from the particular system chosen, and any influence of the matrix properties is only of secondary importance.

However, when a wide range of thermoplastic matrix polymers is examined the general conclusion is that the toughest rubber-modified materials will be those which possess the toughest matrices.[3,78] Thus, rubber-modified polypropylene and polycarbonate, for example, can possess very high impact strengths. The reason why such already relatively tough homopolymers as these are modified by the inclusion of a second rubbery phase is that under high rates of strain, or at low temperatures, they may exhibit notch sensitivity. This was discussed in

Section 6.2 and is illustrated in Table 6.2 and Figs 6.2 and 6.3. It will be recalled that notch sensitivity arises from triaxial stresses being generated which inhibit plastic deformation via shear yielding mechanisms. Under these conditions the presence of a rubbery phase may promote multiple crazing as an additional, and now major, energy absorbing mechanism or may initiate localised shear bands and voids which may relieve the triaxial stress constraint and enable shear yielding to occur more readily. In either case the outcome is a less notch-sensitive material.

Some of the most brittle types of polymer are the polyimides which are thermosetting polymers and typically possess[26,101] fracture energies in the range of 15–70 J m^{-2}. However, since they are capable of withstanding exposures at elevated temperatures of the order of 200–250°C for long periods of time, they are of considerable interest to the aerospace community for use as adhesives and matrices for fibre-composite materials. Recently, efforts have been made to toughen these materials by the incorporation of an elastomeric phase, often a silicone rubber which itself has good thermal resistance. Two-phase microstructures have been obtained[101] resulting in no significant loss in the T_g of the polyimide matrix and a four- to five-fold increase in the value of G_{Ic}.

Turning to rigid-particulate fillers, then the most striking effect is that their inclusion into tough matrices, such as nylon 6.6[7] and poly(phenylene oxide),[102] almost invariably tends to reduce the toughness of the polymer. A possible mechanism for these observations was discussed in Section 11.2.5. In the case of particle-filled brittle polymers, e.g. epoxy resins,[61,62] it is found that the *percentage* increase in toughness is less when somewhat tougher matrices are employed although the composites with the toughest matrices have the highest *absolute* values of toughness.

11.5   TEST VARIABLES

11.5.1   Effect of Temperature and Rate

11.5.1.1   Rubbery Particles
Some of the most mechanistically interesting studies have been conducted by Williams and co-workers[79,103,104] who have examined the effect of temperature on the fracture of HIPS. They found[104] that over

the temperature range from $+20$ to $-120°C$ the stress-intensity factor, K_{Ic}, was not only dependent upon temperature but also upon the specimen thickness. As discussed in Section 3.5, the thickness effect arises from the state of stress at a crack tip being plane strain in a very thick specimen and plane stress in relatively thin ones. Equations (3.59) and (3.60) were employed to deduce plane strain, K'_{Ic}, and plane stress, K''_{Ic}, values of the stress-intensity and these parameters are shown as a function of temperature in Fig. 11.8(a).

The data shown in Fig. 11.8(a) reveal that the value of K'_{Ic} is only slightly dependent upon temperature and its value and temperature dependence are approximately the same as for the polystyrene matrix. In contrast, the values of K''_{Ic} are appreciably higher and increase steadily with temperature down to about $-80°C$, after which there is a decrease. Thus, it appears that under plane-strain conditions the toughening mechanisms are inhibited. Since multiple crazing is the major toughening mechanism in HIPS materials, and plane strain involves a triaxial state of stress, this is a somewhat surprising result. Parvin & Williams,[104] suggested, however, that this is in accord with the Bowden & Oxborough craze criterion (eqns (5.7) to (5.9)) since the stress necessary to produce crazing becomes larger as the Poisson's ratio tends to 0.5 under constraint. Another possible reason is that under triaxial loadings the effective modulus of the rubber particles will be comparatively high and they might not be such effective stress concentrators; thereby reducing the extent of multiple crazing. More convincingly, Bucknall[105,106] has shown that if the effect of the Poisson's contractions upon the applied strains is considered then both the stress concentration and the hydrostatic tensile component, p, of the stress tensor are likely to be lower around a rubber particle in the matrix when the applied stress field is plane strain, as opposed to plane stress. Thus again a rubber particle would be predicted to be a more efficient initiator of crazes when subjected to plane-stress (thin sheet) conditions.

Whatever the fundamental reason, it certainly appears that the toughening occurs in the plane-stress region. This is further reflected by two other features of the data. Firstly, the maximum in K''_{Ic} occurs at approximately the same temperature and rate as the viscoelastic loss maximum at the T_g of the rubbery phase. In plane strain the constraints inhibit such a relaxation of the rubbery phase and the $\tan \delta_r$ value is considerably reduced and hence the value of K'_{Ic} shows no such correlation with the material's relaxation spectrum. Secondly, the

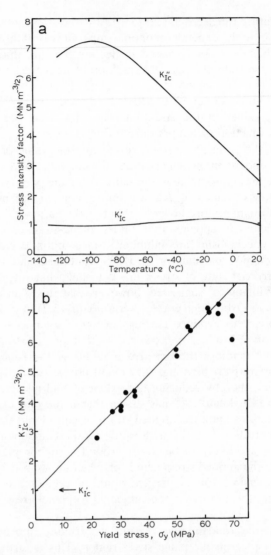

Fig. 11.8. (a) *Effect of temperature on the plane-strain,* K'_{Ic}, *and plane stress,* K''_{Ic}, *stress-intensity factors of HIPS; and* (b) *Relationship between the plane-stress,* K''_{Ic}, *stress-intensity factor and the corresponding value of yield stress,* σ_y, *for HIPS (after Parvin & Williams*[104]).

value of K_{Ic}'' reflects the variation of the yield stress, σ_y, with temperature and this is illustrated in Fig. 11.8(b) where K_{Ic}'' is plotted against σ_y. Above $-80°C$ there is proportionality, with $K_{Ic}'' \to K_{Ic}'$ as $\sigma_y \to 0$. Below $-80°C$ the relaxation of the rubbery phase becomes less pronounced and the interaction of K_{Ic}'' and σ_y decreases. However, unlike many glassy polymers, this proportionality does not result in a strictly constant crack-opening displacement, δ_{tc}, which would have provided a most useful failure criterion. In HIPS the value of δ_{tc} is about 80 μm at room temperature and increases continuously with decreasing temperature to a value of about 145 μm at $-40°C$, below which it remains approximately constant. These values of δ_{tc} are to be compared to values for unmodified polystyrene of the order of only a few micrometres.

In contrast to the above results for HIPS, Newmann & Williams[107] in the case of ABS and Kinloch & Shaw[108] in the case of rubber-modified epoxies have found little dependence of the measured K_{Ic} (or G_{Ic}) value for the onset of crack growth upon specimen thickness. Unlike HIPS these multiphase polymers rely largely upon a multiple shear yielding mechanism for their enhanced toughness. It was suggested earlier that the void initiation which accompanies this mechanism relieves the through-thickness constraint. The lack of any thickness effect would appear to be in agreement with this mechanism.

The work conducted on rubber-modified epoxies[11,15,26,83,108,109] has demonstrated that with these materials the value of K_{Ic} for the onset of crack growth is almost independent of temperature below about 0–20°C, although the value of G_{Ic} may fall slightly as the temperature is decreased since the modulus, E, is increasing and $G_{Ic} = K_{Ic}^2/E$ (eqn. (3.55)). However, as with the HIPS studies, a maximum, albeit a small one, is detectable[26,109] around the viscoelastic loss maximum of the rubbery phase, which is at about $-50°C$ (at 1 Hz) in these toughened epoxies. At temperatures greater than about 20°C the value of K_{Ic} (or G_{Ic}) rises rapidly due to increasing plastic deformation and associated crack tip blunting. Thus, the value of δ_{tc} increases and again a constant δ_{tc} is inapplicable as a general fracture criterion. However, as for the single-phase epoxies (Section 8.5.2), a criterion based upon the attainment of a critical stress acting over a critical distance fits the experimental data—obtained over a wide range of rates and temperatures—extremely well. This is shown in Fig. 11.9 where the ratio K_{Ic}/K_{Ics} is plotted against $\rho_c^{\frac{1}{2}}$. The value of K_{Ics} corresponds to a sharp crack and was taken as the value of K_{Ic} at the lowest temperature studied, and ρ_c

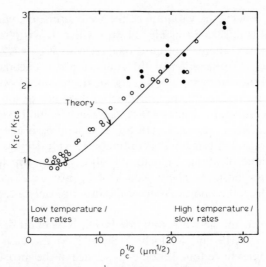

Fig. 11.9. K_{Ic}/K_{Ics} *ratio versus* $\rho_c^{\frac{1}{2}}$ *for rubber-modified epoxy resin over a range of temperatures* ($-90°C$ *to* $+50°C$) *and rates.* ●, *measured* ρ_c *values;* ⊙, *calculated* ρ_c *values. Solid line is the theoretical relation from eqn. (4.23) (after Kinloch et al.*[26,109]*).*

is the crack tip radius corresponding to the measured value of K_{Ic}. Results were obtained for specimens where both natural cracks and artificially blunted cracks (produced by drilling holes) were employed. In the former case the value of ρ_c was taken to be the crack-opening displacement, δ_{tc}, and was deduced from eqn. (3.45) whilst in the latter the value of ρ_c was measured directly. It will be recalled (Section 4.5.2, eqn. (4.23)) that the theoretical relation is

$$\frac{K_{Ic}}{K_{Ics}} = \frac{(1+\rho_c/2c)^{\frac{3}{2}}}{(1+\rho_c/c)}$$

and this is shown as the solid curve in Fig. 11.9. The good agreement with experimental results is evident and this analysis yields a critical stress, σ_{tc}, and distance, c, of 200 MPa and 10 μm, respectively.

These studies also revealed that, as is often observed, increasing the rate of test is equivalent to decreasing the temperature. Hunston and co-workers[15,110] have also found that the value of G_{Ic} for the fracture of rubber-modified epoxies decreased with decreasing temperature or increasing rate and that a master curve of G_{Ic} versus reduced time-of-test, t_f/a_T, could be constructed *below* the T_g of the epoxy matrix.[15,110]

The values of the time–temperature shift factor, a_T, were ascertained experimentally from either fracture or dynamic mechanical relaxation data.[15] Thus, the effects of rate and temperature on the value of G_{Ic} may be simply combined, as shown in Fig. 11.10. Kobayashi & Broutman[81] have reported a more complicated picture in the case of rubber-modified acrylic polymers. The G_{Ic} versus crack growth rate relationships for these polymers contained many peaks, although they were considered to reflect viscoelastic loss relaxations.

If the effects of high rates of test are next considered, then high impact-strength is obviously an important requirement in most rubber-toughened polymers. Indeed, it is the most likely mechanical test to which any such newly developed material will first be subjected. This is reflected in the many references to the impact strength of such polymers in the present chapter and Section 6.2 on impact testing. It is not intended to discuss again the many points covered previously but Fig. 11.11 illustrates[111] several of the important features. This shows the

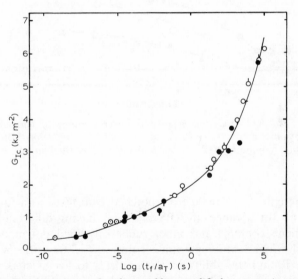

Fig. 11.10. Fracture energy, G_{Ic}, for a rubber-modified epoxy resin as a function of $\log (t_f/a_T)$. The shift factor, a_T, being determined from fracture and dynamic mechanical relaxation data: O, 60°C; Ȯ, 50°C; O–, 40°C; Q, 37°C; –O, 30°C; ●, 23°C; ●–, 15°C; ●, 0°C; –●, –20°C; ●, –40°C; ⊙, –60°C. (After Hunston et al.[110]).

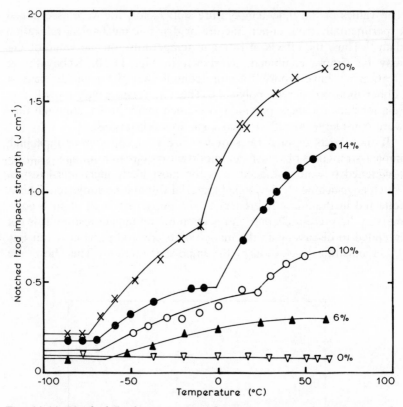

Fig. 11.11. *Notched Izod impact strengths over a range of temperatures for styrene–acrylonitrile copolymer (0 % rubber) and for a series of ABS polymers containing, nominally, 6–20 % polybutadiene (after Bucknall & Street[111]).*

impact strength, determined from notched Izod tests, as a function of temperature for a range of ABS materials having different nominal polybutadiene contents and other rubber-modified polymers exhibit similar behaviour.[3] At temperatures below −75°C the rubbery phase is below its T_g and the ability of the particles to act as sites of stress concentration is poor. The impact strengths of the ABS materials are similar therefore to that of the unmodified styrene–acrylonitrile copolymer (SAN). Above −75°C the T_g of the polybutadiene is exceeded and the impact strengths of the ABS materials begin to rise and stress whitening is observed around the notch. At about −10°C, the

ABS containing 20 % rubber shows a further sharp rise in impact strength, accompanied now by stress whitening over the entire fracture surface. Similar transitions occur at −5°C and at 20°C for the ABS materials containing 14 and 10 % rubber, respectively. Bucknall[3] has offered the following explanation for this second transition in the impact behaviour. At higher temperatures and rubber contents the energy required for crack propagation is greater than the energy stored elastically in the specimen when the crack is initiated, so that additional energy is taken from the pendulum during the propagation stage. At lower temperatures, the crack propagation energy is smaller and there is sufficient stored elastic energy to complete the fracture of the specimens. As mentioned previously, similar impact-strength behaviour has been observed in other rubber-toughened polymers. In toughened-PVC, for example, this transition from moderate to high temperature behaviour is accompanied by a very considerable rise in impact strength.[111]

11.5.1.2 Rigid Particles

There have been few systematic studies of the effect of test temperature upon the fracture behaviour of polymers filled with rigid particles. In the case of thermosetting resins there have only been a few *ad hoc* experiments performed at different temperatures[30,59,112] to determine how the fracture energy is affected by changing the test temperature. It is generally found that for all volume fractions of filler the fracture energy is reduced at low temperatures and raised at high temperatures and this has been explained[30] in terms of less plastic deformation occurring at low temperatures. Alternatively, Lange & Radford[59] have pointed out that at low temperatures there will be microstresses as a result of differential contraction of the resin and particles.

Mai[113] has measured the effect of test temperature upon K_{Ic} for glass-filled polystyrene and found that K_{Ic} decreased as the temperature was increased above ambient. He also showed that K_{Ic} depended upon crack velocity and at a given test temperature dropped as the crack velocity decreased. Mai suggested that crack propagation was controlled by the β_r relaxation process associated with crazing in the glass-filled polystyrene.

A strong dependence of K_{Ic} upon crack velocity has been reported by Young & Beaumont[88] for a silica-filled epoxy resin system where slow crack growth occurs with the value of K_{Ic} increasing as the crack velocity increases. However, in many thermosetting polymers filled with brittle particles crack propagation normally takes place through a stick/slip process and so there is no simple correlation between K_{Ic}, or G_{Ic}, and crack velocity.[61,62]

11.5.1.3 Adhesive Joints

In recent years rubber-modified epoxy materials have become the basis of a new generation of advanced structural adhesives and are currently being widely employed, especially in high technology industries such as aerospace.[114-16] However, whilst the crack growth behaviour in structural joints employing the single-phase epoxy materials is very similar to that of the bulk materials (Section 8.5.2) this is not the case when toughened multiphase adhesives are used.[13,15,83,108,109,117] In a general study of the fracture of polymers the effects of temperature and rate are particularly noteworthy.

Essentially, the more complex behaviour with such adhesives arises from the extensive plasticity that may occur in the vicinity of the crack tip. Firstly, with relatively thin adhesive layers the presence of high modulus substrates, such as steel, may restrict the full volume of the plastic zone from developing. Since the toughness is largely derived from the energy dissipated in forming the plastic zone, the adhesive fracture energy, G_{Ic}(joint), will decrease steadily as the adhesive bond thickness, h_a, is reduced past a certain value. Secondly, however, it has been found[118] that the constraint imposed upon the adhesive layer by the rigid substrates may increase the level of the σ_{11} local tensile stresses of a crack and so extend the length of the plastic zone ahead of the crack tip. The degree of constraint will be greatest with thinner adhesive layers. These two factors combine[108] to give a maximum in the adhesive fracture energy, G_{Ic}(joint), versus adhesive layer thickness, h_a, relation, as may be seen from Fig. 11.12. The maximum value, G_{Icm}(joint), occurs at a certain bond thickness, h_m, but the values of both these parameters are dependent upon rate,[108] and also temperature.[13] Now the maximum, G_{Icm}(joint), results when the adhesive bond thickness and the plastic-zone diameter, $2r''_{yc}$, are approximately equal. Thus, from eqns (3.42) and (3.55) the adhesive thickness, h_m, at G_{Icm}(joint) should be expressed by

$$h_m \equiv 2r''_{yc} = \frac{1}{\pi} \frac{EG_{Ic}}{\sigma_y^2} \qquad (11.10)$$

Values of $2r''_{yc}$, calculated from eqn. (11.10) are shown[108] in Table 11.4

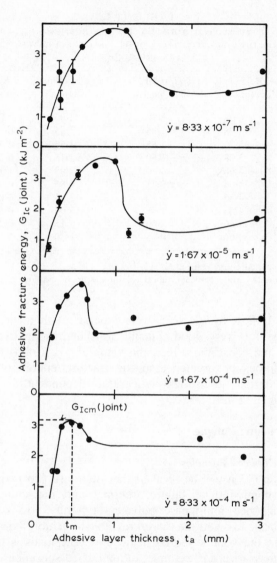

Fig. 11.12. *Adhesive fracture energy, G_{Ic}(joint), as a function of adhesive layer thickness, t_a, for various constant rates of displacement, $\dot{y}$ (after Kinloch & Shaw[108]).*

TABLE 11.4

COMPARISON OF MEASURED ADHESIVE BOND THICKNESS, h_m, AT MAXIMUM ADHESIVE FRACTURE ENERGY, G_{Icm}(JOINT), AND CALCULATED PLASTIC ZONE DIAMETER, $2r''_{yc}$

Temperature (°C)	Rate: log ẏ (m s⁻¹)	$G_{Ic}(kJ\,m^{-2})$ (bulk material)	$G_{Icm}(joint)$ (kJ m⁻²)	h_m (mm)	$2r''_{yc}$ (mm)
20	−6·08	2·10	3·90	1·0	0·85
20	−4·78	1·85	3·65	0·8	0·70
20	−3·78	1·55	3·55	0·55	0·49
20	−3·08	1·50	3·15	0·4	0·43
50	−4·66	4·70	2·95	1·1	1·6
37	−4·66	3·75	2·85	0·9	1·16
25	−4·66	2·70	3·85	0·6	0·57
0	−4·66	1·65	3·00	0·5	0·39
−20	−4·66	1·00	3·15	0·25	0·15
−40	−4·66	0·75	2·50	0·1	0·05

(a) CTBN-toughened epoxy resin used.
(b) Tapered-double-cantilever-beam adhesive joint specimens employed.

together with those of h_m, which were experimentally ascertained, and the agreement is very good. Finally, it is interesting to note that, because of the constraint effect, the value of G_{Icm}(joint) may under many conditions be greater than the fracture energy of the bulk adhesive material and also less temperature dependent, again as indicated in Table 11.4.

11.5.2 Dynamic Fatigue

11.5.2.1 Rubbery Particles

From Section 6.3 it will be recalled that there are two main mechanisms of dynamic-fatigue failure: thermal and mechanical fatigue. Rubber-toughened multiphase polymers typically possess relatively high viscoelastic loss and are therefore liable to exhibit thermal fatigue failure when the volume experiencing the cyclic loads is large. Such conditions may arise, for example, in unnotched specimens, especially at high frequencies and stresses. Alternatively, if thermal failure can be avoided, then the mechanism of failure is via mechanical fatigue and, as a general rule, the presence of a second rubbery phase now increases the dynamic-fatigue resistance. The improvement in this property is, however, far less marked than the increase in impact strength.

Dynamic-fatigue properties have been reported for many rubber-toughened polymers, including HIPS,[119–22] ABS,[120,122–4] rubber-modified PVC,[125] HIPS/poly(phenylene oxide) blends,[121,126] toughened nylon 66[127] and rubber-modified PMMA[120] and have been reviewed recently by Sauer & Richardson[128] and Hertzberg & Manson.[126] As for most materials, the emphasis of these studies has been on the mechanical fatigue mechanism and, even then, crack initiation is largely ignored and only the propagation of cracks which are initially of macroscopic dimensions has been considered. In justification of this emphasis Hertzberg & Manson[126] comment that, even with rubber-toughened multiphase polymers which exhibit relatively high viscoelastic loss, the cyclic loads required to cause significant heating and gross softening are often high compared to the yield stress and may well be outside the design range. Thus, in practice, smaller cyclic loads leading to mechanical fatigue failure via the propagation of existing flaws, surface defects etc., usually represent the more relevant service condition and failure mechanism.

The fatigue crack growth rate, da/dN, in rubber-modified polymers follows the Paris equation (eqn. (6.19))

$$\frac{da}{dN} = A_f \Delta K_I^m$$

where ΔK_I is the stress-intensity factor range. A typical result is shown in Fig. 11.13 where data for an unmodified PVC and one containing a methacrylate–butadiene–styrene rubber are given. As may be seen, at a given ΔK_I value the crack growth rate in the unmodified PVC is about an order of magnitude greater than for the toughened materials. In the case of HIPS and ABS, the improved dynamic crack propagation resistance, compared to polystyrene, is evident from Fig. 6.9.

The micromechanisms of dynamic crack extension in rubber-toughened polymers basically reflect the behaviour of the matrix polymer. Thus, in many such materials, discontinuous crack growth occurs as it does in many single-phase polymers (Section 6.3.4). One difference is that the overall higher viscoelastic loss in the multiphase polymers may lead to a greater extent of hysteretic heating locally around the crack tip (causing the yield stress to fall, the crack tip to blunt and an attenuation of fatigue crack propagation rates), without the necessity of a secondary (β_r) molecular-relaxation transition of the polymer occurring at a similar frequency and temperature to the dynamic-fatigue tests.

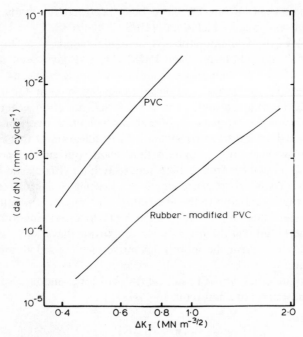

Fig. 11.13. Dynamic-fatigue resistance of unmodified PVC and a meth-acrylate–butadiene–styrene rubber (14 phr) modified PVC (after Skibo et al.[125]).

11.5.2.2   Rigid Particles

Very little work has been reported on the dynamic-fatigue behaviour of rigid-particulate-filled polymers. Nielsen[119] has determined the relation between the stress and number of cycles to failure for an epoxy resin filled with spherical glass particles under one set of test conditions but since the unfilled material was not examined no conclusions may be drawn concerning the effect of filler addition. However, this information may be obtained from several papers[129–31] where the dynamic fatigue of acrylic bone cements has been considered.

Acrylic bone cements typically consist of small spherical particles of PMMA–polystyrene copolymer and up to 10 % w/w of very fine barium sulphate inclusions in a PMMA matrix. Lankford *et al.*[129] have measured the crack growth rate, da/dN, as a function of stress-intensity factor range, ΔK_I, in an acrylic bone cement using single-edge notched specimens. They found that the data could be represented by the Paris equation. Taking pure PMMA as the reference state, then at a given ΔK_I value the dynamic crack growth rate was slower in the filled cement. Further, the value of m for the filled cement was about 4·7, somewhat lower than that for pure PMMA. Thus as the ΔK_I value increased the improvement in the dynamic-fatigue behaviour of the filled material became more marked. Crack pinning was considered to be the major mechanism responsible for this improvement. Evidence for this came from fractographic studies since striation markings on the fracture surface were regular and corresponded to successive positions of the advancing crack front as a result of individual load excursions, except at matrix/particle boundaries where the crack was often pinned for a number of cycles.

11.5.3 Static Fatigue

In one of the few studies on the static fatigue of rubber-toughened polymers Bucknall & Stevens[122] compared the dynamic- and static-fatigue behaviour of ABS. As the dynamic-fatigue experiments were conducted using square-wave loading it was possible to readily measure the duration of tensile loading at fracture and compare these results directly to static-fatigue data. As would be expected from the discussions in Chapter 6, the dynamic conditions resulted in the shorter failure times, especially at the lower applied load levels.

Static fatigue in rigid-particulate-toughened polymers has been examined in the case of acrylic bone cement[132] and epoxy resins containing silica[128,133,134] and glass beads and alumina.[134] In their studies on such materials Young & Beaumont[132,133] employed the fracture mechanics analysis outlined in Section 6.4.3 to predict the static-fatigue lifetimes. This analysis expresses the time-to-failure, t_f, as (eqn. (6.29))

$$t_f = \frac{2A_v^{1/n}}{Q^2\sigma_c^2} \frac{n}{(1-2n)} [K_{Ic}^{(2n-1)/n} - K_{Icf}^{(2n-1)/n}]$$

For an unnotched specimen the initially applied stress-intensity factor, K_{Ic}, is related to the applied stress, σ_c, by

$$K_{Ic} = Q\sigma_c a_0^{\frac{1}{2}} \tag{11.11}$$

where a_0 is, of course, the intrinsic flaw size. Young & Beaumont[132,133] evaluated the parameters A_v, n and K_{Icf} from measuring the crack growth rate, $\dot{a}$, as a function of the stress-intensity factor, K_{Ic}, in

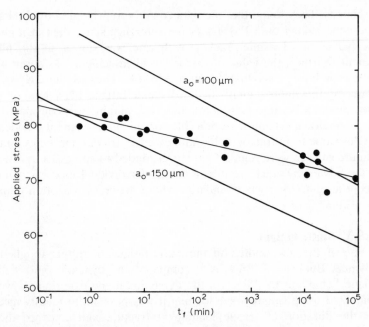

Fig. 11.14. Static-fatigue data for an epoxy resin containing silica particles ($v_{fp} = 0.42$). The points are experimental and the two heavy lines are the theoretical predictions using intrinsic flaw sizes of 100 and 150 μm (after Young & Beaumont[133]).

short-term, constant displacement-rate experiments, using the double-torsion fracture mechanics specimen. For the static-fatigue failure of an epoxy resin containing a volume fraction of 0·42 of irregularly shaped silica particles the experimental relation between applied stress, σ_c, and time-to-failure, t_f, is shown in Fig. 11.14. The theoretical predictions from eqn. (6.29), using eqn. (11.11) to evaluate the applied stress-intensity factor, K_{Ic}, are also plotted for two values of intrinsic flaw size, a_0. It may be seen that, within experimental error, most of the measured values fall within the predictions of 100 μm $< a_0 <$ 150 μm. These values of a_0 are about twice the average particle size, and the average interparticle distance, and are eminently reasonable for such materials, cf., Table 11.2. However, the slope of the measured data is significantly less than that of the predicted relationships, indicating that the strength of the silica-filled epoxy does not fall off as rapidly as the fracture mechanics analysis would imply. This discrepancy probably arises from the need to rely heavily upon the crack growth measurements conducted at very low velocities ($\sim 10^{-8}$ m s^{-1}) and extrapolation of the K_{Ic} versus $\dot{a}$ data to even lower rates. On the other hand, it might also suggest that the time, t_i, required for crack initiation cannot be ignored. In any event, the fracture mechanics analysis does lead to a conservative estimate for the static-fatigue lifetime which will be of comfort to the design engineer.

11.6 CONCLUDING REMARKS

The development of multiphase plastics, especially those based upon the inclusion of a second rubbery phase, has led to significant improvements in the toughness of polymeric materials. The importance of this technology is evident from the considerable interest that has focussed upon the mechanisms of toughening. However, most of the studies have concentrated on rubber-modified plastics, reflecting the industrial importance of such polymers. The mechanisms involved in multiphase polymers employing rigid-particulate fillers, which are generally less effective in improving the toughness but produce lower-cost materials, have yet to be fully explored and benefits may be gained from such studies, especially if materials containing both rigid *and* rubbery particles can be induced to exhibit the many toughening mechanisms that are potentially available.

Also, in the general area of relationships between structure, toughening mechanisms and fracture behaviour, it is only very recently that quantitative studies to ascertain the kinetics and failure criteria of the mechanisms involved have been reported. Until such data are firmly established it is difficult to define structure/property relationships in any detailed, quantitative manner. This obviously inhibits attempts to define the microstructure needed to attain specific fracture properties for any given application.

REFERENCES

1. Kambour, R. P. (1973). *Macromol. Rev.*, **7**, 1.
2. Mann, J. & Williamson, G. R. (1977). In: *The physics of glassy polymers*, Ed. by R. N. Haward, Applied Science Publishers Ltd., London.
3. Bucknall, C. B. (1977). *Toughened plastics*, Applied Science Publishers Ltd., London.

4. Bucknall, C. B. (1978). *Adv. Polym. Sci.*, **27,** 121.
5. Paul, D. R. & Newman, S. (1978). *Polymer blends*, Vols. 1 and 2, Academic Press, New York.
6. Riew, C. K., Rowe, E. H. & Siebert, A. R. (1978). In: *Toughness and brittleness of plastics*, Ed. by R. D. Deanin & A. M. Crugnola, Academic Press, New York.
7. Phillips, D. C. & Harris, B. (1977). In: *Polymer engineering composites*, Ed. by M. O. W. Richardson, Applied Science Publishers Ltd., London, p. 45.
8. Merz, E. H., Claver, G. C. & Baer, M. (1956). *J. Polym. Sci.*, **22,** 325.
9. Newman, S. & Strella, S. (1965). *J. Appl. Polym. Sci.*, **9,** 2297.
10. Kunz-Douglass, S., Beaumont, P. W. R. & Ashby, M. F. (1980). *J. Mater. Sci.*, **15,** 1109.
11. Kunz, S. & Beaumont, P. W. R. (1981). *J. Mater. Sci.*, **16,** 3141.
12. Sultan, J. N. & McGarry, F. J. (1973). *Polym. Eng. Sci.*, **13,** 29.
13. Bascom, W. D. & Cottington, R. L. (1976). *J. Adhesion*, **7,** 333.
14. Bascom, W. D., Ting, R. Y., Moulton, R. J., Riew, C. K. & Siebert, A. R. (1981). *J. Mater. Sci.*, **16,** 2657.
15. Bitner, J. R., Rushford, J. L., Rose, W. S., Hunston, D. L. & Riew, C. K. (1982). *J. Adhesion*, **13,** 3.
16. Goodier, J. N. (1933). *Trans. Am. Soc. Mech. Engs.*, **55,** 39.
17. Oxborough, R. J. & Bowden, P. B. (1974). *Phil. Mag.*, **30,** 171.
18. Broutman, L. J. & Panizza, G. (1971). *Int. J. Polym. Mater.*, **1,** 95.
19. Petrich, R. P. (1973). *Polym. Eng. Sci.*, **13,** 248.
20. Haaf, F., Breuer, H. & Stabenow, J. (1977). *J. Macromol. Sci. Phys.*, **B14,** 387.
21. Donald, A. M. & Kramer, E. J. (1982). *J. Mater. Sci.*, **17,** 1765.
22. Hagerman, E. M. (1973). *J. Appl. Polym. Sci.*, **17,** 2203.
23. Yee, A. F. (1977). *J. Mater. Sci.*, **12,** 757.
24. Yee, A. F., Olszewski, W. V. & Miller, S. (1976). In: *Toughness and brittleness of plastics*, Ed. by R. D. Deanin & A. M. Crugnola, Amer. Chem. Soc., Washington D.C., p. 97.
25. Kinloch, A. J. & Williams, J. G. (1980). *J. Mater. Sci.*, **15,** 987.
26. Kinloch, A. J. & Shaw, S. J. to be published.
27. Lavengood, R. E., Nicolais, L. & Narkis, M. (1973). *J. Appl. Polym. Sci.*, **17,** 1173.
28. Agarwal, B. D. (1972). PhD Thesis, Illinois Inst. of Technology.
29. Agarwal, B. D. & Broutman, L. J. (1974). *Fibre Sci. Technol.*, **7,** 63.
30. Brown, S. K. (1980). *British Polym. J.*, **12,** 24.
31. Bucknall, C. B. & Smith, R. R. (1965). *Polymer*, **6,** 437.
32. Matsuo, M. (1966). *Polymer*, **7,** 421.
33. Kambour, R. P. & Russell, D. R. (1971). *Polymer*, **12,** 237.
34. Matsuo, M., Nozaki, C. & Jyo, Y. (1969). *Polym. Eng. Sci.*, **9,** 197.
35. Matsuo, M., Ueda, A. & Kondon, Y. (1970). *Polym. Eng. Sci.*, **10,** 253.
36. Moore, J. D. (1971). *Polymer*, **12,** 478.
37. Bucknall, C. B., Clayton, D. & Keast, W. E. (1972). *J. Mater. Sci.*, **7,** 1443.
38. Beahan, P., Thomas, A. & Bevis, M. (1976). *J. Mater. Sci.*, **11,** 1207.
39. Kato, K. (1965). *J. Electron Micros.*, **14,** 220.

40. Kato, K. (1967). *Polym. Eng. Sci.,* **7,** 38.
41. Kato, K. (1967). *Koll. Z. u. Z. Polym.,* **220,** 24.
42. Haward, R. N. & Bucknall, C. B. (1976). *Pure and Appl. Chem.,* **46,** 227.
43. Donald, A. M. & Kramer, E. J. (1982). *J. Appl. Polym. Sci.,* to be published.
44. Donald, A. M. & Kramer, E. J. (1982). *J. Mater. Sci.,* **17,** 2351.
45. British Patent, 1,005,681 (1965).
46. Turley, S. G. & Keskkula, H. (1980). *Polymer,* **21,** 466.
47. Argon, A. S. (1975). *Pure and Appl. Chem.,* **43,** 247.
48. Bucknall, C. B. (1969). *J. Mater. Sci.,* **4,** 214.
49. Ricco, T., Oavan, A. & Danusso, F. (1978). *Polym. Eng. Sci.,* **18,** 774.
50. Williams, J. G. & Marshall, G. P. (1975). *Proc. Roy. Soc.,* **A342,** 55.
51. Argon, A. S., Cohen, R. E., Jang, B. Z. & VanderSande, J. B. (1981). *J. Polym. Sci. Polym. Phys.,* **19,** 253.
52. Bucknall, C. B. & Clayton, D. (1972). *J. Mater. Sci.,* **7,** 202.
53. Bucknall, C. B., Clayton, D. & Keast, W. E. (1973). *J. Mater. Sci.,* **8,** 514.
54. Bucknall, C. B., Page, C. J. & Young, V. O. (1973). *J. Mater. Sci.,* **8,** 1800.
55. Truss, R. W. & Chadwick, G. A. (1976). *J. Mater. Sci.,* **11,** 111.
56. Bucknall, C. & Yoshii, T. (1978). *British Polym. J.,* **10,** 53.
57. Coumans, W. J., Heikens, D. & Sjoerdsma, S. D. (1980). *Polymer,* **21,** 103.
58. Ramsteiner, F. (1979). *Polymer,* **20,** 839.
59. Lange, F. F. & Radford, K. C. (1971). *J. Mater. Sci.,* **6,** 1197.
60. Lange, F. F. (1970). *Phil. Mag.,* **22,** 983.
61. Spanoudakis, J. (1981). *Fracture in particle filled epoxy resins,* PhD Thesis, London University, Queen Mary College, London.
62. Spanoudakis, J. & Young, R. J. To be published.
63. Lange, F. F. (1971). *J. Amer. Ceram. Soc.,* **54,** 614.
64. Evans, A. G. (1972). *Phil. Mag.,* **26,** 1327.
65. Evans, A. G. (1974). *J. Mater. Sci.,* **9,** 1145.
66. Green, D. J., Nicholson, P. S. & Embury, J. D. (1979). *J. Mater. Sci.,* **14,** 1413.
67. Green, D. J., Nicholson, P. S. & Embury, J. D. (1979). *J. Mater. Sci.,* **14,** 1657.
68. Owen, A. B. (1979). *J. Mater. Sci.,* **14,** 2521.
69. Chow, T. S. (1980). *J. Mater. Sci.,* **15,** 1873.
70. Radford, K. C. (1971). *J. Mater. Sci.,* **6,** 1286.
71. Mallick, P. K. & Broutman, L. J. (1975). *Mater. Sci. Eng.,* **18,** 63.
72. Nicolais, L. (1975). *Polym. Eng. Sci.,* **15,** 137.
73. Nicolais, L. & Narkis, M. (1971). *Polym. Eng. Sci.,* **11,** 194.
74. Biglione, G., Baer, E. & Radcliffe, S. V. (1969). *Fracture–1969,* Ed. by P. L. Pratt, Chapman and Hall, London, p. 503.
75. Keskkula, H., Turley, S. G. & Boyer, R. F. (1971). *J. Appl. Polym. Sci.,* **15,** 351.
76. Wagner, E. R. & Robeson, L. M. (1970). *Rubb. Chem. Technol.,* **43,** 1129.
77. Sacher, E. (1980). *Polymer,* **21,** 1234.

78. Nikpur, K. & Williams, J. G. (1978). *Plast. Rubb: Mater. Appl.*, **3,** 163.
79. Nikpur, K. & Williams, J. G. (1979). *J. Mater. Sci.*, **14,** 467.
80. Bucknall, C. B. & Street, D. G. (1967). *SCI Monograph. No. 26,* 272.
81. Kobayashi, T. & Broutman, L. J. (1973). *J. Appl. Polym. Sci.*, **17,** 2053.
82. Baum, B. *et al.* (1976). In: *Toughness and brittleness of polymers*, Ed. by R. D. Deanin & A. M. Crugnola, Amer. Chem. Soc., Washington D.C., p. 263.
83. Bascom, W. D., Cottington, R. L., Jones, R. L. & Peyser, P. (1975). *J. Appl. Polym. Sci.*, **19,** 2545.
84. McGarry, F. J., Rowe, E. H. & Riew, C. K. (1977). *32nd Ann. Tech. Conf. of the SPI*, p. 16-C.
85. Sacher, E. (1976). In: *Toughness and brittleness of polymers*, Ed. by R. D. Deanin & A. M. Crugnola, Amer. Chem. Soc., Washington D.C., p. 133.
86. Broutman, L. J. & Sahu, S. (1971). *Mater. Sci. Eng.*, **8,** 98.
87. Hammond, J. C. & Quayle, P. V. (1973). *2nd intern. conf. on yield, deformation and fracture*, Churchill College, Cambridge, Plastics Rubb. Inst., London p. 11.
88. Young, R. J. & Beaumont, P. W. R. (1977). *J. Mater. Sci.*, **12,** 684.
89. Haward, R. N. & Mann, J. (1964). *Proc. Roy. Soc.*, **A282,** 120.
90. Kinloch, A. J. (1980). *J. Mater. Sci.*, **15,** 2141.
91. Durst, R. R., Griffith, R. M., Urbanic, A. J. & Van Essen, W. J. (1976). In: *Toughness and brittleness of polymers*, Ed. by R. D. Deanin & A. M. Crugnola, Amer. Chem. Soc., Washington D.C., p. 239.
92. Aggarwal, S. L. & Livigni, R. A. (1977). *Polym. Eng. Sci.*, **17,** 498.
93. Coumans, W. J., Heikens, D. & Sjoerdsma, S. D. (1980). *Polymer*, **21,** 103.
94. Koenig, J. L. & Shih, P. T. K. (1971). *J. Colloid Interf. Sci.*, **36,** 247.
95. Gettings, M. & Kinloch, A. J. (1977). *J. Mater. Sci.*, **12,** 2511.
96. Sahu, S. & Broutman, L. J. (1972). *Polym. Eng. Sci.*, **12,** 91.
97. Nicholais, L. & Nicodemo, L. (1973). *Polym. Eng. Sci.*, **13,** 469.
98. Leidner, J. & Woodhams, R. T. (1974). *J. Appl. Polym. Sci.*, **18,** 1639.
99. Manzione, L. T., Gillham, J. K. & McPherson, C. A. (1981). *J. Appl. Polym. Sci.*, **26,** 884.
100. Manzione, L. T., Gillham, J. K. & McPherson, C. A. (1981). *J. Appl. Polym. Sci.*, **26,** 907.
101. St. Clair, A. K. & St. Clair, T. L. (1981). *Int. J. Adhes. Adhesives*, **1,** 249.
102. Wambach, A. D., Trachte, K. & Dibenedetto, A. T. (1968). *J. Composite Mater.*, **2,** 266.
103. Ferguson, R. J., Marshall, G. P. & Williams, J. G. (1973). *Polymer*, **14,** 451.
104. Parvin, M. & Williams, J. G. (1976). *J. Mater. Sci.*, **11,** 2045.
105. Bucknall, C. B. (1978). *5th. European Conf. on Plastics and Rubbers*, Paris, p. D.8.
106. Bucknall, C. B. (1982). Private communication.
107. Newmann, L. V. & Williams, J. G. (1980). *J. Mater. Sci.*, **15,** 773.
108. Kinloch, A. J. & Shaw, S. J. (1981). *J. Adhesion*, **12,** 59.
109. Kinloch, A. J., Shaw, S. J. & Hunston, D. L. (1982). *Deformation, yield and fracture of polymers*, Conf., Churchill College, Cambridge, Plastics Rubb. Inst., London, p. 29.

110. Hunston, D. L., Kinloch, A. J., Shaw, S. J. & Wang, S. S. *Adhesive joints: formation, characterisation and testing*, Amer. Chem. Soc. Meeting, Kansas City, Sept. 1982, to be published.
111. Bucknall, C. B. & Street, D. G. (1967). *SCI Monograph. No. 26*, 272.
112. Dibenedetto, A. T. & Wambach, A. D. (1972). *Int. J. Polym. Mater.*, **1**, 159.
113. Mai, Y. W. (1976). *Polym. Eng. Sci.*, **16**, 400.
114. Drake, R. & Siebert, A. (1975). *SAMPE Quart.*, **6**(4), 11.
115. Kinloch, A. J. (Ed.) (1981). *Developments in adhesives—2*, Applied Science Publishers Ltd., London.
116. Lees, W. A. (1981). *J. Adhesion*, **12**, 233.
117. Kinloch, A. J. & Shaw, S. J. (1981). In: *Developments in adhesives—2*, Ed. by A. J. Kinloch, Applied Science Publishers Ltd., London, p. 83.
118. Wang, S. S., Mandell, J. F. & McGarry, F. J. (1978). *Int. J. Fract.*, **14**, 39.
119. Nielsen, L. E. (1975). *J. Compos. Mater.*, **9**, 149.
120. Murukami, R., Shin, N., Jusomots, N. & Motozata, Y. (1976). *Kobunshi Robunshi*, **33**, 107.
121. Bartesh, H. & Williams, D. R. G. (1978). *J. Appl. Polym. Sci.*, **22**, 467.
122. Bucknall, C. B. & Stevens, W. W. (1978). *Toughening of plastics*, Conf. Proc. Plastics and Rubb. Inst., London, p. 24.
123. Menges, G. & Wiegand, E. (1975). *Proc. 21st Ann. Tech. Conf. of SPI*, p. 469.
124. Beardmore, P. & Rabinowitz, S. (1974). *Appl. Polym. Sympos.*, **24**, 25.
125. Skibo, M. D., Manson, J. A., Hertzberg, R. W. & Collins, E. A. (1979). *Durability of macromolecular materials*, Ed. by R. K. Eby, Amer. Chem. Soc., Washington D.C., p. 311.
126. Hertzberg, R. W. & Manson, J. A. (1980). *Fatigue of engineering polymers*, Academic Press, New York, p. 185.
127. Skibo, M. D., Hertzberg, R. W. & Manson, J. A. (1979). *J. Mater. Sci.*, **14**, 2482.
128. Sauer, J. A. & Richardson, G. C. (1980). *Int. J. Fract.*, **16**, 499.
129. Lankford, J., Astleford, W. J. & Asher, M. A. (1976). *J. Mater. Sci.*, **11**, 1624.
130. Freitag, T. A. & Cannon, S. L. (1977). *J. Biomed. Mater. Res.*, **11**, 609.
131. Freitag, T. A. & Cannon, S. L. (1979). *J. Biomed. Mater. Res.*, **13**, 343.
132. Young, R. J. & Beaumont, P. W. R. (1975). *J. Mater. Sci.*, **10**, 1334.
133. Young, R. J. & Beaumont, P. W. R. (1975). *J. Mater. Sci.*, **10**, 1343.
134. Hojo, H., Toyoshima, W., Tamua, M. & Kawamura, N. (1974). *Polym. Eng. Sci.*, **14**, 604.

Author Index

Abbot, B. W., 185, *221*
Adams, R., 216, *225*
Adicoff, A., 411, *420*
Afzal, S. M., 201, *222*
Agarwal, B. D., 427, *468*
Aggarwal, S. L., 407, *419,* 449, *470*
Ahagon, A., 84, *105,* 383, 384, *417*
Ainbinder, S. R., 115, *144*
Airey, R., 216, 219, *225*
Aklonis, J. J., 372, *417*
Alder, W., 314, *323*
Alf, E., 338, 339, *367*
Allan, P., 337, *366*
Allen, S. R., 357–60, *369*
Allport, D. C., 375, 407, *417*
Anderson, G. P., 390, *418*
Anderson, W. E., 204, *223*
Anderton, G. E., 342, *367*
Ando, D. J., 332, *366*
Andrews, E. H., 29, 34, 35, *38,* 48, 50, 52, 55, 57, 58, 59, 61, 63, 68, 70, *71, 72,* 77, 85, 86, *105,* 141, 142, *146,* 158, 160, *179, 180,* 182, 185, 188, 197, 198, 201, 204, 209, 211, 214, *220–4,* 230, 236, 256–8, 261, 270, 273, *280, 282, 284,* 287, 290–7, 301, 302, 305, 308, 311, 313, *321,* 328, 329, 330, 332, 337, 338, 342–4, 351, 352, 356, 357, *365–8,* 371, 376,

Andrews, E. H.,—*contd.*
385–7, 390–4, 415, *416–18, 420*
Andrews, J. M., 332, *366*
Andrews, R. D., 117, 122, 124, 126, *144, 145*
Arad, S., 273, *285*
Argon, A., 31, *38,* 118, 122, 124, 126, 128, *144, 145*
Argon, A. S., 159, 165, 166, 167, *179, 180,* 256, 264, *282, 283,* 288, *321,* 431, 432, *469*
Arsenault, R. J., 199, *222*
Asahina, M., 327, 328, *365*
Ashby, M. F., 423, 424, 442, 444, *468*
Asher, M. A., 464, *471*
Ast, D. G., 153, 154, 156, 158, 169, *178, 179, 180*
Astleford, W. J., 464, *471*
Atkins, A. G., 115, 116, *144,* 171, *180,* 244–9, 254, *282,* 300, 301, *322*
Atkinson, J. R., 338, 339, 341, *367*
Attenburrow, G. E., 339, *367*
Ayscough, P., 57, *72*

Baer, E., 115, 116, 129, *144, 145,* 159, 164, *179, 180,* 236, 260, 261, 263–5, *281, 283,* 442, *469*

Baer, M., 423, 424, *468*
Bair, T. I., 330, 357–61, *366*
Ballard, D. G. H., 13, 15, *38*
Ballou, J. W., 330, 357–61, *366*
Ban, T., 127, *145*
Bandyopadhyay, S., 338, 356, *367, 368*
Barenblatt, G. I., 91, *105*
Barham, P. J., 329–31, *365*
Barns, D. J., 201, *223*
Bartesh, H., 463, *471*
Bascom, W. D., 293, 294, *321,* 393, *418,* 424, 427, 442, 445, 455, 460, *468, 470*
Bassett, D. C., 332, 339, *366, 367*
Batchelder, D. N., 55, 56, *72,* 127, *145,* 328–30, 332, *365, 366*
Bateman, L., 402, 404, 410, *419, 420*
Baughman, R. H., 330, *365*
Baum, B., 442, *470*
Bauwens, J. C., 112, 113, 114, 115, 116, *143, 144,* 158, 165, *179, 180,* 205, 206, 215, *223, 224,* 264, *284*
Bauwens-Crowet, C., 112, 113, 114, *143, 144,* 264, *284*
Beahan, P., 149, 150, 151, 169, 173, *178,* 260, 261, 267, 269, *283,* 428, *468*
Beardmore, P., 176, *181,* 199, *222,* 233, 246, *280,* 463, *471*
Beaumont, P. W. R., 102, *106,* 171, *180,* 216, *225,* 242–5, 277, 278, *281, 285,* 296, 298, 302, 309, *322,* 423, 424, 427, 442, 444–7, 455, 459, 465, 466, *468, 470, 471*
Becht, J., 64, 66, *72*
Beck, R. H., 117, *144*
Beecher, J. F., 407, *419*
Begley, J. A., 82, *105*
Beinert, J., 188, *221,* 299, 301, 315, *322, 323*
Bell, J. P., 290, 291, 316, *321*
Bellin, J. L., 411, *420*
Benbow, J. J., 242, *281*
Benham, P. P., 201, 202, *222, 223*
Bennett, S. J., 390, *418*
Bernier, G. A., 161, *180,* 256, *282*
Berry, J. P., 35, 36, *39,* 46, *71,* 76,

Berry, J. P.,—*contd.*
105, 133, *145,* 230–4, 240, 242, 245, 251, *280, 282,* 289, 291, *321*
Bersch, C., 300, *322*
Bessell, T. J., 338, 339, *367*
Bessonov, M. I., 118, *144,* 155, *179,* 264, *283*
Bevan, L., 160, *180,* 256–8, *282*
Bevis, M., 149, 150, 151, 169, 173, *178,* 260, 261, 265, 267, 269, *283,* 337, *366,* 428, *468*
Bhateja, S. K., 236, *280,* 346, 347, *367*
Biglione, G., 236, *281,* 442, *469*
Billington, E. W., 85, *105*
Binder, G., 110, *143*
Birch, M. W., 193, 196, *222,* 348–51, *367*
Bird, R. J., 267, 268, *284*
Bitner, J. R., 424, 427, 455–7, 460, *468*
Blackley, D. C., 411, *420*
Blades, H., 331, *369*
Blanchard, A. F., 374, *417*
Blasius, J., 59, *72*
Blatz, P. J., 216, *224*
Bloor, D., 55, 56, *72,* 127, *145,* 328–30, 332, *365, 366*
Bluhm, J. I., 97, *106*
Boettner, R. C., 208, *224*
Bolotin, V. V., 219, *225*
Boonstra, B. S., 402, *419*
Bopp, R. C., 96, *106,* 249, *282*
Boudreaux, D. S., 327, 328, 333, 335, 359, *365*
Bowden, P. B., 24, 31, *38,* 108, 109, 110, 111, 113, 116, 117, 118, 119, 120, 121, 122, 123, 124, 125, 127, 128, *143, 144, 145,* 162, 163, *180,* 256, 264, *282, 283,* 288, *321,* 331, 332, *366,* 425, 431, 442, *468*
Boyd, R. H., 327, 328, *365*
Boyer, R., 17, *38*
Boyer, R. F., 442, 445, *469*
Braden, M., 385, *418*
Bradford, R. D., 407, *419*
Brady, T. E., 117, 122, 124, *144, 145*
Braiden, P. M., 216, 219, *225*

Bretz, P. E., 351, 353, *368*
Breuer, H., 137, *146,* 426, 434, *468*
Brinson, H. F., 135, *146,* 262, *283*
Broek, D., 75, 97, *105,* 188, *221*
Broutman, L. J., 83, *105,* 133, *145,* 242, 245, 252, *281, 282,* 291–4, 296, 306, 307, *321,* 425, 427, 439, 442, 445, 447, 450, 457, *468–70,*
Brower, A. L., 24, *38,* 327, 328, 333–5, 359, *365*
Brower, F. M., 237, *281*
Brown, H. R., 36, *39,* 150, 152, 154, 155, 158, *178, 179,* 183, 192, *220,* 233, 240, 249, 250, 256, 257, 260, 261, 267, 270, 271, *280, 282–4,* 296, 298, 306, *321,* 338, 348, 356, *367, 368*
Brown, N., 110, *143,* 234, 235, 246, *280,* 298, *322*
Brown, S. K., 427, 450, 459, *468*
Brown, W., 197, 198, 201, *222*
Brown, W. E., 165, *180*
Brown, W. F., 102, *106*
Bruenner, R. S., 380, 381, 411, *417*
Bryant, G. M., 117, *144*
Bubeck, R. A., 158, *179*
Bucknall, C., 434, 442–5, 451, *469*
Bucknall, C. B., 133, *146,* 165, *180,* 182, 191, *220,* 422, 425, 428, 431–4, 438, 440, 442, 449, 451, 453, 457–9, 463, 465, *467–71*
Bueche, A. M., 413, *420*
Bueche, F., 50, *71,* 374, 375, 404, 413–15, *417, 419, 420*
Bunsell, A. R., 360, *369*
Burke, J. J., 208, *224*
Burns, D. J., 273, *285*
Bush, A. J., 188, *221*

Caddell, R. M., 115, 116, *144,* 245–7, *282*
Campbell, J. D., 288, *321*
Camwell, L., 131, *145,* 261, *283*
Cannon, S. L., 464, *471*
Capaccio, G., 328–32, 357, 358, 361, *365, 366, 368*
Capiati, N., 331, 357, *368*

Carder, D. R., 332, 339, *366*
Cartwright, D. J., 88, *105*
Casale, A., 59, *72*
Cerra, P., 337, *366*
Chadwick, G. A., 434, *469*
Champion, J. V., 287, *321*
Chan, T., 149, 150, 166, *178,* 260, 261, *283*
Charlesby, A., 208, *223*
Chau, C. C., 122, 128, 130, *145,* 261, *283*
Chell, G. G., 82, *105*
Cherry, B. W., 302, *322*
Chin, T. H., 158, *179*
Chow, T. S., 438, *469*
Christiansen, A., 296, 298, *321*
Christiansen, A. W., 115, 133, *144, 145*
Chu, W. H., 404, 405, *419*
Ciferri, A., 328–30, 332, 357–61, *365, 366, 369*
Clark, E. S., 357, 358, *368*
Claver, G. C., 423, 424, *468*
Clayton, D., 133, *146,* 428, 433, 434, *468, 469*
Clements, J., 329, 330, *365*
Clutton, E. Q., 270–2, *284*
Cohen, R. E., 431, 432, *469*
Coleman, B. D., 113, *144,* 216, *224*
Collins, E. A., 463, 464, *471*
Comyn, J., 314, *323*
Connor, A. O., 332, *366*
Constable, I., 141, *146,* 201, *223,* 273, *285*
Cook, N. P., 185, *221*
Cooney, J. L., 212, *224*
Cooper, A. R., 237–9, 271, *281,* 354, 356, *368*
Cooper, S. L., 113, *144,* 375, 407, *417*
Cornes, P. L., 137, 138, *146,* 263, 269, *283*
Cornish, R. H., 185, *221*
Corten, H. T., 93, *106*
Cottington, R. L., 293, 294, *321,* 393, *418,* 424, 427, 442, 445, 455, 460, *468, 470*
Cottrell, A., 44, *71*
Coumans, W. J., 434, 449, *469, 470*

Coutts, L. H., 155, 172, *179,* 242, 243, 245–8, *281,* 298, 300, *322*
Cramer, C., 133, 134, *146*
Crawford, R. J., 201, 202, *222, 223*
Crissman, J. M., 212, *224,* 354, *368*
Crist, B., 24., *38,* 59, *72,* 327, 328, 333–5, 359, *365*
Crook, M., 231, *280*
Crosley, P. B., 102, *106*
Crucker, D. D., 334, *366*
Crugnola, A. M., 422, 427, 442, 445, 449, 450, *468, 470*
Culver, L. E., 141, *146,* 158, *179,* 208, 210, *224,* 242, 244, 245, 256, 257, 259, 273, *281, 282, 285,* 355, *368*
Cunneen, J. I., 404, *419*
Curtis, J. W., 240, 241, 252–4, *281*

Dadek, T., 404, *419*
Dandridge, A., 287, *321*
Daniels, H. E., 173, *180*
Dannenberg, E. M., 375, 410, *417*
Danusso, F., 431, *469*
Darin, S. R., 404, 413, 414, *419, 420*
Davidge, R. W., 216, 218, 219, *225*
Davidson, A. T., 337, *366*
Davis, L. A., 117, *144*
Deanin, R. D., 422, 427, 442, 445, 449, 450, *468, 470*
Dencouer, R. L., 379, *417*
De Sisto, T. S., 188, *221*
Desper, C. R., 357, 358, *368*
Dettenmaier, M., 15, 16, *38*
DeVries, K. L., 53, 54, 55, 56, 57, 62, 64, 66, 67, *72,* 203, *223,* 361–3, *369,* 385, *418*
Diamont, Y., 411, *420*
Dibenedetto, A. T., 256, 259, 260, *283,* 452, 459, *470, 471*
Dickie, R. A., 398, 407, *419*
Diedrich, G., 212, *224*
Diggwa, A. D. S., 293, 294, 296, 298, *321*
Dlugosz, J., 407, *419*
Doak, K. W., 354, *368*

Döll, W., 155, 156, 158, 173, 174, *179,* 208, *223,* 242–4, 247, 260, 267, 268, *281–4*
Donald, A. M., 133, 135, 136, *146,* 149, 150, 166, 175, *178, 180, 181,* 260–3, 265–7, 269, 280, *283,* 306, *322,* 426, 427, 430, 431, 434, *468, 469*
Donald, J. K., 209, *224*
Doolittle, A. K., 373, *417*
Doyle, M. J., 169, 170, 171, *180,* 267–9, *284*
Drake, R., 460, *471*
Dreyfuss, P., 398, 411, *418*
Driscoll, D. E., 188, *221*
Drucker, D. C., 195, *222*
Duckett, R. A., 37, *39,* 96, *106,* 114, *144,* 215, *224,* 236, 240, 249, 250, 267, 271, *281, 282,* 346, 348, *367*
Duckett, R. L., 174, *180*
Dudek, T., 414, *420*
Dugdale, D. S., 91, *105*
Dukes, W. A., 216, 218, *225*
Dulniak, R., 127, *145,* 332, *366*
Dunn, P., 357, *368*
Durst, R. R., 449, *470*
Dušek, K., 287, 308, *321*

Earl, B. L., 231, *280*
Eby, R. K., 212, *224,* 354, *368,* 463, 464, *471*
Eckert, R. E., 58, *72*
Eirich, F. R., 117, *144,* 370, 373–5, 377, 378, 404, 405, 407, 410, 411, *416, 417, 419, 420*
Eldred, R. J., 377, *417*
El-Hakeem, H. A., 208, *224*
Elinyck, J. R., 205, 206, *223*
Embury, J. D., 437, 446, 448, *469*
Enkelmann, V., 328, 330, *365*
Enomoto, S., 327, 328, *365*
Erdogan, F., 203, 204, *223*
Evans, A. G., 216, *225,* 437, 446–8, *469*
Ewing, A., 188, *221*
Eyring, H., 112, 114, *143*

Farrar, N. R., 176, *181,* 260, 261, *283*
Farris, R. J., 357–60, *369,* 411, *420*
Fedors, R. F., 404, 405, *419*
Fellers, J. F., 174, *180*
Feltner, C. E., 208, *224*
Ferguson, R. J., 452, *470*
Ferry, J. D., 26, 29, *38,* 201, *222,* 372, 373, *417*
Fetters, L. J., 407, *419*
Field, J. E., 248, *282*
Filippov, A. G., 357–60, *369*
Fischer, E. W., 15, 16, *38,* 260, *283*
Fischer, H., 66, *72*
Flory, P. J., 13, *38,* 239, *281,* 404, *419*
Foden, E., 201, 208, *222,* 273, 275, *285*
Fogelson, R. A., 110, *143*
Folkes, M. J., 407, *419*
Folman, M., 411, *420*
Ford, H., 111, *143*
Fornet, A., 60, *72*
Fox, P. G., 248, *282*
Frank, F. C., 326, 332, *365, 366*
Fraser, R. A., 96, 97, *106,* 155, *179,* 192, *221,* 246, 249, 250, 260, 271, *282, 284*
Freitag, T. A., 464, *471*
Friedland, K. J., 55, 56, *72,* 361, 363, *369*
Friedrich, K., 122, 128, *145,* 338–40, *367*
Frisch, H. L., 408, 409, *420*
Fukahori, Y., 50, *71,* 85, *105,* 141, 142, *146,* 342, 343, *367,* 371, 376, 392, *416, 417*
Fuller, K. N. G., 248, *282*
Furno, F. J., 185, *221*

Gales, R. D. R., 155, *179*
Galiotis, C., 48, 55, 56, *71, 72,* 328–31, 333–7, 358, 360, *365, 366*
Gaube, E., 212, 213, 215, *224,* 338, 348, 353, *367*
Geil, P. H., 264, *284,* 337, 357, *366, 368*

Gent, A. N., 14, *38,* 69, *73,* 77, 84, 92, *105,* 160, 161, 165, *180,* 204, *223,* 239, *281,* 370, 372–85, 390, 392, 393, 395, 397–9, 405, 407, 411, *416–18*
Gerberich, W. N., 158, *179*
Gerberich, W. W., 210, *224, 273, 285*
Gettings, M., 450, *470*
Gibson, A. G., 328–30, 332, 357, 358, 361, *365*
Gillham, J. K., 451, *470*
Gilman, J. J., 334, *366*
Gledhill, R. A., 96, *106,* 110, *143,* 216, 218, 219, *225,* 296–300, 301, 305, 307–11, 314, 317–19, *322, 323,* 344, 345, *367*
Gleiter, H., 119, *145,* 330, 338, *365, 367*
Godrick, J. A., 122, 124, 126, *145*
Gogolewski, S., 339, *367*
Golden, J. H., 237, 238, *281*
Gomez, M. P., 204, *223*
Gonzalez, H., Jr., 270, *284*
Goodier, J. N., 425, 427, 431, *468*
Gotham, K. V., 182, 191, *220,* 242, *281*
Graham, I. D., 156, 161, *179,* 256, *282*
Granatstein, D. L., 411, *420*
Gray, T. F., Jr., 357–9, *369*
Green, D. J., 437, 446, 448, *469*
Greensmith, H. W., 80, 81, 98, *105,* 216, 217, *225,* 338, 394, 395, 402, 412, 415, *418–20*
Griffith, A. A., 35, *39,* 74, *104,* 289, *321*
Griffith, R. M., 449, *470*
Griffiths, R., 293, 294, *321*
Grosch, K. A., 406, *419*
Groves, G. W., 326, 331, *365*
Gruner, C. L., 158, *179,* 256, 257, *282*
Guinier, A., 60, *72*
Guldemond, W. G., 113, *144*
Gunn, D. A., 115, *144*
Guth, E., 410, *420*

Haaf, F., 137, *146*, 426, 434, *468*
Haaf, W. R., 260, *283*
Hagerman, E. M., 427, 434, *468*
Hakeem, M. I., 254, *282*, 299, 300, *322*
Hall, I. H., 264, *284*, 307, *322*
Halpin, J. C., 50, *71*, 330, *366*, 415, *420*
Hamed, G. R., 376, 393, 407, *417*, *418*
Hammant, B. L., 237, 238, *281*
Hammond, J. C., 445, *470*
Hannon, M. J., 356, *368*
Hannoosh, J. G., 128, *145*, 159, 165, *179*, 256, *282*
Harris, B., 422, 423, 436, 452, *468*
Harris, J. S., 317, *323*
Hartog, J. H., 387, *418*
Harwood, J. A. C., 372, 374, 375, 376, 406, *416*, *417*, *419*
Haward, R. N., 109, 110, 113, 120, 137, 138, 139, *143*, *146*, 149, 159, 160, 173, *178*, *179*, *180*, 197, 222, 263, 269, *283*, *284*, 306, 310, *322*, 407, *419*, 422, 428, 433, 449, *467*, *469*, *470*
Hay, I. L., 332, *366*
Hay, J. N., 137, 139, *146*, 269, *284*
Hazell, E. A., 237, 238, *281*
Heald, P. T., 141, *146*
Hearle, J. W. S., 357, 360, *368*, *369*
Heijboer, J., 196, *222*, 230, 273, *280*, 348, 349, *367*
Heikens, D., 434, 449, *469*, *470*
Henry, A. W., 390, 392, 395, *418*
Hepburn, C., 393, *418*
Hertzberg, R. W., 197, 198, 204–11, *222–4*, 273–6, *285*, 290, 291, 316, *321*, *323*, 351, 353, *367*, *368*, 463, 464, *471*
Hine, P. J., 96, *106*, 249, 250, 267, *282*
Hinton, T., 354, 355, *368*
Hoare, J., 153, 170, *178*, *180*
Hobbs, S. Y., 96, *106*, 249, *282*
Hodgkinson, J. M., 83, *105*, 141, 142, *146*, 193, 196, *222*, 270–2, *284*, 342, 344, 348–51, *367*

Hojo, H., 465, *471*
Holik, A. S., 149, 150, *178*, 249, 269, *282*
Holliday, L., 115, *144*, 327, 328, *365*
Holloway, D. G., 133, *145*, 293, 294, 306, *321*, *322*
Holt, D. L., 112, *143*
Homes, G., 112, 113, 114, *143*, *144*, 205, 206, *223*, 264, *284*
Hoover, W. R., 188, *221*
Hornbogen, E., 339, 340, *367*
Howard, J. B., 354, *368*
Hsiao, C. C., 53, *71*
Hubble, C. L., 127, *145*, 332, *366*
Hull, D., 131, *145*, 149, 150, 151, 153, 169, 173, *178*, *180*, 260, 261, 267–9, *283*, *284*, 286, 301, *320*, *322*, 338, 339, *367*
Hunston, D. L., 313–15, *322*, 424, 427, 455–7, 460, *468*, *470*, *471*

Imai, Y., 234, 246, *280*, 298, *322*
Ireland, D. R., 183, *220*
Irwin, G. R., 75, 78, 86, 88, 91, 93, *104*, *105*, 141, 142, *146*
Ishai, O., 113, *144*
Isherwood, D. P., 342, 343, *367*
Ishikawa, M., 113, 131, 132, *144*, *145*, 261, *283*
Israel, S. J., 158, *179*
Ito, T., 328, 329, *365*

Jackson, W., Jr., 357–9, *369*
Jacoby, G., 133, 134, *146*
Jaffe, R., 314, *323*
Jakeways, R., 329, 330, *365*
Janes, W. H., 375, 407, *417*
Jang, B. Z., 431, 432, *469*
Janiszewski, J., 273, 275, *285*, 290, 291, 316, *321*
Jaques, C. H. M., 159, 161, *180*
Jenkins, A. D., 182, 191, *220*, 330, *365*
Joffe, A. D., 337, *366*
Johnson, F. A., 242, 243, 247, 248, *281*

Johnson, J. F., 13, 14, *38*, 59, *72*, 208, *224*, 237–9, 271, *281*, 354, 356, *368*
Johnson, M. A., 314, *323*
Johnson, T. L., 233, 246, *280*
Johnston, T., 208, *224*
Jones, M., 216, 218, *225*, 293, 294, 297, 304, 317, *321*
Jones, R. L., 293, 294, *321*, 393, *418*, 442, 445, 455, 460, *470*
Jones, T. M., 399, 400, *419*
Jud, K., 269, 270, *284*
Jukes, J. A., 110, 111, 116, 122, 124, *143*
Jusomots, N., 463, *471*
Jyo, Y., 428, *468*

Kadir, A., 84, *105*, 393, *418*
Kalb, B., 358, 359, *369*
Kalthoff, J. F., 188, *221*, 299, 301, 315, *322, 323*
Kambour, R. P., 31, 32, *38*, 118, 133, 134, *144, 146*, 149, 150, 152, 153, 155, 158, 159, 161, 162, 165, 176, *178, 179, 180*, 197, *222*, 230, 231, 236, 240, 249, 256–8, 260–2, 267, 269, 273, 276, 277, *280, 282, 283, 285*, 306, *322*, 330, *365*, 422, 428, 429, 434, *467, 468*
Kanninen, M. F., 314, *323*
Kardos, J. L., 330, *366*
Kasahara, T., 272, *284*
Kastelic, J. R., 263, *283*
Kato, K., 428, *468, 469*
Katz, M. J., 251, *282*
Kausch, H. H., 48, 50, 53, 54, 55, 57, 62, 63, 64, 67, 68, *71, 72*, 212, 213, 215, *224*, 269, 270, 279, *284, 285*, 338, 348, 353, 358, 361–3, *367, 369*
Kawabata, S., 216, *224*
Kawamura, N., 465, *471*
Kazama, Y., 117, *144*
Keast, W. E., 133, *146*, 428, 433, 434, *468, 469*
Kee, B. F., 174, *180*
Keith, H. D., 15, *38*, 339, 356, *367*
Keller, A., 15, *38*, 119, *145*, 329–32, 337, 354, 355, 358, *365, 366, 368*,

Keller, A.,—*contd.*
407, *419*
Kelly, A., 34, *39*, 46, 47, 48, *71*, 74, *104*, 326, 331, *365*
Keskkula, H., 430, 442, 443, 445, *469*
Kiho, H., 337, *366*
Kim, H. J., 84, *105*
Kim, S. L., 205–9, *223, 224*, 273, 275, *285*, 290, 291, 316, *321*
Kin, L., 237, *281*
King, N. E., 287, 290, *321*
King, P. S., 260, 261, *283*
Kinloch, A. J., 77, 92, 96, 101, *105, 106*, 110, 140, 141, *143, 146*, 216, 218, 219, *225*, 286, 296–305, 307–15, 317–19, *320, 322, 323*, 344, 345, *367*, 385, 386, 390, 391, 393, *418*, 427, 438, 449, 450, 452, 455–7, 460, 461, *468, 470, 471*
Kireenko, O. F., 203, *223*
Kisbenyi, M., 193, 196, *222*, 348–51, *367*
Kitagawa, M., 164, *180*
Klempner, D., 408, 409, *420*
Knauss, W. G., 383, 392, 399, 415, *417, 419*
Knight, A. C., 155, 156, *179*
Knollman, G. C., 387, 411, *418, 420*
Knott, J. F., 75, 90, 97, 101, *104*
Knox, A. G., 113, *144*, 216, *224*
Kobayashi, T., 442, 457, *470*
Koenig, J. L., 450, *470*
Kolsky, H., 185, *221*
Konczol, L., 158, *179*, 208, *223*
Kondon, Y., 428, *468*
Konopasek, L., 360, *369*
Koo, G. P., 201, *222*
Kopp, R. W., 152, 153, *178*
Koppenaal, T. J., 188, *221*
Korsukov, V. E., 55, 59, 60, 66, 70, 72, 215, *224*
Koski, L., 332, *366*
Koutsky, J. A., 287, 294, 307, 308, *321, 322*
Kramer, E. J., 32, *38*, 113, 122, 124, 126, 133, 135, *144, 145, 146*, 149, 150, 151, 152, 153, 154, 156, 157, 158, 161, 164, 166, 169, 174, 175,

Kramer, E. J.,—contd.
176, *178–81,* 236, 252, 256, 257, 260–3, 265–9, 280, *280,* 282, *283,* 306, *322,* 356, 357, *368,* 426, 427, 430, 431, 434, *468, 469*
Kraus, G. K., 410, 411, *420*
Krenz, H. G., 153, 154, 156, 158, 169, *178, 179, 180*
Krisch, K. C., 408, 409, *420*
Kruse, R. B., 399, 400, *419*
Kuksenko, V. S., 50, 55, 59, 60, 69, 70, *71, 72, 73,* 361, 363, *369*
Kumagi, Y., 84, *105*
Kunz, S., 423, 424, 427, 442, 444, 445, *468*
Kunz-Douglass, S., 423, 424, 442, 444, *468*
Kurokawa, M., 127, *145*
Kusy, R. P., 251, 252, 267, 268, *282, 284*
Kuvshinshi, E. V., 155, *179*
Kwei, T. K., 408, 409, *420*
Kwolek, S. L., 330, 357–61, *366*

LaGarde, V., 329, *365*
Lainchbury, D. L. G., 260, 261, 265, *283*
Laird, C., 208, *224*
Laka, M. G., 115, *144*
Lake, G. J., 49, 50, *71,* 81, 97, 98, *105, 106,* 197, 198, 204, *222, 223,* 290, *321,* 382, 383, 385, 396, 398, *417, 418*
Landel, R. F., 372, 404, 405, *417, 419*
Landes, J. D., 82, *105*
Lange, F. F., 434, 435, 437, 445–7, 459, *469*
Lankford, J., 464, *471*
Lauterwasser, B. D., 149, 150, 151, 152, 154, 156, 157, 158, 161, 169, *178,* 260, 261, 268, 269, *283*
Lavengood, R. E., 427, 432, 441, 442, *468*
Lazurkin, Yu. S., 110, 113, *143*
Lednicky, F., 287, 308, *321*
Lee, C. S., 245–7, *282*
Lee, H. B., 267, 268, *284*

Lee, L. H., 210, *224*
Lees, W. A., 460, *471*
Leete, N. B., 300, *322*
Legrand, D. G., 240, 260, 271, *281, 283*
Leidner, J., 450, *470*
Leksovskii, A. M., 203, *223,* 360, *369*
Lenz, R. W., 8, 9, *37*
Lepie, A., 411, *420*
Levy, G. M., 158, 160, *179,* 256, 257, *282*
Leyrer, R. J., 328–30, *365*
Li, J. C. M., 122, 125, 126, 128, 129, 130, *145, 261, 283*
Liddell, P., 287, *321*
Liebowitz, H., 189, 203, *221, 223,* 230–4, 240, 242, 245, *280,* 289, 291, *321,* 370, 372, 377, 390, *416*
Lilley, J., 133, *145,* 306, *322*
Lindley, P. B., 49, *71,* 97, 98, *106,* 197, 198, 204, *222, 223,* 378, 379, 381, 382, 383, 385, 396–9, *417, 418*
Lindsey, G. H., 378, 380, 399, *417*
Livigni, R. A., 449, *470*
Lloyd, B. A., 64, 66, *72,* 361, *369*
Loneragan, R. J., 231, *280*
Longman, G. W., 15, *38*
Luňák, S., 287, 308, *321*
Lyons, P. F., 404, *419*
Lyons, W. J., 360, *369*

McClintock, F. A., 142, *146*
McCormick, H. W., 237, *281*
McCrum, N. G., 26, 28, *38,* 244, 245, *281*
McEvily, A. J., 208, *224*
McFarlane, F. E., 357–9, *369*
McGarry, F. J., 133, *145,* 242, 245, 252, *281, 282,* 291–4, 296, 306, 307, *321,* 424, 427, 442, 445, 460, *468, 470, 471*
McGrath, J. E., 385, *418*
Macknight, W. J., 372, *417*
McLaren, J. R., 216, 218, 219, *225*
McMaster, A. D., 273, 275, *285*
McMeeking, R. M., 312, *322*
McMillan, J. C., 314, *323*

McMillan, P. W., 216, *225*
McPherson, C. A., 451, *470*
Maeda, T., 327, 328, 330, *365*
Mai, Y., 206, 207, 210, *223*
Mai, Y. W., 96, *106*, 171, *180*, 244–9, 254, *282*, 300, 301, *322*, 344–6, *367*, 459, *471*
Maiors, I. Yu., 115, *144*
Mallick, P. K., 439, 445, 447, *469*
Mandell, J. F., 460, *471*
Mann, J., 115, *144*, 267, 268, *284*, 422, 449, *467*, *470*
Manson, J. A., 197, 198, 204, 205, 206, 207, 208–11, *222–4*, 273–6, *285*, 290, 291, 295, 316, *321*, *323*, 351, 353, *367*, *368*, 463, 464, *471*
Manzione, L. T., 451, *470*
Maranci, A., 169, 170, *180*, 267–9, *284*
Marker, L., 407, *419*
Marsh, D. M., 334, *366*
Marshall, G. P., 155, 156, 158, 167, 168, 171, 172, 173, *179*, 183, 192, 193, *220*, 242–8, 256, 257, 259, 260, 270, *281*, *282*, *284*, 298, 300, 309, *322*, 355, 356, *368*, 431, 452, *469*, *470*
Martin, C., 411, *420*
Martin, G. C., 210, *224*, 273, *285*
Martin, G. E., 330, 337, *365*
Martin, J. R., 208, *224*, 237–9, 271, *281*, 354, 356, *368*
Martinson, R. H., 387, 411, *418*, *420*
Matsuo, M., 408, 409, *420*, 428, *468*
Matsushige, K., 115, *144*, 164, *180*
Matyi, R. J., 287, 307, 308, *321*
Matz, D. J., 113, *144*
Maxwell, B., 165, *180*
May, C., 387, *321*
Mead, W. T., 330, 332, 357, 358, *366*, *368*
Mears, D. R., 346, *367*
Medalia, A. I., 410, *420*
Meeks, A. C., 293, 294, *321*
Meihuizen, K. E., 330, 357–9, *366*
Menges, G., 338, 339, *367*, 463, *471*
Merkle, J. G., 195, *222*

Merz, E., H., 423, 424, *468*
Mijovic, J., 294, 307, 308, *321*, *322*
Miller, D. B., 307, *322*
Miller, L. E., 252, 253, *282*, 293, 294, 302, *321*
Miller, S., 249, 269, *282*, 427, *468*
Mills, N. J., 131, 132, 135, 137, *145*, *146*, 155, 158, *179*, 205, 206, *223*, 261, 262, 271, *283*, *284*
Miltz, J., 256, 259, 260, *283*
Misra, S., 290, 291, 295, *321*
Mohamed (Kadir), A. K. B., 84, *105*
Mones, E. T., 307, *322*
Moore, C. G., 404, *419*
Moore, J. D., 428, 430, *468*
Moore, N. B., 385, *418*
Morawetz, H., 11, *38*
Morgan, G. P., 155, 173, *179*, 244, 246, 260, *281*
Morgan, P. W., 330, 357–61, *366*
Morgan, R. J., 133, *145*, 306, 307, 314, *322*
Morrow, D. R., 201, 208, *222*, 273, 275, *285*, 337, *366*
Morton, W. E., 357, *368*
Mostovoy, S., 102, *106*, 210, *224*, 291–4, 300, *321*, *322*
Motozata, Y., 463, *471*
Moulton, R. J., 424, 427, *468*
Mueller, H. K., 383, 392, 415, *417*
Muller, F. H., 110, *143*
Mullins, L., 372, 374, 375, 376, 388, 390, 392, 402, 404, 410, *416–20*
Murayama, T., 314, *323*
Murphy, B. M., 110, *143*
Murray, J., 169, *180*, 267, *284*
Murukami, R., 463, *471*

Nadai, A., 120, *145*
Nakame, K., 328, 329, *365*
Narisawa, I., 113, 131, 132, *144*, *145*, 261, *283*, 314, *323*
Narkis, M., 427, 432, 441, 442, *468*, *469*
Natarajan, R., 68, *72*
Neki, K., 264, *284*

Nelson, B. F., 290, 301, 306, 307, *321*
Newman, S., 117, *144*, 422, 423, 425, 426, *468*
Newman, S. B., 133, 134, *146*, 214, *224*
Newmann, L. V., 455, *470*
Nicholais, L., 450, *470*
Nicholson, D. W., 380, *417*
Nicholson, P. S., 437, 446, 448, *469*
Nicodemo, L., 450, *470*
Nicolais, L., 427, 432, 441, 442, *468*, *469*
Nielsen, L. E., 117, *144*, 463, 464, *471*
Niklas, H., 212, 215, *224*
Nikpur, K., 193, *222*, 442, 451, 452, *470*
Nordberg, H., 273, *285*, 316, *323*
Novak, I. I., 55, 56, 59, *72*, 361, 363, *369*
Nozaki, C., 428, *468*
Nurse, P. J., 185, *221*, 270, *284*
Nutting, J., 338, 339, 341, *367*

Oavan, A., 431, *469*
Oberth, A. E., 380, 381, 411, *417*
Odajima, A., 327, 328, 330, *365*
Odian, G., 8, 9, *37*
Ogawa, H., 113, 131, 132, *144, 145*, 261, *283*, 314, *323*
Oldyrev, P. P., 201, *223*
Olf, H. G., 161, *180*
Olszewski, W. V., 427, *468*
O'Neal, J. E., 133, *145*, 306, 307, 314, *322*
Ongchin, L., 110, 115, 116, *143, 144*, 161, 162, 164, *180*
Orowan, E., 74, *104*, 169, 170, *180*, 267–9, *284*
O'Toole, J. L., 201, *222*
Ots, J. M., 112, *143*
Ouano, A. C., 10, *38*
Owen, A. B., 437, *469*
Owen, D. R. J., 160, *180*
Owen, M. J., 133, *145*, 296, 301, 317, *321, 323*
Oxborough, R. J., 118, *144*, 162, 163,

Oxborough, R. J.,—*contd.*
180, 256, *282*, 288, *321*, 425, 431, 442, *468*

Padden, F. J., 15, *38*, 339, 356, *367*
Pae, K. D., 236, *280*, 346, 347, *367*
Page, C. J., 434, *469*
Paipetis, S. A., 133, *145*
Pampillo, C. A., 117, *144*
Panar, M., 330, 357–61, *366*
Panizza, G., 425, *468*
Papazian, H. A., 278, *285*
Parades, E., 260, *283*
Parfeev, V. M., 201, *223*
Paris, P. C., 88, 91, *105*, 195, 204, *222, 223*
Parkinson, D., 374, *417*
Parrish, M. F., 234, 246, *280*
Parry, J. S. C., 115, *144*, 236, *281*
Parvin, M., 95, 97, *106*, 171, 173, *180*, 233, 244–50, 267, 271, *280*, *282, 284*, 452–4, *470*
Patell, Y. R., 337, *366*
Paul, D. R., 422, *468*
Payne, A. R., 372, 374, 375, 376, 406, *416, 417, 419*
Pedemmte, E., 407, *419*
Pennings, A. J., 330, 339, 357–9, *366, 367, 369*
Peterlin, A., 66, 68, *73*, 161, *180*, 332, 337, 361, 363, *366, 369*
Petermann, J., 119, *145*, 335, 338, *366, 367*
Petrich, R. P., 426, *468*
Petrie, S., 256, 259, 260, *283*
Peyser, P., 293, 294, *321*, 393, *418*, 442, 445, 455, 460, *470*
Phillips, D. C., 216, 218, *225*, 293, 294, 297–9, 302, 304, 314, 317, *321, 322*, 422, 423, 436, 452, *468*
Phillips, M. G., 254, *282*, 299, 300, *322*
Pink, E., 288, *321*
Pitman, G., 208, *223*, 273, 274, *285*
Pitman, G. L., 37, *39*, 96, *106*, 155, 174, *179, 180*, 240, 249–51, 260, 267, 271, *281, 282*

Plati, E., 83, *105*, 141, *146*, 183, 193, 194, 195, 196, *220, 222*, 270, *284*, 348, 349, *367*
Plazek, D. J., 405, *419*
Pleštil, J., 287, 308, *321*
Plumbridge, W. J., 203, 210, *223*, 273, *285*
Pogany, G., 115, *144*, 267, 268, *284*
Polley, H. W., 415, *420*
Poole, C. P., 57, 72
Porter, M., 404, *419*
Porter, R. S., 13, 14, *38*, 59, 72, 330–2, 357, 358, *366, 368*
Pozdnyakov, O. F., 59, 72
Prask, H., 329, *365*
Pratt, P. L., 442, *469*
Pregan, S. E., 189, *221*
Preston, F. H., 332, *366*
Preston, J., 357, 359, *369*
Prevorsek, D., 357, 358, 360, *368, 369*
Pritchard, G., 291–7, 301, 302, 305, 306, 308, 311, 313, *321, 322*
Pugh, H. D., 115, *144*
Puttick, K. E., 252, 253, *282*

Quayle, P. V., 445, *470*

Rabinowitz, S., 114, 115, *144, 176, 181*, 199, *222*, 236, *281*, 463, *471*
Racich, J. L., 307, *322*
Radcliffe, S. V., 115, *144*, 164, *180*, 236, *281*, 442, *469*
Radford, K. C., 434, 437, 439, 445–7, 459, *469*
Radok, J. R. M., 375, *417*
Radon, J. C., 210, *224*, 242, 243, 247, 248, 273, *281, 285*
Raff, R. A. V., 354, *368*
Raghava, R., 115, 116, *144*
Raha, S., 31, *38*, 110, 111, 118, 122, 125, *143, 144*, 236, 256, 257, 264, *280, 282, 283*, 288, *321*
Rahm, L. F., 165, *180*
Ramsteiner, F., 434, *469*
Ratner, M. A., 24, *38*, 327, 328, 333–5,

Ratner, M. A.,—*contd.*
359, *365*
Raymond, L., 188, *221*
Read, R. T., 338, *367*
Ree, T., 112, 114, *143*
Reed, B. E., 26, 28, *38*, 244, 245, *281*
Reed, N. L., 208, *224*
Reed, P. E., 48, 50, 52, 55, 57, 58, 59, 61, 63, 68, 70, *71, 72*, 182, 185, 188, *220, 221*, 270, *284*
Regel, V. R., 59, 70, *72, 73*, 165, *180*, 203, *223*, 278, *285*, 360, *369*
Reimschuessel, A. C., 357, *368*
Reynolds, R. J. W., 393, *418*
Rhoades, G. V., 293, 296, 301, 302, 306, *321*
Ricco, T., 431, *469*
Rice, T. R., 82, 83, 87, 92, *105*, 195, 222, 314, *323*
Richard, K., 212, *224*
Richardson, G. C., 197, 201, 205, 209, *222*, 273–5, *285*, 463, 465, *471*
Richardson, M. O. W., 286, *320*, 422, 423, 436, 452, *468*
Riddell, M. N., 199, 200, 201, *222*
Rider, J. G., 252, 253, *282*, 332, *366*
Riew, C. K., 422, 424, 427, 442, 455–7, 460, *468, 470*
Rimnac, C. M., 273, *285*
Rinde, J. A., 398, *419*
Ripling, E. J., 102, *106*, 210, *224*, 291–4, 300, *321, 322*
Ritchie, J. M., 332, *366*
Rivlin, R. S., 76, 79, 80, 83, 97, 98, 101, *105*
Robertson, R. E., 112, 113, 118, 127, *143, 144, 145*, 175, *181*, 251, 252, *282*, 330, *365*
Robeson, L. M., 442, 443, 445, *469*
Roche, E., 357, *368*
Rockhill, A. T., 59, 69, *72*
Roesler, F. C., 242, *281*
Roetling, J. A., 112, *143*
Romagosa, E. E., 158, *179*, 256, 257, *282*
Rooke, D. P., 88, *105*
Rooney, G., 267, 268, *284*
Rose, R. G., 133, *145*, 296, 298, 301,

Rose, R. G.,—*contd.*
317, *321–3*
Rose, W. S., 424, 427, 455–7, 460, *468*
Rosenfield, A., 314, *323*
Rosengren, G. F., 314, *323*
Rosenthal, J., 176, *181,* 240, *281*
Rosner, M., 184, *221*
Rowe, E. H., 422, 442, *468, 470*
Roylance, D. K., 55, 56, 64, 66, 72, 361, *369*
Rusch, K. C., 117, *144*
Rushford, J. L., 424, 427, 455–7, 460, *468*
Russell, D. R., 149, 150, *178,* 428, 429, *468*
Ryan, J. T., 271, *284*

Sacher, E., 442, 445, 450, *469, 470*
Saffman, P. G., 166, *180*
Sahu, S., 445, 450, *470*
St. Clair, A. K., 452, *470*
St. Clair, T. L., 452, *470*
Sakurada, I., 328, 329, *365*
Salama, M. M., 165, 166, 167, *180,* 256, *282*
Salloum, R. J., 58, 72
Sambrook, R. W., 410, 411, *420*
Sansom, G. F., 357, *368*
Sardar, D., 115, *144*
Sauer, J. A., 197, 201, 205, 208, 209, *222, 223,* 273–5, *285,* 337, 346, *366, 367,* 463, 465, *471*
Saville, B., 404, *419*
Savin, J. R., 24, *38,* 327, 328, 333–5, 359, *365*
Schaefgen, J. R., 330, 357–61, *366*
Schafer, J. K., 122, 128, *145*
Schapery, R. A., 380, *417*
Schelten, J., 13, 15, *38*
Schinker, M. G., 208, *223*
Schleier, G., 328, 330, *365*
Schultz, J., 356, *368*
Schultz, J. M., 60, *72,* 77, *105,* 337, *366*
Scott, J. M., 216, 218, *225,* 293, 294, 297–9, 302, 304, 314, 317, *321, 322*

Scott, L. S., 357, 358, *368*
Seidelmann, U., 158, *179*
Selby, K., 293, 294, 302, *321*
Sendfeld, N., 330, *365*
Server, W. L., 188, *221*
Shânahan, M. E. R., 356, *368*
Shauffele, R. F., 328, 329, *365*
Shaw, S. J., 101, *106,* 216, 218, *225,* 302–4, 313–15, 317–19, *322, 323,* 386, 393, *418,* 427, 438, 452, 455–7, 460, 461, *468, 470, 471*
Shea, M., 372, *417*
Sheikh, M. W., 411, *420*
Shih, P. T. K., 450, *470*
Shih, T. T., 219, *225*
Shimanouchi, T., 327–9, *365*
Shin, N., 463, *471*
Shortall, J. B., 338, 339, *367*
Shorthall, J. B., 133, *145,* 296, 298, *321*
Siebert, A., 460, *471*
Siebert, A. R., 422, 424, 427, *468*
Sih, G. C., 88, *105*
Silano, A. A., 346, *367*
Silverman, A., 110, *143*
Simonson, E. R., 385, *418*
Sims, G. L. A., 342, 343, *367*
Sims, K. J., 164, *180*
Singleton, C. J., 357, *368*
Sjoerdsma, S. D., 434, 449, *469, 470*
Skibo, M. D., 204, 205, 206, 208, 209, *223, 224,* 273, 275, 276, *285,* 290, 291, 316, *321,* 463, 464, *471*
Slutsker, A. I., 59, 70, *72, 73*
Smith, C. G., 208, *224*
Smith, K., 137, 138, *146,* 263, 269, *283*
Smith, R. R., 428, *468*
Smith, T. L., 370, 374, 376, 398, 400, 402, 403, 404, 405, 407, *416, 417, 419, 420*
Sneddon, I. N., 155, *179*
Soni, P. L., 357, *368*
Spanoudakis, J., 435, 437, 445, 446, 448, 450, 452, 460, *469*
Spath, W., 184, *221*
Sperling, L. H., 290, 291, 295, *321,* 375, 408, *417*

Spink, G. M., 141, *146*
Squires, H. V., 185, *221,* 270, *284*
Srawley, J. E., 102, *106*
Sridharan, N. S., 83, *105*
Stabenow, J., 137, *146,* 426, 434, *468*
Stamm, M., 15, 16, *38*
Stark, C. F., 189, *221*
Steele, W. J., 307, *322*
Stein, R. S., 377, *417*
Sternstein, S. S., 110, 115, 116, *143, 144,* 161, 162, 164, 177, *180, 181,* 240, *281*
Stevens, G., 155, 158, *179*
Stevens, G., C., 287, *321,* 332, *366*
Stevens, W. W., 463, 465, *471*
Stoeckel, T. M., 59, *72*
Stork, S. T., 169, 170, *180,* 267–9, *284*
Stowell, W. J., 270, *284*
Street, D. G., 442, 457–9, *470, 471*
Strella, S., 117, *144,* 423, 425, 426, *468*
Sultan, J. N., 133, *145,* 424, 427, 445, *468*
Sutton, S. A., 316, *323*

Tada, H., 88, *105*
Tai, C. L., 375, *417*
Takemori, M., T., 276, 277, *285*
Tamua, M., 465, *471*
Tamuzs, V. P., 50, 55, 60, 69, 70, *71,* 361, 363, *369*
Tanaka, Y., 287, *321*
Taneja, N., 296, 298, 301, *321, 322*
Tappin, G., 216, 219, *225*
Tauchert, T. R., 201, *222*
Taylor, G., 404, *419*
Taylor, G. I., 166, *180*
Taylor, G. R., 413, 414, *420*
Taylor, W. N., 357, 358, *368*
Teh, J. W., 204, 209, *223,* 351, 352, *368*
Tetelman, A. S., 188, *221*
Thackray, G., 110, 113, *143*
Theocaris, P. S., 133, *145*
Thierry, A., 118, *144,* 288, *321*
Thomas, A., 428, *468*

Thomas, A. G., 14, *38,* 50, 69, *71, 73,* 76, 79, 80, 83, 84, 97, 98, 101, *105, 106,* 204, *223,* 239, *281,* 290, *321,* 383, 387, 388, 393, 395, 397, 402, 404, *417–19*
Tnomas, E. L., 12, *38,* 158, *179,* 264, *284,* 307, *322,* 357–60, *369*
Thomson, K. W., 302, *322*
Ting, R. Y., 424, 427, *468*
Tobin, N. R., 374, 375, *417*
Tobolsky, A. V., 404, *419*
Tomashevsky, E. E. 50, 52, 59, *71, 72,* 215, *224,* 361, *369*
Tomkins, B., 203, *223*
Tompkins, D. A., 379, *417*
Toyoshima, W., 465, *471*
Trachte, K., 452, *470*
Treloar, L. R. G., 25, *38,* 173, *180,* 327, 328, 330, 342, 356, *365, 367, 368,* 370, 398, *416, 419*
Trevino, S., 329, *365*
Truss, R. W., 215, *224,* 346, 348, *367,* 434, *469*
Tsangaris, J. M., 133, *145*
Turley, S. G., 272, *284,* 430, 442, 443, 445, *469*
Turner, C. E., 82, *105,* 183, 192, 193, 220, 242, 270, *281, 284*
Turner, D. J., 239, *281*
Turner, D. T., 251, 252, 267, 268, 282, *284,* 290, 301, 306, 307, *321*
Turner, S., 182, 185, 188, 211, *220, 224*

Ueda, A., 428, *468*
Uhlmann, D. R., 12, *38,* 264, *284,* 287, 307, 308, *321*
Urbanic, A. J., 449, *470*

Vadimsky, R. G., 15, *38,* 339, 356, *367*
Valanis, K. C., 216, *225*
Valenti, B., 357, 359, *369*
Van den Boogaart, A., 133, *145,* 242, 267, *281, 284,* 306, 310, *322*
VanderSande, J. B., 431, 432, *469*

Van Essen, W. J., 449, *470*
Verheulpen-Heymans, N., 155, 158, 165, *179, 180*
Vettegren, V. I., 55, 56, *72*, 361, 363, *369*
Villars, D. S., 402, *419*
Vincent, P. I., 48, 49, *71*, 110, 120, 141, *143, 145, 146*, 182, 190, 191, *220*, 230, 233, 236–40, 242, 256, 257, 270–2, *280, 281, 282*, 348, 349, *367*
Voigt-Martin, I. G., 338, *366*

Wada, Y., 272, *284*
Wagner, E. R., 442, 443, 445, *469*
Walker, B. J., 204, 209, *223*, 351, *368*
Walker, N., 137, 139, *146*, 155, 158, *179*, 205, 206, *223*, 269, *284*
Wambach, A. D., 452, 459, *470, 471*
Wang, S. S., 456, 457, 460, *471*
Wang, T. T., 330, *365*
Wann, R. J., 210, *224*
Ward, I. M., 26, 37, *38, 39*, 96, 97, *106*, 108, 110, 114, 115, *143, 144*, 155, 173, 174, *179, 180*, 192, 208, 215, *221, 223, 224*, 236, 240, 244, 246, 249, 250, 251, 260, 267, 271, 273, 274, *281–5*, 296, 298, 306, 317, *321, 323*, 328–32, 346, 348, 357–61, *365–9*
Warty, S., 208, *223*
Way, J. L., 338, 339, 341, *367*
Webb, R. S., 185, *221*
Webler, S. M., 273, *285*
Webner, G., 9, *37*, 328–30, 332, *365, 366*
Weidmann, G. W., 155, 156, 173, 174, *179*, 242–4, 247, 256, 260, *281–3*
Weil, N. A., 185, *221*
Weiss, V., 189, 208, *221, 224*
Wellinghoff, S., 129, *145*, 159, *179*, 260, 261, 263–5, *283*
Wells, A. A., 91, *105*
Wells, G. M., 297, 298, 302, 314, *322*
West, J. C., 375, 407, *417*
Westergaard, H. M., 86, *105*

Wettling, W., 328–30, *365*
White, E. F. T., 110, *143*
White, J. R., 204, 209, *223*, 351, 352, *368*
White, J. W., 327, 328, *365*
Whitney, W., 117, 122, 124, 126, *144, 145*
Whittle, J. M., 402, *419*
Wiederhorn, S. M., 216, *225*
Wiegand, E., 463, *471*
Wignall, G. D., 13, 15, *38*
Williams, A. L., 411, *420*
Williams, D. R. G., 463, *471*
Williams, G., 26, 28, *38*, 244, 245, *281*
Williams, H. L., 411, *420*
Williams, J. G., 20, 22, 27, 34, *38*, 48, *71*, 78, 83, 92, 95, 97, 101, *105, 106*, 111, 139, 140, 141, 142, *143, 146*, 155, 156, 158, 161, 167, 168, 171, 172, 173, *179, 180*, 183, 192, 193, 194, 195, 196, 201, 206–10, 212, 218, *220, 222–5*, 233, 242–50, 255–7, 259, 260, 269–73, 276, 277, *280–2, 284, 285*, 298, 300, 302, 304, 309, 311, 312, 314, 315, *322*, 342–6, 348–51, 353, 355, 356, *367, 368*, 427, 431, 442, 451–5, *468–70*
Williams, J. R., 398, 411, *418*
Williams, M. L., 64, 66, *72*, 203, *223*, 361, *369*, 372, 380, 385, 390, *416, 418*
Williamson, G. R., 422, *467*
Willis, J., 158, 160, *179*, 256, 257, *282*
Winkler, S., 188, *221*, 299, 301, 315, *322, 323*
Wolock, 1., 133, 134, *146*, 214, *224*
Wolstenholme, W. E., 189, *221*
Woodhams, R. T., 450, *470*
Wool, R. P., 55, 59, 69, *72*, 327, 328, 361, *365, 369*
Wooten, W. C., 357–9, *369*
Worthington, P. J., 141, *146*
Wu, J. B. C., 122, 125, 126, 128, 129, *145*, 261, *283*
Wu, J. C. B., 234, 235, 246, *280*
Wu, W. C., 273, *285*

Wunderlich, B., 15, *38*, 324, 326, 329, 332, 339, *365*
Wysgoski, M. G., 159, 161, *180*, 264, 271, 272, *283*

Yamini, S., 31, *38*, 110, 118, 140, 141, *143, 144, 146*, 264, *283*, 288, 293, 295–300, 302–5, 309–12, 314, 315, *321, 322*
Yee, A. F., 427, 434, *468*
Yeh, G. S., 12, *38*, 115, 117, 122, 124, *144, 145*, 264, 271, 272, *283, 284*
Yilmazer, U., 216, *225*
Yoshii, T., 434, 422–5, 451, *469*
Young, J. K., 357, *368*
Young, R. J., 2–5, 7–12, 14, 15, 17, 22, 24, 26, 27, 29, 31, *37*, 44, 46, 48, *71*, 101, 102, *106*, 110, 118, 119, 127, 133, 140, 141, *143–6*, 171,

Young, R. J.,—*contd.*
180, 216, *225*, 242–5, 264, 277, 278, *281, 283, 285*, 288, 291–305, 308–15, *321, 322*, 324, 326, 328–32, 334, 335, 337–9, 341, 342, 348, *365–7*, 435, 445–8, 450, 452, 459, 460, 465, 466, *469–71*
Young, V. O., 434, *469*

Zachariades, A. E., 330, 332, 357, 358, *366*
Zakrevskii, V. A., 59, 60, 70, 72
Zapas, L. J., 212, *224*, 354, *368*
Zaukelies, D. A., 127, *145*
Zbinden, R., 10, *38*
Zhurkov, S. N., 50, 52, 54, 55, 59, 60, 66, 69, 70, *71, 72, 73*, 215, *224*, 278, *285*, 360, 361, *369*
Zichy, E. L., 161, *179*, 256, *282*
Ziegler, E. E., 165, *180*
Zimmerman, J., 330, 357–61, *366*

Subject Index

ABS, 425, 426, 430, 434, 449, 458–9, 463, 465
Activation energy, 203, 215
Activation volume, 113, 203, 264
Addition polymerisation, 8
Adhesive bonding, 378
Adhesive joints, 318, 460–2
Adiabatic/isothermal transitions, 247–9
Alumina trihydrate, 435, 439
Amorphous polymers, 12–14, 23, 28, 31, 122–7, 205
Annealing effects, 37, 240, 263, 265, 271

Boltzmann distribution, 118
Boltzmann superposition principle, 26
Bond
    breakage, 57–60
    rupture, 51
    straining, 55–7
Branching, 9, 15, 17
Brittle/ductile transition, 251
Brittle fracture, 68, 132–4, 142, 148, 177, 183, 191
    glassy thermoplastics, 230–40
    glassy thermosets, 287–91
Bulk inelastic behaviour, 84–6
Bulk non-linear elastic behaviour, 79–84
Burgers vector, 118, 119

Carbon black fillers, 394, 402, 410
Carbon–carbon bond, 384
Chain direction modulus, 327, 328, 330–1
Chain scission, 70
Chemical structure, 16, 177, 237
cis state, 118
Cleavage
    cracks, 337
    intermolecular, 337–8
Condensation polymerisation, 8
Considère's construction, 109, 120
Cooling rate, 18
Copolymers, 2
Covalent bonds, 173
Crack
    extension, 204, 218
    growth, 75, 79, 80, 83, 88, 93, 97, 102, 135, 141, 203, 205–8, 210, 315, 353, 356, 467
        relaxation-controlled, 244
        stick/slip, 394
    healing, 269–70
    initiation, 184, 199, 203, 214, 220
        shear yielding, and, 128–32
    length, 100, 101, 193, 217, 312
    opening displacement, 91, 92, 172, 207, 218, 312
    pinning, toughened multiphase plastics, 434–8, 447–8
    propagation, 79, 82, 101, 203, 205,

489

Crack—*contd.*
  propagation—*contd.*
    209, 210, 218, 220, 267–9, 355
    continuous, 309
    criteria for, 139–42
    glassy thermoplastics, 241–55
    glassy thermosets, 291–304
    molecular relaxation, and, 247
    rubbers, 386–98
    semicrystalline polymers, 342–6
    shear yielding, and, 132–42
    stable brittle, 302
    stable ductile, 302–4
    unstable, 300–1
      brittle, 302
  resistance, 177
  tip blunting, 139, 141, 218, 254
  tip radius, 140
  velocity, 242, 247, 298–301
Craze
  cavities, 257
  fibrils, 174, 266
    creep, 158
    mechanical behaviour, 153–4
  length, 259, 260
  thickness, 257
Crazing, 31–2, 69–70, 107, 122, 129,
    131, 133, 143, 147–81, 205,
    206, 208, 214, 234, 236, 254,
    306–7, 320, 354–7
  air-grown, 150, 152, 153, 158, 169
  breakdown criteria, 173
  breakdown mechanisms, 169–71
  brittle, 132
  chemical structure, effect of, 177
  environmental, 169, 256–60
  fracture via, 156
  growth, 256, 259
    criteria, 167
    flow-controlled, 260
    kinetics, 167, 171–3
    mechanisms, 165–6
    meniscus instability, by, 166
    relaxation-controlled, 260
  importance of, 147, 148
  initiation, 147, 148, 256
    growth and breakdown, 173
    kinetics, 165

Crazing—*contd.*
  initiation—*contd.*
    mechanisms and criteria, 158–65
    kinetics, 256
    loaded air-grown, 152
    localised, 36
    mechanical properties, 152–5
    micromechanics, 152–8
    microstructure, 149–52
    molecular entanglements, role of,
      175–6
    multiple, 147, 148, 255, 453
    orientation effects, 176
    polymer structure, effect of, 174–7
    refractive index, 152
    shape models, 155
    shear yielding, vs., 263–7
    solvent-grown, 158
    stress distribution, 155
    structure, 260–1
    surface stress, 156
    toughened multiphase plastics, 428–
      34
    wedge-shaped, 169
Creep rupture, 361
Critical stress/distance criterion, 311–
    15
Cross-linking, 3, 31, 49, 50, 61, 68,
    77, 80, 84, 133, 136, 177, 216,
    267, 271, 290–1, 306, 377, 383,
    384, 403–5, 411
Cryogenic temperatures, 236
Crystal moduli, 327–30
Crystalline polymer(s), 15, 119, 127,
    205, 324–69
  deformation, 326–32
  dynamic fatigue, 351–3
  fibres, 64–8
  fracture, 332–8
  mechanical behaviour, 324–6
  mechanical properties, 325
Crystallisation, 15–18
  temperature, 17

Deformation, 23–32, 43
  crystalline polymers, 326–32
  elastic, 23–5, 326–31

Deformation—*contd.*
elastically isotropic solid, 45
energy dissipative, 178
homogeneous, 119
inhomogeneous, 119–27
causes, 120
types of, 120
molecular, 54–61
fracture during, 62–9
plastic, 31, 139, 142, 148, 173, 331–2
shear, 111
viscoelastic, 173
Diamond cavities, 137–9
Diethylene triamine (DETA), 294
Diphenylpicrylhydrazal (DPPH), 58
Disulphur dinitride, 337
Doolittle equation, 373
Drawing, 332
Ductile/brittle transition, 33, 36, 48, 149, 183, 190, 265, 270, 279, 347
Ductile failure, 191
Ductile fracture, 132, 134, 262
Ductile polymers, 233
Dugdale line plastic-zone model, 91, 92, 135, 155, 158, 172, 173, 206, 208, 262, 276, 309, 312
Dynamic mechanical behaviour, 28

Elastic constants, 23
Elastic properties, 23, 24
Elastic shear modulus, 379
Electron spin resonance (ESR) spectroscopy, 57, 58, 59, 63, 64, 66, 68, 333, 361, 363, 364
Energy
absorption, 421, 433, 437
balance
analysis, 380
fracture mechanics, 75–86
criterion, 74, 75
dissipation, 178, 201, 371, 405–6
losses, 77, 80
Engineering strain, 20
Entanglements, 13, 17, 69, 137, 175–6, 263–7, 280, 306

Environment effects, 254
Environmental stress cracking, 236, 354, 356, 357
Epoxy resins, 1, 31, 216, 287–91, 293, 294, 296, 297, 299, 303, 308, 309, 313, 314, 316, 317, 422, 434, 436, 439, 446, 448, 457, 460, 466
mechanical properties, 307
Equilibrium modulus, 25
Ethylene–propylene rubber, 50
Extension ratio, 20, 81, 135, 137, 265, 266, 398
Extrinsic yield point, 109
Eyring theory, 112, 117

Failure
criteria, glassy thermosets, 309–15
mechanisms,
glassy thermosets, 301–8
oriented polymers, 361–3
Fatigue
curves, 199
dynamic, 197–211, 273–7, 316–17, 351–3, 462–5
experimental considerations, 197–200
failure, 197
mechanical, 202–11
rubbers, 395–8
static, fracture mechanics approach, 216–20
thermal, 200–2
life,
prediction, 214
static, 216
oriented polymers, 360–1
static, 211–20, 277–9, 317–20, 353–4, 465–7
mechanisms, 212–20
strength, 289–90
tests, 197
Fibres, high-strength, 331
Flaws, 36, 47, 49, 74, 212, 214, 231, 237, 289, 438, 465
Flexible polymers, 97
Flory–Rehner equation, 404

Fourier transform, 155
Fractography, 351
Fracture, 32–7, 43
  criteria, 75, 76, 88
  crystalline polymers, 332–8
  energy, 35, 36, 48, 49, 75, 81, 83, 85, 93, 148, 193, 196, 218, 219, 231, 249, 289–90, 317, 343, 382–6, 438, 446, 457
  environmental, 354–7
  general approaches, 32
  general behaviour, 33
  Griffith, 35–6
  initiation, rubbers 377–86
  isotropic semicrystalline polymers, 338–57
  kinetic approach, 50–4
  mechanics, 74–106
    energy balance approach, 75–86
    experimental considerations, 97–104
    glassy thermosets, 291–3
    impact tests, 192–7
    rubbers, 412
    static fatigue failure, 216–20
    stress-intensity factor approach, 86–92
  micromechanisms, 61–70
  molecular, 44–50, 61, 333–7
    techniques for studying, 54–61
    theory, 47, 214
  post-yield, 137
  rubbers, 370
  semicrystalline polymers, 357–63
  strength, 35, 239
  stress, 33, 238, 336, 398
  surface, 128, 267
  toughness, 344
Free energy change, 51
Free radicals, 59, 63, 64, 65, 67

Gel-permeation chromatography (GPC), 10
Geometry factor (Z), 193
Glass-transition temperature, 14, 117, 148, 287, 325, 421
Glassy polymers, 68, 122–7, 149

Glassy polymers—contd.
  thermoplastics. See Glassy thermoplastics
  thermosets. See Glassy thermosets
Glassy thermoplastics, 149, 229–85
  brittle fracture, 230–40
  crack propagation, 241–55
  mechanical properties, 229
  micromechanisms, 255–70
Glassy thermosets, 286–323
  brittle fracture, 287–91
  crack propagation, 291–304
  failure criteria, 309–15
  failure mechanisms, 301–8
  fatigue, 316–20
  fracture mechanics, 291–3
  impact properties, 315–16
  material variables, 293–6
  microstructure, 307
  testing variables, 296–8
Griffith fracture, 35–6
Guinier formula, 61

High-impact polystyrene (HIPS), 422, 423, 428–34, 440–2, 449, 452–5, 463
Homopolymers, 2
Hooke's law, 22, 26, 29, 46
Hoop stress, 213
Hydrogen bonding, 17
Hydrostatic pressure, 114, 115, 212, 236, 237, 346
Hysteresis, 29–31, 80, 85, 372, 376, 390, 395, 410

Impact
  properties, glassy thermosets, 315–16
  strength, 183, 190, 191, 245
    experimental methods of measuring, 185–8
  tests, 182–97, 270–3
    blunt-notch, 189, 194
    fracture mechanics approach, 192–7
    notched-beam, 189

Impact—*contd.*
  tests—*contd.*
    semicrystalline polymers, 348–51
    specimen geometry, effect of, 188–92
    toughness, 184
Infra-red (IR) spectroscopy, 55–7, 59
Internal friction, 372
Interpenetrating polymer network (IPN), 408
Intrinsic yield point, 109
Irradiation effects, 337

J-contour integral, 82, 83, 195, 342

Kevlar, 359

Linear elastic fracture mechanics (LEFM), 77–9, 88, 92, 93, 100, 142, 192, 195, 204, 229, 242, 257, 273, 277, 278, 279, 291, 314, 320, 344, 364
Lorentz–Lorenz equation, 152
Loss compliance, 201
Loss function, 77, 85

Mackerel pattern, 170
Macromolecules in solution, 10
Magnetic moment, 57
Martensitic transformation, 332
Mechanical properties, 9, 12, 19, 26, 47, 152–5, 229, 307, 325, 331, 337
Mechanical tests, 110–11
Melt spinning, 359
Melt-crystallised polymers, 15
Melt-flow index, 354
Melting, 15–18
  temperature, 15, 17
Methacrylate–butadiene–styrene rubber, 464
Microshear bands, 122–5
Microvoids, 69–70, 131, 147, 165

Mohr–Coulomb yield criterion, 115, 116
Molar gas constant, 25
Molar mass, 7, 9, 25, 137, 173, 174, 237–40, 251–2, 271
  distribution of, 7
  measurement of, 10
Molecular approach, rubbers 413–15
Molecular aspects, 43–73
Molecular relaxation, 113, 167, 171, 247
Molecular structure, 9, 279
Molecular theories, 117–19, 214
Molecules, types of, 2
Mullins effect, 374

Newton's law, 26
Nodular structure, 264
Non-Hookean behaviour, 29
Notch sensitivity, 195
Notched compression tests, 129
Nylon(s), 17, 339
Nylon-6, 362
Nylon-66, 345, 346

Orientation effects, 176, 240, 252–4, 357–63
Osmotic pressure, 10
Ozone concentration, 396

Paris equation, 351, 463
Particle deformation, 423–4
Patch pattern, 170
Phase angle, 27
Phase lag, 27
Physical properties, 18
Plane strain, 22, 93, 95
  compression test, 22, 111
  fracture toughness, 93
Plane stress, 20–2, 35, 90, 93, 95
Plastic constraint factor, 89, 90
Plastic flow, 29–31
Plastic zone radius, 91
Poisson's ratio, 22, 23, 35, 88, 90
Polyamides, 17

Poly(p-benzamide) (PBA), 359
Polybutadiene, 431, 432
Poly(butylene terephthalate), 249
Polycarbonates, 37, 86, 131, 153, 167,
    174, 229, 233, 235, 237, 240,
    244–7, 249, 250, 256, 260, 269,
    276, 279
Polydiacetylene, 329, 333, 334, 336,
    337, 338
Poly(dimethylsiloxane), 414
Poly(ether sulphone) (PES), 249,
    255, 257
Polyethylene, 17, 59, 85, 119, 142,
    204, 212, 327, 330, 331, 333,
    334, 335, 337, 338, 339, 342,
    343, 344, 346–9, 351, 353–6,
    359, 361
Poly(ethylene terephthalate), 12
Polymerisation, 8, 9
Polymer(s)
  applications, 1
  classification, 3
  definitions, 1, 2
  identification, 10
  structure, 237–41
Poly(methyl methacrylate) (PMMA),
    53, 76, 122, 124, 131, 153, 155,
    156, 161–4, 167, 170, 173, 174,
    177, 192, 201, 208–10, 216,
    229–31, 233, 234, 236–42, 244,
    245–9, 251, 252, 254, 256–60,
    267–70, 276, 278, 279, 291,
    298, 300, 307, 310, 317, 449,
    464–5
Polyolefins, 342
Polyoxymethylene, 329, 337
Poly(p-phenylenebenzobisthiazole)
    (PBT), 360
Polypropylene, 9, 18, 327, 337–41,
    343, 345–8
Polystyrene, 9, 13, 14, 124, 125, 129,
    152, 153, 158, 166, 167, 170,
    173, 178, 209, 229, 231, 232,
    235, 237, 240, 241, 244–7, 249,
    251, 252, 254, 261, 268, 269,
    276, 279, 443
Polytetrafluoroethylene (PTFE), 329,
    339, 341, 342, 349, 350

Polyurethane, 298, 407
Poly(vinyl chloride), 85, 131, 137,
    212, 215, 236, 279, 426, 427,
    449, 464
Poly(vinylidene fluoride), 353
Post-yield fracture, 137
Pressure effects. See Hydrostatic
    pressure
Principal stresses, 18
Probit transformation, 187
Proportionality constant, 80

Quenching, 37

Ree–Eyring model, 114
Refractive index, 152
Relaxation behaviour, 171, 244, 263,
    356
Resonant Raman scattering (RRS),
    55–6
Rigid fillers, 411
Rigid particles, 445–51, 459–60, 464
Rigid particulate fillers, 380–2, 422,
    435
Rigid polymers, 97
Root mean square (RMS), 10
Rubber(s), 1, 3, 25, 49, 68, 370–420
  amorphous, 388–93
  crack propagation, 386–98
  deformation of domains, 375–7
  failure processes, 1
  fatigue failure, 395–8
  filled, 373, 394–5
  fracture, 370
    initiation, 377–86
    mechanics, 412
  molecular approach, 413–15
  multiphase, 406–11
  strain crystallising, 393–4
  structural breakdown, 375
  tensile failure, 411–15
  tensile fracture, 398–415
  thermoplastic, 407
  toughening, 37
  viscoelastic behaviour, 415

Rubbery particles, 442–5, 448–9, 452–9, 462–3
Rubbery state, 25

Self-toughening mechanism, 319
Semicrystalline polymers, 15, 18, 24, 31, 53, 60, 329–31
   crack propagation, 342–6
   elastic deformation, 330–1
   impact tests, 348–51
   isotropic, 338–57
   oriented, 357–63
   static fatigue, 353–4
Shear
   bands, 122–7, 177, 261, 433
      propagation kinetics, 126
      structure of, 124
   modulus, 22, 23
   stresses, 18
   yielding, 31, 107–46, 148, 261–3, 320, 421
      bulk, 263
      crack initiation, and, 128–32
      crack propagation, and, 132–42
      crazing vs., 263–7
      criteria for, 114–17, 162–4
      importance of, 107
      localised, 36, 133, 177
         plane-strain, 261
      molecular theories, 117–19
      toughened multiphase plastics, 425–8, 432–4
Shift factor, 29, 405, 457
Single crystals, 332–7
Slip, 119, 331, 332
Small-angle X-ray scattering, 70, 260
Small-scale yielding, 88–92
S–N curves, 199
Solid polymers, structure 12–18
Solid-state polymerisation, 9, 329
Solvent cracking, 354
Staircase analysis, 187
Stick/slip propagation, 254, 268, 292, 296, 301, 309, 311, 312, 319, 394
Stiffness constant, 22
Strain, 20
   amplitude, 27

Strain—contd.
   hardening, 154
   rate, 112, 113, 123, 124, 125, 183, 400, 452–62
   softening, 109, 123, 135
Strain–energy density, 377
Strain-induced crystallisation, 373
Strength–probability–time (SPT) curves, 220
Stress, 18–19
   amplitude, 27
   concentration, 177
      factor, 191, 381
   crack-tip, 33–5
   distribution, 90, 155
      crack-tip, 386
   softening, 374
   tensor, 18, 19, 107, 115, 162
Stress-intensity factor, 75, 92, 140, 148, 204, 207, 217, 255, 277, 293, 298, 312, 445, 454, 465
   fracture mechanics approach, 86–92
Stress/strain
   behaviour, 22, 230
   curves, 153, 235, 288, 324, 325, 329, 333, 334, 378, 414, 438–42
   properties, 153
Styrene–acrylonitrile copolymer (SAN), 458
Styrene–butadiene rubber (SBR), 50, 216, 374, 388, 390, 393, 397–400, 405, 407, 409, 415
Styrene–butadiene styrene (SBS), 407
Synthesis, 8

Tacticity, 9
Temperature effects, 16–19, 233–6, 245, 296, 400, 452–62
Tensile fracture, 128, 130, 131
   rubbers, 398–415
Tensile strength, oriented polymers, 358–60
Tensile tests, 110
Tensile yield stress, 160
Testing rate, 29

Tetraethylenepentamine (TEPA), 319, 320
Thermoplastics, 3
   common types, 4
   see also Glassy thermoplastics
Thermosets, 3, 49
   see also Glassy thermosets
Thickness effects, 93–7, 249–51
Tie molecules, 15
Time–temperature superposition, 29
Torsion tests, 111
Toughened multiphase plastics, 421–71
   crack pinning, 434–8, 447–8
   crazing, 428–34
   matrix properties, 451–2
   particle/matrix adhesion, 448–51
   second-phase particles, 442–8
   shear yielding, 425–8, 432–4
   stress/strain curves, 438–42
   structure/property relationships, 442–52
   test variables, 452–67
Toughening mechanisms, 36, 423–38
trans state, 118
Tresca yield criterion, 90, 94, 115
Triaxial stresses, 378–82
Triethylene tetramine (TETA), 294
Twinning, 332

Urey–Bradley force field, 327

van der Waals bonds, 47
van der Waals forces, 76

Verheulpen–Heymans–Bauwens model, 157, 158
Vinyl polymers, 9
Viscoelastic relaxation, 28
Viscoelasticity, 26–9, 111–14, 172, 173, 298, 356, 372, 375, 415
Voids, 60–1, 152
Voigt model, 330
Volume fraction, 446, 447
von Mises criterion, 94, 115, 116

Weibull modulus, 219
Weibull statistics, 218–19
WLF equation, 29, 372, 373, 390, 402, 405

X-ray diffraction, 329

Yield
   behaviour, 108–19
   criterion, 88
   definitions, 108–10
   point, 31, 123
      extrinsic, 109
      intrinsic, 109
   stress, 37, 110, 111, 113, 115, 158, 202, 209, 311, 314
   viscoelastic nature of, 111–14
Young's modulus, 22, 23, 33, 35, 46, 74, 91, 92, 167, 231, 289, 295, 309, 326, 331

Ziegler–Natta catalysts, 9